543.01   71125
A m3r

DATE DUE			

GAYLORD M-2   PRINTED IN U.S.A.

REAGENT

CHEMICALS

 AMERICAN CHEMICAL SOCIETY
SPECIFICATIONS 4 **TH**

EDITION

Copyright © 1968 by
AMERICAN CHEMICAL SOCIETY

All Rights Reserved

Library of Congress Catalog Card No. 68-29955
PRINTED IN THE UNITED STATES OF AMERICA

Prepared by the
1967 COMMITTEE ON ANALYTICAL REAGENTS

OFFICIAL FROM DECEMBER 1, 1968

**Edited and Produced by
AMERICAN CHEMICAL
SOCIETY PUBLICATIONS
Washington, D.C.
1968**

FOREWORD

Chemical analysis is the handmaiden of research in chemistry and the indispensable partner of production—sometimes its master—in industry. Gone are the days when "chemically pure" was enough to say of a reagent, when the source of a compound was the criterion of its purity.

With the acceptance of chemical analyses as the criteria of reagent purity came the need for standards. The development and improvement of these standards have been the concern of successive committees of the American Chemical Society; the history of their work is outlined in the prefaces that follow.

The present committee includes representatives of manufacturers and of users of reagent chemicals. All have contributed personally and through their organizations to the immense labor of study, laboratory testing, and revision that was required to produce this volume. Special tribute is due to W. Stanley Clabaugh, chairman of the committee during most of the interim since the Edition of 1960, to Vernon A. Stenger, present chairman, and to William E. Schmidt who, as editorial consultant, has consolidated the work of revision.

RICHARD L. KENYON
Director of Publications
American Chemical Society

CONTENTS

Preface to Edition of 1950

As a result of comments regarding the quality of reagent chemicals, the Council of the American Chemical Society in 1903 appointed a Committee on the Purity of Chemical Reagents consisting of John H. Long, chairman; W. F. Hillebrand, secretary; Charles Baskerville, L. M. Dennis, and H. P. Talbot.

The committee held one meeting and outlined a program of preparation of specifications. Although no publication of specifications was produced, the committee did exert influence towards better quality of reagents and a decrease in instances of discrepancies between labels and contents of packages of reagent chemicals. The committee was not reappointed when its appointment expired at the spring meeting in New Orleans in 1915.

Analysts continued to be disturbed about the quality of reagent chemicals on the market. Dr. Hillebrand referred to the problem in his Chandler Foundation Lecture at Columbia University, November 27, 1916 [Our Analytical Chemistry and Its Future, *J. Ind. Eng. Chem.*, **9**, 170 (1917)]. He emphasized the need for concerted action by chemists to raise the standards of quality and reliability of available reagent chemicals. In 1916 a local section of the American Chemical Society requested the Council of the Society to take steps to learn just the extent to which a manufacturer or dealer might be held accountable for erroneous statements on labels. The communication cited an instance of serious embarrassment to a member of the section who had naïvely trusted a grossly inaccurate statement as to the amount of an impurity in a reagent chemical. In January 1917 a Committee on Analyzed Reagents was appointed consisting of W. F. Hillebrand, chairman, Charles Baskerville, and W. D. Bigelow.

This committee's report to the council meeting in April 1917 proposed that an effort be made to obtain the appropriation by Congress of funds to enable the National Bureau of Standards to purchase reagents on the open market and publish results of analyses of the samples along with the analyses on the labels. This proposed procedure would be in line with the practice of state agricultural experiment stations in regard to fertilizers. The committee report recommended the appointment of a permanent committee of the Society to act in an advisory capacity to the Bureau of Standards and the manufacturers of reagents. The committee appointed consisted of W. D. Bigelow, chairman, Charles Baskerville, and C. C. McDonnell. The appropriation for work by the Bureau of Standards was not obtained. The committee reports for 1918 and 1919 give summaries of experiences in the testing of reagents at the Bureau of Standards.

At the meeting of the Council of the American Chemical Society in April 1919 the subject of apparatus was added to the field of work of the committee. The name of the committee was changed accordingly and several additional members were appointed.

In August 1921 the committee published specifications for hydrochloric, nitric, and sulfuric acids and ammonium hydroxide in about the style that has been followed in the later publication of specifications by the committee. No additional specifications for reagents were issued by the Committee on Guaranteed Reagents and Standard Apparatus.

In accordance with a recommendation in the committee report for 1924, the committee was divided into two committees and some new members were added to the Committee on Guaranteed Reagents.

The present collection of specifications may be considered a summary of the work on reagents done by the committee under different names since the original appointment in 1917 of the Committee on Analyzed Reagents. However, the present set of specifications was started in 1925 and is the product of those holding membership in the committee from that time. The final decisions on practically all points have been made in committee meetings, usually attended by all members. The 1950 committee is responsible for the preparation of the present edition.

The following list shows the period of membership of each person who has served on the committee after the preparation of the report for 1924.

ASHLEY, SAMUEL E. Q.	1948-1950	FREEMAN, JOHN V.	1930-1942
BAXTER, GREGORY P.	1930-1931	MARSIGLIO, E. F.	1939
BERILLA, JOHN J.	1945-1946	MESSINGER, P. H.	1939-1944
BUTLER, ALBERT Q.	1942-1950	OSBORN, R. A.	1933-1950
CLARKE, BEVERLY L.	1948-1950	ROSIN, JOSEPH	1925-1947
COLLINS, W. D.	1925-1950	ROSS, JOHN F.	1940-1950
Chairman	1925-1942	SPENCER, G. C.	1925-1932
EISENHAUER, F. S.	1941	WICHERS, EDWARD	1925-1950
	1945-1950	Chairman	1943-1950
FARR, H. V.	1925-1939	WILLARD, HOBART H.	1932-1942
FLAGG, JOHN F.	1947	WOLF, JOHN P.	1947-1950

Committee membership has been from one spring meeting to the next, except for 1948 and later years, and the years shown are the years closing a period of membership; 1925 means the committee year ending in April 1925; 1948 refers to the period ending in March 1948; 1949 and 1950 refer to calendar years. Some who have served on the committee contributed largely to its work while they were not members. Others who have never served as members have furnished valuable assistance in the preparation of specifications, especially some members of staffs of laboratories represented on the committee.

Of these, particular mention should be made of W. Stanley Clabaugh of the National Bureau of Standards, who has supplied technical assistance at every step of the compilation of the specifications into their final form. Full utilization has been made of his special skill in appraisal and development of methods, which has been acquired in years of testing products from many producers.

The work of the committee is continuing, looking towards an extension of the list of reagent specifications, modification of existing specifications as better reagents become available, and the improvement of methods of test. Comments and suggestions along these lines will be welcomed by the committee.

Preface to Edition of 1955

Plans for the continuing work of the Committee on Analytical Reagents, as of the time of publication of the edition of 1950, are stated in the last paragraph of the Preface to that edition. This continuing work resulted in the publication in 1953 of an appendix to the book [*Anal. Chem.* **25,** 365-80 (1953)] which contained 10 additional specifications, more than 200 changes in requirements, and 60-odd revisions of the test procedures. This material now appears in the new edition of the book, together with seven more new specifications and a substantial additional number of changes in requirements and in test procedures.

It is apparent that during the past 5 years more of the committee's time and energy has gone into the revision of existing specifications than into the development of new ones. This has seemed necessary on the grounds that the existing specifications cover the majority of the reagents that are in common use and that keeping these specifications up to date is more important than adding to their number. This is not to say that no more reagent chemicals need to be standardized. The committee recognizes that there is a continuing need for additional specifications, and several of them are in process of development. It seems likely, however, that emphasis will continue to be placed on the further revision and improvement of the published specifications.

The Preface to the edition of 1950 listed all persons who had served as members of the committee since 1924. Three changes in the composition of the committee have occurred since 1950. Samuel E. Q. Ashley withdrew at the end of 1953, and W. Stanley Clabaugh, C. A. Flanders, and Mark O. Lamar were added in 1954.

Preface to Edition of 1960

It would be inconsistent with the times if, in the five years since the latest edition, no significant advance had been made in either the manufacture or testing of reagent chemicals. Were this true, only a reprint of the 1955 edition would have been needed.

Actually, there have been many changes. Manufacturers have continually improved the quality of their chemicals; many new reagents have been added to the list, and scores of revisions have been made in the specifications and methods of test. In some instances, better and more reliable reagents have been introduced—for example, the brucine test for nitrate. In others, improved methods and instruments are specified, such as the flame photometer for the determination of sodium, potassium, calcium, and strontium. As a result, it has frequently been possible to replace the expression "To pass test" by a numerical limit. Similarly, the tests for "Free acid" or "Free alkali" are replaced with a definite pH range determined with an accurate pH meter.

The users of reagent chemicals have kept pressure on the manufacturers to produce higher grade materials. The demand has been satisfied, but there appears to be a repeating pattern of ask-and-receive. This is good for both participants. Thus, it is logical to assume, certainly to hope, that this trend continues and that the next edition, in every respect, will be better than the present. Again the committee asks readers to suggest new reagents for consideration and to point out errors.

A new section, "The Gravimetric Determination of Small Amounts of Impurities," has been added, wherein are details and precautions for the precipitation, collection, filtration, ignition, and weighing of small precipitates and residues. This addition is necessary and appropriate because experience has shown that at times the book is used by the less skilled analyst.

Since 1955 four changes have taken effect in the membership of the committee: Albert Q. Butler and R. A. Osborn resigned in 1958 and 1959, respectively, and were replaced by Samuel M. Tuthill and Henry W. Loy.

Preface to Fourth Edition

Since the publication of the edition of 1960, the rapid advance of analytical chemistry has greatly affected the field of reagent testing. For example, the realization that "trace impurities" may produce beneficial as well as harmful effects has resulted in closer controls on all items. This in turn has placed added responsibility on analysts and a consequent demand for still purer reagents.

Many improvements have been adopted for the existing requirements and methods of testing of the common reagents used in wet analyses. Meanwhile, a growing demand has been developing for reagents of special quality to use in instrumental methods. A number of these reagents have been included in the fourth edition, but a tremendous amount of additional laboratory work will be required to determine adequate specifications for many such chemicals.

During the period from 1960 through 1967 the size of the Committee on Analytical Reagents expanded from 11 to 18 active members representing government, private business, and educational institutions. W. Stanley Clabaugh, who served as chairman during the preparation of the previous edition and during all but one of the years devoted to the completion of the fourth edition, retired from government service, and was succeeded by Vernon A. Stenger in 1967. Hence, for the first time since its establishment 50 years ago, the chairman is a chemist from private industry.

The following list shows the period of membership of each person who has served on the Committee following the preparation of the edition of 1960.

ALLEN, HARRY C.	1963	LINGANE, JAMES J.	1966-1967
CLABAUGH, W. STANLEY	1954-1967	LOY, HENRY W.	1959-1964**
Chairman	1956-1966	MARTELLO, NATHAN A.	1967
COLLINS, W. D.	1925-1967*	MEARS, THOMAS W.	1966
Chairman	1925-1942	MEINKE, W. WAYNE	1964-1965
Chairman Emeritus	1963-1967	MORECOMBE, FRED	1966-1967
COOPER, MAURICE D.	1963-1967	MURPHY, THOMAS J.	1967
CORLEY, J. W.	1966-1967	ROHRBOUGH, WALLACE G.	1965-1967
EISENHAUER, FRANKLIN S.	1941	ROSS, JOHN F.	1940-1965
	1945-1965	STENGER, VERNON A.	1962-1967
FLANDERS, CLIFFORD A.	1954-1967	Chairman	1967
FUESS, JAMES T.	1965-1967	TUTHILL, SAMUEL M.	1958-1967
GREEN, FLOYD J.	1963-1967	WICHERS, EDWARD	1925-1967
HANSON, ROBERT W.	1961-1967	Chairman	1943-1955
HUBBARD, WILLARD D.	1965-1967	WOLF, G. EDWARD	1966-1967
JIMINEZ, LAWRENCE R.	1961-1962	WOLF, JOHN P.	1947-1967

* Deceased May 8, 1967   ** Deceased November 30, 1964

As in the past the Committee urges the readers to report any errors and to suggest new reagents and new methods of testing to evaluate. Only one chemical has been deleted from REAGENT CHEMICALS since 1960, while 38 reagents have been added. In addition, several polarographic and gas chromatographic methods have been adopted in testing procedures for the first time.

The desirability of promoting early use of newly adopted techniques and specifications is apparent. To facilitate this goal the Committee plans to issue one or two supplements prior to publication of the next full edition. These will be published in *Analytical Chemistry,* and reprints sized to fit this book will be made available. Cards for requesting the supplement reprints, when announced in *Analytical Chemistry,* are in the back of this edition.

DEFINITIONS,

PROCEDURES,

AND STANDARDS

The specifications prepared by the Committee on Analytical Reagents of the American Chemical Society are intended to serve for reagents to be used in precise analytical work. The requirements and the details of tests are based on published work, on the experience of members of the committee in the examination of reagent chemicals on the market, and on studies of the tests made by members of the committee. It is recognized that there may be special uses for which reagents conforming to these specifications must be further purified with respect to one or more particular impurities.

In determining quality levels to be defined by new or revised specifications the committee is guided by the following general principles:

When a specification is first prepared it will in general be based on the highest level of purity (of the reagent to which it applies) that is competitively available in the United States. If a higher level of purity subsequently becomes available on a competitive basis, the specification will be revised accordingly.

Since the requirements of a specification relating to the content of designated impurities must necessarily be expressed in terms of maximum permissible limits, products conforming to the specification will normally contain less than the maximum permissible proportion of some or all of these impurities. A given preparation of a reagent chemical that has less than the maximum content of one or more impurities permitted by the specification is, therefore, not considered as of higher quality than that defined by the specification.

A lower permissible limit for a given impurity will be adopted only if it is significantly different from the one it is intended to supersede. In general a new requirement for an impurity whose content is not greater than 0.01 per cent will not be considered significantly different unless it decreases the maximum permissible content of the impurity by at least 50 per cent. This principle will also be approximated in the revision of those requirements defined by the term, "To pass test."

Tests as written are considered to be applicable only to the accompanying requirements. Modification of a requirement, especially if the change is toward a higher level of purity, will necessitate reconsideration, and often revision, of the test to ensure its validity.

INTERPRETATION OF REQUIREMENTS

The requirements for reagent chemicals can be divided into two main classes—namely, an assay or quantitative determination of the principal or active constituent and the determination of the impurities or minor constituents. By far, the majority of the requirements belong to the latter class.

Assay Requirements. Assay requirements are included in these specifications only when they are essential to the definition of quality. Such requirements are included, for example, in specifications for standards, for acid-water systems to control strength, for alkalies to limit the content of water and carbonate, for oxidizing or reducing substances which may change strength on storage, and for some hydrates to control, within reasonable limits, the amount of water indicated by the formula.

In most other instances assays would serve only as a form of identity test of uncertain reliability. Unless described in great detail and carried out with exceptional skill and care, available assay methods seldom are accurate enough to permit using a weighed quantity of a reagent, so assayed, in a precise stoichiometric operation. This use of reagents should be limited to those designated standards. In this connection see the statement concerning mother liquor in crystals under "Unlisted Impurities," page 3.

For comparison of analytical results with requirements for assays, the results are rounded off to the number of places carried in the requirement. A requirement of a minimum of 46 per cent will be met by a product whose analysis shows 45.6 per cent, but not by one whose analysis shows 45.4 per cent. A minimum of 46.0 per cent would demand 45.95 per cent; 45.9 per cent would fail. Rounding off is according to the commonly used practice of rejecting or increasing numbers less than or greater than 5. When the number to be considered is exactly 5, it is rejected or increased by 5, whichever gives an even number for the last number retained. Thus, 36.465 and 36.455 are both rounded off to 36.46. The formula weights and factors for computing results are based on the 1967 International Atomic Weights given on page 30. The formula weights are rounded off to two decimal places.

Impurity Requirements. Requirements for impurities are expressed (1) as numerical limits, (2) in terms of the expression "To pass test," with an accompanying approximate numerical limit, or (3) in terms of the expression "To pass test" without an approximate numerical limit. The distinction between these forms of expression is based on the committee's opinion as to the relative quantitative significance of the prescribed methods of test. The methods given for determining conformity to requirements of the first type are considered to yield, in competent hands, what are usually thought of as "quantitative" results, whereas those of the second type can be expected to yield only approximate values. Those in class 3 give definitions that cannot be expressed in numbers. It is obvious, however, that these distinctions as to quantitative significance cannot be sharp, and that even the numerically expressed requirements are not all defined with equal accuracy. The final and essential definition of any requirement must, therefore, reside in the prescribed method of test, rather than in its numerical expression.

If a method of test yields results that are adequately reproducible on repeated trials in different laboratories, it offers a satisfactory definition of the content of an impurity, whether or not the result can be expressed by a number. Although the committee has endeavored to base requirements, so far as possible, on methods of testing that meet this criterion, there are a considerable number that are based on essentially undefined statements such as "no turbidity," "no color," or "the color shall not be completely discharged in —— minutes." While some of the requirements of this kind could be replaced by others based on quantitative comparisons or measurements, to do so would require more costly or time-consuming procedures than appear, at this time, to be justified. The approach to an ultimate goal of replacing in every instance the word "none," or its equivalent, by the expression "not more than ——" therefore is limited both by deficiencies of knowledge and by practical considerations of expediency.

Unlisted Impurities. Reagents may contain certain impurities other than those included in the listed requirements. Some of these may be "natural" impurities in the sense that they are commonly present in the source material from which the reagent is prepared, or result from the method of manufacture, but which are considered to be without significant effect on the common uses of the reagent. An example is water retained as mother liquor in crystals prepared from an aqueous solution. The presumption that "natural" impurities are not significant obviously cannot apply to new or unusually demanding uses of a reagent.

In some instances residual amounts of substances may be present that have been added as aids in the process of purification. An example is provided by the use of complexing agents added to keep certain metal ions in solution during recrystallization. Some reagents may contain stabilizers, intentionally added to retard or inhibit natural processes of deterioration.

When the Committee becomes aware of an unlisted impurity that affects adversely the known uses of a reagent, a new requirement is added to the specification, provided a suitable method of test is available. If a stabilizer is known to be used, an explanatory note is included in the specification.

Users of reagents can protect themselves against the effects of unlisted impurities on a specific analytical procedure by applying, *ad hoc,* an appropriate "suitability" test.

Identity Requirements. Identity requirements and tests are not included in the specifications. If there is any question as to the identity of a chemical, identity can be made by methods outlined in well-known texts on qualitative analysis.

Particle Size for Granular Materials. When a mesh range is stated on a label, at least 95 per cent shall pass through the coarse sieve and at least 70 per cent shall be retained on the fine sieve. This statement applies only to materials that are 60 mesh or coarser. Unless otherwise noted for individual reagent chemicals, the procedure will be by dry sieving, without brushing, using U. S. standard sieve sizes.

PRECAUTIONS FOR TESTS

The descriptions of the individual tests are intended to give all essential details without repetition of considerations that should be obvious to an experienced analyst. A few suggestions are given for precautions and procedures that are particularly applicable to the routine testing of reagent chemicals.

Samples for Testing

To eliminate accidental contamination or possible change in composition, samples for test must be taken from freshly opened containers.

Reagents

Reagents used in the testing should conform to ACS specifications. Reagents not covered by ACS specifications should be of the best grade obtainable and should be examined carefully for interfering impurities.

Blank Tests

It must be kept in mind that many of the tests are for minute quantities of the impurities sought. Therefore, complete blank tests must be made on the water and all reagents used in each step of the tests—including, for example, filtration and ignition. Frequently, however, the directions include a control, a blank, or other device that corrects for possible impurities in the water and the reagents (see page 26).

GENERAL DIRECTIONS

Gravimetric Method for Determining Small Amounts of Impurities

In many of the reagent specifications it is directed that a precipitate or residue be collected and either dried or ignited so as to provide certain information concerning the purity of the reagent. Detailed instructions for every reagent would be unnecessarily repetitious, so the following procedures are provided. Except wherein it is directed otherwise in the specific reagent tests, these directions and precautions will be employed in collecting, drying, and igniting precipitates and residues.

General Considerations

It is imperative that the analyst use the best techniques in performing any of the operations included in this book. Exceptional cleanliness and protection against accidental contamination from dirt and fumes are rigid requirements for acceptable results. The choice of equipment is generally left to the discretion of the analyst, but it must provide satisfactory precision and accuracy. All weighings must be determined with an uncertainty of not more than ± 0.0002 gram.

When the use of a tared container is specified, the container will be carried through a series of operations identical to those employed in the procedure, including drying, igniting, cooling in a suitable desiccator, and weighing. The length of the drying or ignition and the temperature employed must be the same as specified in the procedure in which the tared equipment is to be used. Where it is directed to dry or ignite to constant weight, two separate weighings may differ by not more than ± 0.0002 gram, the second weighing following a second drying or ignition period.

In those operations wherein a filtering crucible is specified, a Gooch crucible with an asbestos mat, a fritted-glass crucible, a porous porcelain crucible, or a crucible having a sponge platinum mat may be used. The preparation and use of a Gooch crucible with asbestos mat should conform to the directions given in reputable texts (*cf.* Hillebrand, Lundell, Bright, and Hoffman, "Applied Inorganic Analysis," 2nd edition, pp. 99-100, John Wiley & Sons, New York, 1953). Also, both fritted glass and porcelain are affected by strongly alkaline solutions. Even platinum sponge mats are attacked by hydrochloric acid unless the crucible is first washed with boiling water to remove oxygen.

Collection of Precipitates and Residues

In many of the tests the amount of residue or precipitate may be so small as to escape easy detection. Therefore, the absence of a weighable residue or precipitate must never be assumed. However small, it must be properly collected, washed, and dried or ignited. The size of the filter paper to be used is selected according to the amount of precipitate to be collected, not by the volume of solution to be filtered.

Often when ammonia is added in slight excess to precipitate the R_2O_3 group of elements, the amount of precipitate produced is so small that it is hard to see and collect. If a small amount of a suspension of ashless filter paper pulp is added toward the end of the period of digestion on the steam bath or hot plate, the flocculation and collection of the hydroxides are facilitated.

Some precipitates have a strong tendency to "creep"; others, like magnesium ammonium phosphate, stick fast to the walls of the container. The use of the rubber-tip "policeman" is recommended, sometimes supplemented by a small segment of ashless filter paper. The analyst should guard against the possibility of any of the precipitate escaping beyond the upper rim of the filter paper.

Precipitates, especially if but recently produced, are all partially soluble and proper precautions should be taken with respect to both their formation and subsequent washing. For example, a large excess of ammonia should be avoided when the R_2O_3 hydroxides are precipitated, since aluminum hydroxide is measurably soluble in excess ammonia.

In general, precipitates should not be washed with water alone but with water containing a small amount of common ion to decrease the solubility of the precipitate. It is much better to wash with several small portions of washing solution than with fewer and larger portions. Calcium oxalate precipitates should be washed with dilute (about 0.1 per cent) ammonium oxalate solution; therefore, mixed precipitates which may contain calcium oxalate and magnesium ammonium phosphate should be washed with a 1 per cent ammonia solution containing also 0.1 per cent ammonium oxalate.

Ignition of Precipitates

The proper conditions for obtaining the precipitate are given in the individual monograph test directions. The precipitate is collected on a suitable piece of good quality ashless filter paper, the residue and paper are thoroughly washed with the proper solution, and the moist filter paper is folded about the residue. The filter paper is then placed in a suitable tared crucible, and the paper dried. The drying may be accomplished by using a 105°C. oven, by heating on a hot plate, with an infrared lamp, or by the careful use of an Argand burner. When dry, the paper is charred at the lowest possible temperature, the charred paper destroyed by gentle ignition, and the crucible finally ignited at 800° ± 25°C. for 15 minutes. The ignited crucible is cooled in a suitable desiccator and weighed.

Insoluble Residue Tests

These tests are designed and intended to determine the amount of foreign matter (filter lint, wood chips, etc.) that may be in chemicals.

The specified weight of sample and the volume of solvent are placed in a beaker of suitable size, heated to boiling, then digested in the covered beaker on the steam bath for 1 hour. The hot solution is then passed through a tared filtering crucible and the beaker thoroughly rinsed with small portions of hot solvent, which are also poured through the filter. The outside of the crucible is wiped clean, after which it is dried to constant weight at 105° to 110°C., cooled in a suitable desiccator, and weighed.

Water is the solvent usually specified, but the solubility of the chemical or its chemical nature may require that an acid, alkaline, or organic solution be used as the solvent. In these cases the particular monograph specifications will direct the amount of acid or alkali or organic solvent to be used.

Residue after Evaporation Tests

These tests are designed and intended to determine the amount of any higher boiling impurities or nonvolatile dissolved material that may be in a chemical. They are chiefly used in the testing of organic solvents and some of the inorganic acids.

The specified volume of reagent is placed in a clean, tared container and the liquid evaporated gently, at a rate such that boiling does not occur, and in a hood, protected from any possibility of contamination. The residue is then dried as directed in the particular monograph specification, cooled in a suitable desiccator, and weighed.

The residue is not dried to constant weight in this case, since continued heating may slowly volatilize some of the higher boiling impurities. The drying conditions specified in the individual reagent monograph will, however, yield reproducible and reliable results, so that drying to constant weight is unnecessary.

Residue after Ignition Tests

These tests are designed and intended to determine the amount of non-volatile inorganic material that may be in a reagent. They are applied to those inorganic reagents that can be sublimed or volatilized without decomposition and to various organic reagents. Among those chemicals so tested are ammonium salts, mercury salts, and some inorganic acids.

The interpretation of the instructions to "ignite" has varied widely. Directions to "ignite gently," "ignite at cherry redness," and "ignite at a low red heat" are not specific enough to assure the same procedure by different analysts.

After considerable study of the various residues involved, a temperature of $800° \pm 25°C.$ for a time of 15 minutes has been adopted. This should assure constant conditions for conversion of the residues to the desired composition without causing appreciable loss of the impurities themselves.

Although detailed directions are given in each monograph wherein this test is required, the following *General Procedure* is recommended:

> Ignite X grams in a tared crucible or dish. The rate of heating should be such that from 1 to 2 hours is required to volatilize the sample. When nearly all the sample has been volatilized, cool and moisten the residue with 0.10 ml. of sulfuric acid. Continue the heating until the remainder of the sample and excess sulfuric acid have been volatilized. Finally, ignite at $800° \pm 25°C.$ for 15 minutes. The weight of the residue should not exceed $0.00X$ gram.

It is obvious that the above *General Procedure* is not inflexible. In particular, certain organic reagents are difficult to volatilize and slight variations in the test have been suggested here and there. Reagents with a high water content should be dried before ignition to prevent loss of sample. It is left to the discretion of the analyst as to the method of heating to be used, whether a hot plate, Argand burner, or infrared lamp. The final ignition at higher temperature should be done under oxidizing conditions.

"Substances Not Precipitated by _____" Procedures

These procedures are designed and intended to determine those soluble impurities that remain after the principal constituent has been removed by precipitation, as prescribed in the monograph.

In these tests a solution of the reagent in question is treated with a particular precipitating agent, the precipitate is removed by filtration, and a specified volume of the filtrate is used for the determination. The aliquot portion is transferred to a tared dish on a steam bath and the liquid evaporated without boiling or spattering. A moist residue, often an ammonium salt, may remain. When volatilizing this salt, great care must be taken to avoid spattering, which may cause a loss of some of the residue. After the salt has been volatilized, the residue is ignited as directed in the particular reagent specification.

Weights of Precipitates and Residues

With few exceptions, the weight of the sample used in the test will insure that at least 0.0010 gram of the impurity to be determined will be present if the sample fails the test.

Volumes of Reagents

The addition of small volumes of liquid reagents is generally stated to the nearest 0.05 ml. (0.05 ml., 0.10 ml., 0.15 ml., etc.). Use of the term "drop" to represent 0.05 ml. is avoided.

Colorimetric and Turbidimetric Methods
for Determining Impurities

Conditions and quantities for colorimetric or turbidimetric tests have been chosen to produce colors or turbidities that can be observed easily. These conditions and quantities approach but do not reach the minimum that can be observed. A time of 5 minutes, unless some other time is specified, must be allowed for the development of the colors or turbidities before the comparisons are made. If solutions of samples contain any turbidity or insoluble matter that might interfere with the later observation of colors or turbidities, they must be filtered before the addition of the reagent used to produce the color or turbidity. Conditions of the tests will vary from one reagent to another, but most of the tests fall close to the limits indicated in the table.

Usual Limits for Colorimetric or Turbidimetric Standards

	Quantity Used for Comparison, Mg.	Approximate Volume, Ml.
Ammonium (NH_4)	0.01	50
Arsenic (As)	0.002-0.003	—
Barium (Ba) chromate test	0.05-0.10	50
Chloride (Cl)	0.01	25
Copper (Cu)		
Dithizone extraction	0.006	10-20
Hydrogen sulfide	0.02	50
Pyridine-thiocyanate	0.02	10-20
Heavy metals (as Pb)	0.02	50
Iron (Fe)		
1,10-Phenanthroline	0.01	25
Thiocyanate	0.01	50
Lead (Pb)		
Chromate	0.05	25
Dithizone	0.002	10-20
Sodium sulfide	0.01-.02	50
Manganese (Mn)	0.01	50
Nitrate (NO_3)		
Brucine sulfate	0.005-0.02	50
Diphenylamine	0.005	25
Phosphate (PO_4)		
Direct molybdenum blue	0.02	25
Molybdenum blue ether		
extraction	0.01	25
Sulfate (SO_4)	0.04-0.06	12
Zinc (Zn)		
Dithizone extraction	0.006-0.01	10-20

GENERAL PROCEDURES

The ACS specifications for reagent chemicals are for the most part complete in themselves. However, for the determination of arsenic, boiling range, density at 25°C., freezing point, and melting point details are given below that have been found well adapted to the testing of reagent chemicals. These directions are not repeated in the specifications.

In addition, brief descriptions are given of general features of the tests for heavy metals, iron, nitrate, and phosphate. These tests are described in the individual specifications with details adapted to the testing of each reagent.

Finally, apparatus and methods are described for the determination of the pH of a solution of a pure reagent salt with the pH meter, alkalies and alkaline earths by means of the flame photometer, and the use of dithizone tests. These tests are described in the individual specifications with details adapted to the testing of each reagent.

Arsenic

The widely used Gutzeit method, which is described for testing reagents, depends upon the measurement or comparison of stains produced by the action of evolved arsine on strips of paper that have been impregnated with mercuric bromide from an alcoholic solution. Details of the method are given in collections of official methods of analysis and in textbooks. Because of the nature of the test, it is important to have the greatest possible uniformity in the preparation of the stains from samples and from measured amounts of arsenic.

Apparatus. A wide-mouthed bottle of about 60-ml. capacity serves for the generator. It carries a glass tube about 1 cm. in diameter and 6 to 7 cm. long, which is constricted at the bottom to pass through the stopper of the bottle. The tube is used to hold glass wool, purified cotton, or similar material, moistened with a 10 per cent lead acetate solution. All tubes of a set of generators should be charged with equal amounts of this material. The solution serves to hold back any hydrogen sulfide generated in the bottle, and also helps to maintain a uniform content of moisture in the evolved gases.

Above the lead acetate tube is a narrow glass tube 2.6 to 2.7 mm. in internal diameter and 10 to 12 cm. long which holds the strip of mercuric bromide paper. The diameter of this tube must not be large enough to permit curling of the paper strip. The paper strips are best obtained by the purchase of commercially cut strips that are of uniform width of 2.5 mm. and are generally supplied in a manner which facilitates their preparation for use. The strips are soaked about an hour in a 5 per cent solution of mercuric bromide in alcohol. They are drained and allowed to dry in clean air. It is essential that all strips used for a particular test be sensitized in the same manner and at the same time.

Procedure. Place the sample in the generator bottle with water and about 5 ml. of acid. The acid may be either sulfuric or hydrochloric, but in any set of determinations the kind and the amounts of acid in all the bottles must be the same. If acid is consumed in dissolving the sample, the amount used must be replaced and the bottles for preparation of standards must contain an amount of arsenic-free salt equal to that resulting from the action of the acid on the sample. Add 7.5 ml. of potassium iodide solution (10 per cent solution in water) and 0.20 ml. of stannous chloride solution (40 per cent solution of $SnCl_2 \cdot 2H_2O$ in concentrated hydrochloric acid). Mix, allow to stand 30 minutes at not less than 25°C., and dilute to 40 ml. Prepare the lead acetate tube, removing excess solution, and insert the paper strip in the small tube. Add to the bottle the required amount of zinc, which may be 10 to 15 grams of stick zinc or 2 to 5 grams of granulated zinc. Insert the stopper carrying the tubes and immerse the generator bottle in a water bath that is maintained at a constant temperature of from 20° to 25°C. At the end of 1.5 hours remove the paper strips and compare the stains.

The character of the stain is affected by variables which should be controlled as closely as possible. Moisture is a factor which is regulated in part by the lead acetate solution on the inert material in the tube next to the generator. A major factor is the rate of evolution of arsine and hydrogen. The kind and concentration of acid in the generator can be regulated fairly easily, but special pains must be taken to have the zinc the same in all generators of a set. Uniformity in a set is much more important than the form of the zinc. Good results may be obtained with pieces of stick zinc, mossy zinc, or granulated zinc. The best concentration of acid may depend on the form of the zinc and the amount used in each generator.

Attention to all the details is necessary to make certain that stains from equal amounts of arsenic in samples and standards shall be of equal length and appearance. This factor must be emphasized if the practice is followed of making a series of standard stains and using a graph based on the relation between amounts of arsenic and length of stain. A control of average arsenic content should give a stain whose length falls on the graph. A blank will show any significant amount of arsenic in the reagents used.

Boiling Range

In order to avoid complicated precautions or corrections involved in the determination of actual boiling points at various elevations and with variable atmospheric pressure, the character of most volatile reagents with respect to boiling is indicated by the requirement that the boiling range be within narrow limits, without specifying an actual boiling temperature. The "boiling range" for purposes of testing most analytical reagent quality solvents is defined in two terms: first, the difference between the temperatures when 1 ml. and 95 ml. have distilled, and second, the difference between the temperatures when 95 ml. and when all of the material (dry point) have distilled. The distillation must be conducted essentially as described.

Apparatus. The preferred apparatus for the determination of boiling ranges is the all-glass apparatus with standard-taper ground joints. The separate pieces are a 250-ml. round-bottomed short-necked flask (with a 24/40 standard-taper joint), a three-way connecting tube with 24/40 standard-taper joints for connecting the flask to a West-type condenser which has a 24/40 standard-taper joint, a water jacket about 50 cm. long, and a bent delivery tube. It is immaterial whether the thermometer outlet of the connecting tube has a ground joint or is unground. The wide outlet to the side arm is important and the bent delivery tube is desirable. An asbestos board 3 to 5 mm. thick and approximately 18 cm. square with a centrally placed circular opening 4 cm. in diameter should be used to support the flask. A cylindrical shield of asbestos to protect the flask from drafts will be useful in many laboratories. Because the requirements for boiling range usually specify merely a range of the order of 1°C., there is no need for a rigid specification for the thermometer. The subdivisions on the thermometer scale should not be greater than 0.2°C.

Procedure. All apparatus must be clean and dry. Measure 100 ml. of the liquid in a graduated cylinder and transfer it to the boiling flask together with some device to prevent bumping. Use the cylinder as the receiver. Place the flask on the asbestos board, which is supported on a ring stand or other suitable support, and place in position the cylindrical shield for the flask if it is to be used. Connect the flask and condenser by the connecting tube and fasten the thermometer in place so that it is well centered in the vertical arm of the connecting tube with the top of the thermometer bulb just below the bottom of the outlet to the side arm. For heating use a small flame or other source which will confine the heating to the exposed bottom of the distilling flask, and adjust the heat so that all the liquid will distill in from 20 to 30 minutes. Make a preliminary trial if necessary to determine the adjustment for the proper rate of heating. Read the thermometer when 1 ml. has distilled and thereafter at volumes of distillate of 5, 10, 40, 50, 60, 90, and 95 ml. and when the last drop has volatilized from the bottom of the flask. The 1-ml. to 95-ml. boiling range is the difference between the temperatures observed when 1 ml. and 95 ml. have distilled. The 95-ml. to dryness boiling range is the difference between the temperatures observed when 95 ml. have distilled and when the last drop of liquid has volatilized from the bottom of the flask.

Density at 25°C.

Density (grams per milliliter) may be determined by any reliable method in use in the testing laboratory. A satisfactory method employs a 5-ml. U-shaped bicapillary pycnometer described in *Ind. Eng. Chem., Anal. Ed.,* **16**, 55 (1944) and adopted by ASTM [*Anal. Chem.* **22**, 1452 (1950)].

Procedure. Tare a pycnometer, the volume of which has been accurately determined at 25°C. Fill the pycnometer with the liquid to be tested and immerse in a constant temperature $(25° \pm 0.01°C.)$ water bath for at least 30 minutes. Observe the volume of liquid at this temperature. Remove the pycnometer from the bath, wipe it dry, and weigh.

$$D \text{ at } 25°C. = \frac{W}{V} + 0.0010$$

where

W = weight of liquid in pycnometer at 25°C.
V = volume of liquid in pycnometer at 25°C.
0.0010 = correction factor to compensate for buoyancy

The correction of 0.0010 for air buoyancy is accurate to ± 0.0001 (gram per ml.) if the density varies from 0.7079 (gram per ml.) (anhydrous ethyl ether) to 1.585 (gram per ml.) (carbon tetrachloride) and the pycnometer is weighed at a temperature of from 20° to 30°C., at an atmospheric pressure of from 720-mm. to 775-mm. mercury pressure.

Dithizone Tests

Because dithizone is extremely sensitive to many metal ions, all glassware used must be specially cleaned. After the usual cleaning, it should be thoroughly rinsed with warm dilute nitric acid $(1 + 1)$ and finally rinsed with reagent water. All glassware used in the preparation and storage of reagents and in performing the tests must be made of lead-free glass.

Flame Photometry

The techniques of flame photometric measurements have been adapted to the determination of calcium, potassium, sodium, and strontium occurring as impurities in certain salts. These impurities can be determined most expediently and accurately with the flame photometer, and no better reason seems necessary for using such an instrument. The determination must be made with adequate apparatus, and several instruments with sufficient selectivity are available.

The type of flame photometer that has proved useful for determining all of the impurities listed is one that is equipped with a red-sensitive phototube, a multiplier phototube, a monochromator, an adjustable exit slit-width control, a selector switch, and a sensitivity control. Any flame photometer may be used, provided the operator proves that the instrument will accurately determine the amount of impurities allowed in the reagent to be tested.

The test is a semi-internal-standard method and requires two solutions. For Sample Solution A, a definite amount of the sample is dissolved and diluted to a definite volume. For Control Solution B, an equal amount of sample plus specified quantities of various impurities to be determined is dissolved and diluted to the same volume as Sample Solution A. Adjust the flame photometer to give as near as possible to 100 per cent transmittance at the designated characteristic wavelength of the impurity to be determined with Control Solution B and record this value. Without changing the adjustment of the slit-width and sensitivity controls, or the selector switch, determine the emission of Sample Solution A at this wavelength. Readjust *only* the monochromator by the small specified amount and determine the emission of Sample Solution A at this new wavelength. This latter value is used to correct the emission of Sample Solution A for background emission produced by the salt and solvent. The salt being tested contains less than the specified amount of impurity if the difference (D_1) between the intensities observed for Sample Solution A at the characteristic wavelength of the impurity and at the wavelength used to correct for background is less than the difference (D_2) between the intensities observed for Sample Solution A and Control Solution B at the characteristic wavelength of the impurity. This test is designed for a limiting test; the determination of the actual amount of impurity present requires a more elaborate procedure, especially with regard to controls and calibration curves.

The preparation of the various solutions and the adjustments required for the flame photometer are described in each particular test. However, no absolute directions that are infallible can be given. This type of analysis, like every other, depends on experimental conditions and the analytical technique of the operator.

Calcium.   Use a flame photometer of the type previously described. Set the slit-width control at 0.03 mm. and the selector switch at 0.1. Adjust the instrument to give the maximum emission with Control Solution B at the 422.7-mμ calcium line and note this reading. Without changing the slit-width and sensitivity controls, or the selector switch, determine the emission of Sample Solution A at this wavelength. Change only the monochromator by the amount specified in the particular test and determine the emission of Sample Solution A at this new wavelength.

The directions for preparing Sample Solution A and Control Solution B as well as the calculations are specified in each test.

Potassium.   Use a flame photometer of the type previously described and use the red-sensitive phototube. Set the slit-width control at 0.1 mm. (except for magnesium salts, 0.3 mm., and for lithium carbonate, 0.03 mm.) and the selector switch at 0.1. If the salt being tested is a calcium salt, one must use an oxyhydrogen burner, not an oxyacetylene burner.

Adjust the instrument to give the maximum emission with Control Solution B at the 766.5-mμ potassium line and note this reading. Without changing the slit-width and sensitivity controls, or the selector switch, determine the emission of Sample Solution A at this wavelength. Change only the monochromator by the amount specified in the particular test and determine the emission of Sample Solution A at this new wavelength.

The directions for preparing Sample Solution A and Control Solution B as well as the calculations are specified in each test.

Sodium. Use a flame photometer of the type previously described. Set the slit-width control at 0.01 mm. (except for lithium carbonate, 0.03 mm.) and the selector switch at 0.1. Adjust the instrument to give the maximum emission with Control Solution B at the 589-mμ sodium line and note this reading. Without changing the slit-width and sensitivity controls, or the selector switch, determine the emission of Sample Solution A at this wavelength. Change only the monochromator by the amount specified in the particular test and determine the emission of Sample Solution A at this new wavelength.

The directions for preparing Sample Solution A and Control Solution B as well as the calculations are specified in each test.

Strontium. Use a flame photometer of the type previously described. Set the slit-width control at 0.03 mm. and the selector switch at 0.1. Adjust the instrument to give the maximum emission with Control Solution B at the 460.7-mμ strontium line and note this reading. Without changing the slit-width and sensitivity controls, or the selector switch, determine the emission of Sample Solution A at this wavelength. Change only the monochromator by the amount specified in the particular test and determine the emission of Sample Solution A at this new wavelength.

The directions for preparing Sample Solution A and Control Solution B as well as the calculations are specified in each test.

Freezing Point

Place 15 ml. of sample in a test tube (20 × 150 mm.) in which is centered an accurate thermometer. The sample tube is centered by corks in an outer tube about 38 × 200 mm. Cool the whole apparatus, without stirring, in a bath of shaved or crushed ice with water enough to wet the outer tube. When the temperature is about 3° below the normal freezing point of the reagent, stir to induce freezing and read the thermometer every half minute. The temperature which remains constant for 1 or 2 minutes is the freezing point.

Melting Point

The capillary tube method described in textbooks on organic preparations may be used, or the analyst may prefer one of the more refined types of apparatus—for example, the hot stage or the heated copper bar equipped with a thermocouple to measure the temperature.

Heavy Metals (as Pb)

The test for heavy metals as lead does not mean that lead is the only heavy metal that might be present. The test is designed to include many of the so-called hydrogen sulfide metals. The comparison is usually made with the color developed on the addition of 10 ml. of hydrogen sulfide water to a solution containing 0.02 mg. of lead in a volume of 40 ml., the pH of which is adjusted prior to final dilution to between 3 and 4 (using a pH meter). The color comparison should be made, using matched 50-ml. Nessler tubes, by viewing vertically over a white background. In some instances, an appropriate amount of the sample is added to the control because the color developed in the test may be affected by the sample being tested. In other instances, no such effect occurs and the standard may be prepared without any of the sample.

Iron

Thiocyanate. The test for iron with thiocyanate is usually made by dissolving the sample, adding 2 ml. of hydrochloric acid, diluting to 50 ml., and adding 30 to 50 mg. of ammonium persulfate crystals and 3 ml. of ammonium thiocyanate reagent solution (about 30 per cent). These quantities of hydrochloric acid and thiocyanate were selected so that the production of the red color would not be affected significantly by anything except the iron. The use of persulfate to oxidize the iron prevents fading of the color and eliminates the need for immediate comparison with the standard. For barium salts permanganate is used to oxidize the iron.

1,10-Phenanthroline. The test for iron in phosphates is usually made by adjustment of the pH, if necessary, addition of 6 ml. of hydroxylamine hydrochloride reagent solution (10 per cent) and 4 ml. of 1,10-phenanthroline reagent solution (0.1 per cent), and dilution to 25 ml. The hydroxylamine hydrochloride solution must be the unacidified reagent solution and not the acidified solution used in the dithizone test for lead and other metals.

ACS SPECIFICATIONS   **17**

pH Range

The purpose of this test is to limit the amount of free acid or alkali that is allowed in a reagent grade salt. The pH of the solution is determined by means of any reliable pH meter equipped with a standard calomel electrode and a glass electrode. The meter and electrodes are standardized at pH 4.01 at 25°C. with 0.05M potassium hydrogen phthalate ($KHC_8H_4O_4$) and at pH 9.18 at 25°C. with 0.01M N.B.S. sodium borate ($Na_2B_4O_7 \cdot 10H_2O$). Since the pH values are reported to only 0.1 pH unit, the meter and electrodes are considered to be in satisfactory working order if they show an error of less than 0.05 pH unit in the pH range of 4.01 to 9.18. Unless otherwise specified, the solution for testing is prepared by dissolving 10 grams of the sample in 200 ml. of carbon dioxide- and ammonia-free water.

Reported in each test is the pH of a 5 per cent solution of the pure salt. This value was determined experimentally for each salt by dissolving 10 grams in approximately 200 ml. of water, then making the solution slightly acid and titrating with standard alkali. Another similar solution was prepared, made slightly alkaline, and titrated with standard acid. Graphs were constructed for each titration by plotting pH versus milliliters of titrating solution and the average of the two end points so determined is reported as the pH of a 5 per cent solution containing no free acid or alkali.

Nitrate

Brucine Sulfate. It is recognized that the sensitivity of brucine sulfate for determining small amounts of nitrate varies with the conditions of each particular test. Therefore, the tests are designed so that the sensitivity of the brucine sulfate for determining the small amounts of nitrate is determined under the particular conditions of the test. The prescribed test must be followed carefully to insure the development of a reproducible color.

Diphenylamine. The prescribed tests must be followed carefully to insure the development of a reproducible and stable color. Under slightly different conditions the oxidation reaction may produce a somewhat different color, which is not stable.

Phosphate

Direct Molybdenum Blue Test. The molybdenum blue test for phosphate is used for some of the reagents. The sample is dissolved in 25 ml. of approximately 0.5N sulfuric or hydrochloric acid and 1 ml. of ammonium molybdate reagent solution and 1 ml. of p-methylaminophenol sulfate reagent solution are added. The blue color developed after standing at room temperature for 2 hours is constant and reproducible.

Extracted Molybdenum Blue Test. In some of the tests for phosphate, conditions are established that allow only the phosphomolybdate to be extracted into ether, thus eliminating any interference from arsenate or silicate.

Silicate

Small amounts of silica or silicate are now determined by a molybdenum blue method. Conditions have been established that allow the extraction of the silicomolybdate and thus eliminate any interference from arsenate or phosphate.

REAGENT SOLUTIONS

Throughout the specifications the term "reagent solution" is used to designate a solution described below. The tests and limits in the specifications are based on the use of the solutions in the strength indicated in the descriptions.

Wherever the use of ammonium hydroxide or an acid is prescribed with no indication of strength or dilution, the reagent is to be used in full strength described in its specification. Dilutions are indicated either by the percentage of some constituent or by the volumes of reagents and water mixed to prepare a dilute reagent. Dilute acid or ammonium hydroxide $(1 + X)$ means a dilute solution prepared by mixing 1 volume of the strong acid or ammonium hydroxide with X volumes of reagent water.

Unless otherwise indicated, the reagent solutions are prepared and diluted with reagent water.

Reagent Water

Throughout the specifications the term "water" means distilled water, or deionized water, which meets the requirements of **Water Reagent,** page 631. In tests for nitrogen compounds water should be "ammonia-free" or "nitrogen-free." For some tests freshly boiled water must be used in order to assure freedom from material absorbed from the air, such as ammonia, carbon dioxide, or oxygen.

Strength of Reagent Solutions

Acetic Acid, 1N

Dilute 57.5 ml. of glacial acetic acid with water to a volume of 1 liter.

Alcohol

The term "alcohol" without any qualification refers to reagent ethyl alcohol, 95 per cent by volume.

Ammonia-Cyanide Mixture, Lead-Free

Dissolve 20 grams of potassium cyanide in 150 ml. of ammonium hydroxide and dilute to 1 liter with water. Remove lead by shaking the solution with small portions of dithizone extraction solution in chloroform until the dithizone retains its original green color, rejecting the extraction solution.

Ammonium Citrate, Lead-Free

Dissolve 40 grams of citric acid in 100 ml. of water and make alkaline to phenol red with ammonium hydroxide. Remove lead by shaking the solution with small portions of dithizone extraction solution in chloroform until the dithizone solution retains its original green color, rejecting the extraction solution.

Ammonium Hydroxide, 10 Per Cent NH_3

Dilute 400 ml. of ammonium hydroxide with water to make a volume of 1 liter.

Ammonium Hydroxide, 2.5 Per Cent NH_3

Dilute 100 ml. of ammonium hydroxide with water to make a volume of 1 liter.

Ammonium Molybdate (for Direct Colorimetric Phosphate)

Dissolve 50 grams of ammonium molybdate, $(NH_4)_6Mo_7O_{24}\cdot4H_2O$, in 1 liter of $1N$ sulfuric acid.

Ammonium Oxalate

Dissolve 35 grams of ammonium oxalate, $(COONH_4)_2\cdot H_2O$, in water and dilute to 1 liter.

Ammonium Phosphate

Dissolve 130 grams of dibasic ammonium phosphate, $(NH_4)_2HPO_4$, in water and dilute to 1 liter.

Ammonium Thiocyanate

Dissolve 300 grams of ammonium thiocyanate, NH_4SCN, in water and dilute to 1 liter.

Barium Chloride

Dissolve 120 grams of barium chloride, $BaCl_2 \cdot 2H_2O$, in water and dilute to 1 liter.

Bromine Water

A saturated aqueous solution of bromine. Add enough liquid bromine to water in a bottle so that when the mixture is shaken, undissolved bromine remains in a separate phase.

Bromophenol Blue Indicator

Dissolve 0.10 gram of the salt form of bromophenol blue in water and dilute to 100 ml.

Bromothymol Blue Indicator

Dissolve 0.10 gram of bromothymol blue in 100 ml. of dilute alcohol $(1 + 1)$, and filter if necessary.

Brucine Sulfate

See the test for *Sensitivity to nitrate* under **Brucine Sulfate,** page 120.

Chromotropic Acid

Dissolve 1 gram of chromotropic acid, 4,5-dihydroxy-2,7-naphthalenedisulfonic acid, in water and dilute to 100 ml.

5,5-Dimethyl-1,3-cyclohexanedione, 5 Per Cent in Alcohol

Dissolve 5 grams of 5,5-dimethyl-1,3-cyclohexanedione in alcohol and dilute to 100 ml. with alcohol.

Dimethylglyoxime

Dissolve 1 gram of dimethylglyoxime in alcohol and dilute to 100 ml. with alcohol.

Diphenylamine

Dissolve 10 mg. of colorless diphenylamine in 100 ml. of sulfuric acid. In a separate beaker dissolve 2 grams of ammonium chloride in 200 ml. of water. Cool both solutions in an ice bath and cautiously add the sulfuric acid solution to the water solution, taking care to keep the resulting solution cold. The solution should be nearly colorless.

Dithizone Extraction Solutions

In Carbon Tetrachloride. Dissolve 30 mg. of dithizone in 1 liter of carbon tetrachloride. Store the solution in a refrigerator.

In Chloroform. Dissolve 30 mg. of dithizone in 1 liter of chloroform plus 5 ml. of alcohol. Store the solution in a refrigerator.

Dithizone Standard Solutions

In Carbon Tetrachloride. Dissolve 10 mg. of dithizone in 1 liter of carbon tetrachloride.

In Chloroform. Dissolve 10 mg. of dithizone in 1 liter of chloroform.

Keep the solutions in glass-stoppered lead-free bottles protected from light and stored in a refrigerator.

Ferric Ammonium Sulfate Indicator

Dissolve 80 grams of clear crystals of ferric ammonium sulfate, $FeNH_4(SO_4)_2 \cdot 12H_2O$, in water and dilute to 1 liter. A few drops of sulfuric acid may be added, if necessary, to clear the solution.

Ferric Chloride

Dissolve 100 grams of ferric chloride, $FeCl_3 \cdot 6H_2O$, in dilute hydrochloric acid $(1 + 99)$ and dilute to 1 liter with the dilute acid.

Furfural

Dissolve 9 ml. of freshly distilled furfural in water and dilute to 1 liter.

Hydrochloric Acid, 20 Per Cent HCl

Dilute 470 ml. of hydrochloric acid with water to 1 liter.

Hydrochloric Acid, 10 Per Cent HCl

Dilute 235 ml. of hydrochloric acid with water to 1 liter.

Hydrogen Sulfide Water

Saturate water with hydrogen sulfide gas. This solution must be freshly prepared.

Hydroxylamine Hydrochloride

Dissolve 10 grams of hydroxylamine hydrochloride, $NH_2OH \cdot HCl$, in water and dilute to 100 ml.

Hydroxylamine Hydrochloride for Dithizone Test

Dissolve 20 grams of hydroxylamine hydrochloride, $NH_2OH \cdot HCl$, in about 65 ml. of water and add 0.10 to 0.15 ml. of thymol blue indicator solution. Add ammonium hydroxide until a yellow color appears. Add 5 ml. of a 4 per cent solution of sodium diethyldithiocarbamate. Mix thoroughly and allow to stand for 5 minutes. Extract with successive portions of chloroform until no yellow color is developed in the chloroform layer when the extract is shaken with a dilute solution of a copper salt. Add hydrochloric acid until the indicator turns pink, and dilute to 100 ml.

Indigo Carmine

Dissolve 1 gram of FD&C Blue No. 2, dried at 105°C., in a mixture of 800 ml. of water and 110 ml. of sulfuric acid, and dilute to 1 liter. FD&C Blue No. 2, the disodium salt of 5,5'-indigotindisulfonic acid, $C_{16}H_8N_2O_2(SO_3Na)_2$, is one of the dyes which may be certified under the Federal Food, Drug, and Cosmetic Act as suitable for use in foods, drugs, and cosmetics.

Lead Acetate

Dissolve 100 grams of lead acetate, $(CH_3COO)_2Pb \cdot 3H_2O$, in water. If necessary, add a few drops of acetic acid to clear the solution and dilute to 1 liter.

p-Methylaminophenol Sulfate

Dissolve 2 grams of p-methylaminophenol sulfate in 100 ml. of water. To 10 ml. of this solution add 90 ml. of water and 20 grams of sodium bisulfite. Confirm the suitability of the reagent solution by the following test:

Add 1 ml. of this reagent solution to each of four solutions containing 25 ml. of 0.5N sulfuric acid and 1 ml. of ammonium molybdate 5 per cent reagent solution. Add 0.005 mg. of phosphate ion (PO_4) to one of the solutions, 0.01 mg. to a second, and 0.02 mg. to a third. Allow to stand at room temperature for 2 hours. The solutions in the three tubes should show readily perceptible differences in blue color corresponding to the relative amounts of phosphate added, and the one to which 0.005 mg. of phosphate was added should be perceptibly bluer than the blank.

Methyl Orange Indicator

Dissolve 0.10 gram of methyl orange in 100 ml. of water.

Methyl Red Indicator

Dissolve 0.10 gram of methyl red in 100 ml. of alcohol. See page 376 for a description of the three forms of methyl red.

Nessler Reagent

Dissolve 143 grams of sodium hydroxide in 700 ml. of water. Dissolve 50 grams of red mercuric iodide and 40 grams of potassium iodide in 200 ml. of water. Pour the iodide solution into the hydroxide solution and dilute to 1 liter. Allow to settle and use the clear supernatant liquid. Nessler reagent prepared by any of the recognized methods may be used, but the reagent described reacts promptly and consistently.

Nitric Acid, 10 Per Cent HNO$_3$

Dilute 105 ml. of nitric acid with water to 1 liter.

Nitric Acid, 1 Per Cent HNO$_3$

Dilute 10.5 ml. of nitric acid with water to 1 liter.

Oxalic Acid

Dissolve 40 grams of oxalic acid, $(COOH)_2 \cdot 2H_2O$, in water and dilute to 1 liter.

1,10-Phenanthroline

Dissolve 0.1 gram of 1,10-phenanthroline monohydrate,

CH:CHCH:NC:CCH:CHC:CN:CHCH:CH·H$_2$O, in 100 ml. of water containing 0.1 ml. of 10 per cent hydrochloric acid reagent solution.

Phenoldisulfonic Acid

Dissolve 50 grams of phenol, C_6H_5OH, in 300 ml. of sulfuric acid, add 150 ml. of fuming sulfuric acid (15 per cent SO$_3$), and heat at 100°C. for 2 hours.

Phenolphthalein Indicator

Dissolve 1 gram of phenolphthalein in 100 ml. of alcohol.

Phenol Red Indicator

Dissolve 0.10 gram of phenol red in 100 ml. of alcohol, and filter if necessary.

Potassium Chromate

Dissolve 100 grams of potassium chromate, K_2CrO_4, in water and dilute to 1 liter.

Potassium Cyanide, Lead-Free

Dissolve 100 grams of potassium cyanide, KCN, in sufficient water to make 200 ml. Remove lead by shaking with portions of dithizone extraction solution. Part of the dithizone remains in the aqueous phase but can be removed, if desired, by shaking with chloroform. Dilute the potassium cyanide solution to 1 liter.

Potassium Dichromate

Dissolve 10 grams of potassium dichromate, $K_2Cr_2O_7$, in water and dilute to 100 ml. with water.

Potassium Ferricyanide

Dissolve 5 grams of potassium ferricyanide, $K_3Fe(CN)_6$, in 100 ml. of water. The solution must be freshly prepared.

Potassium Ferrocyanide

Dissolve 10 grams of potassium ferrocyanide, $K_4Fe(CN)_6 \cdot 3H_2O$, in 100 ml. of water. The solution must be freshly prepared.

Potassium Hydroxide, 0.5N in Methanol

Dissolve 34 to 36 grams of potassium hydroxide, KOH, in 20 ml. of water and add methanol to make a volume of 1 liter. Allow the solution to stand in a stoppered bottle for 24 hours. Decant the clear supernatant solution into a bottle provided with a tight-fitting stopper.

Potassium Iodide

Dissolve 100 grams of potassium iodide, KI, in water and dilute to 1 liter.

Silver Nitrate

Dissolve 17 grams of silver nitrate, $AgNO_3$, in 1 liter of water.

Sodium Cyanide

Dissolve 100 grams of sodium cyanide, NaCN, in water and dilute to 1 liter.

Sodium Diethyldithiocarbamate

Dissolve 1.0 gram of sodium diethyldithiocarbamate in water and dilute to 1 liter.

Sodium Hydroxide

Dissolve 100 grams of sodium hydroxide, NaOH, in water and dilute to 1 liter.

Stannous Chloride

Dissolve 2 grams of stannous chloride, $SnCl_2 \cdot 2H_2O$, in hydrochloric acid and dilute to 100 ml. with hydrochloric acid.

Starch Indicator

Mix 1 gram of soluble starch with 10 mg. of red mercuric iodide and enough cold water to make a thin paste, add 200 ml. of boiling water, and boil for 1 minute while stirring. Cool before use.

Sulfuric Acid, 25 Per Cent H_2SO_4

Slowly add 170 ml. of sulfuric acid to 750 ml. of water, cool, and dilute to 1 liter.

Sulfuric Acid, 10 Per Cent H_2SO_4

Slowly add 60 ml. of sulfuric acid to 750 ml. of water, cool, and dilute to 1 liter.

Thymol Blue Indicator

Dissolve 0.10 gram of thymol blue in 100 ml. of alcohol.

Thymolphthalein Indicator

Dissolve 0.10 gram of thymolphthalein in 100 ml. of alcohol.

STANDARD SOLUTIONS

For Preparing Controls and Standards

Many of the tests for impurities require the comparison of the color or the turbidity produced under specified conditions by an impurity ion with the color or the turbidity produced under similar conditions by a known amount of the impurity. Three types of solutions are used to determine amounts of impurities in reagent chemicals: (1) the blank, (2) the standard, and (3) the control.

(1) Blank. A solution containing the quantities of solvents and reagents used in the test. A blank is required primarily in gravimetric tests.

(2) Standard. A solution containing the quantities of solvents and reagents used in the test plus an added known amount of the impurity to be determined.

(3) Control. A solution containing the quantities of solvents and reagents used in the test plus an added known amount of the impurity to be determined *and* a known amount of the reagent chemical being tested. Some of the chemical being tested must be added to the solution because it is known that the chemical interferes with the test.

Throughout this book in the expressions "for the control" or "for the standard" add X mg. of Y ion means to add the proper aliquot of one of the following solutions. These solutions must be freshly prepared or at least checked often enough to make certain that the tests will not be vitiated by changes in strength of the standard solution during storage. Calibrated volumetric glassware must be used in preparing these solutions.

Aluminum (0.01 mg. Al in 1 ml.)

Dissolve 0.100 gram of metallic aluminum, Al, in 10 ml. of dilute hydrochloric acid $(1 + 1)$ and dilute to 100 ml. To 10 ml. of this solution add 25 ml. of dilute hydrochloric acid $(1 + 1)$ and dilute with water to 1 liter.

Ammonium (0.01 mg. NH₄ in 1 ml.)

Dissolve 0.296 gram of ammonium chloride, NH_4Cl, in water and dilute to 100 ml. Dilute 10 ml. of this solution to 1 liter.

Arsenic (0.001 mg. As in 1 ml.)

Dissolve 0.132 gram of arsenic trioxide, As_2O_3, in 10 ml. of 10 per cent sodium hydroxide reagent solution, neutralize with 10 per cent sulfuric acid reagent solution, add an excess of 10 ml., and dilute to 1 liter. To 10 ml. of this solution add 10 ml. of 10 per cent sulfuric acid reagent solution and dilute to 1 liter.

Barium (0.10 mg. Ba in 1 ml.)

Dissolve 0.178 gram of barium chloride, $BaCl_2 \cdot 2H_2O$, in water and dilute to 1 liter.

Bismuth (0.01 mg. Bi in 1 ml.)

Dissolve 0.232 gram of bismuth trinitrate pentahydrate, $Bi(NO_3)_3 \cdot 5H_2O$, in 10 ml. of dilute nitric acid $(1 + 9)$ and dilute to 100 ml. Dilute 10 ml. of this solution plus 10 ml. of nitric acid with water to 1 liter.

Bromide (0.10 mg. Br in 1 ml.)

Dissolve 1.49 grams of potassium bromide, KBr, in water and dilute to 100 ml. Dilute 10 ml. of this solution to 1 liter.

Cadmium (0.025 mg. Cd in 1 ml.)

Dissolve 0.10 gram of cadmium chloride crystals, $CdCl_2 \cdot 2\frac{1}{2}H_2O$, in water, add 1 ml. of hydrochloric acid, and dilute to 500 ml. To 25 ml. of this solution add 1 ml. of hydrochloric acid and dilute to 100 ml.

Calcium (0.10 mg. Ca in 1 ml.)

Dissolve 0.250 gram of calcium carbonate, $CaCO_3$, in 20 ml. of water plus 5 ml. of 10 per cent hydrochloric acid reagent solution and dilute to 1 liter.

Chloride (0.01 mg. Cl in 1 ml.)

Dissolve 0.165 gram of sodium chloride, NaCl, in water and dilute to 100 ml. Dilute 10 ml. of this solution to 1 liter.

Copper Stock Solution (0.10 mg. Cu in 1 ml.)

Dissolve 0.393 gram of cupric sulfate, $CuSO_4 \cdot 5H_2O$, in water and dilute to 1 liter.

Copper Standard for Dithizone Test (0.001 mg. Cu in 1 ml.)

Dilute 1 ml. of the copper stock solution to 100 ml. This dilute solution must be freshly prepared immediately before use.

Iodide (0.01 mg. I in 1 ml.)

Dissolve 0.131 gram of potassium iodide, KI, in water and dilute to 100 ml. Dilute 10 ml. of this solution to 1 liter.

Iron (0.01 mg. Fe in 1 ml.)

Dissolve 0.702 gram of ferrous ammonium sulfate, $Fe(NH_4)_2(SO_4)_2 \cdot 6H_2O$, in 10 ml. of 10 per cent sulfuric acid reagent solution and dilute to 100 ml. with water. To 10 ml. of this solution add 10 ml. of 10 per cent sulfuric acid reagent solution and dilute to 1 liter.

Lead Stock Solution (0.10 mg. Pb in 1 ml.)

Dissolve 0.160 gram of lead nitrate, $Pb(NO_3)_2$, in 100 ml. of dilute nitric acid $(1 + 99)$ and dilute to 1 liter. The solution should be prepared and stored in containers free from lead. Its strength should be checked every few months to determine whether the lead content has changed by reaction with the container.

Lead Standard for Dithizone Test (0.001 mg. Pb in 1 ml.)

Dilute 1 ml. of the lead stock solution to 100 ml. with dilute nitric acid $(1 + 99)$. This solution must be freshly prepared immediately before use.

Lead Standard for Heavy Metals Test (0.01 mg. Pb in 1 ml.)

Dilute 10 ml. of the lead stock solution to 100 ml. with water. This dilute solution must be freshly prepared.

Magnesium (0.01 mg. Mg in 1 ml.)

Dissolve 1.014 grams of clear crystals of magnesium sulfate heptahydrate, $MgSO_4 \cdot 7H_2O$, in water and dilute to 100 ml. Dilute 10 ml. of this solution to 1 liter.

Manganese (0.01 mg. Mn in 1 ml.)

Dissolve 3.08 grams of manganese sulfate monohydrate, $MnSO_4 \cdot H_2O$, in water and dilute to 1 liter. Dilute 10 ml. of this solution to 1 liter.

Mercury (0.05 mg. Hg in 1 ml.)

Dissolve 1.35 grams of mercuric chloride, $HgCl_2$, in water, add 8 ml. of hydrochloric acid, and dilute to 1 liter. To 50 ml. of this solution add 8 ml. of hydrochloric acid and dilute to 1 liter.

Molybdenum (0.01 mg. Mo in 1 ml.)

Dissolve 0.150 gram of molybdenum trioxide, MoO_3, in 10 ml. of dilute ammonium hydroxide $(1 + 9)$ and dilute to 100 ml. Dilute 10 ml. of this solution to 1 liter.

Nickel (0.01 mg. Ni in 1 ml.)

Dissolve 0.448 gram of nickel sulfate, $NiSO_4 \cdot 6H_2O$, in water and dilute to 100 ml. Dilute 10 ml. of this solution to 1 liter.

Nitrate (0.01 mg. NO_3 in 1 ml.)

Dissolve 0.163 gram of potassium nitrate, KNO_3, in water and dilute to 100 ml. Dilute 10 ml. of this solution to 1 liter.

International Atomic Weights 1967

	Symbol	Atomic No.	Atomic Weight		Symbol	Atomic No.	Atomic Weight
Actinium	Ac	89	...	Mercury	Hg	80	200.59
Aluminum	Al	13	26.9815	Molybdenum	Mo	42	95.94
Americium	Am	95	...	Neodymium	Nd	60	144.24
Antimony	Sb	51	121.75	Neon	Ne	10	20.179[b]
Argon	Ar	18	39.948	Neptunium	Np	93	...
Arsenic	As	33	74.9216	Nickel	Ni	28	58.71
Astatine	At	85	...	Niobium	Nb	41	92.906
Barium	Ba	56	137.34	Nitrogen	N	7	14.0067
Berkelium	Bk	97	...	Nobelium	No	102	...
Beryllium	Be	4	9.0122	Osmium	Os	76	190.2
Bismuth	Bi	83	208.980	Oxygen	O	8	15.9994[a]
Boron	B	5	10.811[a]	Palladium	Pd	46	106.4
Bromine	Br	35	79.904[b]	Phosphorus	P	15	30.9738
Cadmium	Cd	48	112.40	Platinum	Pt	78	195.09
Calcium	Ca	20	40.08	Plutonium	Pu	94	...
Californium	Cf	98	...	Polonium	Po	84	...
Carbon	C	6	12.01115[a]	Potassium	K	19	39.102
Cerium	Ce	58	140.12	Praseodymium	Pr	59	140.907
Cesium	Cs	55	132.905	Promethium	Pm	61	...
Chlorine	Cl	17	35.453[b]	Protactinium	Pa	91	...
Chromium	Cr	24	51.996	Radium	Ra	88	...
Cobalt	Co	27	58.9332	Radon	Rn	86	...
Copper	Cu	29	63.546[b]	Rhenium	Re	75	186.2
Curium	Cm	96	...	Rhodium	Rh	45	102.905
Dysprosium	Dy	66	162.50	Rubidium	Rb	37	85.47
Einsteinium	Es	99	...	Ruthenium	Ru	44	101.07
Erbium	Er	68	167.26	Samarium	Sm	62	150.35
Europium	Eu	63	151.96	Scandium	Sc	21	44.956
Fermium	Fm	100	...	Selenium	Se	34	78.96
Fluorine	F	9	18.9984	Silicon	Si	14	28.086[a]
Francium	Fr	87	...	Silver	Ag	47	107.868[b]
Gadolinium	Gd	64	157.25	Sodium	Na	11	22.9898
Gallium	Ga	31	69.72	Strontium	Sr	38	87.62
Germanium	Ge	32	72.59	Sulfur	S	16	32.064[a]
Gold	Au	79	196.967	Tantalum	Ta	73	180.948
Hafnium	Hf	72	178.49	Technetium	Tc	43	...
Helium	He	2	4.0026	Tellurium	Te	52	127.60
Holmium	Ho	67	164.930	Terbium	Tb	65	158.924
Hydrogen	H	1	1.00797[a]	Thallium	Tl	81	204.37
Indium	In	49	114.82	Thorium	Th	90	232.038
Iodine	I	53	126.9044	Thulium	Tm	69	168.934
Iridium	Ir	77	192.2	Tin	Sn	50	118.69
Iron	Fe	26	55.847[b]	Titanium	Ti	22	47.90
Krypton	Kr	36	83.80	Tungsten	W	74	183.85
Lanthanum	La	57	138.91	Uranium	U	92	238.03
Lead	Pb	82	207.19	Vanadium	V	23	50.942
Lithium	Li	3	6.939	Xenon	Xe	54	131.30
Lutetium	Lu	71	174.97	Ytterbium	Yb	70	173.04
Magnesium	Mg	12	24.305	Yttrium	Y	39	88.905
Manganese	Mn	25	54.9380	Zinc	Zn	30	65.37
Mendelevium	Md	101	...	Zirconium	Zr	40	91.22

[a] Atomic weights so designated are known to be variable because of natural variations in isotopic condition. The observed ranges are: boron, ±0.003; carbon, ±0.00005; hydrogen, ±0.00001; oxygen, ±0.0001; silicon, ±0.001; and sulfur, ±0.003.
[b] Atomic weights so designated are believed to have the following experimental uncertainties: bromine, ±0.001; chlorine, ±0.001; copper, ±0.001; iron, ±0.003; neon, ±0.003; and silver, ±0.001.

Nitrogen (0.01 mg. N in 1 ml.)

Dissolve 0.382 gram of ammonium chloride, NH_4Cl, in water and dilute to 100 ml. Dilute 10 ml. of this solution to 1 liter.

Phosphate (0.01 mg. PO_4 in 1 ml.)

Dissolve 0.143 gram of monobasic potassium phosphate, KH_2PO_4, in water and dilute to 100 ml. Dilute 10 ml. of this solution to 1 liter.

Platinum-Cobalt Stock Solution (APHA No. 500)

Dissolve 1.246 grams of potassium chloroplatinate, K_2PtCl_6, and 1.000 gram of cobalt chloride, $CoCl_2 \cdot 6H_2O$, in water. Add 100 ml. of hydrochloric acid and dilute to 1 liter with water.

Potassium (0.01 mg. K in 1 ml.)

Dissolve 0.191 gram of potassium chloride, KCl, in water and dilute to 1 liter. Dilute 100 ml. of this solution to 1 liter.

Silicate (0.01 mg. SiO_2 in 1 ml.)

Dissolve 0.473 gram of sodium silicate, $Na_2SiO_3 \cdot 9H_2O$, in 100 ml. of water in a platinum or polyethylene dish. Dilute 10 ml. of this solution (polyethylene graduate) to 1 liter in a polyethylene bottle.

Silver (0.10 mg. Ag in 1 ml.)

Dissolve 0.157 gram of silver nitrate, $AgNO_3$, in water and dilute to 1 liter.

Sodium (0.01 mg. Na in 1 ml.)

Dissolve 0.254 gram of sodium chloride, NaCl, in water and dilute to 1 liter. Dilute 100 ml. of this solution to 1 liter.

Strontium (0.01 mg. Sr in 1 ml.)

Dissolve 0.242 gram of strontium nitrate, $Sr(NO_3)_2$, in water and dilute to 100 ml. Dilute 10 ml. of this solution to 1 liter.

Sulfate (0.01 mg. SO_4 in 1 ml.)

Dissolve 0.148 gram of anhydrous sodium sulfate, Na_2SO_4, in water and dilute to 100 ml. Dilute 10 ml. of this solution to 1 liter.

Sulfide (0.01 mg. S in 1 ml.)

Dissolve 0.75 gram of sodium sulfide, $Na_2S \cdot 9H_2O$, in water and dilute to 100 ml. Dilute 10 ml. of this solution to 1 liter. This solution must be freshly prepared immediately before use.

Tin (0.05 mg. Sn in 1 ml.)

Dissolve 0.100 gram of metallic tin (Sn) in 10 ml. of dilute hydrochloric acid $(1 + 1)$ and dilute to 100 ml. Dilute 5 ml. of this solution to 100 ml. with dilute hydrochloric acid $(1 + 9)$. This solution must be freshly prepared immediately before use.

Titanium (0.10 mg. Ti in 1 ml.)

Dissolve 0.739 gram of potassium titanyl oxalate, $K_2TiO(C_2O_4)_2 \cdot 2H_2O$, in water and dilute to 1 liter.

Zinc Stock Solution (0.10 mg. Zn in 1 ml.)

Dissolve 0.124 gram of zinc oxide, ZnO, in 10 ml. of dilute sulfuric acid $(1 + 9)$ and dilute to 1 liter with water.

Zinc Standard for Dithizone Tests (0.001 mg. Zn in 1 ml.)

Dilute 1 ml. of the zinc stock solution to 100 ml. This dilute solution must be freshly prepared immediately before use.

Notes

Notes

Acetic Acid, Glacial

CH$_3$COOH   Formula Wt. 60.05

REQUIREMENTS

Assay.   Not less than 99.7 per cent CH$_3$COOH.
Color (APHA).   Not more than 10.
Dilution test.   To pass test.
Residue after evaporation.   Not more than 0.0010 per cent.
Chloride (Cl).   Not more than 0.0001 per cent.
Sulfate (SO$_4$).   Not more than 0.0001 per cent.
Heavy metals (as Pb).   Not more than 0.00005 per cent.
Iron (Fe).   Not more than 0.00002 per cent.
Substances reducing dichromate.   To pass test.

TESTS

Assay.   The freezing point should not be below 16.0°C.

Color (APHA).   For the color standard dilute a 2-ml. aliquot of platinum-cobalt stock solution (APHA No. 500) to 100 ml. with water. Compare this solution (APHA No. 10) with 100 ml. of the acetic acid in 100-ml. Nessler tubes, viewed vertically over a white background.

Dilution test.   Dilute 1 volume of the acid with 3 volumes of water and allow to stand for 1 hour. The solution should be as clear as an equal volume of water.

Residue after evaporation.   Evaporate 95 ml. (100 grams) to dryness in a tared dish on the steam bath and dry the residue at 105°C. for 30 minutes. The weight of the residue should not exceed 0.0010 gram.

Chloride.   Dilute 9.5 ml. (10 grams) with 10 ml. of water and add 1 ml. of silver nitrate reagent solution. Prepare a standard containing 0.01 mg. of chloride ion (Cl) in 20 ml. of water and add 1 ml. of silver nitrate reagent solution. Evaporate the solutions to dryness on the steam bath. Dissolve the residues with 0.5 ml. of ammonium hydroxide, dilute with 20 ml. of water, and add 1.5 ml. of nitric acid. Any turbidity in the solution of the sample should not exceed that in the standard.

Sulfate.   To 48 ml. (50 grams) add about 10 mg. of sodium carbonate and evaporate to dryness on the steam bath. Dissolve the residue in 4 ml. of water plus 1 ml. of dilute hydrochloric acid (1 + 19) and filter through a small filter. Wash with two 2-ml. portions of water, dilute to 10 ml., and add 1 ml. of barium chloride reagent solution. Any turbidity should not exceed that produced by 0.05 mg. of sulfate ion (SO$_4$) in an equal volume of solution containing the quantities of reagents used in the test. Compare 10 minutes after adding the barium chloride to the sample and standard solutions.

Heavy metals.   To 38 ml. (40 grams) add about 10 mg. of sodium carbonate, evaporate to dryness on the steam bath, dissolve the residue in about 20 ml. of water, and dilute to 25 ml. For the standard dilute a solution containing 0.02 mg. of lead ion (Pb) to 25 ml. Adjust the pH of the standard and sample solutions to between 3 and 4 (using a pH meter) with 1N acetic acid or ammonium hydroxide (10 per cent NH₃), dilute to 40 ml., and mix. Add 10 ml. of freshly prepared hydrogen sulfide water to each and mix. Any color in the solution of the sample should not exceed that in the standard.

Iron.   To 48 ml. (50 grams) add 10 mg. of sodium carbonate and evaporate to dryness. Dissolve the residue in 2 ml. of hydrochloric acid and dilute to 50 ml. Add 30 to 50 mg. of ammonium persulfate crystals and 3 ml. of ammonium thiocyanate reagent solution. Any red color should not exceed that produced by 0.01 mg. of iron (Fe) in an equal volume of solution containing the quantities of reagents used in the test.

Substances reducing dichromate.   To 10 ml. add 1.0 ml. of 0.1N potassium dichromate and cautiously add 10 ml. of sulfuric acid. Cool the solution to room temperature and allow to stand for 30 minutes. While the solution is swirled, dilute slowly and cautiously with 50 ml. of water, cool, and add 1 ml. of freshly prepared potassium iodide reagent solution. Titrate the liberated iodine with 0.1N thiosulfate, using starch as the indicator. Not more than 0.40 ml. of the 0.1N potassium dichromate should be consumed (not less than 0.60 ml. of the 0.1N thiosulfate should be required). Correct for a complete blank.

Notes

Acetic Anhydride

$(CH_3CO)_2O$ Formula Wt. 102.09

REQUIREMENTS

Assay.   Not less than 97 per cent $(CH_3CO)_2O$.
Residue after evaporation.   Not more than 0.003 per cent.
Chloride (Cl).   Not more than 0.0005 per cent.
Phosphate (PO_4).   Not more than 0.001 per cent.
Sulfate (SO_4).   Not more than 0.0005 per cent.
Heavy metals (as Pb).   Not more than 0.0002 per cent.
Iron (Fe).   Not more than 0.0005 per cent.
Substances reducing permanganate.   To pass test.

TESTS

Assay.   Carefully pipet 50 ml. of morpholine methanolic solution* into each of two 250-ml. glass-stoppered flasks. For the sample weigh accurately 1.8 to 2.0 grams of the acetic anhydride from a Lunge pipet into the first flask and swirl to effect dissolution. Reserve the second flask for the determination of the quantity of morpholine mixed with the sample. Allow the flasks to stand at room temperature for 5 minutes. Add 0.20 to 0.25 ml. of methyl yellow-methylene blue mixed indicator.* Titrate each solution with 0.5N hydrochloric acid methanolic solution* to the end point at which the green color changes to amber. Calculate the *Assay* value as follows:

$$\text{Per cent } (CH_3CO)_2O = 10.209 \frac{(V_2 - V_1)N}{W}$$

where,

$V_1 =$ volume, in ml., of 0.5N HCl added to the first flask
$V_2 =$ volume, in ml., of 0.5N HCl added to the second flask
$N =$ exact normality of HCl methanolic solution
$W =$ weight, in grams, of sample

*Reagents. 1. Hydrochloric Acid Methanolic Solution, 0.5N.   Transfer 84 ml. of 6N hydrochloric acid to a 1-liter volumetric flask and dilute to volume with reagent methanol. Standardize daily against 0.5N sodium hydroxide using phenolphthalein indicator. The reagent is best handled in an automatic buret assembly.

2. Morpholine Methanolic Solution, 0.5N.   Transfer 44 ml. of redistilled morpholine to a 1-liter reagent bottle and dilute to 1 liter with reagent methanol. To facilitate removal of aliquots fit the bottle with a 2-hole rubber stopper and insert a 50-ml. pipet through one hole so that the tip dips below the surface of the liquid. Through the other hole insert a short piece of glass tubing to which is attached a rubber atomizer bulb.

3. Methyl Yellow-Methylene Blue Mixed Indicator. Dissolve 1.0 gram of methyl yellow (*N,N*-dimethyl-*p*-phenylazoaniline) and 0.1 gram of methylene blue in 125 ml. of methanol.

Residue after evaporation. Evaporate 46 ml. (50 grams) to dryness in a tared dish on the steam bath and dry the residue at 105°C. for 30 minutes. The weight of the residue should not exceed 0.0015 gram.

Sample Solution A. Dilute 37.0 ml. (40 grams) of the sample to 200 ml. (1 ml. = 0.2 gram).

Chloride. Dilute 10 ml. of Sample Solution A (2-gram sample) to 20 ml., filter if necessary through a chloride-free filter, and add 1 ml. of nitric acid and 1 ml. of silver nitrate reagent solution. Any turbidity should not exceed that produced by 0.01 mg. of chloride ion (Cl) in an equal volume of solution containing the quantities of reagents used in the test.

Phosphate. Evaporate 10 ml. of Sample Solution A (2-gram sample) to dryness on the steam bath. Dissolve the residue in 25 ml. of approximately 0.5N sulfuric acid, add 1 ml. of ammonium molybdate reagent solution and 1 ml. of *p*-methylaminophenol sulfate reagent solution, and allow to stand for 2 hours at room temperature. Any blue color should not exceed that produced by 0.02 mg. of phosphate ion (PO_4) in an equal volume of solution containing the quantities of reagents used in the test.

Sulfate. To 50 ml. of Sample Solution A (10-gram sample) add about 10 mg. of sodium carbonate and evaporate to dryness on the steam bath. Dissolve the residue in 4 ml. of water plus 1 ml. of dilute hydrochloric acid (1 + 19), filter through a small filter, and wash with two 2-ml. portions of water. Dilute the filtrate to 10 ml. and add 1 ml. of barium chloride reagent solution. Any turbidity should not exceed that produced by 0.05 mg. of sulfate ion (SO_4) in an equal volume of solution containing the quantities of reagents used in the test. Compare 10 minutes after adding the barium chloride to the sample and standard solutions.

Heavy metals. To 50 ml. of Sample Solution A (10-gram sample) add about 10 mg. of sodium carbonate, evaporate to dryness on the steam bath, dissolve the residue in about 20 ml. of water, and dilute to 25 ml. For the standard dilute a solution containing 0.02 mg. of lead ion (Pb) to 25 ml. Adjust the pH of the standard and sample solutions to between 3 and 4 (using a pH meter) with 1N acetic acid or ammonium hydroxide (10 per cent NH_3), dilute to 40 ml., and mix. Add 10 ml. of freshly prepared hydrogen sulfide water to each and mix. Any color in the solution of the sample should not exceed that in the standard.

Iron. To 10 ml. of Sample Solution A (2-gram sample) in a beaker add about 10 mg. of sodium carbonate and evaporate to dryness. Dissolve the residue in 2 ml. of hydrochloric acid and dilute to 50 ml. Add 30 to 50 mg. of ammonium persulfate crystals and 3 ml. of ammonium thiocyanate reagent solution. Any red color should not exceed that produced by 0.01 mg. of iron (Fe) in an equal volume of solution containing the quantities of reagents used in the test.

Substances reducing permanganate. To 10 ml. of Sample Solution A (2-gram sample) add 0.4 ml. of 0.1N potassium permanganate and allow to stand for 5 minutes. The pink color should not be entirely discharged.

Notes

Acetone

(CH₃)₂CO

$(CH_3)_2CO$ Formula Wt. 58.08

REQUIREMENTS

Color (APHA). Not more than 10.
Density (gram per ml.) at 25°C. Not above 0.7857.
Boiling range. 1 ml. to 95 ml., not more than 0.5°C.; 95 ml. to dryness, not more than 0.5°C.
Residue after evaporation. Not more than 0.001 per cent.
Solubility in water. To pass test.
Acidity (as CH₃COOH). Not more than 0.002 per cent.
Alkalinity (as NH₃). Not more than 0.001 per cent.
Aldehyde (as HCHO). Not more than 0.002 per cent.
Methanol (CH₃OH). To pass test (limit about 0.05 per cent).
Substances reducing permanganate. To pass test.

TESTS

Color (APHA). For the color standard dilute a 2-ml. aliquot of platinum-cobalt stock solution (APHA No. 500) to 100 ml. with water. Compare this solution (APHA No. 10) with 100 ml. of the acetone in 100-ml. Nessler tubes, viewed vertically over a white background.

Boiling range. Distill 100 ml. by the method described on page 12. The difference between the temperatures when 1 ml. and 95 ml. have distilled should not exceed 0.5°C., and the difference in temperatures when 95 ml. have distilled and when the dry point is reached should not exceed 0.5°C. The boiling point of pure acetone at 760-mm. mercury pressure is 56.1°C.

Residue after evaporation. Evaporate 125 ml. (100 grams) to dryness in a tared dish on the steam bath and dry the residue at 105°C. for 30 minutes. The weight of the residue should not exceed 0.0010 gram.

Solubility in water. Mix 38 ml. (30 grams) with 38 ml. of carbon dioxide-free water. The solution should remain clear for 30 minutes. Reserve this solution for the test for *Acidity*.

Acidity. Add 0.10 ml. of phenolphthalein indicator solution to the solution prepared in the preceding test. Not more than 0.1 ml. of 0.1N sodium hydroxide should be required to produce a pink color.

Alkalinity. Mix 23 ml. (18 grams) with 25 ml. of water and add 0.05 ml. of methyl red indicator solution. Not more than 0.1 ml. of 0.1N acid should be required to produce a red color.

Aldehyde. Dilute 2.5 ml. (2 grams) with water to 10 ml. Prepare a standard containing 0.04 mg. of formaldehyde in 10 ml. of water. To each add 0.15 ml. of a 5 per cent solution of 5,5-dimethyl-1,3-cyclohexanedione in alcohol. Evaporate each on the steam bath until the acetone is volatilized (as judged by odor of acetone). Dilute each to 10 ml. and cool quickly in an ice bath while stirring vigorously. Any turbidity in the solution of the sample should not exceed that in the standard.

Methanol. Dilute 10 ml. with water to 100 ml. To 1 ml. of the solution add 0.2 ml. of dilute phosphoric acid (1 + 9) and 0.25 ml. of 5 per cent potassium permanganate solution. Allow to stand for 15 minutes, add 0.3 ml. of 10 per cent sodium bisulfite solution, and shake until colorless. Add slowly 5 ml. of ice-cold 80 per cent sulfuric acid (3 volumes of acid to 1 volume of water), keeping the mixture cold during the addition. Add 0.1 ml. of a 1 per cent aqueous solution of chromotropic acid, mix, and digest on the steam bath for 20 minutes. Any violet color should not exceed that produced by 0.04 mg. of methanol in 1 ml. of water treated exactly like the 1 ml. of diluted sample.

Substances reducing permangate. Add 0.05 ml. of $0.1N$ potassium permanganate to 10 ml. of the sample and allow to stand for 15 minutes at 25°C. The pink color should not be entirely discharged.

Notes

Acetone

(Suitable for use in ultraviolet spectrophotometry)

(CH$_3$)$_2$CO   Formula Wt. 58.08

REQUIREMENTS

Absorbance.   To pass test.
Density (gram per ml.) at 25°C.   Not above 0.7857.
Boiling range.   1 ml. to 95 ml., not more than 0.5°C.; 95 ml. to dryness, not more than 0.5°C.
Residue after evaporation.   Not more than 0.001 per cent.
Solubility in water.   To pass test.
Acidity (as CH$_3$COOH).   Not more than 0.002 per cent.
Alkalinity (as NH$_3$).   Not more than 0.001 per cent.
Aldehyde (as HCHO).   Not more than 0.002 per cent.
Methanol (CH$_3$OH).   To pass test (limit about 0.05 per cent).
Substances reducing permanganate.   To pass test.

TESTS

Absorbance.   Determine the absorbance of the sample in a 1.00-cm. cell throughout the range of 330 mμ to 400 mμ, against water in a similar matched cell set at zero absorbance as the reference liquid. The absorbance should not exceed 1.00 at 330 mμ, 0.10 at 340 mμ, 0.02 at 350 mμ, and 0.01 at 400 mμ. The spectral absorbance curve recorded through the wavelengths indicated should be smooth throughout the prescribed range and should not show any extraneous impurity peaks within this range.

Other tests are the same as for **Acetone,** page 39, except *Color (APHA),* which is superseded by the *Absorbance* test.

Notes

Acetonitrile

CH$_3$CN   Formula Wt. 41.05

REQUIREMENTS

Appearance. Clear.
Color (APHA). Not more than 10.
Odor. Characteristic ethereal odor with no odor of amines.
Density (gram per ml.) at 25°C. Not less than 0.775 nor more than 0.780.
Boiling range. 1 ml. to 95 ml., not more than 1.0°C.; 95 ml. to dryness, not more than 1.0°C.
Residue after evaporation. Not more than 0.005 per cent.
Acidity (as CH$_3$COOH). Not more than 0.05 per cent.
Alkalinity (as NH$_3$). Not more than 0.001 per cent.
Water (H$_2$O). Not more than 0.3 per cent.

TESTS

Color (APHA). For the color standard dilute a 2-ml. aliquot of platinum-cobalt stock solution (APHA No. 500) to 100 ml. with water. Compare this solution (APHA No. 10) with 100 ml. of the acetonitrile in 100-ml. Nessler tubes, viewed vertically over a white background.

Boiling range. Distill 100 ml. by the method described on page 12. The difference between the temperatures when 1 ml. and 95 ml. have distilled should not exceed 1.0°C., and the difference in the temperatures when 95 ml. have distilled and the dry point is reached should not exceed 1.0°C. The boiling point of pure acetonitrile at 760-mm. mercury pressure is 81.6°C.

Residue after evaporation. Evaporate 50 ml. (40 grams) to dryness in a tared platinum dish on the steam bath, in a well ventilated hood, and dry the residue at 105°C. for 30 minutes. The weight of the residue should not exceed 0.0020 gram.

Acidity. Mix 13 ml. (10 grams) with 13 ml. of carbon dioxide-free water. Add 0.10 ml. of phenolphthalein indicator solution. Not more than 0.8 ml. of 0.1N sodium hydroxide solution should be required in the titration.

Alkalinity. To 100 ml. in a 250-ml. conical flask, add 0.30 ml. of 0.05 per cent solution of bromocresol green in alcohol and 0.10 ml. of 0.2 per cent solution of methyl red indicator solution. Titrate with 0.1N hydrochloric acid to a light orange-pink end point. Not more than 0.45 ml. of 0.1N hydrochloric acid should be required.

Water. Place 25 ml. of methanol in a dry titration flask and add Karl Fischer reagent to a visually or electrometrically determined end point. Add 10 ml. (7.7 grams) of the sample, taking care to protect the sample and contents of the flask from moisture. Stir vigorously and titrate with Karl Fischer reagent to the same end point. Calculate the water content of the sample from the titer and volume of Karl Fischer reagent consumed by the sample.

Notes

Aluminum

Al

Atomic Wt. 26.98

REQUIREMENTS

Insoluble in dilute hydrochloric acid. Not more than 0.050 per cent.
Silicon (Si). Not more than 0.10 per cent.
Nitrogen compounds (as N). Not more than 0.001 per cent.
Copper (Cu). Not more than 0.02 per cent.
Iron (Fe). Not more than 0.10 per cent.
Manganese (Mn). Not more than 0.002 per cent.
Titanium (Ti). Not more than 0.03 per cent.

TESTS

Insoluble in dilute hydrochloric acid. Dissolve 10 grams in 200 ml. of dilute hydrochloric acid (1 + 1). If the sample is finely divided, it should be added to the acid in small portions. Filter through a tared filtering crucible. Retain the filtrate, without washings, for Sample Solution A. Wash thoroughly, rejecting the washings, and dry at 105°C. The weight of the residue should not exceed 0.0050 gram.

Sample Solution A. Dilute to 250 ml. the filtrate, without washings, obtained in the test for *Insoluble in dilute hydrochloric acid* (1 ml. = 0.04 gram).

Silicon. Note. The molybdenum blue test for silicon is extremely sensitive; therefore, all solutions that are more alkaline than pH 4 should be handled in containers other than glass or porcelain. Nickel beakers and plastic graduates are recommended. The 10 per cent solution of sodium hydroxide is prepared and measured in plastic.

Dissolve 0.25 gram in 10 ml. of 10 per cent sodium hydroxide solution. Add the aluminum to the sodium hydroxide solution in small portions, particularly if the sample is finely divided. When the vigorous reaction has subsided, digest in the covered container on the steam bath until dissolution is complete. Uncover and evaporate to a moist residue. Dissolve the residue in 10 ml. of water, and add 0.05 to 0.10 ml. of 30 per cent hydrogen peroxide. Boil the solution gently to decompose the excess peroxide, cool, and dilute to 100 ml. Adjust the acidity of the solution to a pH of 2 (external indicator) by adding dilute sulfuric acid (1 + 1). Digest on the steam bath until any precipitate is dissolved and the solution is clear. If necessary, add more of the dilute sulfuric acid (1 + 1). When dissolution is complete, cool, and dilute to 250 ml. Prepare a blank solution by treating 10 ml. of the 10 per cent sodium hydroxide solution exactly as described above, but omit the 0.25-gram sample. Dilute 5 ml. of the sample solution to 80 ml. For the standard add 0.01 mg. of SiO_2 to 5 ml. of the blank solution and dilute to 80 ml. To each solution add 5 ml. of a freshly prepared 10 per cent solution of ammonium molybdate. Adjust the pH of each solution to 1.7 to 1.9 (using a pH meter) with dilute hydrochloric acid $(1 + 9)$ or silica-free ammonium hydroxide. Heat the solutions just to boiling, cool, add 20 ml. of hydrochloric acid, and dilute to 110 ml. Transfer the solutions to separatory funnels, add 50 ml. of butyl alcohol, and shake vigorously. Allow the layers to separate, and draw off and discard the aqueous phase. Wash the butyl alcohol three times with 20-ml. portions of dilute hydrochloric acid $(1 + 99)$, discarding each aqueous phase. Add 0.5 ml. of a freshly prepared 2 per cent solution of stannous chloride in hydrochloric acid and shake. If the butyl alcohol is turbid, wash it with 10 ml. of dilute hydrochloric acid $(1 + 99)$. Any blue color in the butyl alcohol from the solution of the sample should not exceed that in the butyl alcohol from the standard.

Nitrogen compounds. To 2.5 grams in a flask connected through a spray trap to a condenser, the end of which dips beneath the surface of 10 ml. of $0.1N$ hydrochloric acid, add 60 ml. of freshly boiled 10 per cent sodium hydroxide reagent solution. Allow to stand until solution of the aluminum is complete, add 50 ml. of water, slowly distill about 45 ml., and dilute the distillate to 60 ml. To 30 ml. of the diluted distillate add 1 ml. of 10 per cent sodium hydroxide reagent solution, dilute to 50 ml., and add 2 ml. of Nessler reagent. Any color should not exceed that produced when 0.5 gram of the aluminum and a quantity of an ammonium salt containing 0.02 mg. of nitrogen (N) are treated exactly like the sample.

Copper. Dissolve 0.25 gram in 10 ml. of dilute hydrochloric acid $(1 + 1)$ by digesting on the steam bath. Cool and add 1 ml. of 30 per cent hydrogen peroxide. Let stand for 5 minutes without heating, then boil for 1 to 2 minutes. Add about 150 ml. of water, adjust the pH to 1.0 to 1.5 (using a pH meter) with $1N$ sodium hydroxide (about 1 ml. will be required), and dilute to 200 ml. To a 20-ml. aliquot in a separatory funnel add 5 ml. of standard dithizone solution in carbon tetrachloride. Shake for 2 minutes, and draw off the carbon tetrachloride layer. Any pink color in the carbon tetrachloride extract should not exceed that produced by a standard containing 0.005 mg. of copper ion (Cu) in 20 ml. of $0.05N$ hydrochloric acid treated exactly like the solution of the sample.

Iron. Dilute 5 ml. of Sample Solution A (0.2-gram sample) to 100 ml. To 5 ml. of this solution add 2 ml. of hydrochloric acid and dilute to 50 ml. Add 30 to 50 mg. of ammonium persulfate crystals and 3 ml. of ammonium thiocyanate reagent solution. Any red color should not exceed that produced by 0.01 mg. of iron (Fe) in an equal volume of solution containing the quantities of reagents used in the test.

Manganese. To 12.5 ml. of Sample Solution A (0.5-gram sample) add 20 ml. of nitric acid and 10 ml. of sulfuric acid. Prepare a standard containing 0.01 mg. of manganese ion (Mn) in 7.5 ml. of water plus 5 ml. of hydrochloric acid, 20 ml. of nitric acid, and 10 ml. of sulfuric acid. Evaporate each solution to dense fumes of sulfur trioxide, cool, and cautiously add 50 ml. of water, 20 ml. of nitric acid, and 5 ml. of phosphoric acid. Dilute to 100 ml. and boil gently for 5 minutes. Cool, add 0.25 gram of potassium periodate to each, and again boil gently for 5 minutes. Cool and dilute to 100 ml. Any pink color in the solution of the sample should not exceed that in the standard.

Titanium. To 25 ml. of Sample Solution A (1.0-gram sample) add 3 ml. of phosphoric acid and 0.5 ml. of 30 per cent hydrogen peroxide. Any color should not exceed that produced by 0.3 mg. of titanium ion (Ti) in an equal volume of solution containing the quantities of reagents used in the test.

Notes

Aluminum Potassium Sulfate

$AlK(SO_4)_2 \cdot 12H_2O$ Formula Wt. 474.39

REQUIREMENTS

Insoluble matter. Not more than 0.005 per cent.
Chloride (Cl). Not more than 0.0005 per cent.
Ammonium (NH$_4$). Not more than 0.005 per cent.
Arsenic (As). Not more than 0.0002 per cent.
Heavy metals (as Pb). Not more than 0.001 per cent.
Iron (Fe). Not more than 0.001 per cent.
Sodium (Na). Not more than 0.02 per cent.

TESTS

Insoluble matter. Dissolve 20 grams in 150 ml. of hot water, heat to boiling, and digest in a covered beaker on the steam bath for 1 hour. Filter through a tared filtering crucible, wash thoroughly with hot water, and dry at 105°C. The weight of the residue should not exceed 0.0010 gram.

Chloride. Dissolve 2 grams in warm water, filter if necessary through a small chloride-free filter, dilute to 20 ml., and add 1 ml. of nitric acid. Cool to room temperature and add 1 ml. of silver nitrate reagent solution. Any turbidity should not exceed that produced by 0.01 mg. of chloride ion (Cl) in an equal volume of solution containing the quantities of reagents used in the test.

Ammonium. Dissolve 1 gram in 100 ml. of ammonia-free water. To 20 ml. of this solution add 10 per cent sodium hydroxide reagent solution until the precipitate first formed is redissolved. Dilute to 50 ml. and add 2 ml. of Nessler reagent. Any color should not exceed that produced by 0.01 mg. of ammonium ion (NH$_4$) in an equal volume of solution containing the quantities of reagents used in the test.

Arsenic. Determine the arsenic in 1 gram by the Gutzeit method (page 11). The amount of stain should not exceed that produced by 0.002 mg. of arsenic (As).

Heavy metals. Dissolve 5 grams in about 40 ml. of water and dilute to 50 ml. For the control add 0.02 mg. of lead ion (Pb) to a 10-ml. (1-gram) aliquot of the solution and dilute to 30 ml. For the sample use a 30-ml. (3-gram) aliquot. Adjust the pH of the control and sample solutions to between 3 and 4 (using a pH meter) with 1N acetic acid or ammonium hydroxide (10 per cent NH$_3$), dilute to 40 ml., and mix. Add 10 ml. of

freshly prepared hydrogen sulfide water to each and mix. Any color in the solution of the sample should not exceed that in the control.

Iron.   Dissolve 1 gram in 40 ml. of water plus 2 ml. of hydrochloric acid, dilute to 50 ml., and add 30 to 50 mg. of ammonium persulfate crystals and 3 ml. of ammonium thiocyanate reagent solution. Any red color should not exceed that produced by 0.01 mg. of iron (Fe) in an equal volume of solution containing the quantities of reagents used in the test.

Sodium.   Determine the sodium by the flame photometric method described on page 14. Dissolve 10 grams in 80 ml. of dilute hydrochloric acid (1 + 40) and digest in a covered beaker on the steam bath for 20 minutes. Cool and dilute to 100 ml.

Sample Solution A.   Dilute a 10-ml. aliquot of the solution to 100 ml. with water.

Control Solution B.   To another 10-ml. aliquot of the solution add 0.20 mg. of sodium ion (Na) and dilute to 100 ml. with water.

Observe the emission of Control Solution B at the 589-mμ sodium line. Observe the emission of Sample Solution A at the 589-mμ sodium line and at a wavelength of 580 mμ. The difference (D_1) between the intensities observed for Sample Solution A at 580 mμ and 589 mμ should not exceed the difference (D_2) observed at 589 mμ between Sample Solution A and Control Solution B.

Notes

Ammonium Acetate

CH_3COONH_4 Formula Wt. 77.08

REQUIREMENTS

Insoluble matter.   Not more than 0.005 per cent.
Residue after ignition.   Not more than 0.010 per cent.
pH of a 5 per cent solution.   From 6.7 to 7.3 at 25°C.
Chloride (Cl).   Not more than 0.0005 per cent.
Nitrate (NO_3).   Not more than 0.001 per cent.
Sulfate (SO_4).   Not more than 0.001 per cent.
Heavy metals (as Pb).   Not more than 0.0005 per cent.
Iron (Fe).   Not more than 0.0005 per cent.

TESTS

Insoluble matter.   Dissolve 20 grams in 200 ml. of water, heat to boiling, and digest in a covered beaker on the steam bath for 1 hour. Filter through a tared filtering crucible, wash thoroughly, and dry at 105°C. The weight of the residue should not exceed 0.0010 gram.

Residue after ignition.   Ignite 10 grams in a tared crucible or dish. The rate of heating should be such that from 1 to 2 hours is required to volatilize the sample. When nearly all the sample has been volatilized, cool, and moisten the residue with 0.10 ml. of sulfuric acid. Continue the heating until the remainder of the sample and excess sulfuric acid have been volatilized. Finally, ignite at 800° ± 25°C. for 15 minutes. The weight of the residue should not exceed 0.0010 gram.

pH of a 5 per cent solution.   Dissolve 10 grams in 200 ml. of carbon dioxide- and ammonia-free water. Determine the pH by the method described on page 18. The pH should be from 6.7 to 7.3 at 25°C. The pH of a 5 per cent solution of pure ammonium acetate would be 7.0 at 25°C.

Chloride.   Dissolve 2 grams in water, filter if necessary through a small chloride-free filter, dilute to 20 ml., and add 1 ml. of nitric acid and 1 ml. of silver nitrate reagent solution. Any turbidity should not exceed that produced by 0.01 mg. of chloride ion (Cl) in an equal volume of solution containing the quantities of reagents used in the test.

Nitrate.

Sample Solution A.   Dissolve 1.0 gram in 3 ml. of water by heating in a boiling water bath. Dilute to 50 ml. with brucine sulfate reagent solution.

Control Solution B. Dissolve 1.0 gram in 2 ml. of water and 1.0 ml. of the standard nitrate solution containing 0.01 mg. of nitrate ion (NO_3) by heating in a boiling water bath. Dilute to 50 ml. with brucine sulfate reagent solution.

Blank Solution C. Use 50 ml. of brucine sulfate reagent solution.

Heat the three solutions in a preheated (boiling) water bath for 10 minutes. Cool rapidly in an ice bath to room temperature. Set a spectrophotometer at 410 mμ and, using 1-cm. cells, adjust the instrument to read 0 absorbance with Blank Solution C in the light path, then determine the absorbance of Sample Solution A. Adjust the instrument to read 0 absorbance with Sample Solution A in the light path and determine the absorbance of Control Solution B. The absorbance of Sample Solution A should not exceed that of Control Solution B.

Sample Solution A and Blank Solution B for determining Sulfate, Heavy Metals, and Iron.

Sample Solution A. Dissolve 15 grams in 15 ml. of water and add about 10 mg. of sodium carbonate, 2 ml. of hydrogen peroxide, 15 ml. of hydrochloric acid, and 25 ml. of nitric acid.

Blank Solution B. Prepare a solution containing the quantities of reagents used in Sample Solution A.

Digest each in covered beakers on the steam bath until reaction ceases, uncover, and evaporate to dryness. Dissolve each in 3 ml. of 1N acetic acid plus 15 ml. of water, filter through a small filter, and dilute to 30 ml. (1 ml.= 0.5 gram).

Sulfate. To 10 ml. of Sample Solution A (5-gram sample) add 1 ml. of dilute hydrochloric acid (1 + 19). For the standard add 0.05 mg. of sulfate ion (SO_4) and 1 ml. of dilute hydrochloric acid (1 + 19) to 10 ml. of Blank Solution B. Add 1 ml. of barium chloride reagent solution to each. Any turbidity in the solution of the sample should not exceed that in the standard. Compare 10 minutes after adding the barium chloride to the sample and standard solutions.

Heavy metals. Dilute 8 ml. of Sample Solution A (4-gram sample) to 25 ml. For the standard add 0.02 mg. of lead ion (Pb) to 8 ml. of Blank Solution B and dilute to 25 ml. Adjust the pH of the standard and sample solutions to between 3 and 4 (using a pH meter) with 1N acetic acid or ammonium hydroxide (10 per cent NH_3), dilute to 40 ml., and mix. Add 10 ml. of freshly prepared hydrogen sulfide water to each and mix. Any color in the solution of the sample should not exceed that in the standard.

Iron. To 4 ml. of Sample Solution A (2-gram sample) add 2 ml. of hydrochloric acid and dilute to 50 ml. For the standard add 0.01 mg. of iron (Fe) and 2 ml. of hydrochloric acid to 4 ml. of Blank Solution B and dilute to 50 ml. To each solution add 30 to 50 mg. of ammonium persulfate crystals and 3 ml. of ammonium thiocyanate reagent solution. Any red color in the solution of the sample should not exceed that in the standard.

Notes

Ammonium Carbonate

Note. This product is a mixture of variable proportions of ammonium carbonate and ammonium carbamate.

REQUIREMENTS

Assay. Not less than 30 per cent NH_3.
Insoluble matter. Not more than 0.005 per cent.
Nonvolatile matter. Not more than 0.01 per cent.
Chloride (Cl). Not more than 0.0005 per cent.
Sulfur compounds (as SO_4). Not more than 0.002 per cent.
Heavy metals (as Pb). Not more than 0.0005 per cent.
Iron (Fe). Not more than 0.0005 per cent.

TESTS

Assay. Tare a glass-stoppered flask containing about 25 ml. of water. Add from 2.0 to 2.5 grams of the sample and weigh. Add slowly 50.0 ml. of $1N$ hydrochloric acid and titrate the excess with $1N$ alkali (sodium hydroxide or potassium hydroxide), using methyl orange indicator. One milliliter of $1N$ acid corresponds to 0.01703 gram of NH_3.

Insoluble matter. Dissolve 20 grams in 100 ml. of water, heat to boiling, and digest in a covered beaker on the steam bath for 1 hour. Filter through a tared filtering crucible, wash thoroughly, and dry at 105°C. The weight of the residue should not exceed 0.0010 gram.

Nonvolatile matter. To 20 grams in a tared dish add 10 ml. of water, volatilize on the steam bath, and dry for 1 hour at 105°C. The weight of the residue should not exceed 0.0020 gram. Retain the residue for the test for *Heavy metals*.

Chloride. Dissolve 2 grams in 25 ml. of hot water, add about 10 mg. of sodium carbonate, and evaporate to dryness on the steam bath. Dissolve the residue in 20 ml. of water, filter if necessary through a chloride-free filter, and add 1 ml. of nitric acid and 1 ml. of silver nitrate reagent solution. Any turbidity should not exceed that produced by 0.01 mg. of chloride ion (Cl) in an equal volume of solution containing the quantities of reagents used in the test.

Sulfur compounds. Dissolve 2 grams in 20 ml. of water, add about 10 mg. of sodium carbonate, and evaporate to dryness. Dissolve the residue in a slight excess of hydrochloric acid, add 2 ml. of bromine water, and again evaporate to dryness. Dissolve the residue in 4 ml. of water plus 1 ml. of dilute hydrochloric acid (1 + 19). Filter through a small filter, wash with two 2-ml. portions of water, dilute to 10 ml., and add 1 ml. of barium chloride reagent solution. Any turbidity should not exceed that produced by 0.04 mg. of sulfate ion (SO_4) in an equal volume of solution containing the quantities of reagents used in the test. Compare 10 minutes after adding the barium chloride to the sample and standard solutions.

Heavy metals. Dissolve the residue from the test for *Nonvolatile matter* in 5 ml. of 1N acetic acid and dilute to 50 ml. Dilute a 10-ml. aliquot of this solution to 25 ml. For the standard dilute a solution containing 0.02 mg. of lead ion (Pb) to 25 ml. Adjust the pH of the standard and sample solutions to between 3 and 4 (using a pH meter) with 1N acetic acid or ammonium hydroxide (10 per cent NH_3), dilute to 40 ml., and mix. Add 10 ml. of freshly prepared hydrogen sulfide water to each and mix. Any color in the solution of the sample should not exceed that in the standard.

Iron. To 2 grams add 5 ml. of water and evaporate on the steam bath. Dissolve the residue in 2 ml. of hydrochloric acid plus 20 ml. of water, filter if necessary, and dilute to 50 ml. Add 30 to 50 mg. of ammonium persulfate crystals and 3 ml. of ammonium thiocyanate reagent solution. Any red color should not exceed that produced by 0.01 mg. of iron (Fe) in an equal volume of solution containing the quantities of reagents used in the test.

Notes

Ammonium Chloride

NH_4Cl Formula Wt. 53.49

REQUIREMENTS

Insoluble matter. Not more than 0.005 per cent.
Residue after ignition. Not more than 0.010 per cent.
pH of a 5 per cent solution. From 4.5 to 5.5 at 25°C.
Phosphate (PO_4). Not more than 0.0002 per cent.
Sulfate (SO_4). Not more than 0.002 per cent.
Calcium and magnesium precipitate. Not more than 0.002 per cent.
Heavy metals (as Pb). Not more than 0.0005 per cent.
Iron (Fe). Not more than 0.0002 per cent.

TESTS

Insoluble matter. Dissolve 20 grams in 200 ml. of water, heat to boiling, and digest in a covered beaker on the steam bath for 1 hour. Filter through a tared filtering crucible, wash thoroughly, and dry at 105°C. The weight of the residue should not exceed 0.0010 gram.

Residue after ignition. Ignite 50 grams in a tared crucible or dish. The rate of heating should be such that from 1 to 2 hours is required to volatilize the sample. When nearly all the sample has been volatilized, cool, and moisten the residue with 0.10 ml. of sulfuric acid. Continue the heating until the remainder of the sample and excess sulfuric acid have been volatilized. Finally, ignite at 800° ± 25°C. for 15 minutes. The weight of the residue should not exceed 0.0050 gram. Retain the residue for the test for *Calcium and magnesium precipitate.*

pH of a 5 per cent solution. Dissolve 10 grams in 200 ml. of carbon dioxide- and ammonia-free water. Determine the pH by the method described on page 18. The pH should be from 4.5 to 5.5 at 25°C. The pH of a 5 per cent solution of pure ammonium chloride would be 4.7 at 25°C.

Sample Solution A and Blank Solution B for determining Phosphate, Sulfate, Heavy metals, and Iron.

Sample Solution A. Dissolve 25 grams in 75 ml. of water and add about 10 mg. of sodium carbonate, 10 ml. of hydrogen peroxide, and 50 ml. of nitric acid.

Blank Solution B. To 75 ml. of water add about 10 mg. of sodium carbonate, 10 ml. of hydrogen peroxide, and 50 ml. of nitric acid.

Digest Sample Solution A and Blank Solution B in covered beakers on the steam bath until reaction ceases, uncover, and evaporate to dryness. Dissolve the two residues in separate 20-ml. portions of water, filter if necessary, and dilute each to 100 ml. (1 ml. of Sample Solution A = 0.25 gram).

Phosphate. For the sample evaporate 40 ml. of Sample Solution A (10 gram sample) to dryness on the steam bath. For the standard add 0.02 mg. of phosphate ion (PO_4) to 40 ml. of Blank Solution B and evaporate to dryness on the steam bath. Dissolve the residues in 25 ml. of approximately $0.5N$ sulfuric acid, add to each 1 ml. of ammonium molybdate reagent solution and 1 ml. of p-methylaminophenol sulfate reagent solution, and allow to stand for 2 hours at room temperature. Any blue color in the solution of the sample should not exceed that in the standard.

Sulfate. To 10 ml. of Sample Solution A (2.5-gram sample) add 1 ml. of dilute hydrochloric acid (1 + 19). For the standard add 0.05 mg. of sulfate ion (SO_4) and 1 ml. of dilute hydrochloric acid (1 + 19) to 10 ml. of Blank Solution B. To each solution add 1 ml. of barium chloride reagent solution. Any turbidity in the solution of the sample should not exceed that in the standard. Compare 10 minutes after adding the barium chloride to the sample and standard solutions.

Calcium and magnesium precipitate. Warm the residue obtained in the test for *Residue after ignition* with 1 ml. of hydrochloric acid and 3 ml. of water. Add 2 ml. of ammonium hydroxide, filter, and wash with a few milliliters of water. Add to the filtrate 2 ml. of ammonium oxalate reagent solution and 2 ml. of ammonium phosphate reagent solution, and allow to stand overnight. Filter, wash with a solution containing 2.5 per cent of ammonia and 0.1 per cent ammonium oxalate, and ignite. The weight of the residue should not exceed 0.0010 gram.

Heavy metals. Dilute 16 ml. of Sample Solution A (4-gram sample) to 25 ml. For the standard add 0.02 mg. of lead ion (Pb) to 16 ml. of Blank Solution B and dilute to 25 ml. Adjust the pH of the standard and sample solutions to between 3 and 4 (using a pH meter) with $1N$ acetic acid or ammonium hydroxide (10 per cent NH_3), dilute to 40 ml., and mix. Add 10 ml. of freshly prepared hydrogen sulfide water to each and mix. Any color in the solution of the sample should not exceed that in the standard.

Iron. To 20 ml. of Sample Solution A (5-gram sample) add 2 ml. of hydrochloric acid and dilute to 50 ml. For the standard add 0.01 mg. of iron (Fe) and 2 ml. of hydrochloric acid to 20 ml. of Blank Solution B and dilute to 50 ml. To each solution add 30 to 50 mg. of ammonium persulfate crystals and 3 ml. of ammonium thiocyanate reagent solution. Any red color in the solution of the sample should not exceed that in the standard.

Notes

Ammonium Citrate, Dibasic

$(NH_4)_2HC_6H_5O_7$ Formula Wt. 226.19

REQUIREMENTS

Assay. Not less than 98 nor more than 103 per cent $(NH_4)_2HC_6H_5O_7$.
Insoluble matter. Not more than 0.005 per cent.
Residue after ignition. Not more than 0.010 per cent.
Chloride (Cl). Not more than 0.001 per cent.
Oxalate (C_2O_4). To pass test (limit about 0.05 per cent).
Phosphate (PO_4). Not more than 0.0005 per cent.
Sulfur compounds (as SO_4). Not more than 0.005 per cent.
Heavy metals (as Pb). Not more than 0.0005 per cent.
Iron (Fe). Not more than 0.001 per cent.

TESTS

Assay. Weigh accurately about 3 grams and dissolve in 40 ml. of water. Dilute 20 ml. of formaldehyde solution with 20 ml. of water, add phenolphthalein indicator solution, and neutralize with 0.1N sodium hydroxide. Add the formaldehyde solution to the solution of the sample, mix, and allow to stand 30 minutes. Add 0.10 to 0.15 ml. of phenolphthalein indicator solution and titrate with 1N sodium hydroxide to a pink color which persists for 5 minutes. One milliliter of 1N sodium hydroxide corresponds to 0.07540 gram of $(NH_4)_2HC_6H_5O_7$.

Insoluble matter. Dissolve 20 grams in 200 ml. of water, heat to boiling, and digest in a covered beaker on the steam bath for 1 hour. Filter through a tared filtering crucible, wash thoroughly, and dry at 105°C. The weight of the residue should not exceed 0.0010 gram.

Residue after ignition. Ignite 10 grams in a tared crucible or dish. The rate of heating should be such that from 1 to 2 hours is required to volatilize the sample. When nearly all the sample has been volatilized, cool and moisten the residue with 0.10 ml. of sulfuric acid. Continue the heating until the remainder of the sample and excess sulfuric acid have been volatilized. Finally, ignite at 800° ± 25°C. for 15 minutes. The weight of the residue should not exceed 0.0010 gram.

Chloride. Dissolve 1 gram in 20 ml. of water, filter if necessary through a chloride-free filter, and add 1 ml. of nitric acid and 1 ml. of silver nitrate reagent solution. Any turbidity should not exceed that produced by 0.01 mg. of chloride ion (Cl) in an equal volume of solution containing the quantities of reagents used in the test.

Oxalate. Dissolve 5 grams in 25 ml. of water and add 3 ml. of glacial acetic acid and 2 ml. of 10 per cent solution of calcium acetate. No turbidity or precipitate should appear after standing 4 hours.

Phosphate. To 4 grams in a 150-ml. beaker add 0.2 ml. of ammonium vanadate solution* and 10 ml. of nitric acid. Digest in a covered beaker on the steam bath until reaction ceases, rinse and remove the watch glass, and evaporate to dryness. Add another 10 ml. of nitric acid, repeat the digestion and evaporation, and dissolve the residue by warming with about 10 ml. of water and 0.05 ml. of nitric acid. Cool and transfer to a 50-ml. Nessler tube. Dilute to about 25 ml. and add in order, mixing between each addition, 5 ml. of nitric acid $(1 + 2)$, 5 ml. of ammonium vanadate solution,* and 5 ml. of ammonium molybdate solution.* Dilute to 50 ml. Any yellow color should not exceed that produced by 0.02 mg. of phosphate ion (PO_4) taken through the entire procedure with the sample. Compare 5 minutes after adding the ammonium molybdate to the sample and standard solutions.**

* **Reagents. 1. Ammonium Vanadate Solution.** Dissolve 2.5 grams of ammonium vanadate, NH_4VO_3, in 500 ml. of boiling water, cool, and add 20 ml. of nitric acid. Cool, dilute to 1 liter, and store in a polyethylene bottle.

2. Ammonium Molybdate Solution. Dissolve 50 grams of ammonium molybdate, $(NH_4)_6Mo_7O_{24}\cdot4H_2O$, in 1 liter of water and store in a polyethylene bottle.

**If results are near the limit, the absorbance may be measured at 460 mμ, in 5-cm. cells, using a suitable spectrophotometer. The absorbance of the sample should not exceed that of the standard.

Sulfur compounds. To 1 gram add 1 ml. of hydrochloric acid and 3 ml. of nitric acid. Prepare a standard containing 0.05 mg. of sulfate ion (SO_4), 1 ml. of hydrochloric acid, and 3 ml. of nitric acid. Digest each in a covered beaker on the steam bath until the reaction ceases, remove the covers, and evaporate to dryness. Add 0.2 to 0.5 mg. of ammonium vanadate and 10 ml. of nitric acid and digest in covered beakers on the steam bath until reactions cease. Remove the covers and evaporate to dryness. Add 10 ml. more nitric acid and repeat the digestions and evaporations. Add 5 ml. of dilute hydrochloric acid $(1 + 1)$ and evaporate to dryness. Dissolve the residues in 4 ml. of water plus 1 ml. of dilute hydrochloric acid $(1 + 19)$, and filter through a small filter. Wash with two 2-ml. portions of water, dilute to 10 ml., and add 1 ml. of barium chloride reagent solution to each. Any turbidity in the solution of the sample should not exceed that in the standard. Compare 10 minutes after adding the barium chloride to the sample and standard solutions.

Heavy metals.   Dissolve 6 grams in about 20 ml. of water, add 5 ml. of dilute hydrochloric acid (1 + 1), and dilute to 30 ml. For the control add 0.02 mg. of lead ion (Pb) to a 5-ml. aliquot of the solution and dilute to 25 ml. For the sample use the remaining 25-ml. portion. Adjust the pH of the control and sample solutions to between 3 and 4 (using a pH meter) with $1N$ acetic acid or ammonium hydroxide (10 per cent NH_3), dilute to 40 ml., and mix. Add 10 ml. of freshly prepared hydrogen sulfide water to each and mix. Any color in the solution of the sample should not exceed that in the control.

Iron.   Dissolve 1 gram in about 40 ml. of water plus 2 ml. of hydrochloric acid, dilute to 50 ml., and add 30 to 50 mg. of ammonium persulfate crystals and 3 ml. of ammonium thiocyanate reagent solution. Any red color should not exceed that produced by 0.01 mg. of iron (Fe) in an equal volume of solution containing the quantities of reagents used in the test.

Notes

Ammonium Hydroxide

NH$_4$OH   Formula Wt. 35.05

REQUIREMENTS

Appearance.   Colorless and free from suspended matter or sediment.
Assay.   Not less than 28 nor more than 30 per cent NH$_3$.
Residue after ignition.   Not more than 0.002 per cent.
Carbon dioxide (CO$_2$).   Not more than 0.002 per cent.
Chloride (Cl).   Not more than 0.00005 per cent.
Phosphate (PO$_4$).   Not more than 0.0002 per cent.
Total sulfur (as SO$_4$).   Not more than 0.0002 per cent.
Heavy metals (as Pb).   Not more than 0.00005 per cent.
Iron (Fe).   Not more than 0.00002 per cent.
Substances reducing permanganate.   To pass test.

TESTS

Appearance.   Mix the material in the original container, pour 10 ml. into a test tube (20 × 150 mm.), and compare with distilled water in a similar tube. The liquids should be equally clear and free from suspended matter; looking across the columns by means of transmitted light should reveal no apparent difference in color between the two liquids.

Assay.   Tare a small glass-stoppered Erlenmeyer flask containing 15 ml. of water. Quickly add about 2 ml. of the ammonium hydroxide, stopper, and weigh. Titrate with 1N acid, using methyl red as indicator. One milliliter of 1N acid is equivalent to 0.01703 gram of NH$_3$.

Residue after ignition.   Evaporate 56 ml. (50 grams) of the sample to dryness in a tared dish and ignite at 800° ± 25°C. for 15 minutes. The weight of the residue should not exceed 0.0010 gram.

Carbon dioxide.   Dilute 11 ml. (10 grams) of the sample with 10 ml. of water free from carbon dioxide and add 5 ml. of a saturated solution of barium hydroxide. Any turbidity should not be greater than is produced when the same quantity of barium hydroxide solution is added to 21 ml. of water (free from carbon dioxide) containing 0.5 mg. of sodium carbonate.

Chloride.   To 22 ml. (20 grams) add about 10 mg. of sodium carbonate and evaporate to dryness. Dissolve the residue in 20 ml. of dilute nitric acid (1 + 19), filter if necessary through a chloride-free filter, and add 1 ml. of silver nitrate reagent solution. Any turbidity should not exceed that produced by 0.01 mg. of chloride ion (Cl) in an equal volume of solution containing the quantities of reagents used in the test.

Phosphate. Evaporate 11 ml. (10 grams) to dryness on the steam bath. Dissolve the residue in 25 ml. of approximately 0.5N sulfuric acid, add 1 ml. of ammonium molybdate reagent solution and 1 ml. of p-methyl-aminophenol sulfate reagent solution, and allow to stand for 2 hours at room temperature. Any blue color should not exceed that produced by 0.02 mg. of phosphate ion (PO_4) in an equal volume of solution containing the quantities of reagents used in the test.

Total sulfur. To 33 ml. (30 grams) add about 10 mg. of sodium carbonate and evaporate to about 5 ml. Add 1 ml. of bromine water and evaporate to dryness. Dissolve the residue in 4 ml. of water plus 1 ml. of dilute hydrochloric acid (1 + 19), filter through a small filter, wash with two 2-ml. portions of water, and dilute the filtrate to 10 ml. Add 1 ml. of barium chloride reagent solution. Any turbidity should not exceed that produced by 0.06 mg. of sulfate ion (SO_4) in an equal volume of solution containing the quantities of reagents used in the test. Compare 10 minutes after adding the barium chloride to the sample and standard solutions.

Heavy metals. To 44 ml. (40 grams) add about 10 mg. of sodium chloride and evaporate to dryness on the steam bath. Dissolve the residue in about 20 ml. of water and dilute to 25 ml. For the standard add 0.02 mg. of lead ion (Pb) to 20 ml. of water and dilute to 25 ml. Adjust the pH of the standard and sample solutions to between 3 and 4 (using a pH meter) with 1N acetic acid or ammonium hydroxide (10 per cent NH_3), dilute to 40 ml., and mix. Add 10 ml. of freshly prepared hydrogen sulfide water to each and mix. Any color in the solution of the sample should not exceed that in the standard.

Iron. To 56 ml. (50 grams) add about 10 mg. of sodium carbonate and evaporate to dryness on the steam bath. Dissolve the residue in 3 ml. of hydrochloric acid and dilute to 50 ml. To this solution add 30 to 50 mg. of ammonium persulfate crystals and 3 ml. of ammonium thiocyanate reagent solution. Any red color should not exceed that produced by 0.01 mg. of iron (Fe) in an equal volume of solution containing the quantities of reagents used in the test.

Substances reducing permanganate. Dilute 3 ml. of the sample with 5 ml. of water and add 50 ml. of 10 per cent sulfuric acid reagent solution. Add 0.05 ml. of 0.1N potassium permanganate, heat to boiling, and keep at this temperature for 5 minutes. The pink color should not be entirely discharged.

Ammonium Iodide

NH_4I Formula Wt. 144.94

REQUIREMENTS

Insoluble matter.   Not more than 0.005 per cent.
Residue after ignition.   Not more than 0.05 per cent.
Chloride and bromide (as Cl).   Not more than 0.005 per cent.
Phosphate (PO_4).   Not more than 0.001 per cent.
Sulfate (SO_4).   Not more than 0.05 per cent.
Barium (Ba).   Not more than 0.002 per cent.
Heavy metals (as Pb).   Not more than 0.001 per cent.
Iron (Fe).   Not more than 0.0005 per cent.

TESTS

Insoluble matter.   Dissolve 20 grams in 200 ml. of water, heat to boiling, and digest in a covered beaker on the steam bath for 1 hour. Filter through a tared filtering crucible, wash thoroughly, and dry at 105°C. The weight of the residue should not exceed 0.0010 gram.

Residue after ignition.   Ignite 2 grams in a tared crucible or dish. The rate of heating should be such that from 1 to 2 hours is required to volatilize the sample. When nearly all the sample has been volatilized, cool, and moisten the residue with 0.10 ml. of sulfuric acid. Continue the heating until the remainder of the sample and excess sulfuric acid have been volatilized. Finally, ignite at 800° ± 25°C. for 15 minutes. The weight of the residue should not exceed 0.0010 gram.

Chloride and bromide.   Dissolve 1 gram in 100 ml. of water in a distilling flask. Add 1 ml. of hydrogen peroxide and 1 ml. of phosphoric acid, heat to boiling, and boil gently until all the iodine is expelled and the solution is colorless. Cool, wash down the sides of the flask, and add 0.5 ml. of hydrogen peroxide. If an iodine color develops, boil until the solution is colorless and for 10 minutes longer. If no color develops, boil for 10 minutes, filter if necessary through a chloride-free filter, and dilute to 100 ml. Dilute a 20-ml. aliquot to 23 ml., and add 1 ml. of nitric acid and 1 ml. of silver nitrate reagent solution. Any turbidity should not exceed that produced by 0.01 mg. of chloride ion (Cl) in an equal volume of solution containing the quantities of nitric acid and silver nitrate used in the test.

Sample Solution A and Blank Solution B for determining Phosphate, Sulfate, Barium, Heavy metals, and Iron.

Sample Solution A.   Dissolve 20 grams in 40 ml. of water in a 600-ml. beaker and add about 10 mg. of sodium carbonate. Add 16 ml. of hydrochloric acid and 32 ml. of nitric acid, cover with a watch glass, and warm on the steam bath. When the rapid evolution of iodine ceases, add an additional 16 ml. of nitric acid and 24 ml. of hydrochloric acid. Digest in the covered beaker until the bubbling ceases, remove the watch glass, and evaporate to dryness.

Blank Solution B. Evaporate to dryness the quantities of acids and sodium carbonate used to prepare Sample Solution A.

Dissolve the residues in separate 20-ml. portions of water, filter if necessary, and dilute each to 100 ml. (1 ml. of Sample Solution A = 0.2 gram).

Phosphate. Evaporate 10 ml. of Sample Solution A (2-gram sample) to dryness. For the standard add 0.02 mg. of phosphate ion (PO_4) to 10 ml. of Blank Solution B and evaporate to dryness. Dissolve each residue in 25 ml. of approximately $0.5N$ sulfuric acid, add 1 ml. of ammonium molybdate reagent solution and 1 ml. of p-methylaminophenol sulfate reagent solution, and allow to stand at room temperature for 2 hours. Any blue color in the solution of the sample should not exceed that produced in the standard.

Sulfate. To 0.5 ml. of Sample Solution A (0.1-gram sample) add 1 ml. of dilute hydrochloric acid (1 + 19) and dilute to 10 ml. For the standard add 0.05 mg. of sulfate ion (SO_4) and 1 ml. of dilute hydrochloric acid (1 + 19) to 0.5 ml. of Blank Solution B, and dilute to 10 ml. Add 1 ml. of barium chloride reagent solution to each. Any turbidity in the solution of the sample should not exceed that in the standard. Compare 10 minutes after adding the barium chloride to the sample and standard solutions.

Barium. To 20 ml. of Sample Solution A (4-gram sample) add 5 ml. of a 1 per cent solution of potassium sulfate. For the standard add 0.08 mg. of barium ion (Ba) and 5 ml. of a 1 per cent solution of potassium sulfate to 20 ml. of Blank Solution B. Any turbidity in the solution of the sample should not exceed that in the standard. Compare 10 minutes after adding the potassium sulfate to the sample and standard solutions.

Heavy metals. Dilute a 10-ml. aliquot of Sample Solution A (2-gram sample) to 25 ml. For the standard add 0.02 mg. of lead ion (Pb) to a 10-ml. aliquot of Blank Solution B and dilute to 25 ml. Adjust the pH of the standard and sample solutions to between 3 and 4 (using a pH meter) with $1N$ acetic acid or ammonium hydroxide (10 per cent NH_3), dilute to 40 ml., and mix. Add 10 ml. of freshly prepared hydrogen sulfide water to each and mix. Any color in the solution of the sample should not exceed that in the standard.

Iron.   Dilute 10 ml. of Sample Solution A (2-gram sample) to 50 ml. For the standard add 0.01 mg. of iron (Fe) to 10 ml. of Blank Solution B and dilute to 50 ml. To each solution add 2 ml. of hydrochloric acid, 30 to 50 mg. of ammonium persulfate crystals, and 3 ml. of ammonium thiocyanate reagent solution. Any red color in the solution of the sample should not exceed that in the standard.

Notes

Ammonium Molybdate

(NH$_4$)$_6$Mo$_7$O$_{24}$·4H$_2$O   Formula Wt. 1235.86

REQUIREMENTS

Assay.   Not less than 81.0 nor more than 83.0 per cent MoO$_3$.
Insoluble matter.   Not more than 0.005 per cent.
Chloride (Cl).   Not more than 0.002 per cent.
Nitrate (NO$_3$).   To pass test (limit about 0.003 per cent).
Arsenate, phosphate, and silicate (as SiO$_2$).   Not more than 0.0005 per cent.
Sulfate (SO$_4$).   Not more than 0.02 per cent.
Heavy metals (as Pb).   Not more than 0.001 per cent.
Magnesium and allied cations.   Not more than 0.02 per cent.

TESTS

Assay.   Weigh accurately about 1 gram and dissolve in 10 ml. of water plus 1 ml. of ammonium hydroxide. Transfer to a 250-ml. flask, dilute to volume, and mix thoroughly. To a 50.0-ml. aliquot (filtered if necessary) in a 600-ml. beaker add 250 ml. of water, 20 grams of ammonium chloride, 15 ml. of hydrochloric acid, and 0.15 ml. of methyl orange indicator solution. Heat nearly to boiling and add 18 ml. of 10 per cent lead acetate solution. To the hot solution add, slowly and with constant stirring, a saturated ammonium acetate solution until the solution is alkaline, and then add an excess of 15 ml. of the acetate solution. Digest in the covered beaker on the hot plate below the boiling temperature until the precipitate has settled (from one-half to 1 hour). Filter through a tared Gooch crucible or a porous porcelain crucible, wash 7 or 8 times with a solution containing 10 ml. of nitric acid and 100 ml. of saturated ammonium acetate solution in a liter, and finally wash 3 times with hot water. Ignite to constant weight in a muffle furnace at 560° to 625°C. The weight of the lead molybdate times 0.3921 corresponds to the weight of MoO$_3$.

Insoluble matter.   Dissolve 20 grams in 200 ml. of water, heat to boiling, and digest in a covered beaker on the steam bath for 1 hour. Filter through a tared filtering crucible, wash thoroughly, and dry at 105°C. The weight of the residue should not exceed 0.0010 gram.

Chloride.   Dissolve 1 gram in 50 ml. of water, and filter if necessary through a chloride-free filter. To 25 ml. of the solution add 2 ml. of nitric acid and 1 ml. of silver nitrate reagent solution. Any turbidity should not exceed that produced by 0.01 mg. of chloride ion (Cl) in an

equal volume of solution containing the quantities of reagents used in the test.

Nitrate. Dissolve 1 gram in 10 ml. of water containing 5 mg. of sodium chloride. Add 0.10 ml. of indigo carmine solution and 10 ml. of sulfuric acid. The blue color should not be completely discharged in 5 minutes.

Arsenate, phosphate, and silicate. Dissolve 2.5 grams in 70 ml. of water. For the control dissolve 0.5 gram in 70 ml. of water and add 0.01 mg. of silica (SiO_2). These solutions, to avoid excess silica contamination, are prepared in containers other than glass. Adjust the pH to 3 to 4 (pH paper) with dilute hydrochloric acid $(1 + 9)$, then transfer to glass containers and treat each solution as follows: add 1 to 2 ml. of bromine water and adjust the pH to 1.7 to 1.9 (using a pH meter) with dilute hydrochloric acid $(1 + 9)$. Heat just to boiling, but do not boil, and cool to room temperature. Dilute to 90 ml., add 10 ml. of hydrochloric acid, and transfer to a separatory funnel. Add 1 ml. of butyl alcohol and 30 ml. of 4-methyl-2-pentanone, shake vigorously, and allow the phases to separate. Draw off and discard the aqueous phase and wash the ketone phase three times with 10-ml. portions of dilute hydrochloric acid $(1 + 99)$, discarding each aqueous phase. To the washed ketone phase add 10 ml. of dilute hydrochloric acid $(1 + 99)$ to which has just been added 0.2 ml. of a freshly prepared 2 per cent solution of stannous chloride in hydrochloric acid. Any blue color in the solution of the sample should not exceed that in the control.

Sulfate. Dissolve 1 gram in hot water, add 5 ml. of nitric acid, and evaporate to dryness on the steam bath. Dissolve the residue in 4 ml. of water plus 1 ml. of dilute hydrochloric acid $(1 + 19)$, filter through a small filter, wash with two 2-ml. portions of water, and dilute to 40 ml. To 10 ml. of the solution add 1 ml. of barium chloride reagent solution. Any turbidity should not exceed that produced by 0.05 mg. of sulfate ion (SO_4) in an equal volume of solution containing the quantities of reagents used in the test. Compare 10 minutes after adding the barium chloride to the sample and standard solutions.

Heavy metals. Dissolve 2 grams in about 20 ml. of water, add 10 ml. of 10 per cent sodium hydroxide reagent solution and 2 ml. of ammonium hydroxide, and dilute to 40 ml. For the control add 0.01 mg. of lead ion (Pb) to a 10-ml. aliquot of the solution and dilute to 40 ml. For the sample dilute the remaining portion to 40 ml. Add 10 ml. of freshly prepared hydrogen sulfide water to each. Any color in the solution of the sample should not exceed that in the control.

Magnesium and allied cations. Dissolve 5 grams in 50 ml. of water, filter if not perfectly clear, and add 0.5 gram of sodium carbonate and 25 ml. of 10 per cent sodium hydroxide reagent solution. Boil the solution gently for 5 minutes, cool, filter, wash with 2.5 per cent ammonia solution, and ignite at 800° ± 25°C. for 30 minutes. The weight of the residue should not exceed 0.0010 gram.

Notes

Ammonium Nitrate

NH_4NO_3 Formula Wt. 80.04

REQUIREMENTS

Insoluble matter.   Not more than 0.005 per cent.
Residue after ignition.   Not more than 0.010 per cent.
pH of a 5 per cent solution.   From 4.5 to 6.0 at 25°C.
Chloride (Cl).   Not more than 0.0005 per cent.
Nitrite (NO_2).   To pass test (limit about 0.0005 per cent).
Phosphate (PO_4).   Not more than 0.0005 per cent.
Sulfate (SO_4).   Not more than 0.002 per cent.
Heavy metals (as Pb).   Not more than 0.0005 per cent.
Iron (Fe).   Not more than 0.0002 per cent.

TESTS

Insoluble matter.   Dissolve 20 grams in 200 ml. of water, heat to boiling, and digest in a covered beaker on the steam bath for 1 hour. Filter through a tared filtering crucible, wash thoroughly, and dry at 105°C. The weight of the residue should not exceed 0.0010 gram.

Residue after ignition.   Ignite 10 grams in a tared crucible or dish. The rate of heating should be such that from 1 to 2 hours is required to volatilize the sample. When nearly all the sample has been volatilized, cool, and moisten the residue with 0.10 ml. of sulfuric acid. Continue heating until the remainder of the sample and excess sulfuric acid have been volatilized. Finally, ignite at 800° ± 25°C. for 15 minutes. The weight of the residue should not exceed 0.0010 gram.

pH of a 5 per cent solution.   Dissolve 10 grams in 200 ml. of carbon dioxide- and ammonia-free water. Determine the pH by the method described on page 18. The pH should be from 4.5 to 6.0 at 25°C. The pH of a 5 per cent solution of pure ammonium nitrate would be 4.8 at 25°C.

Chloride.   Dissolve 2 grams in water, filter if necessary through a small chloride-free filter, dilute to 20 ml., and add 1 ml. of nitric acid and 1 ml. of silver nitrate reagent solution. Any turbidity should not exceed that produced by 0.01 mg. of chloride ion (Cl) in an equal volume of solution containing the quantities of reagents used in the test.

Nitrite.   Dissolve 1 gram in 10 ml. of water and add 1 ml. of 10 per cent sulfuric acid and 1 ml. of colorless 0.5 per cent m-phenylenediamine hydrochloride solution. No yellowish or brownish color should be produced in 5 minutes.

Note. *m*-Phenylenediamine hydrochloride solution can be decolorized by treating with a little activated carbon and filtering.

Phosphate. Dissolve 4 grams in 25 ml. of approximately 0.5N sulfuric acid, add 1 ml. of ammonium molybdate reagent solution and 1 ml. of *p*-methylaminophenol sulfate reagent solution, and allow to stand at room temperature for 2 hours. Any blue color should not exceed that produced by 0.02 mg. of phosphate ion (PO_4) in an equal volume of solution containing the quantities of reagents used in the test.

Sample Solution A and Blank Solution B for determining Sulfate, Heavy metals, and Iron.

Sample Solution A. Dissolve 20 grams in 20 ml. of water, add 10 mg. of sodium carbonate, 5 ml. of 30 per cent hydrogen peroxide, 20 ml. of hydrochloric acid, and 20 ml. of nitric acid.

Blank Solution B. Prepare a solution containing the quantities of reagents used in Sample Solution A.

Digest each in covered beakers on the steam bath until reaction ceases, uncover, and evaporate to dryness. Dissolve the residues in 5 ml. of 1N acetic acid and 50 ml. of water, filter if necessary, and dilute to 100 ml. (1 ml. = 0.2 gram).

Sulfate. To 10 ml. of Sample Solution A (2-gram sample) add 1 ml. of dilute hydrochloric acid (1 + 19). For the standard add 0.04 mg. of sulfate ion (SO_4) and 1 ml. of dilute hydrochloric acid to 10 ml. of Blank Solution B. To each solution add 1 ml. of barium chloride reagent solution. Any turbidity in the solution of the sample should not exceed that in the standard. Compare 10 minutes after adding the barium chloride to the sample and standard solutions.

Heavy metals. Dilute 20 ml. of Sample Solution A (4-gram sample) to 25 ml. For the standard add 0.02 mg. of lead ion (Pb) to 20 ml. of Blank Solution B and dilute to 25 ml. Adjust the pH of the standard and sample solutions to between 3 and 4 (using a pH meter) with 1N acetic acid or ammonium hydroxide (10 per cent NH_3), dilute to 40 ml., and mix. Add 10 ml. of freshly prepared hydrogen sulfide water to each and mix. Any color in the solution of the sample should not exceed that in the standard.

Iron. To 25 ml. of Sample Solution A (5-gram sample) add 2 ml. of hydrochloric acid and dilute to 50 ml. For the standard add 0.01 mg. of iron (Fe) and 2 ml. of hydrochloric acid to 25 ml. of Blank Solution B and dilute to 50 ml. To each solution add 30 to 50 mg. of ammonium persulfate crystals and 3 ml. of ammonium thiocyanate reagent solution. Any red color in the solution of the sample should not exceed that in the standard.

Notes

Ammonium Oxalate

$(COONH_4)_2 \cdot H_2O$ Formula Wt. 142.11

REQUIREMENTS

Insoluble matter. Not more than 0.005 per cent.
Residue after ignition. Not more than 0.020 per cent.
Chloride (Cl). Not more than 0.002 per cent.
Sulfate (SO$_4$). Not more than 0.002 per cent.
Heavy metals (as Pb). Not more than 0.0005 per cent.
Iron (Fe). Not more than 0.0002 per cent.

TESTS

Insoluble matter. Dissolve 20 grams in 400 ml. of hot water, heat to boiling, and digest in a covered beaker on the steam bath for 1 hour. Filter through a tared filtering crucible, wash thoroughly with hot water, and dry at 105°C. The weight of the residue should not exceed 0.0010 gram.

Residue after ignition. Dry 5 grams in a tared crucible or dish for 1 hour at 105° to 110°C., then ignite slowly. The rate of heating should be such that from 1 to 2 hours is required to volatilize the sample. When nearly all the sample has been volatilized, cool, and moisten the residue with 0.10 ml. of sulfuric acid. Continue the heating until the remainder of the sample and excess sulfuric acid have been volatilized. Finally, ignite at 800° ± 25°C. for 15 minutes. The weight of the residue should not exceed 0.0010 gram.

Chloride. Dissolve 2 grams in water plus 10 ml. of nitric acid, filter if necessary through a chloride-free filter, and dilute to 100 ml. To 25 ml. of the solution add 1 ml. of silver nitrate reagent solution. Any turbidity should not exceed that produced by 0.01 mg. of chloride ion (Cl) in an equal volume of solution containing the quantities of reagents used in the test.

Sample Solution A and Blank Solution B for determining Sulfate, Heavy metals, and Iron.

Sample Solution A. Digest 20 grams of sample plus 10 mg. of sodium carbonate with 40 ml. of nitric acid plus 35 ml. of hydrochloric acid in a covered beaker on the steam bath until no more bubbles of gas are evolved. Remove the cover and evaporate until a small amount of crystals form in the beaker. Add 10 ml. of 30 per cent hydrogen peroxide, cover the beaker, and digest on the steam bath until reaction ceases. Add an additional 10 ml. of 30 per cent hydrogen peroxide, re-cover the beaker, digest on the steam bath until reaction ceases, remove the cover, and evaporate to dryness. Add 5 ml. of dilute hydrochloric acid $(1 + 1)$, cover, digest on the steam bath for 15 minutes, remove the cover, and evaporate to dryness. Dissolve the residue in about 50 ml. of water, filter if necessary, and dilute to 100 ml. $(1 \text{ ml.} = 0.2 \text{ gram})$.

Blank Solution B. Prepare a similar solution containing the quantities of reagents used in preparing Sample Solution A and treated in the identical manner.

Sulfate. To 10 ml. of Sample Solution A (2-gram sample) add 1 ml. of dilute hydrochloric acid $(1 + 19)$ and filter if necessary. For the standard add 0.04 mg. of sulfate ion (SO_4) and 1 ml. of the dilute hydrochloric acid to 10 ml. of Blank Solution B and filter if necessary. To each solution add 1 ml. of barium chloride reagent solution. Any turbidity in the solution of the sample should not exceed that in the standard. Compare 10 minutes after adding the barium chloride to the sample and standard solutions.

Heavy metals. For the sample dilute a 20-ml. aliquot of Sample Solution A (4-gram sample) to 25 ml. For the standard add 0.02 mg. of lead ion (Pb) to a 20-ml. aliquot of Blank Solution B and dilute to 25 ml. Adjust the pH of the standard and sample solutions to between 3 and 4 (using a pH meter) with $1N$ acetic acid or ammonium hydroxide (10 per cent NH_3), dilute to 40 ml., and mix. Add 10 ml. of freshly prepared hydrogen sulfide water to each and mix. Any color in the solution of the sample should not exceed that in the standard.

Iron. Add 2 ml. of hydrochloric acid to 25 ml. of Sample Solution A (5-gram sample) and dilute to 50 ml. For the standard add 0.01 mg. of iron (Fe) and 2 ml. of hydrochloric acid to 25 ml. of Blank Solution B and dilute to 50 ml. To each solution add 30 to 50 mg. of ammonium persulfate crystals and 3 ml. of ammonium thiocyanate reagent solution. Any red color in the solution of the sample should not exceed that in the standard.

Notes

Ammonium Persulfate

$(NH_4)_2S_2O_8$ Formula Wt. 228.20

Note. Because of inherent instability this reagent may be expected to decrease in strength and to increase in acidity during storage. After storage for some time the reagent may fail to meet the specified requirements for assay and acidity.

REQUIREMENTS

Assay. Not less than 98 per cent $(NH_4)_2S_2O_8$.
Insoluble matter. Not more than 0.005 per cent.
Residue after ignition. Not more than 0.05 per cent.
Acidity (as H_2SO_4). Not more than 0.20 per cent.
Chloride and chlorate (as Cl). Not more than 0.001 per cent.
Heavy metals (as Pb). Not more than 0.005 per cent.
Iron (Fe). Not more than 0.001 per cent.
Manganese (Mn). Not more than 0.00005 per cent.

TESTS

Assay. Weigh accurately about 0.5 gram and add it to 25.0 ml. of standard ferrous sulfate solution (about $0.2N$, described below)* in a glass-stoppered flask. Stopper the flask, allow it to stand for 1 hour with frequent shaking, and titrate the excess ferrous sulfate with $0.1N$ potassium permanganate. One milliliter of $0.1N$ potassium permanganate corresponds to 0.01141 gram of $(NH_4)_2S_2O_8$.

* **Standard Ferrous Sulfate Solution.** Dissolve 7 grams of clear crystals of ferrous sulfate in 90 ml. of freshly boiled and cooled distilled water, and add sulfuric acid to make 100 ml. Standardize the solution with $0.1N$ potassium permanganate. The solution must be freshly prepared and standardized.

Insoluble matter. Dissolve 20 grams in 200 ml. of water, heat to boiling, and digest in a covered beaker on the steam bath for 1 hour. Filter through a tared filtering crucible, wash thoroughly, and dry at 105°C. The weight of the residue should not exceed 0.0010 gram.

Residue after ignition. Ignite 5 grams in a tared crucible or dish. The rate of heating should be such that from 1 to 2 hours is required to volatilize the sample. When nearly all the sample has been volatilized, cool, and moisten the residue with 0.10 ml. of sulfuric acid. Continue the heating until the remainder of the sample and excess sulfuric acid have been volatilized. Finally, ignite at $800° \pm 25°C$. for 15 minutes. The weight of the residue should not exceed 0.0025 gram.

Acidity. Dissolve 10 grams in 100 ml. of water and add 0.10 ml. of methyl red indicator solution. If a red color is produced, not more than 4.0 ml. of $0.1N$ alkali should be required to discharge it.

Chloride and chlorate. Mix 1 gram with 1 gram of sodium carbonate and heat until no more gas is evolved. Dissolve the residue in 20 ml. of water, neutralize with nitric acid, and add an excess of 1 ml. of the acid. Filter if necessary through a chloride-free filter, and add 1 ml. of silver nitrate reagent solution. Any turbidity should not exceed that produced by 0.01 mg. of chloride ion (Cl) in an equal volume of solution containing the quantities of reagents used in the test.

Heavy metals. Gently ignite 2 grams (not in platinum), and to the residue add 1 ml. of hydrochloric acid, 1 ml. of nitric acid, and about 10 mg. of sodium carbonate. Evaporate to dryness on the steam bath, dissolve the residue in about 20 ml. of water, and dilute to 50 ml. For the sample dilute a 10-ml. aliquot of this solution to 25 ml. For the standard dilute a solution containing 0.02 mg. of lead ion (Pb) to 25 ml. Adjust the pH of the standard and sample solutions to between 3 and 4 (using a pH meter) with $1N$ acetic acid or ammonium hydroxide (10 per cent NH_3), dilute to 40 ml., and mix. Add 10 ml. of freshly prepared hydrogen sulfide water to each and mix. Any color in the solution of the sample should not exceed that in the standard.

Iron. To 1 gram add 5 ml. of water and 10 ml. of hydrochloric acid and evaporate to dryness. Moisten the residue with 2 ml. of hydrochloric acid, dissolve in about 40 ml. of water, and dilute to 50 ml. Add 30 to 50 mg. of ammonium persulfate crystals and 3 ml. of ammonium thiocyanate reagent solution. Any red color should not exceed that produced by 0.01 mg. of iron (Fe) when treated exactly like the 1-gram sample.

Manganese. Gently ignite 20 grams (not in platinum) until the sample is decomposed, and finally ignite at 600°C. until the sample is volatilized. Dissolve the residue by boiling for 5 minutes with 35 ml. of water plus 10 ml. of nitric acid, 5 ml. of sulfuric acid, and 5 ml. of phosphoric acid and cool. Prepare a standard containing 0.01 mg. of manganese ion (Mn) in an equal volume of solution containing the quantities of reagents used to dissolve the residue. To each solution add 0.25 gram of potassium periodate, boil gently for 5 minutes, and cool. Any pink color in the solution of the sample should not exceed that in the standard.

Ammonium Phosphate, Dibasic

Diammonium Hydrogen Phosphate

$(NH_4)_2HPO_4$ Formula Wt. 132.06

REQUIREMENTS

Insoluble matter.   Not more than 0.005 per cent.
Ammonium hydroxide precipitate.   Not more than 0.005 per cent.
pH of a 0.2M solution.   From 7.7 to 8.1 at 25°C.
Chloride (Cl).   Not more than 0.001 per cent.
Nitrate (NO_3).   Not more than 0.003 per cent.
Sulfur compounds (as SO_4).   Not more than 0.004 per cent.
Arsenic (As).   Not more than 0.0002 per cent.
Heavy metals (as Pb).   Not more than 0.001 per cent.
Iron (Fe).   Not more than 0.001 per cent.
Potassium (K).   Not more than 0.005 per cent.
Sodium (Na).   Not more than 0.005 per cent.

TESTS

Insoluble matter.   Dissolve 20 grams in 200 ml. of water, heat to boiling, and digest in a covered beaker on the steam bath for 1 hour. Filter through a tared porous porcelain or platinum filtering crucible, wash thoroughly, and dry at 105°C. The weight of the insoluble residue should not exceed 0.0010 gram. Save the filtrate separate from the washings for the test for *Ammonium hydroxide precipitate.*

Ammonium hydroxide precipitate.   To the filtrate from the test for *Insoluble matter* add successively enough hydrochloric acid to make the solution acid to methyl red and enough ammonium hydroxide to make the solution again alkaline to methyl red. Heat to boiling, boil gently for 5 minutes, and cool. Filter, wash, and ignite the precipitate. The weight of the residue should not exceed 0.0010 gram.

pH of a 0.2M solution.   Dissolve 2.64 grams in 100 ml. of water. Determine the pH by the method described on page 18. The pH should be from 7.7 to 8.1 at 25°C.

Chloride.   Dissolve 1 gram in 20 ml. of water, filter if necessary through a chloride-free filter, and add 3 ml. of nitric acid and 1 ml. of silver nitrate reagent solution. Any turbidity should not exceed that produced by 0.01 mg. of chloride ion (Cl) in an equal volume of solution containing the quantities of reagents used in the test.

Nitrate.

Sample Solution A. Dissolve 0.5 gram in 3 ml. of water by heating in a boiling water bath. Dilute to 50 ml. with brucine sulfate reagent solution.

Control Solution B. Dissolve 0.5 gram in 1.5 ml. of water and 1.5 ml. of the standard nitrate solution containing 0.01 mg. of nitrate ion (NO_3) per ml. by heating in a boiling water bath. Dilute to 50 ml. with brucine sulfate reagent solution.

Blank Solution C. Use 50 ml. of brucine sulfate reagent solution.

Heat the three solutions in a preheated (boiling) water bath for 10 minutes. Cool rapidly in an ice bath to room temperature. Set a spectrophotometer at 410 mμ and, using 1-cm. cells, adjust the instrument to read 0 absorbance with Blank Solution C in the light path, then determine the absorbance of Sample Solution A. Adjust the instrument to read 0 absorbance with Sample Solution A in the light path and determine the absorbance of Control Solution B. The absorbance of Sample Solution A should not exceed that of Control Solution B.

Sulfur compounds. Dissolve 10 grams in about 80 ml. of water, add 5 ml. of bromine water, and heat to boiling. Add 12 ml. of hydrochloric acid, heat to boiling again, and add 5 ml. of barium chloride reagent solution. Digest in a covered beaker on the steam bath for 2 hours and allow to stand overnight. If a precipitate is formed, filter, wash thoroughly, and ignite. The weight of the precipitate should not be more than 0.0010 gram greater than the weight obtained in a complete blank test.

Arsenic. Determine the arsenic in 1 gram by the Gutzeit method (page 11). The amount of stain should not exceed that produced by 0.002 mg. of arsenic (As).

Heavy metals. Dissolve 4 grams in 10 ml. of water, add 15 ml. of 2N hydrochloric acid, and dilute to 32 ml. For the control add 0.02 mg. of lead ion (Pb) to an 8-ml. aliquot of the solution and dilute to 25 ml. For the sample dilute the remaining 24-ml. portion to 25 ml. Adjust the pH of the control and sample solutions to between 3 and 4 (using a pH meter) with 1N acetic acid or ammonium hydroxide (10 per cent NH_3), dilute to 40 ml., and mix. Add 10 ml. of freshly prepared hydrogen sulfide water to each and mix. Any color in the solution of the sample should not exceed that in the control.

Iron. Dissolve 1 gram in 10 ml. of water. Add 6 ml. of hydroxylamine hydrochloride reagent solution and 4 ml. of 1, 10-phenanthroline reagent solution and dilute to 25 ml. Any red color should not exceed that produced by 0.01 mg. of iron (Fe) in an equal volume of solution containing the quantities of reagents used in the test. Compare 1 hour after adding the reagents to the sample and standard solutions.

Potassium and Sodium.

Sample Solution A. Dissolve 5 grams and dilute to 100 ml.

Control Solution B. Dissolve 5 grams, add 0.25 mg. of sodium ion (Na) and 0.25 mg. of potassium ion (K), and dilute to 100 ml.

Potassium. Determine the potassium by the flame photometric method described on page 14. Observe the emission of Control Solution B at the 767-mμ potassium line. Observe the emission of Sample Solution A at the 767-mμ potassium line and at a wavelength of 750 mμ. The difference (D_1) between the intensities observed at 767 mμ and 750 mμ should not exceed the difference (D_2) observed at 767 mμ between Sample Solution A and Control Solution B.

Sodium. Determine the sodium by the flame photometric method described on page 14. Observe the emission of Control Solution B at the 589-mμ sodium line. Observe the emission of Sample Solution A at the 589-mμ sodium line and at a wavelength of 580 mμ. The difference (D_1) between the intensities observed for Sample Solution A at 580 mμ and 589 mμ should not exceed the difference (D_2) observed at 589 mμ between Sample Solution A and Control Solution B.

Notes

Ammonium Phosphate, Monobasic

Ammonium Dihydrogen Phosphate

$NH_4H_2PO_4$ Formula Wt. 115.03

REQUIREMENTS

Insoluble matter. Not more than 0.005 per cent.
Ammonium hydroxide precipitate. Not more than 0.005 per cent.
pH of a 5 per cent solution. From 3.8 to 4.4 at 25°C.
Chloride (Cl). Not more than 0.0005 per cent.
Nitrate (NO_3). Not more than 0.001 per cent.
Sulfur compounds (as SO_4). Not more than 0.005 per cent.
Arsenic (As). Not more than 0.00005 per cent.
Heavy metals (as Pb). Not more than 0.0005 per cent.
Iron (Fe). Not more than 0.001 per cent.
Potassium (K). Not more than 0.005 per cent.
Sodium (Na). Not more than 0.005 per cent.

TESTS

Insoluble matter. Dissolve 20 grams in 200 ml. of water, heat to boiling, and digest in a covered beaker on the steam bath for 1 hour. Filter through a tared filtering crucible, wash thoroughly, and dry at 105°C. The weight of the residue should not exceed 0.0010 gram. Save the filtrate separate from the washings for the test for *Ammonium hydroxide precipitate.*

Ammonium hydroxide precipitate. To the filtrate from the test for *Insoluble matter* add enough ammonium hydroxide to make the solution alkaline to methyl red. Heat to boiling, boil gently for 5 minutes, cool, filter, and wash. Ignite the precipitate. The weight of the residue should not exceed 0.0010 gram.

pH of a 5 per cent solution. Dissolve 10 grams in 200 ml. of carbon dioxide- and ammonia-free water and protect from the atmosphere. Determine the pH by the method described on page 18. The pH should be from 3.8 to 4.4 at 25°C. The pH of a 5 per cent solution of pure ammonium phosphate, monobasic, would be 4.1 at 25°C.

Chloride. Dissolve 2 grams in 20 ml. of water, filter if necessary through a chloride-free filter, and add 3 ml. of nitric acid and 1 ml. of silver nitrate reagent solution. Any turbidity should not exceed that produced by 0.01 mg. of chloride ion (Cl) in an equal volume of solution containing the quantities of reagents used in the test.

Nitrate.

Sample Solution A. Dissolve 1.5 grams in 3 ml. of water by heating in a boiling water bath. Dilute to 50 ml. with brucine sulfate reagent solution.

Control Solution B. Dissolve 1.5 grams in 1.5 ml. of water and 1.5 ml. of the standard nitrate solution containing 0.01 mg. of nitrate ion (NO_3) per ml. by heating in a boiling water bath. Dilute to 50 ml. with brucine sulfate reagent solution.

Blank Solution C. Use 50 ml. of brucine sulfate reagent solution.

Heat the three solutions in a preheated (boiling) water bath for 10 minutes. Cool rapidly in an ice bath to room temperature. Set a spectrophotometer at 410 mμ and, using 1-cm. cells, adjust the instrument to read 0 absorbance with Blank Solution C in the light path, then determine the absorbance of Sample Solution A. Adjust the instrument to read 0 absorbance with Sample Solution A in the light path and determine the absorbance of Control Solution B. The absorbance of Sample Solution A should not exceed that of Control Solution B.

Sulfur compounds. Dissolve 10 grams in 100 ml. of water, add 6 ml. of hydrogen peroxide, and boil the solution for a few minutes. Add 6.5 ml. of hydrochloric acid, boil, add 5 ml. of barium chloride reagent solution, digest in a covered beaker on the steam bath for 2 hours, and allow to stand overnight. If a precipitate is formed, filter, wash thoroughly, and ignite. The weight of the precipitate should not be more than 0.0012 gram greater than the weight obtained in a complete blank test.

Arsenic. Determine the arsenic in 4 grams by the Gutzeit method (page 11). The stain should not exceed that produced by 0.002 mg. of arsenic (As).

Heavy metals. Dissolve 6 grams in 30 ml. of water. For the control add 0.02 mg. of lead ion (Pb) to a 5-ml. aliquot of the solution and dilute to 25 ml. For the sample use the remaining 25-ml. portion. Adjust the pH of the control and sample solutions to between 3 and 4 (using a pH meter) with 1N acetic acid or ammonium hydroxide (10 per cent NH_3), dilute to 40 ml., and mix. Add 10 ml. of freshly prepared hydrogen sulfide water to each and mix. Any color in the solution of the sample should not exceed that in the control.

Iron. Dissolve 1 gram in 10 ml. of water and add 3 ml. of dilute ammonium hydroxide (1 + 4). Add 6 ml. of hydroxylamine hydrochloride reagent solution and 4 ml. of 1,10-phenanthroline reagent solution and dilute to 25 ml. Any red color should not exceed that produced by 0.01 mg. of iron (Fe) in an equal volume of solution containing the quantities of reagents used in the test except the dilute ammonium hydroxide. Compare 1 hour after adding the reagents to the sample and standard solutions.

Potassium and Sodium.

Sample Solution A. Dissolve 2 grams and dilute to 100 ml.

Control Solution B. Dissolve 2 grams, add 0.10 mg. of sodium ion (Na) and 0.10 mg. of potassium ion (K), and dilute to 100 ml.

Potassium. Determine the potassium by the flame photometric method described on page 14. Observe the emission of Control Solution B at the 767-mμ potassium line. Observe the emission of Sample Solution A at the 767-mμ potassium line and at a wavelength of 750 mμ. The difference (D_1) between the intensities observed at 767 mμ and 750 mμ should not exceed the difference (D_2) observed at 767 mμ between Sample Solution A and Control Solution B.

Sodium. Determine the sodium by the flame photometric method described on page 14. Observe the emission of Control Solution B at the 589-mμ sodium line. Observe the emission of Sample Solution A at the 589-mμ sodium line and at a wavelength of 580 mμ. The difference (D_1) between the intensities observed for Sample Solution A at 580 mμ and 589 mμ should not exceed the difference (D_2) observed at 589 mμ between Sample Solution A and Control Solution B.

Notes

Ammonium Sulfate

(NH₄)₂SO₄

Formula Wt. 132.14

REQUIREMENTS

Insoluble matter. Not more than 0.005 per cent.
Residue after ignition. Not more than 0.005 per cent.
pH of a 5 per cent solution. From 5.0 to 6.0 at 25°C.
Chloride (Cl). Not more than 0.0005 per cent.
Nitrate (NO_3). Not more than 0.001 per cent.
Phosphate (PO_4). Not more than 0.0005 per cent.
Arsenic (As). Not more than 0.00002 per cent.
Heavy metals (as Pb). Not more than 0.0005 per cent.
Iron (Fe). Not more than 0.0005 per cent.

TESTS

Insoluble matter. Dissolve 20 grams in 200 ml. of water, heat to boiling, and digest in a covered beaker on the steam bath for 1 hour. Filter through a tared filtering crucible, wash thoroughly, and dry at 105°C. The weight of the residue should not exceed 0.0010 gram.

Residue after ignition. Ignite 20 grams in a tared crucible or dish. The rate of heating should be such that from 1 to 2 hours is required to volatilize the sample. When nearly all the sample has been volatilized, cool, and moisten the residue with 0.10 ml. of sulfuric acid. Continue the heating until the remainder of the sample and excess sulfuric acid have been volatilized. Finally, ignite at 800° ± 25°C. for 15 minutes. The weight of the residue should not exceed 0.0010 gram.

pH of a 5 per cent solution. Dissolve 10 grams in 200 ml. of carbon dioxide- and ammonia-free water. Determine the pH by the method described on page 18. The pH should be from 5.0 to 6.0 at 25°C. The pH of a 5 per cent solution of pure ammonium sulfate would be 5.2 at 25°C.

Chloride. Dissolve 2 grams in water, filter if necessary through a small chloride-free filter, dilute to 20 ml., and add 1 ml. of nitric acid and 1 ml. of silver nitrate reagent solution. Any turbidity should not exceed that produced by 0.01 mg. of chloride ion (Cl) in an equal volume of solution containing the quantities of reagents used in the test.

Nitrate.

Sample Solution A. Dissolve 1 gram in 3 ml. of water by heating in a boiling water bath. Dilute to 50 ml. with brucine sulfate reagent solution.

Control Solution B.   Dissolve 1 gram in 2 ml. of water and 1 ml. of the standard nitrate solution containing 0.01 mg. of nitrate ion (NO_3) per ml. by heating in a boiling water bath. Dilute to 50 ml. with brucine sulfate reagent solution.

Blank Solution C.   Use 50 ml. of brucine sulfate reagent solution.

Heat the three solutions in a preheated (boiling) water bath for 10 minutes. Cool rapidly in an ice bath to room temperature. Set a spectrophotometer at 410 mμ and, using 1-cm. cells, adjust the instrument to read 0 absorbance with Blank Solution C in the light path, then determine the absorbance of Sample Solution A. Adjust the instrument to read 0 absorbance with Sample Solution A in the light path and determine the absorbance of Control Solution B. The absorbance of Sample Solution A should not exceed that of Control Solution B.

Phosphate.   Dissolve 4 grams in 25 ml. of approximately $0.5N$ hydrochloric acid, add 1 ml. of ammonium molybdate reagent solution and 1 ml. of p-methylaminophenol sulfate reagent solution, and allow to stand at room temperature for 2 hours. Any blue color should not exceed that produced by 0.02 mg. of phosphate ion (PO_4) in an equal volume of solution containing the quantities of reagents used in the test.

Arsenic.   Determine the arsenic in 10 grams by the Gutzeit method (page 11). The amount of stain should not exceed that produced by 0.002 mg. of arsenic (As).

Heavy metals.   Dissolve 6 grams in about 20 ml. of water and dilute to 30 ml. For the control add 0.02 mg. of lead ion (Pb) to a 5-ml. aliquot of the solution and dilute to 25 ml. For the sample use the remaining 25-ml. portion. Adjust the pH of the control and sample solutions to between 3 and 4 (using a pH meter) with $1N$ acetic acid or ammonium hydroxide (10 per cent NH_3), dilute to 40 ml., and mix. Add 10 ml. of freshly prepared hydrogen sulfide water to each and mix. Any color in the solution of the sample should not exceed that in the control.

Iron.   Dissolve 2 grams in about 30 ml. of water plus 2 ml. of hydrochloric acid, dilute to 50 ml., and add 30 to 50 mg. of ammonium persulfate crystals and 3 ml. of ammonium thiocyanate reagent solution. Any red color should not exceed that produced by 0.01 mg. of iron (Fe) in an equal volume of solution containing the quantities of reagents used in the test.

Ammonium Thiocyanate

NH₄SCN   Formula Wt. 76.12

REQUIREMENTS

Appearance. Colorless or white crystals.
Insoluble matter. Not more than 0.005 per cent.
Residue after ignition. Not more than 0.025 per cent.
pH of a 5 per cent solution. From 4.5 to 6.0 at 25°C.
Chloride (Cl). Not more than 0.005 per cent.
Sulfate (SO₄). Not more than 0.005 per cent.
Heavy metals (as Pb). Not more than 0.0005 per cent.
Iron (Fe). Not more than 0.0003 per cent.
Iodine-consuming substances. To pass test (not more than 0.2 ml. of
   0.1N iodine solution per gram).

TESTS

Insoluble matter. Dissolve 20 grams in 150 ml. of water, heat to boiling, and digest in a covered beaker on the steam bath for 1 hour. Filter through a tared filtering crucible, wash thoroughly, and dry at 105°C. The weight of the residue should not exceed 0.0010 gram.

Residue after ignition. Ignite 4 grams in a tared crucible or dish. The rate of heating should be such that from 1 to 2 hours is required to volatilize the sample. When nearly all the sample has been volatilized, cool, and moisten the residue with 0.10 ml. of sulfuric acid. Continue heating until the remainder of the sample and excess sulfuric acid have been volatilized. Finally, ignite at 800° ± 25°C. for 15 minutes. The weight of the residue should not exceed 0.0010 gram. Retain the residue for the test for *Iron*.

pH of a 5 per cent solution. Dissolve 10 grams in 200 ml. of carbon dioxide- and ammonia-free water. Determine the pH by the method described on page 18. The pH should be from 4.5 to 6.0 at 25°C. The pH of a 5 per cent solution of pure ammonium thiocyanate would be 4.9 at 25°C.

Chloride. Dissolve 1 gram in 20 ml. of water in a small flask. Add 10 ml. of 25 per cent sulfuric acid reagent solution and 7 ml. of 30 per cent hydrogen peroxide. Evaporate to 20 ml. by boiling *in a well ventilated hood,* add 17 ml. of water, and evaporate again. Repeat until all the cyanide has been volatilized. Cool, filter if necessary through a chloride-free filter, and dilute to 100 ml. To 20 ml. of this solution add 1 ml. of nitric acid and 1 ml. of silver nitrate reagent solution. Any turbidity should not exceed that produced by 0.01 mg. of chloride ion (Cl) in an equal volume of solution containing the quantities of reagents used in the test.

Sulfate. Dissolve 10 grams in 100 ml. of hot water, filter if necessary, and add 1 ml. of hydrochloric acid and 5 ml. of barium chloride reagent solution. Digest in a covered beaker on the steam bath for 2 hours and allow to stand overnight. If any precipitate is formed, filter, wash thoroughly, and ignite. The weight of the precipitate should not be more than 0.0012 gram greater than the weight of the precipitate obtained in a complete blank test.

Heavy metals. Dissolve 6 grams in about 20 ml. of water and dilute to 30 ml. For the control add 0.02 mg. of lead ion (Pb) to a 5-ml. aliquot of the solution and dilute to 25 ml. For the sample use the remaining 25-ml. portion. Adjust the pH of the control and sample solutions to between 3 and 4 (using a pH meter) with $1N$ acetic acid or ammonium hydroxide (10 per cent NH_3), dilute to 40 ml., and mix. Add 10 ml. of freshly prepared hydrogen sulfide water to each and mix. Any color in the solution of the sample should not exceed that in the control.

Iron. To the *Residue after ignition* add 3 ml. of dilute hydrochloric acid $(1 + 1)$, cover with a watch glass, and digest on the steam bath for 15 to 20 minutes. Remove the watch glass and evaporate to dryness. Dissolve in 2 ml. of hydrochloric acid, filter if necessary, and dilute to 50 ml. Add 30 to 50 mg. of ammonium persulfate crystals and 3 ml. of ammonium thiocyanate reagent solution. Any red color should not exceed that produced by 0.012 mg. of iron (Fe) in an equal volume of solution containing the quantities of reagents used in the test.

Iodine-consuming substances. Dissolve 5 grams in 50 ml. of water plus 1.7 ml. of 10 per cent sulfuric acid reagent solution. Add 1 gram of potassium iodide and 2 ml. of starch indicator solution and titrate with $0.1N$ iodine solution. Not more than 1.0 ml. of the iodine solution should be required.

Notes

Aniline

$C_6H_5NH_2$ Formula Wt. 93.13

REQUIREMENTS

Appearance. Not more than a pale yellow.
Boiling range. Not more than 3°C.
Residue after ignition. Not more than 0.005 per cent.
Chlorobenzene (C_6H_5Cl). Not more than 0.010 per cent.
Hydrocarbons. To pass test.
Nitrobenzene ($C_6H_5NO_2$). To pass test (limit about 0.0010 per cent).

TESTS

Boiling range. Distill 100 ml. by the method described on page 12. The difference between the temperatures when 1 ml. and 95 ml. have distilled should not exceed 3°C. The boiling point of pure aniline at 760-mm. mercury pressure is 184.4°C. Save the distillate for the test for *Chlorobenzene*.

Residue after ignition. Evaporate 20 ml. (20 grams) to dryness in a tared dish on the steam bath *in the hood* and ignite the residue at 800 ± 25°C. for 15 minutes. The weight of the residue should not exceed 0.0010 gram.

Chlorobenzene.

Note. Specification applies only to freshly distilled aniline. If aniline is colored, distill prior to test. The distillate obtained in the test for *Boiling range* may be used.

To 25 ml. of 2,2,4-trimethylpentane in a 100-ml. separatory funnel, add 5 ml. (5.1 grams) of the sample and 50 ml. of cool, dilute hydrochloric acid (1 + 4). Mix, allow the layers to separate, and discard the lower layer. Add 10 ml. of dilute hydrochloric acid (1 + 4), mix, separate, and discard the lower layer. Rinse the 2,2,4-trimethylpentane layer with 10 ml. of water. Transfer a portion of the 2,2,4-trimethylpentane layer to a 1-cm. optical cell and determine the spectral absorption curve between 240 mμ and 290 mμ, using a similarly treated 2,2,4-trimethylpentane blank for reference. Draw a baseline through the two lowest points of the curve that occur immediately on each side of the 264 mμ to 265 mμ region and measure the absorbance between the baseline and the peak in this region. The absorbance should not be greater than that obtained from a standard containing 0.5 mg. of chlorobenzene per 25 ml. of 2,2,4-trimethylpentane.

Hydrocarbons. Mix 5 ml. with 10 ml. of hydrochloric acid. The solution while still hot from the mixing should be clear and should remain clear after dilution with 15 ml. of cold water.

Nitrobenzene.

> **Sample Solution A.** Place 10 ml. of methanol in a 25-ml. glass-stoppered cylinder.

> **Control Solution B.** Place 10 ml. of methanol in a 25-ml. glass-stoppered cylinder and add 1 ml. of a methanol solution containing 0.10 mg. of nitrobenzene per ml.

Immerse the cylinders in a beaker of water at or below room temperature, and add 10 ml. of the aniline and 2.5 ml. of hydrochloric acid to each. Mix well and bring to room temperature.

Transfer a portion of Sample Solution A to a polarographic cell and deaerate with nitrogen or hydrogen. Record the polarogram from -0.2 to -0.7 volt (vs. saturated calomel electrode) with a current sensitivity of 0.02 microampere per millimeter. Repeat this procedure with Control Solution B. The diffusion current in Sample Solution A should not exceed the difference in diffusion current between Control Solution B and Sample Solution A.

Notes

Arsenic Trioxide

(A primary standard)

As_2O_3 Formula Wt. 197.84

REQUIREMENTS

> **Residue after ignition.**   Not more than 0.020 per cent.
> **Insoluble in dilute hydrochloric acid.**   Not more than 0.010 per cent.
> **Chloride (Cl).**   Not more than 0.005 per cent.
> **Sulfide (S).**   To pass test (limit about 0.001 per cent).
> **Antimony (Sb).**   Not more than 0.002 per cent.
> **Lead (Pb).**   Not more than 0.001 per cent.
> **Iron (Fe).**   Not more than 0.0005 per cent.

TESTS

Residue after ignition.   Ignite 5 grams in a tared platinum dish under a well ventilated hood. The rate of heating should be such that no more than 30 minutes is required to volatilize the entire sample. Finally, ignite at 800° ± 25°C. for 15 minutes. The weight of the residue should not exceed 0.0010 gram. Retain the residue for the test for *Iron*.

Insoluble in dilute hydrochloric acid.   To 10 grams add 90 ml. of dilute hydrochloric acid (3 + 7) and 10 ml. of hydrogen peroxide. Cover with a watch glass and allow to stand until the sample goes into solution, heating if necessary. Heat to boiling, digest in a covered beaker on the steam bath for 1 hour, filter through a tared filtering crucible, wash thoroughly, and dry at 105°C. The weight of the residue should not exceed 0.0010 gram.

Chloride.   Dissolve 1 gram in 10 ml. of dilute ammonium hydroxide (1 + 2) with the aid of gentle heat and dilute to 100 ml. Neutralize 20 ml. with nitric acid, add an excess of 1 ml. of the acid, filter if necessary through a chloride-free filter, and add 1 ml. of silver nitrate reagent solution. Any turbidity should not exceed that produced by 0.01 mg. of chloride ion (Cl) in an equal volume of solution containing the quantities of reagents used in the test.

Sulfide.   Dissolve 1 gram in 10 ml. of 10 per cent sodium hydroxide reagent solution and add 0.05 ml. of lead acetate solution (about 10 per cent). The color should be the same as that of an equal volume of the sodium hydroxide solution to which only the lead acetate is added.

Antimony.   Dissolve 2 grams in 50 ml. of hydrochloric acid plus 25 ml.

of water, warm if necessary to dissolve the sample completely, cool to room temperature, and dilute to 100 ml. Mix well and transfer 5 ml. to a small separatory funnel. Prepare a standard containing 0.002 mg. of antimony ion (Sb) in 5 ml. of dilute hydrochloric acid (1 + 1) in a second separatory funnel. Carry the sample and standard together through the following steps.

Add 0.15 ml. of 10 per cent sodium nitrite solution and mix. Add 10 ml. of water, 5 ml. of a 0.01 per cent aqueous solution of rhodamine B, and 15 ml. of toluene. Shake for 1 minute, allow the layers to separate, and draw off and discard the lower aqueous layer. Add 5 ml. of dilute hydrochloric acid (1 + 1) and 10 ml. of water, shake for 1 minute, and again draw off and discard the aqueous layer.

Transfer the toluene layer to a glass-stoppered graduate and dilute to 20 ml. with a small portion of toluene that has been used to rinse the separatory funnel. Add 0.5 gram of granular anhydrous sodium sulfate and shake until the solution is clear (approximately 1 minute). Transfer to comparison tubes and compare immediately. The intensity of the color in the solution of the sample should not exceed that in the standard.

Notes. 1. The initial solution to be treated must not contain more than 0.2 gram of As_2O_3 or 0.02 mg. of Sb.

2. The antimony standard solution may be prepared conveniently from antimonyl potassium tartrate (tartar emetic U.S.P.) which has been rendered anhydrous by drying at 105°C. A weight of 2.6687 grams of $K(SbO)C_4H_4O_6$ corresponds to 1 gram of Sb.

3. If desired, the transmittance of the toluene extract may be read on a spectrophotometer at 562 mμ against a toluene blank. The transmittance vs. concentration curve obeys Beer's law for concentrations below 0.02 mg. of antimony (as the rhodamine complex) in 20 ml. of toluene.

4. The toluene solution of the complex is unstable and comparisons or measurements must be made within one-half hour.

Lead. Dissolve 2 grams in 10 ml. of 10 per cent sodium hydroxide reagent solution. Add 50 ml. of water and 5 ml. of hydrochloric acid, and dilute to 100 ml. Transfer 10 ml. to a separatory funnel, and add 10 ml. of ammonium citrate lead-free reagent solution and 2 ml. of hydroxylamine hydrochloride reagent solution for dithizone test. Add 0.15 ml. of phenol red indicator solution, make almost alkaline to phenol red, and add 4 ml. of 10 per cent potassium cyanide lead-free reagent solution. (*Caution. Use hood. Use bulb for pipetting.*) Immediately extract the solution with 5-ml. portions of dithizone extraction solution in chloroform, draining off each extract into another separatory funnel until the lead is completely removed and the dithizone retains its original green color. If it is necessary to release the pressure during extraction, do not open the stopcock, since portions of the solution of the sample may be blown into the stem and become a source of contamination in future determinations. Remove the lead from the combined chloroform extracts by shaking the mixture with 20 ml. of 1 per cent nitric acid and discard the chloroform layer.

To the 1 per cent nitric acid containing the lead, add 4 ml. of ammonia-cyanide mixture, lead-free, and 5 ml. of standard dithizone solution in chloroform and immediately shake for half a minute. Drain the dithizone extract into a clean, dry test tube and observe the color over a white background. The color of this final extract should be a shade of violet no deeper than the color of the extract obtained from the treatment of 2 ml. of lead standard solution for dithizone test (0.002 mg. of Pb) and 8 ml. of water in the same manner as the 10 ml. of diluted sample solution.

Iron. Warm the residue from the test for *Residue after ignition* with 3 ml. of dilute hydrochloric acid (1 + 1). Add 5 ml. of hydrochloric acid and dilute to 125 ml. To 50 ml. of this solution add 30 to 50 mg. of ammonium persulfate crystals and 3 ml. of ammonium thiocyanate reagent solution. Any red color should not exceed that produced by 0.01 mg. of iron (Fe) in an equal volume of solution containing the quantities of reagents used in the test.

Notes

Aurintricarboxylic Acid Ammonium Salt

Aluminon

$(HOC_6H_3COONH_4)_2C:C_6H_3(COONH_4):O$ Formula Wt. 473.44

REQUIREMENTS

Insoluble matter. Not more than 0.10 per cent.
Residue after ignition. Not more than 0.20 per cent.
Sensitivity to aluminum. To pass test.

TESTS

Insoluble matter. Dissolve 1 gram in 100 ml. of water and 0.5 ml. of dilute ammonium hydroxide (10 per cent NH_3). Filter through a tared filtering crucible, wash thoroughly, and dry at 105°C. The weight of the residue should not exceed 0.0010 gram.

Residue after ignition. Gently ignite 0.5 gram in a tared crucible or dish until charred. Cool, moisten the residue with 0.5 ml. of sulfuric acid, and ignite again slowly until all carbon and excess sulfuric acid have been volatilized. Finally, ignite at 800° ± 25°C. for 15 minutes. The weight of the residue should not exceed 0.0010 gram.

Sensitivity to aluminum. Dissolve 25 mg. in 20 ml. of water and 0.1 ml. of dilute ammonium hydroxide (10 per cent NH_3). Add 0.1 ml. of this solution and 0.1 ml. of acetic acid to 10 ml. of a solution containing 0.001 mg. of aluminum ion (Al). A distinct pink color should appear within 15 minutes.

Notes

Barium Acetate

(CH₃COO)₂Ba

$(CH_3COO)_2Ba$

Formula Wt. 255.43

REQUIREMENTS

Insoluble matter. Not more than 0.010 per cent.
Chloride (Cl). Not more than 0.001 per cent.
Oxidizing substances (as NO₃). Not more than 0.005 per cent.
Substances not precipitated by sulfuric acid. Not more than 0.10 per cent.
Calcium (Ca). Not more than 0.05 per cent.
Heavy metals (as Pb). Not more than 0.0005 per cent.
Iron (Fe). Not more than 0.001 per cent.
Strontium (Sr). To pass test (limit about 0.2 per cent).

TESTS

Insoluble matter. Dissolve 10 grams in 100 ml. of water, heat to boiling, and digest in a covered beaker on the steam bath for 1 hour. Filter through a tared filtering crucible, wash thoroughly, and dry at 105°C. The weight of the residue should not exceed 0.0010 gram.

Chloride. Dissolve 1 gram in water, filter if necessary through a small chloride-free filter, dilute to 20 ml., and add 1 ml. of nitric acid and 1 ml. of silver nitrate reagent solution. Any turbidity should not exceed that produced by 0.01 mg. of chloride ion (Cl) in an equal volume of solution containing the quantities of reagents used in the test.

Oxidizing substances. Place 0.1 gram in a dry beaker. Cool the beaker thoroughly in an ice bath and add 22 ml. of sulfuric acid which has been cooled to ice-bath temperature. Allow the mixture to warm to room temperature and swirl the beaker at intervals to effect gentle dissolution with slow evolution of the acetic acid vapor. When dissolution is complete, add 3 ml. of diphenylamine reagent solution and digest on the steam bath for 90 minutes. Prepare a standard by evaporating to dryness a solution containing 0.005 mg. of nitrate (0.5 ml. of the nitrate standard solution) and 0.01 gram of sodium carbonate. Treat the residue exactly like the sample. Any color produced in the solution of the sample should not exceed that in the standard.

Substances not precipitated by sulfuric acid. Dissolve 5 grams in 150 ml. of water. Add 1 ml. of hydrochloric acid and heat to boiling. Add 25 ml. of 10 per cent sulfuric acid reagent solution, cool, dilute to 250 ml., and allow to stand overnight. Decant through a filter and evaporate 100 ml. of the filtrate to dryness in a tared dish. Ignite gently to remove the excess acids, and finally ignite at 800° ± 25°C. for 15 minutes. The weight of the residue should not exceed 0.0020 gram.

Calcium. Determine the calcium by the flame photometric method described on page 14.

Sample Solution A. Dissolve 1 gram in water, add 2 ml. of hydrochloric acid, and dilute to 100 ml.

Control Solution B. Dissolve 1 gram in water, add 2 ml. of hydrochloric acid plus 0.50 mg. of calcium ion (Ca), and dilute to 100 ml.

Observe the emission of Control Solution B at the 422.7-mμ calcium line. Observe the emission of Sample Solution A at the 422.7-mμ calcium line and at a wavelength of 418 mμ. The difference (D_1) between the intensities observed for Sample Solution A at 418 mμ and 422.7 mμ should not exceed the difference (D_2) observed at 422.7 mμ between Sample Solution A and Control Solution B.

Heavy metals. Dissolve 6 grams in about 15 ml. of water, add 8 ml. of dilute hydrochloric acid (1 + 1), and dilute to 30 ml. For the control add 0.02 mg. of lead ion (Pb) to a 5-ml. aliquot of this solution and dilute to 25 ml. For the sample use the remaining 25-ml. portion. Adjust the pH of the control and sample solutions to between 3 and 4 (using a pH meter) with 1N acetic acid or ammonium hydroxide (10 per cent NH_3), dilute to 40 ml., and mix. Add 10 ml. of freshly prepared hydrogen sulfide water to each and mix. Any color in the solution of the sample should not exceed that in the control.

Iron. Dissolve 1 gram in 40 ml. of water. For the standard add 0.01 mg. of iron (Fe) to 40 ml. of water. Add 2 ml. of hydrochloric acid to each, dilute to 50 ml., and add 0.10 ml. of 0.1N potassium permanganate. Allow to stand for 5 minutes and add 3 ml. of ammonium thiocyanate reagent solution. Any red color in the solution of the sample should not exceed that in the standard.

Strontium. Determine the strontium by the flame photometric method described on page 14. Dissolve 1 gram in water, add 2 ml. of hydrochloric acid, and dilute to 100 ml.

Sample Solution A. Add 2 ml. of hydrochloric acid to a 10-ml. aliquot of this solution and dilute to 100 ml.

Control Solution B. Add 2 ml. of hydrochloric acid and 0.2 mg. of strontium ion (Sr) to another 10-ml. aliquot of the solution, and dilute to 100 ml.

Observe the emission of Control Solution B at the 460.7-mμ strontium line. Observe the emission of Sample Solution A at the 460.7-mμ strontium line and at a wavelength of 458.7-mμ. The difference (D_1) between the intensities observed for Sample Solution A at 458.7 mμ and 460.7 mμ should not exceed the difference (D_2) observed at 460.7 mμ between Sample Solution A and Control Solution B.

Notes

Barium Carbonate

BaCO$_3$ Formula Wt. 197.35

REQUIREMENTS

Insoluble in dilute hydrochloric acid. Not more than 0.015 per cent.
Chloride (Cl). Not more than 0.002 per cent.
Hydroxide and alkali carbonate. To pass test.
Oxidizing substances (as NO$_3$). Not more than 0.005 per cent.
Sulfide (S). To pass test (limit about 0.001 per cent).
Substances not precipitated by sulfuric acid. Not more than 0.25 per cent.
Calcium (Ca). Not more than 0.05 per cent.
Heavy metals (as Pb). Not more than 0.001 per cent.
Iron (Fe). Not more than 0.002 per cent.
Strontium (Sr). To pass test (limit about 0.3 per cent).

TESTS

Insoluble in dilute hydrochloric acid. Cautiously dissolve 10 grams in 100 ml. of dilute hydrochloric acid (1 + 9) and dilute to 200 ml. Heat the solution to boiling and digest in a covered beaker on the steam bath for 1 hour. Filter through a tared filtering crucible, wash thoroughly, and dry at 105°C. The weight of the residue should not exceed 0.0015 gram.

Chloride. To 1 gram add 20 ml. of water and gradually add, with stirring, 3 ml. of nitric acid. Filter if necessary through a chloride-free filter, wash with a little hot water, and dilute to 50 ml. To 25 ml. of the solution add 1 ml. of silver nitrate reagent solution. Any turbidity should not exceed that produced by 0.01 mg. of chloride ion (Cl) in an equal volume of solution containing the quantities of reagents used in the test.

Hydroxide and alkali carbonate. Shake 5 grams for 5 minutes with 50 ml. of carbon dioxide-free water, cool, and filter. To 30 ml. of the filtrate add 0.10 ml. of phenolphthalein indicator solution. If a pink color is produced, it should be discharged by 0.05 ml. of 0.1N hydrochloric acid.

Oxidizing substances. Place 0.1 gram in a dry beaker. Cool the beaker thoroughly in an ice bath and add 22 ml. of sulfuric acid which has been cooled to ice-bath temperature. Allow the mixture to warm to room temperature and swirl the beaker at intervals to effect gentle dissolution with slow evolution of carbon dioxide. When dissolution is complete, add 3 ml. of diphenylamine reagent solution and digest on the steam bath for 90 minutes. Prepare a standard by evaporating to dryness a solution containing 0.005 mg. of nitrate (0.5 ml. of the nitrate standard solution) and 0.01 gram of sodium carbonate. Treat the residue exactly like the sample. Any color produced in the solution of the sample should not exceed that in the standard.

Sulfide. Dissolve 1 gram in a mixture of 8 ml. of water and 2 ml. of glacial acetic acid. As soon as dissolution is effected, add 1 ml. of silver nitrate reagent solution. The solution should not darken in 5 minutes.

Substances not precipitated by sulfuric acid. Cautiously dissolve 2 grams in 30 ml. of dilute hydrochloric acid $(1 + 9)$ and dilute to 80 ml. Heat the solution to boiling, add 15 ml. of $2N$ sulfuric acid, cool, dilute to 100 ml., mix well, and allow to stand overnight. Decant the solution through a dry filter paper and evaporate 50 ml. of the filtrate to dryness in a tared dish. Ignite carefully to remove the excess acids, and finally ignite at $800° \pm 25°C$. for 15 minutes. The weight of the residue should not exceed 0.0025 gram.

Calcium. Determine the calcium by the flame photometric method described on page 14. Cautiously dissolve 4 grams in 50 ml. of dilute hydrochloric acid $(1 + 9)$ and evaporate to dryness on the steam bath. Dissolve the residue in about 80 ml. of dilute hydrochloric acid $(1 + 49)$ and dilute to 100 ml. with more of the dilute hydrochloric acid.

> **Sample Solution A.** Dilute 25 ml. of the solution to 100 ml. with dilute hydrochloric acid $(1 + 49.)$

> **Control Solution B.** Add 0.5 mg. of calcium ion (Ca) to another 25-ml. aliquot of the solution and dilute to 100 ml. with dilute hydrochloric acid $(1 + 49)$.

Observe the emission of Control Solution B at the 422.7-mμ calcium line. Observe the emission of Sample Solution A at the 422.7-mμ calcium line and at a wavelength of 418 mμ. The difference (D_1) between the intensities observed for Sample Solution A at 418 mμ and 422.7 mμ should not exceed the difference (D_2) observed at 422.7 mμ between Sample Solution A and Control Solution B.

Heavy metals. Cautiously dissolve 5 grams in 30 ml. of dilute hydrochloric acid $(1 + 4)$ and evaporate to dryness on the steam bath. Dissolve the residue in about 20 ml. of water and dilute to 25 ml. For the control add 0.02 mg. of lead ion (Pb) to a 5-ml. aliquot of the solution and dilute to 25 ml. For the sample dilute a 15-ml. aliquot of the solution to 25 ml. Adjust the pH of the control and sample solutions to between 3 and 4 (using a pH meter) with $1N$ acetic acid or ammonium hydroxide (10 per cent NH_3), dilute to 40 ml., and mix. Add 10 ml. of freshly prepared hydrogen sulfide water to each and mix. Any color in the solution of the sample should not exceed that in the control.

Iron. Cautiously dissolve 1 gram in 15 ml. of dilute hydrochloric acid $(1 + 2)$. For the standard add 0.02 mg. of iron (Fe) to 15 ml. of dilute hydrochloric acid $(1 + 2)$. Evaporate both solutions to dryness on the steam bath. Dissolve each residue in about 20 ml. of water, add 4 ml. of hydrochloric acid, and dilute to 100 ml. To 50 ml. of each solution add 0.10 ml. of $0.1N$ potassium permanganate solution, allow to stand for 5 minutes, and add 3 ml. of ammonium thiocyanate reagent solution. Any red color in the solution of the sample should not exceed that in the standard.

Strontium. Determine the strontium by the flame photometric method described on page 14. Cautiously dissolve 1 gram in 10 ml. of dilute hydrochloric acid $(1 + 5)$ and evaporate to dryness on the steam bath. Dissolve the residue in 20 ml. of dilute hydrochloric acid $(1 + 9)$ and dilute to 100 ml. with water.

Sample Solution A. Add 2 ml. of hydrochloric acid to a 10-ml. aliquot of the solution and dilute to 100 ml.

Control Solution B. Add 0.3 mg. of strontium ion (Sr) plus 2 ml. of hydrochloric acid to another 10-ml. aliquot of the solution and dilute to 100 ml.

Observe the emission of Control Solution B at the 460.7-mμ strontium line. Observe the emission of Sample Solution A at the 460.7-mμ strontium line and at a wavelength of 458.7 mμ. The difference (D_1) between the intensities observed for Sample Solution A at 458.7 mμ and 460.7 mμ should not exceed the difference (D_2) observed at 460.7 mμ between Sample Solution A and Control Solution B.

Notes

Barium Chloride

BaCl$_2$·2H$_2$O   Formula Wt. 244.28

REQUIREMENTS

Insoluble matter. Not more than 0.005 per cent.
pH of a 5 per cent solution. From 5.2 to 8.2 at 25°C.
Oxidizing substances (as NO$_3$). Not more than 0.005 per cent.
Substances not precipitated by sulfuric acid. Not more than 0.050 per cent.
Calcium (Ca). Not more than 0.05 per cent.
Heavy metals (as Pb). Not more than 0.0005 per cent.
Iron (Fe). Not more than 0.0002 per cent.
Strontium (Sr). To pass test (limit about 0.10 per cent).

TESTS

Insoluble matter. Dissolve 20 grams in 200 ml. of water, heat to boiling, and digest in a covered beaker on the steam bath for 1 hour. Filter through a tared filtering crucible, wash thoroughly, and dry at 105°C. The weight of the residue should not exceed 0.0010 gram.

pH of a 5 per cent solution. Dissolve 10 grams in 200 ml. of carbon dioxide- and ammonia-free water. Determine the pH by the method described on page 18. The pH should be from 5.2 to 8.2 at 25°C. The pH of a 5 per cent solution of pure barium chloride would be 6.9 at 25°C.

Oxidizing substances. Place 0.1 gram in a dry beaker. Cool the beaker thoroughly in an ice bath and add 22 ml. of sulfuric acid which has been cooled to ice-bath temperature. Allow the mixture to warm to room temperature and swirl the beaker at intervals to effect slow dissolution with gentle evolution of hydrogen chloride. When dissolution is complete, add 3 ml. of diphenylamine reagent solution and digest on the steam bath for 90 minutes. Prepare a standard by evaporating to dryness a solution containing 0.005 mg. of nitrate ion (NO$_3$) and 0.01 gram of sodium carbonate. Treat the residue exactly like the sample. Any color produced in the solution of the sample should not exceed that in the standard.

Substances not precipitated by sulfuric acid. Dissolve 5 grams in about 150 ml. of water. Add 1 ml. of hydrochloric acid, heat to boiling, and add 50 ml. of 1N sulfuric acid. Cool the solution, dilute to 250 ml., and allow to stand overnight. Decant through a dry filter paper and evaporate 100 ml. of the filtrate to dryness in a tared dish. Ignite gently to volatilize the excess acids, and finally ignite at 800° ± 25°C. for 15 minutes. The weight of the residue should not exceed 0.0010 gram.

Calcium. Determine the calcium by the flame photometric method described on page 14.

Sample Solution A. Dissolve 1 gram in 100 ml. of dilute hydrochloric acid (1 + 49).

Control Solution B. Dissolve 1 gram in about 80 ml. of dilute hydrochloric acid (1 + 49), add 0.5 mg. of calcium ion (Ca), and dilute to 100 ml. with dilute hydrochloric acid (1 + 49).

Observe the emission of Control Solution B at the 422.7-mμ calcium line. Observe the emission of Sample Solution A at the 422.7-mμ calcium line and at a wavelength of 418 mμ. The difference (D_1) between the intensities observed for Sample Solution A at 418 mμ and 422.7 mμ should not exceed the difference (D_2) observed at 422.7 mμ between Sample Solution A and Control Solution B.

Heavy metals. Dissolve 6 grams in about 20 ml. of water and dilute to 30 ml. For the control add 0.02 mg. of lead ion (Pb) to a 5-ml. aliquot of the solution and dilute to 25 ml. For the sample use the remaining 25-ml. portion. Adjust the pH of the control and sample solutions to between 3 and 4 (using a pH meter) with 1N acetic acid or ammonium hydroxide (10 per cent NH_3), dilute to 40 ml., and mix. Add 10 ml. of freshly prepared hydrogen sulfide water to each and mix. Any color in the solution of the sample should not exceed that in the control.

Iron. Dissolve 5 grams in 40 ml. of water plus 2 ml. of hydrochloric acid. Prepare a standard containing 0.01 mg. of iron (Fe) in 40 ml. of water plus 2 ml. of hydrochloric acid. Add 0.10 ml. of 0.1N potassium permanganate to each, dilute to 50 ml., and allow to stand for 5 minutes. Add 3 ml. of ammonium thiocyanate reagent solution to each. Any red color in the solution of the sample should not exceed that in the standard.

Strontium. Determine the strontium by the flame photometric method described on page 14. Dissolve 5 grams in dilute hydrochloric acid (1 + 49) and dilute to 100 ml. with dilute hydrochloric acid (1 + 49).

Sample Solution A. Dilute a 10-ml. aliquot (0.5-gram sample) of the solution to 100 ml. with dilute hydrochloric acid (1 + 49).

Control Solution B. Add 0.5 mg. of strontium ion (Sr) to another 10-ml. aliquot of the solution and dilute to 100 ml. with dilute hydrochloric acid (1 + 49).

Observe the emission of Control Solution B at the 460.7-mμ strontium line. Observe the emission of Sample Solution A at the 460.7-mμ strontium line and at a wavelength of 458.7 mμ. The difference (D_1) between the intensities observed for Sample Solution A at 458.7 mμ and 460.7 mμ should not exceed the difference (D_2) observed at 460.7 mμ between Sample Solution A and Control Solution B.

Notes

Barium Hydroxide

$Ba(OH)_2 \cdot 8H_2O$ Formula Wt. 315.48

REQUIREMENTS

Assay. Not less than 98 per cent $Ba(OH)_2.8H_2O$.
Carbonate (as $BaCO_3$). Not more than 2.0 per cent.
Insoluble in dilute hydrochloric acid. Not more than 0.010 per cent.
Chloride (Cl). Not more than 0.001 per cent.
Sulfide (S). To pass test (limit about 0.001 per cent).
Substances not precipitated by sulfuric acid. Not more than 0.20 per
    cent.
Calcium (Ca). Not more than 0.05 per cent.
Heavy metals (as Pb). Not more than 0.0005 per cent.
Iron (Fe). Not more than 0.001 per cent.
Strontium (Sr). To pass test (limit about 0.8 per cent).

TESTS

Assay. Weigh accurately 4 to 5 grams of clear crystals and dissolve in
about 200 ml. of carbon dioxide-free water. Add 0.10 ml. of phenolphthalein indicator solution and titrate with $1N$ hydrochloric acid. Reserve this solution for the determination of *Carbonate*. Each milliliter
of $1N$ acid corresponds to 0.1577 gram of $Ba(OH)_2 \cdot 8H_2O$.

Carbonate. To the solution reserved from the test for *Assay* add 5.00
ml. of $1N$ hydrochloric acid, heat to boiling, boil gently to expel all of the
carbon dioxide, and cool. Add 0.10 ml. of methyl orange indicator and
titrate the excess acid with $1N$ sodium hydroxide. Each milliliter of $1N$
hydrochloric acid consumed corresponds to 0.09868 gram of $BaCO_3$.

Insoluble in dilute hydrochloric acid. Dissolve 10 grams in 100 ml. of
dilute hydrochloric acid $(1 + 9)$. Heat the solution to boiling, then
digest in a covered beaker on the steam bath for 1 hour. Filter through
a tared filtering crucible, wash thoroughly, and dry at 105°C. The
weight of the residue should not exceed 0.0010 gram.

Chloride. Dissolve 2 grams in 25 ml. of water, add 0.05 ml. of phenolphthalein indicator solution, and neutralize with nitric acid. If the solution is not perfectly clear, filter it through a chloride-free filter and dilute
the filtrate to 50 ml. To 25 ml. of the solution add 1 ml. of nitric acid
and 1 ml. of silver nitrate reagent solution. Any turbidity should not
exceed that produced by 0.01 mg. of chloride ion (Cl) in an equal volume of solution containing the quantities of reagents used in the test.

Sulfide. Dissolve 1 gram in 8 ml. of warm water and add 0.25 ml. of alkaline lead solution (prepared by adding sodium hydroxide solution to a 10 per cent lead acetate solution until the precipitate is redissolved) and 2 ml. of glacial acetic acid. No darkening should occur.

Substances not precipitated by sulfuric acid. Dissolve 5 grams in 150 ml. of water plus 5 ml. of hydrochloric acid. Heat the solution to boiling, and add 25 ml. of 10 per cent sulfuric acid reagent solution. Allow the solution to cool, dilute to 250 ml., and allow to stand overnight. Decant the solution through a dry filter and evaporate 100 ml. to dryness in a tared dish. Heat gently to volatilize the excess acids, and finally ignite at $800° \pm 25°C$. for 15 minutes. The weight of the residue should not exceed 0.0040 gram.

Calcium. Determine the calcium by the flame photometric method described on page 14.

Sample Solution A. Dissolve 1 gram in about 50 ml. of water, add 0.05 ml. of phenolphthalein indicator solution, neutralize with hydrochloric acid, add 2-ml. excess hydrochloric acid, and dilute to 100 ml.

Control Solution B. Dissolve 1 gram in about 50 ml. of water, add 0.50 mg. of calcium ion (Ca), and treat exactly like Sample Solution A.

Observe the emission of Control Solution B at the 422.7-$m\mu$ calcium line. Observe the emission of Sample Solution A at the 422.7-$m\mu$ calcium line and at a wavelength of 418 $m\mu$. The difference (D_1) between the intensities observed for Sample Solution A at 418 $m\mu$ and 422.7 $m\mu$ should not exceed the difference (D_2) observed at 422.7 $m\mu$ between Sample Solution A and Control Solution B.

Heavy metals. To 5 grams in a 150-ml. beaker add 25 ml. of water, mix, and cautiously add 10 ml. of hydrochloric acid. For the control dissolve 1 gram of the sample in 25 ml. of water, add 0.02 mg. of lead ion (Pb), and cautiously add 10 ml. of hydrochloric acid. Evaporate both solutions to dryness on the steam bath, dissolve each residue in about 2 ml. of water, and dilute to 25 ml. Adjust the pH of the control and sample solutions to between 3 and 4 (using a pH meter) with $1N$ acetic acid or ammonium hydroxide (10 per cent NH_3), dilute to 40 ml., and mix. Add 10 ml. of freshly prepared hydrogen sulfide water to each and mix. Any color in the solution of the sample should not exceed that in the control.

Iron. Dissolve 1 gram in 40 ml. of water. For the standard add 0.01 mg. of iron (Fe) to 40 ml. of water. Add 2.5 ml. of hydrochloric acid to each, dilute to 50 ml., and add 0.10 ml. of potassium permanganate solution. Allow to stand for 5 minutes and add 3 ml. of ammonium thiocyanate reagent solution. Any red color in the solution of the sample should not exceed that in the standard.

Strontium.   Determine the strontium by the flame photometric method described on page 14. Dissolve 5 grams in 100 ml. of dilute hydrochloric acid $(1 + 19)$.

Sample Solution A.   Dilute a 1-ml. aliquot to 100 ml. with dilute hydrochloric acid $(1 + 49)$.

Control Solution B.   Add 0.4 mg. of strontium ion (Sr) to another 1-ml. aliquot of the solution and dilute to 100 ml. with dilute hydrochloric acid $(1 + 49)$.

Observe the emission of Control Solution B at the 460.7-mμ strontium line. Observe the emission of Sample Solution A at the 460.7-mμ strontium line and at a wavelength of 458.7 mμ. The difference (D_1) between the intensities observed for Sample Solution A at 460.7 mμ and 458.7 mμ should not exceed the difference (D_2) observed at 460.7 mμ between Sample Solution A and Control Solution B.

Notes

Barium Nitrate

Ba(NO$_3$)$_2$ Formula Wt. 261.35

REQUIREMENTS

Insoluble matter.   Not more than 0.010 per cent.
pH of a 5 per cent solution.   From 5.0 to 8.0 at 25°C.
Chloride (Cl).   Not more than 0.0005 per cent.
Substances not precipitated by sulfuric acid.   Not more than 0.050 per cent.
Calcium (Ca).   Not more than 0.05 per cent.
Heavy metals (as Pb).   Not more than 0.0005 per cent.
Iron (Fe).   Not more than 0.0002 per cent.
Strontium (Sr).   To pass test (limit about 0.05 per cent).

TESTS

Insoluble matter.   Dissolve 10 grams in 150 ml. of hot water, heat to boiling, and digest in a covered beaker on the steam bath for 1 hour. Filter through a tared filtering crucible, wash thoroughly, and dry at 105°C. The weight of the residue should not exceed 0.0010 gram.

pH of a 5 per cent solution.   Dissolve 10 grams in 200 ml. of carbon dioxide- and ammonia-free water. Determine the pH by the method described on page 18. The pH should be from 5.0 to 8.0 at 25°C. The pH of a 5 per cent solution of pure barium nitrate would be 6.9 at 25°C.

Chloride.   Dissolve 2 grams in 30 ml. of warm water, filter if necessary through a chloride-free filter, and add 0.10 ml. of nitric acid and 1 ml. of silver nitrate reagent solution. Any turbidity should not exceed that produced by 0.01 mg. of chloride ion (Cl) in an equal volume of solution containing the quantities of reagents used in the test.

Substances not precipitated by sulfuric acid.   Dissolve 5 grams in about 150 ml. of water plus 1 ml. of hydrochloric acid. Heat the solution to boiling, add 25 ml. of approximately 2N sulfuric acid, cool, dilute to 250 ml., and allow to stand overnight. Decant the solution through a dry filter and evaporate 100 ml. of the filtrate to dryness in a tared porcelain or silica dish. Heat gently to volatilize the excess acid, and finally ignite at 800° ± 25°C. for 15 minutes. The weight of the residue should not exceed 0.0010 gram.

Calcium.   Determine the calcium by the flame photometric method described on page 14.

Sample Solution A. Dissolve 1 gram in about 80 ml. of water, add 2 ml. of nitric acid, and dilute to 100 ml.

Control Solution B. Dissolve 1 gram in about 80 ml. of water, add 0.50 mg. of calcium ion (Ca) and 2 ml. of nitric acid, and dilute to 100 ml.

Observe the emission of Control Solution B at the 422.7-mμ calcium line. Observe the emission of Sample Solution A at the 422.7-mμ calcium line and at a wavelength of 418 mμ. The difference (D_1) between the intensities observed for Sample Solution A at 418 mμ and 422.7 mμ should not exceed the difference (D_2) observed at 422.7 mμ between Sample Solution A and Control Solution B.

Heavy metals. Dissolve 4 grams in about 50 ml. of water and dilute to 60 ml. For the control add 0.01 mg. of lead ion (Pb) to a 15-ml. aliquot of the solution and dilute to 45 ml. For the sample use the remaining 45-ml. portion. Adjust the pH of the control and sample solutions to between 3 and 4 (using a pH meter) with 1N acetic acid or ammonium hydroxide (10 per cent NH_3), dilute to 48 ml., and mix. Add 10 ml. of freshly prepared hydrogen sulfide water to each and mix. Any color in the solution of the sample should not exceed that in the control.

Iron. Dissolve 5 grams in 45 ml. of hot water plus 2 ml. of hydrochloric acid and allow to cool. Prepare a standard containing 0.01 mg. of iron (Fe) in 45 ml. of water plus 2 ml. of hydrochloric acid. Add 0.10 ml. of 0.1N potassium permanganate to each, allow to stand for 5 minutes, and add 3 ml. of ammonium thiocyanate reagent solution. Any red color in the solution of the sample should not exceed that in the standard.

Strontium. Determine the strontium by the flame photometric method described on page 14.

Sample Solution A. Dissolve 1 gram in about 80 ml. of water, add 2 ml. of nitric acid, and dilute to 100 ml.

Control Solution B. Dissolve 1 gram in about 80 ml. of water, add 0.50 mg. of strontium ion (Sr) and 2 ml. of nitric acid, and dilute to 100 ml.

Observe the emission of Control Solution B at the 460.7-mμ strontium line. Observe the emission of Sample Solution A at the 460.7-mμ strontium line and at a wavelength of 458.7 mμ. The difference (D_1) between the intensities observed for Sample Solution A at 458.7 mμ and 460.7 mμ should not exceed the difference (D_2) observed at 460.7 mμ between Sample Solution A and Control Solution B.

Benzene

C₆H₆

C_6H_6

Formula Wt. 78.11

REQUIREMENTS

Color (APHA).   Not more than 10.
Boiling range.   1 ml. to 95 ml., not more than 0.5°C.; 95 ml. to dryness,
    not more than 0.5°C.
Freezing point.   Not below 5.2°C.
Residue after evaporation.   Not more than 0.001 per cent.
Substances darkened by sulfuric acid.   To pass test.
Thiophene.   To pass test (limit about 0.0001 per cent).
Sulfur compounds (as S).   Not more than 0.005 per cent.
Water (H₂O).   Not more than 0.05 per cent.

TESTS

Color (APHA).   For the color standard dilute a 2-ml. aliquot of platinum-cobalt stock solution (APHA No. 500) to 100 ml. with water. Compare this solution (APHA No. 10) with 100 ml. of the benzene in 100-ml. Nessler tubes, viewed vertically over a white background.

Boiling range.   Distill 100 ml. by the method described on page 12. The difference between the temperatures when 1 ml. and 95 ml. have distilled should not exceed 0.5°C., and the difference in temperatures when 95 ml. have distilled and when the dry point is reached should not exceed 0.5°C. The boiling point of pure benzene at 760-mm. mercury pressure is 80.1°C.

Freezing point.   Place 15 ml. in a test tube (20 × 150 mm.) in which is centered an accurate thermometer. The sample tube is centered by corks in an outer tube about 38 × 200 mm. Cool the whole apparatus, without stirring, in a bath of shaved or crushed ice with water enough to wet the outer tube. When the temperature is about 2°C., stir to start the freezing and read the thermometer every half minute. The temperature which remains constant for 1 or 2 minutes is the freezing point.

Residue after evaporation.   Evaporate 115 ml. (100 grams) to dryness in a tared dish on the steam bath and dry the residue at 105°C for 30 minutes. The weight of the residue should not exceed 0.0010 gram.

Substances darkened by sulfuric acid.   Shake 25 ml. with 15 ml. of sulfuric acid for 15 to 20 seconds and allow to separate. Neither the benzene nor the acid should be darkened.

Thiophene.   Add 5.0 ml. of freshly prepared isatin reagent solution* to a dry, clean 50-ml. porcelain crucible. Carefully overlay with 5.0 ml. of the sample, allow to stand undisturbed for 1 hour, and compare to a blank containing 5.0 ml. of isatin reagent solution in a 50-ml. porcelain crucible. No bluish-green color should be present.

* Isatin Reagent Solution

Solution A. Dissolve 0.25 grams of isatin in 25 ml. of sulfuric acid.

Solution B. Dissolve 0.25 grams of ferric chloride in 1 ml. of water. Dilute to 50 ml. with sulfuric acid and allow the evolution of gas to cease.

To 2.5 ml. of Solution A add 5.0 ml. of Solution B and dilute to 100 ml. with sulfuric acid.

Sulfur compounds. Place 30 ml. of 0.5N potassium hydroxide in methanol in an Erlenmeyer flask, add 6 ml. of the sample, and boil the mixture gently for 30 minutes under a reflux condenser, avoiding the use of a rubber stopper or connection. Detach the condenser, dilute with 50 ml. of water, and heat on the steam bath until the benzene and methanol are evaporated. Add 50 ml. of saturated bromine water and heat for 15 minutes longer. Transfer the solution to a beaker, neutralize with dilute hydrochloric acid (1 + 3), add an excess of 1 ml. of the acid, and concentrate to about 50 ml. Filter if necessary, heat the filtrate to boiling, add 5 ml. of barium chloride reagent solution, digest in a covered beaker on the steam bath for 2 hours, and allow to stand overnight. If a precipitate is formed, filter, wash thoroughly, and ignite. The weight of the precipitate should not be more than 0.0020 gram greater than the weight obtained in a complete blank test.

Water. Place 25 ml. of methanol in a dry titration flask and add Karl Fischer reagent to a visually or electrometrically determined end point. Add 20 ml. (17.4 grams) of the sample, taking care to protect the sample and contents of the flask from moisture. Stir vigorously and titrate with Karl Fischer reagent to the same end point. Calculate the water content of the sample from the titer and volume of Karl Fischer reagent consumed by the sample.

Notes

Benzene

(Suitable for use in ultraviolet spectrophotometry)

C_6H_6 Formula Wt. 78.11

REQUIREMENTS

Absorbance.   To pass test.
Boiling range.   1 ml. to 95 ml., not more than 0.5°C.; 95 ml. to dryness, not more than 0.5°C.
Freezing point.   Not below 5.2°C.
Residue after evaporation.   Not more than 0.001 per cent.
Substances darkened by sulfuric acid.   To pass test.
Thiophene.   To pass test (limit about 0.0001 per cent).
Sulfur compounds (as S).   Not more than 0.005 per cent.
Water (H_2O).   Not more than 0.05 per cent.

TESTS

Absorbance.   Determine the absorbance of the sample in a 1.00-cm. cell throughout the range of 280 mμ to 400 mμ, against water in a similar matched cell set at zero absorbance as the reference liquid. The absorbance should not exceed 1.00 at 280 mμ, 0.30 at 290 mμ, 0.10 at 300 mμ, 0.04 at 330 mμ, 0.02 at 350 mμ, and 0.01 at 380 mμ to 400 mμ. The spectral absorbance curve recorded through the wavelengths indicated should be smooth throughout the prescribed range and should not show extraneous impurity peaks within this range.

Other tests are the same as for **Benzene,** page 105, except *Color* (*APHA*), which is superseded by the *Absorbance* test.

Notes

Benzidine Dihydrochloride

$(C_6H_4NH_2)_2 \cdot 2HCl$ Formula Wt. 257.16

Caution. This reagent is reported to be carcinogenic. *Avoid contact.*

REQUIREMENTS

Insoluble matter. Not more than 0.020 per cent.
Residue after ignition. Not more than 0.050 per cent.
Sulfate (SO_4). Not more than 0.015 per cent.
Sensitivity for detecting blood. To pass test.

TESTS

Insoluble matter. Dissolve 5 grams in 200 ml. of water, heat to boiling, and digest in a covered beaker on the steam bath for 1 hour. Filter through a tared filtering crucible, wash thoroughly, and dry at 105°C. The weight of the residue should not exceed 0.0010 gram.

Residue after ignition. Ignite 2 grams in a tared crucible or dish. The rate of heating should be such that from 1 to 2 hours is required to volatilize the sample. When nearly all the sample has been volatilized, cool, and moisten the residue with 0.5 ml. of sulfuric acid. Continue the heating until the remainder of the sample and excess sulfuric acid have been volatilized. Finally, ignite at 800° ± 25°C. for 15 minutes. The weight of the residue should not exceed 0.0010 gram.

Sulfate. Moisten 1 gram with 10 ml. of 10 per cent sodium carbonate solution, evaporate to dryness, and carefully ignite, protecting from sulfur in the flame. Treat the residue with 20 ml. of water and 2 ml. of 30 per cent hydrogen peroxide and heat on the steam bath for 15 minutes. Add 5 ml. of hydrochloric acid and evaporate to dryness on the steam bath. Dissolve the residue in 10 ml. of water, filter through a small filter, wash thoroughly, and dilute the filtrate to 25 ml. To 10 ml. of the solution add 1 ml. of dilute hydrochloric acid (1 + 19) and 1 ml. of barium chloride reagent solution. Any turbidity should not exceed that in a standard prepared as follows: treat 10 ml. of 10 per cent sodium carbonate with 2 ml. of 30 per cent hydrogen peroxide and 5 ml. of hydrochloric acid and evaporate to dryness on the steam bath. Dissolve the residue in 25 ml. of water. To 10 ml. add 0.06 mg. of sulfate ion (SO_4), 1 ml. of dilute hydrochloric acid (1 + 19), and 1 ml. of barium chloride reagent solution. Compare 10 minutes after adding the barium chloride to the sample and standard solutions.

Sensitivity for detecting blood. Dissolve 1 gram in 100 ml. of water without heating. Dilute 0.10 ml. of blood with water to 100 ml. and dilute a 1-ml. aliquot of this solution to 500 ml. To 1 ml. of the latter solution in a test tube add, in the order named, with mixing after each addition: 1 ml. of the solution of the sample, 1 ml. of diluted 30 per cent hydrogen peroxide (1 + 9), and 1 ml. of 1 per cent sodium acetate solution. After 1 minute the mixed solution should show a distinct blue color when compared with a blank prepared in the same manner but containing 1 ml. of water instead of the 1 ml. of diluted blood solution. The solution of the sample must be freshly prepared for this test.

Notes

Benzoic Acid

C_6H_5COOH Formula Wt. 122.12

REQUIREMENTS

Freezing point.   Not below 122°C. nor above 123°C.
Residue after ignition.   Not more than 0.005 per cent.
Insoluble in methanol.   Not more than 0.005 per cent.
Chlorine compounds (as Cl).   To pass test (limit about 0.005 per cent).
Sulfur compounds (as S).   To pass test (limit about 0.002 per cent).
Heavy metals (as Pb).   Not more than 0.0005 per cent.
Substances reducing permanganate.   To pass test.

TESTS

Freezing point.   Place 12 to 15 grams in test tube (20 × 150 mm.), and heat gently to melt the benzoic acid. Insert an accurate thermometer in the test tube so that the bulb of the thermometer is centrally located, and heat gently to about 130°C. Place the tube containing the melted sample in a larger test tube (38 × 200 mm.) and keep it centered by means of corks. Allow the sample to cool slowly. If crystallization does not start when the temperature is about 120°C., stir gently with the thermometer to start freezing, and read the thermometer every half minute. The temperature that remains constant for 2 to 3 minutes is the freezing point.

Residue after ignition.   Heat 20 grams in a platinum dish at a temperature sufficient to volatilize the acid slowly, but do not char or ignite it. When nearly all the acid has been volatilized, cool, and moisten the residue with 0.15 ml. of sulfuric acid. Continue the heating until the remainder of the sample and excess sulfuric acid have been volatilized. Finally, ignite at 800° ± 25°C. for 15 minutes. The weight of the residue should not exceed 0.0010 gram.

Insoluble in methanol.   Dissolve 20 grams in 200 ml. of methanol and digest under complete reflux for 30 minutes. Filter through a tared filtering crucible, wash thoroughly with methanol, and dry at 105°C. The weight of the residue should not exceed 0.0010 gram.

Chlorine compounds.   Mix 1 gram with 0.5 gram of sodium carbonate and add 10 to 15 ml. of water. Evaporate on the steam bath and ignite until the mass is thoroughly charred, avoiding an unduly high temperature. Extract the fusion with 20 ml. of water and 5.5 ml. of nitric acid. Filter through a chloride-free filter, wash with two 10-ml. portions of water, and dilute to 50 ml. Dilute 10 ml. of the solution to 25 ml. and add 1 ml. of silver nitrate reagent solution. Any turbidity should not exceed that produced by 0.01 mg. of chloride ion (Cl) in an equal volume of solution containing 0.1 gram of sodium carbonate, 1.1 ml. of nitric acid, and 1 ml. of silver nitrate reagent solution.

Sulfur compounds.   Mix 2 grams with 1 gram of sodium carbonate and add in small portions 15 ml. of water. Evaporate and thoroughly ignite, protected from sulfur in the flame. Treat the residue with 20 ml. of water and 2 ml. of 30 per cent hydrogen peroxide and heat on the steam bath for 15 minutes. Add 5 ml. of hydrochloric acid and evaporate to dryness on the steam bath. Dissolve the residue in 10 ml. of water, filter, wash with two 5-ml. portions of water, and dilute to 25 ml. Add to this solution 0.5 ml. of 1N hydrochloric acid and 2 ml. of barium chloride reagent solution. Any turbidity should not exceed that in a standard prepared as follows: treat 1 gram of sodium carbonate with 2 ml. of 30 per cent hydrogen peroxide and 5 ml. of hydrochloric acid and evaporate to dryness on the steam bath. Dissolve the residue and 0.12 mg. of sulfate ion (SO_4) in sufficient water to make 25 ml. and add 0.5 ml. of 1N hydrochloric acid and 2 ml. of barium chloride reagent solution. Compare 10 minutes after adding the barium chloride to the sample and standard solutions.

Heavy metals.   For the sample volatilize 4 grams over a low flame. For the standard use a solution containing 0.02 mg. of lead ion (Pb). To each add 5 ml. of nitric acid and about 10 mg. of sodium carbonate, evaporate to dryness on the steam bath, dissolve each residue in about 20 ml. of water and dilute to 25 ml. Adjust the pH of the standard and sample solutions to between 3 and 4 (using a pH meter) with 1N acetic acid or ammonium hydroxide (10 per cent NH_3), dilute to 40 ml., and mix. Add 10 ml. of freshly prepared hydrogen sulfide water to each and mix. Any color in the solution of the sample should not exceed that in the standard.

Substances reducing permanganate.   Dissolve 1 gram in 100 ml. of water containing 1 ml. of sulfuric acid. Heat to 85°C. (steam bath temperature) and add 0.5 ml. of 0.1N potassium permanganate solution. The pink color should not be entirely discharged in 5 minutes.

Boric Acid

H_3BO_3 Formula Wt. 61.83

REQUIREMENTS

Insoluble in methanol. Not more than 0.005 per cent.
Nonvolatile with methanol. Not more than 0.05 per cent.
Chloride (Cl). Not more than 0.001 per cent.
Phosphate (PO_4). Not more than 0.001 per cent.
Sulfate (SO_4). Not more than 0.010 per cent.
Arsenic (As). Not more than 0.0001 per cent.
Calcium (Ca). Not more than 0.005 per cent.
Heavy metals (as Pb). Not more than 0.001 per cent.
Iron (Fe). Not more than 0.001 per cent.

TESTS

Insoluble in methanol. Heat 20 grams with 200 ml. of methanol under complete reflux until the acid is dissolved, then reflux for 30 minutes. Filter through a tared filtering crucible, wash thoroughly with hot methanol, and dry at 105°C. The weight of the insoluble residue should not exceed 0.0010 gram.

Nonvolatile with methanol. To 2 grams of the powdered acid in a platinum dish, add 25 ml. of methanol and 0.5 ml. of hydrochloric acid and evaporate to dryness. Add 15 ml. of methanol and 0.3 ml. of hydrochloric acid and repeat the evaporation. Add to the residue 0.10 or 0.15 ml. of sulfuric acid and ignite at 800° ± 25°C. for 15 minutes. The weight of the residue should not exceed 0.0010 gram.

Chloride. Dissolve 2 grams in 40 ml. of warm water, and filter if necessary through a chloride-free filter. To 20 ml. add 1 ml. of nitric acid and 1 ml. of silver nitrate reagent solution. Any turbidity should not exceed that produced by 0.01 mg. of chloride ion (Cl) in an equal volume of solution containing the quantities of reagents used in the test.

Sample Solution A for the determination of Phosphate, Sulfate, Calcium, Heavy metals, and Iron. To 10 grams add 10 mg. of sodium carbonate, 100 ml. of methanol, and 5 ml. of hydrochloric acid. Digest in a covered beaker on the steam bath to effect dissolution, then uncover and evaporate to dryness. Add 75 ml. of methanol and 5 ml. of hydrochloric acid and repeat the digestion and evaporation. Dissolve the residue in 5 ml. of $1N$ acetic acid and digest in a covered beaker on the steam bath for 15 minutes. Filter and dilute to 100 ml. (1 ml. = 0.1 gram).

Phosphate. Add 0.5 ml. of nitric acid to 20 ml. of Sample Solution A (2-gram sample) and evaporate to dryness. Dissolve the residue in 25 ml. of approximately 0.5N sulfuric acid. Add 1 ml. of ammonium molybdate reagent solution and 1 ml. of p-methylaminophenol sulfate reagent solution, and allow to stand for two hours at room temperature. Any blue color produced should not exceed that produced by 0.02 mg. of phosphate ion (PO_4) in an equal volume of solution containing the quantities of reagents used in the test.

Sulfate. Dilute 5 ml. of Sample Solution A (0.5-gram sample) to 10 ml. and add 1 ml. of dilute hydrochloric acid (1 + 19) and 1 ml. of barium chloride reagent solution. Any turbidity should not exceed that produced by 0.05 mg. of sulfate ion (SO_4) in an equal volume of solution containing the quantities of reagents used in the test. Compare 10 minutes after adding the barium chloride to the sample and standard solutions.

Arsenic. Determine the arsenic in 2 grams by the Gutzeit method (page 11). The amount of stain should not exceed that produced by 0.002 mg. of arsenic (As).

Calcium. Determine the calcium by the flame photometric method described on page 14.

Sample Solution A-1. Dilute a 20-ml. aliquot of Sample Solution A (2-gram sample) to 100 ml.

Control Solution B. Add 0.1 mg. of calcium ion (Ca) to another 20-ml. aliquot of Sample Solution A and dilute to 100 ml.

Observe the emission of Control Solution B at the 422.7-mμ calcium line. Observe the emission of Sample Solution A-1 at the 422.7-mμ calcium line and at a wavelength of 413 mμ. The difference (D_1) between the intensities observed for Sample Solution A-1 at 422.7 mμ and 413 mμ should not exceed the difference (D_2) observed at 422.7 mμ between Sample Solution A-1 and Control Solution B.

Heavy metals. Dilute 20 ml. of Sample Solution A (2-gram sample) to 25 ml. For the standard dilute a solution containing 0.02 mg. of lead ion (Pb) to 25 ml. Adjust the pH of the standard and sample solutions to between 3 and 4 (using a pH meter) with 1N acetic acid or ammonium hydroxide (10 per cent NH_3), dilute to 40 ml., and mix. Add 10 ml. of freshly prepared hydrogen sulfide water to each and mix. Any color in the solution of the sample should not exceed that in the standard.

Iron. Add 2 ml. of hydrochloric acid to 10 ml. of Sample Solution A

(1-gram sample) and dilute to 50 ml. Add 30 to 50 mg. of ammonium persulfate crystals and 3 ml. of ammonium thiocyanate reagent solution. Any red color should not exceed that produced by 0.01 mg. of iron in an equal volume of solution containing the quantities of reagents used in the test.

Notes

Bromine

Br

Atomic Wt. 79.904

REQUIREMENTS

Residue after evaporation. Not more than 0.005 per cent.
Chlorine (Cl). Not more than 0.05 per cent.
Iodine (I). Not more than 0.001 per cent.
Organic bromine compounds. To pass test.
Sulfur compounds (as S). Not more than 0.001 per cent.
Heavy metals (as Pb). Not more than 0.0002 per cent.
Nickel (Ni). Not more than 0.0005 per cent.

TESTS

Residue after evaporation. Evaporate 10 ml. (31 grams) to dryness from a tared container on the steam bath *under a hood* and dry the residue at 105°C. for 30 minutes. The weight of the residue should not exceed 0.0015 grams. Reserve the residue for the test for *Heavy metals.*

Chlorine. To each of two 250-ml. wide-mouth Erlenmeyer flasks, add 0.5 ml. of dilute sulfuric acid (1 + 4), 5 ml. of potassium bromide solution (0.75 gram KBr per liter), and 35 ml. of water. For the sample add 1 ml. (3 grams) of the bromine to one of the flasks. For the standard add 1.5 mg. of chloride ion (3.2 mg. KCl) to the other flask. Digest each on the steam bath until the sample solution is colorless, add 2.5 ml. of potassium persulfate solution (1.0 gram per 100 ml.), and wash down the sides of the flask with a little water. Digest again on the the steam bath for 15 minutes, cool, and dilute to 100 ml. Dilute a 10-ml. aliquot of each solution to 100 ml., dilute a 6.0-ml. aliquot of these solutions to 23 ml., and add 1 ml. of nitric acid and 1 ml. of silver nitrate reagent solution to each. Any turbidity in the solution of the sample should not exceed that in the standard.

Iodine. To each of two 250-ml. wide-mouth Erlenmeyer flasks, add 1.0 ml. of 10 per cent potassium chloride solution, 50 ml. of water, and a few silicon carbide boiling chips. For the sample add 3.5 ml. (10.5 grams) of the bromine to one of the flasks. For the control add 0.3 ml. of the bromine and 0.1 mg. of iodide ion (0.13 mg. KI) to the other flask. Boil cautiously *in a hood* to remove the excess bromine, adding water as required to maintain a volume of not less than 50 ml. When no trace of yellow color remains in either flask, cool, and add 5 ml. of 10 per cent potassium iodide solution and 5 ml. of dilute sulfuric acid

$(1 + 4)$ to each. Any color in the solution of the sample should not exceed that in the control.

Organic bromine compounds. Use matching infrared cells consisting of rock salt windows separated by ½-inch Teflon spacers. Fill one of the cells with bromine from a pipet inserted through an opening drilled in the plastic. Scan the sample from 2.5 μ to 15 μ, using the empty matching cell for reference. The absorbance of the sample should not exceed 0.10 in the region from 2.5 μ to 12 μ (except for possible water bands at 2.6 μ to 2.9 μ and 6.3 μ) or 0.20 in the region from 12 μ to 15 μ.

Sulfur compounds. To 2.6 ml. (8 grams) add 5 ml. of water and evaporate to dryness on the steam bath. To the residue add 5 ml. of dilute hydrochloric acid $(1 + 19)$, filter if necessary, dilute to 50 ml. with water, and add 1 ml. of barium chloride reagent solution to a 10-ml. aliquot. Any turbidity should not exceed that produced by 0.05 mg. of sulfate ion (SO_4) in an equal volume of solution containing the quantities of reagents used in the test. Compare 10 minutes after adding the barium chloride to the sample and standard solutions. Reserve the remaining solution for the test for *Nickel*.

Heavy metals. For the sample use the residue reserved from the test for *Residue after evaporation*. For the standard use a solution containing 0.06 mg. of lead ion (Pb). To each add 3 ml. of nitric acid, 1 ml. of water, and about 10 mg. of sodium carbonate. Evaporate to dryness on the steam bath, dissolve the residues in about 20 ml. of water, and dilute to 25 ml. Adjust the pH of the standard and sample solutions to between 3 and 4 (using a pH meter) with 1N acetic acid or ammonium hydroxide (10 per cent NH_3), dilute to 40 ml., and mix. Add 10 ml. of freshly prepared hydrogen sulfide water to each and mix. Any color in the solution of the sample should not exceed that in the standard.

Nickel. To 25 ml. of the solution reserved from the test for *Sulfur compounds*, add 5 ml. of bromine water. Stir and add ammonium hydroxide $(1 + 1)$ until the bromine color is discharged. Add 5 ml. of 1 per cent dimethylglyoxime solution in ethyl alcohol and 5 ml. of 10 per cent sodium hydroxide reagent solution. Any red color should not exceed that produced by 0.02 mg. of nickel ion (Ni) in an equal volume of solution containing the quantities of reagents used in the test. Compare 10 minutes after adding the dimethylglyoxime to the sample and standard solutions.

Notes

Bromocresol Green

3',3'',5',5''-Tetrabromo-m-cresolsulfonphthalein

α,α-bis(3,5-Dibromo-4-hydroxy-o-tolyl)-α-hydroxy-o-toluene γ-Sultone

Note. This specification applies both to the free acid form and to the salt form of this indicator.

REQUIREMENTS

Insoluble matter. To pass test.
Visual transition interval. From pH 4.0 (yellow) to pH 5.4 (blue).

TESTS

Insoluble matter. If the indicator is the acid form, dissolve 0.1 gram in 100 ml. of alcohol. If the indicator is a salt form, dissolve 0.1 gram in 100 ml. of water. Not more than a faint trace of turbidity or insoluble matter should remain. Reserve the solution for the test for *Visual transition interval*.

Visual transition interval. Dissolve 1 gram of potassium chloride in 100 ml. of water. Adjust the pH of the solution to 4.00 (using a pH meter as described on page 18) with 0.01N acid. Add 0.10 to 0.30 ml. of the 0.1 per cent solution reserved from the test for *Insoluble matter*. The color of the solution should be yellow, with not more than a faint trace of green color. Titrate the solution with 0.01N sodium hydroxide to a pH of 4.5 (using the pH meter). The color of the solution should be green. Continue the titration to a pH of 5.4. The color of the solution should be blue. Not more than 1.3 ml. of 0.01N sodium hydroxide should be consumed in the entire titration.

Notes

Bromophenol Blue

3′,3″,5′,5″-Tetrabromophenolsulfonphthalein

α,α-bis(3,5-Dibromo-4-hydroxyphenyl)-α-hydroxy-o-toluene γ-Sultone

Note. This specification applies both to the free acid form and to the salt form of this indicator.

REQUIREMENTS

Insoluble matter. To pass test.
Visual transition interval. From pH 3.0 (yellow) to pH 4.6 (blue).

TESTS

Insoluble matter. If the indicator is the acid form, dissolve 0.1 gram in 100 ml. of alcohol. If the indicator is the salt form, dissolve 0.1 gram in 100 ml. of water. Not more than a faint trace of turbidity or insoluble matter should remain. Reserve the solution for the test for *Visual transition interval.*

Visual transition interval. Dissolve 1 gram of potassium chloride in 100 ml. of water. Adjust the pH of the solution to 3.00 (using a pH meter as described on page 18) with 0.01N acid. Add 0.10 to 0.30 ml. of the 0.1 per cent solution of the indicator reserved from the test for *Insoluble matter.* The color of the solution should be yellow with a slight greenish hue. Titrate the solution with 0.01N sodium hydroxide to a pH of 3.4 (using the pH meter). The color of the solution should be green. Continue the titration to pH 4.6. The color of the solution should be blue. Not more than 13.0 ml. of 0.01N sodium hydroxide should be consumed in the entire titration.

Notes

Bromothymol Blue

3',3''-Dibromothymolsulfonphthalein

α,α-bis(6-Bromo-5-hydroxycarvacryl)-α-hydroxy-o-toluene γ-Sultone

Note. This specification applies both to the free acid form and to the salt form of this indicator.

REQUIREMENTS

Insoluble matter.   To pass test.
Visual transition interval.   From pH 6.0 (yellow) to pH 7.6 (blue).

TESTS

Insoluble matter.   If the indicator is the acid form, dissolve 0.1 gram in 100 ml. of alcohol. If the indicator is a salt form, dissolve 0.1 gram in 100 ml. of water. Not more than a faint trace of turbidity or insoluble matter should remain. Reserve the solution for the test for *Visual transition interval*.

Visual transition interval.   Dissolve 1 gram of potassium chloride in 100 ml. of water. Adjust the pH of the solution to 6.00 (using a pH meter as described on page 18) with 0.01N acid or alkali. Add 0.10 to 0.30 ml. of the 0.1 per cent solution reserved from the test for *Insoluble matter*. The color of the solution should be yellow, with not more than a faint trace of green color. Titrate the solution with 0.01N sodium hydroxide to a pH of 6.7 (using the pH meter). The color of the solution should be green. Continue the titration to pH 7.6. The color of the solution should be blue. Not more than 0.3 ml. of 0.01N sodium hydroxide should be consumed in the entire titration.

Notes

Brucine Sulfate

$(C_{23}H_{26}N_2O_4)_2 \cdot H_2SO_4 \cdot 7H_2O$ Formula Wt. 1013.13

REQUIREMENTS

Insoluble matter.   To pass test.
Loss on drying at 105°C.   Not more than 13.0 per cent.
Residue after ignition.   Not more than 0.10 per cent.
Sensitivity to nitrate.   To pass test.

TESTS

Insoluble matter.   Dissolve 1 gram in 100 ml. of water and digest in a covered beaker on the steam bath for 1 hour. The solution should be as colorless and clear as an equal volume of water.

Loss on drying at 105°C.   Weigh accurately about 1 gram and dry in a tared dish for 6 hours at 105°C. The loss in weight should not exceed 13.0 per cent.

Residue after ignition.   Gently ignite 1 gram in a tared crucible or dish until charred. Continue the gentle ignition until all the carbon has been volatilized, and finally ignite at 800° ± 25°C. for 15 minutes. The weight of the residue should not exceed 0.0010 gram.

Sensitivity to nitrate.

Preparation of Brucine Sulfate Solution.   Dissolve 0.6 gram in dilute sulfuric acid (2 + 1), previously cooled to room temperature, and dilute to 1 liter with the dilute acid. The sulfuric acid should be nitrate-free acid prepared as follows: dilute the concentrated sulfuric acid (about 96 per cent H_2SO_4) to about 80 per cent H_2SO_4 by adding it to water, heat to dense fumes of sulfur trioxide, and cool. Repeat the dilution and fuming 3 or 4 times.

Test Solutions 1, 2, 3, and 4.   Place 50 ml. of the brucine sulfate solution, prepared as described above, in each of four test tubes, and add nitrate ion (NO_3) to each as follows: No. 1, none; No. 2, 0.01 mg.; No. 3, 0.02 mg.; and No. 4, 0.03 mg.

Heat the four test tubes in a preheated (boiling) water bath for 10 minutes. Cool rapidly in an ice bath to room temperature. Set a spectrophotometer at 410 mμ and, using 1-cm. cells, adjust the instrument to read 0 absorbance with Solution 1 in the light path. Determine the absorbance for Solutions 2, 3, and 4 at this adjustment, using similar cells. The absorbances for Solutions 2, 3, and 4 should not be less than 0.025, 0.050, and 0.075, respectively, and the plot of absorbances *vs.* nitrate concentrations should be linear.

Notes

Butyl Alcohol

1-Butanol

$CH_3(CH_2)_2CH_2OH$ Formula Wt. 74.12

REQUIREMENTS

Color (APHA).   Not more than 10.
Boiling range.   Not more than 2.0°C.
Residue after evaporation.   Not more than 0.005 per cent.
Acidity [as $CH_3(CH_2)_2COOH$].   Not more than 0.01 per cent.
Aldehydes and ketones.   To pass test (limit about 0.05 per cent).

TESTS

Color (APHA).   For the color standard dilute a 2-ml. aliquot of platinum-cobalt stock solution (APHA No. 500) to 100 ml. with water. Compare this solution (APHA No. 10) with 100 ml. of the butyl alcohol in 100-ml. Nessler tubes, viewed vertically over a white background.

Boiling range.   Distill 100 ml. by the method described on page 12. The difference between the temperatures when 1 ml. and 95 ml. have distilled should not exceed 2.0°C. The boiling point of pure butyl alcohol at 760-mm. mercury pressure is 117.5°C.

Residue after evaporation.   Evaporate 25 ml. (20 grams) to dryness in a tared platinum dish on the steam bath and dry the residue at 105°C. for 30 minutes. The weight of the residue should not exceed 0.0010 gram.

Acidity.   Transfer 20 ml. (16 grams) to a glass-stoppered flask. Add 20 ml. of water, shake for about 1 minute, and add 0.05 ml. of bromothymol blue indicator solution. If a yellow color is produced, it should be changed to a blue color by not more than 0.2 ml. of 0.1N sodium hydroxide.

Aldehydes and ketones.   To 17.5 ml. (14 grams) in a glass-stoppered cylinder add 15 ml. of water and 50 ml. of hydroxylamine hydrochloride reagent solution.* Mix thoroughly and allow to stand for 5 minutes. Titrate the solution with 0.1N sodium hydroxide until the color matches the color of 90 ml. of the hydroxylamine hydrochloride in a similar cylinder. Not more than 1.0 ml. of 0.1N sodium hydroxide should be consumed.

* **Hydroxylamine hydrochloride reagent solution.**   Dissolve 5 grams of hydroxylamine hydrochloride in 240 ml. of ethyl alcohol and dilute to about 400 ml. with water. Add 5 ml. of bromophenol blue reagent

solution and titrate with 0.1N sodium hydroxide to a greenish end point. Dilute the solution to 500 ml. with water.

Notes

Cadmium Chloride, Anhydrous

CdCl₂ $\qquad$ Formula Wt. 183.31

REQUIREMENTS

Assay. Not less than 99 per cent $CdCl_2$.
Insoluble matter. Not more than 0.010 per cent.
Nitrate and nitrite (as NO_3). Not more than 0.003 per cent.
Sulfate (SO_4). Not more than 0.010 per cent.
Ammonium (NH_4). Not more than 0.010 per cent.
Copper (**Cu**). Not more than 0.001 per cent.
Iron (**Fe**). Not more than 0.001 per cent.
Lead (**Pb**). To pass test (limit about 0.005 per cent).
Substances not precipitated by hydrogen sulfide (as sulfates). Not more than 0.30 per cent.
Zinc (**Zn**). Not more than 0.1 per cent.

TESTS

Assay. Weigh accurately about 0.35 gram, dissolve in about 100 ml. of water in a 200-ml. volumetric flask, and add 5 ml. of nitric acid and 50.0 ml. of 0.1N silver nitrate. Shake vigorously, dilute to volume, mix well, and filter through a dry paper into a dry flask or beaker, rejecting the first 20 ml. of the filtrate. To 100 ml. of the subsequent filtrate add 2 ml. of ferric ammonium sulfate indicator solution, and titrate the excess silver nitrate with 0.1N thiocyanate. One milliliter of 0.1N silver nitrate corresponds to 0.009165 gram of $CdCl_2$.

Insoluble matter. Dissolve 10 grams in 150 ml. of water, heat to boiling, and digest in a covered beaker on the steam bath for 1 hour. Filter through a tared filtering crucible, wash thoroughly, and dry at 105°C. The weight of the residue should not exceed 0.0010 gram. Retain the filtrate and washings for the test for *Sulfate*.

Nitrate and nitrite.

Sample Solution A. Dissolve 0.3 gram in a 50-ml. centrifuge tube in 3 ml. of water by heating in a boiling water bath. Add 20 ml. of nitrate-free sulfuric acid (2 + 1) and cool in an ice bath. Centrifuge for 10 minutes, decant the solution into a 200-mm. test tube, and dilute to 50 ml. with brucine sulfate reagent solution.

Control Solution B. Dissolve 0.3 gram in a 50-ml. centrifuge tube in 2 ml. of water and 1 ml. of the standard nitrate solution containing 0.01 mg. of nitrate ion (NO_3) per ml. by heating in a boiling water bath. Add 20 ml. of nitrate-free sulfuric acid (2 + 1) and cool in an ice bath. Centrifuge for 10 minutes, decant the solution into a 200-mm. test tube, and dilute to 50 ml. with brucine sulfate reagent solution.

Blank Solution C.   Use 50 ml. of brucine sulfate reagent solution.

Heat the three solutions in a preheated (boiling) water bath for 10 minutes. Cool rapidly in an ice bath to room temperature. Set a spectrophotometer at 410 mμ and, using 1-cm. cells, adjust the instrument to read 0 absorbance with Blank Solution C in the light path, then determine the absorbance of Sample Solution A. Adjust the instrument to read 0 absorbance with Sample Solution A in the light path and determine the absorbance of Control Solution B. The absorbance of Sample Solution A should not exceed that of Control Solution B.

Sulfate.   Add 2 ml. of hydrochloric acid to the filtrate and washings obtained in the test for *Insoluble matter* and heat to boiling. Add 10 ml. of barium chloride reagent solution, digest in a covered beaker on the steam bath for 2 hours, and allow to stand overnight. If a precipitate is formed, filter, wash thoroughly, and ignite. The weight of the precipitate should not be more than 0.0024 gram greater than the weight obtained in a complete blank test.

Ammonium.   Dissolve 1 gram in 80 ml. of water and add with stirring 20 ml. of freshly boiled 10 per cent sodium hydroxide reagent solution. After allowing the precipitate to settle, dilute 10 ml. of the clear supernatant liquid to 50 ml., and add 2 ml. of Nessler reagent. Any color should not exceed that produced by 0.01 mg. of ammonium ion (NH_4) in an equal volume of solution containing 4 ml. of the sodium hydroxide solution and 2 ml. of the Nessler reagent.

Copper.   Dissolve 1 gram in 10 ml. of water and transfer the solution to a separatory funnel. For the standard add 0.01 mg. of copper ion (Cu) to 10 ml. of water in another separatory funnel. To each solution add 10 ml. of 40 per cent ammonium citrate reagent solution and 1 ml. of 0.1 per cent sodium diethyldithiocarbamate reagent solution and shake. Add 5 ml. of isopentyl alcohol, shake for 1 minute, and allow the layers to separate. Any yellow color in the isopentyl alcohol from the solution of the sample should not exceed that in the isopentyl alcohol from the standard.

Iron.   Dissolve 1 gram in 40 ml. of water plus 2 ml. of hydrochloric acid, dilute to 50 ml., and add 30 to 50 mg. of ammonium persulfate crystals and 3 ml. of ammonium thiocyanate reagent solution. Any red color should not exceed that produced by 0.01 mg. of iron (Fe) in an equal volume of solution containing the quantities of reagents used in the test.

Lead. Dissolve 1 gram in 25 ml. of water, add 0.25 ml. of glacial acetic acid, and filter if necessary. Add 2 ml. of 1 per cent potassium chromate solution. Any turbidity or precipitate should not exceed that produced by 0.05 mg. of lead ion (Pb) in an equal volume of solution containing the quantities of reagents used in the test.

Substances not precipitated by hydrogen sulfide. Dissolve 2 grams in 150 ml. of water containing 15 ml. of approximately 1N sulfuric acid. Heat to boiling and pass a rapid stream of hydrogen sulfide through the solution as it cools to room temperature. Filter the solution, but do not wash the precipitate. Add 0.25 ml. of sulfuric acid to 75 ml. of the clear filtrate and evaporate to dryness in a tared dish. Finally, ignite at 800° ± 25°C. for 15 minutes. The weight of the residue should not exceed 0.0030 gram.

Zinc. Dissolve 1 gram in 50 ml. of dilute hydrochloric acid (2 + 25). For the standard add 1.0 mg. of zinc ion (Zn) to 50 ml. of dilute hydrochloric acid (2 + 25). Transfer the solutions to separatory funnels. To each solution add 25 ml. of ammonium thiocyanate reagent solution and 25 ml. of ether. Shake vigorously, allow the layers to separate, and draw off and reserve the ether. Repeat the extractions three more times. Combine the respective ether extracts, add 10 ml. of 25 per cent sulfuric acid reagent solution to each, and heat on the steam bath until all the ether has evaporated. Add about 100 ml. of water to each, filter, wash thoroughly, and dilute the filtrate plus washings to 1 liter. Adjust the pH of an 8-ml. aliquot of each solution to between 5.0 and 5.5 (using a pH meter) with 0.5N sodium acetate solution that has been extracted with dithizone extraction solution before use. Add 1 ml. of 0.1N sodium thiosulfate to each, transfer the solutions to separatory funnels, add 5 ml. of dithizone standard solution in carbon tetrachloride, and shake vigorously for about 2 minutes. Draw off the dithizone layers. Repeat with successive portions of dithizone standard solution until the color of the dithizone solution remains unchanged. Combine the extracts from each and dilute to the smallest uniform volume with dithizone standard solution. Any red color, producing a purplish hue in the extract from the sample, should not exceed that in the extract from the standard. The color intensities may be determined with a spectrophotometer at a wavelength of 535 mμ.

If desired, the monocolor method may be used. Transfer 10 ml. of each carbon tetrachloride extract to separate separatory funnels. Wash the carbon tetrachloride twice with 10-ml. portions of water, discarding the aqueous phase. Then wash the carbon tetrachloride extract with 5-ml. portions of a freshly prepared dilute solution of sodium sulfide

(20 ml. of a freshly prepared 1 per cent solution of sodium sulfide diluted to 500 ml. with water) until the aqueous phase remains colorless. Any red color in the carbon tetrachloride extract from the sample should not exceed that in the carbon tetrachloride extract from the standard.

Notes

Cadmium Chloride, Crystals

$CdCl_2 \cdot 2\frac{1}{2}H_2O$ Formula Wt. 228.34

REQUIREMENTS

Assay.   Not less than 79.5 nor more than 81.0 per cent $CdCl_2$.
Insoluble matter.   Not more than 0.005 per cent.
Nitrate and nitrite (as NO_3).   Not more than 0.003 per cent.
Sulfate (SO_4).   Not more than 0.005 per cent.
Ammonium (NH_4).   Not more than 0.005 per cent.
Copper (Cu).   Not more than 0.0005 per cent.
Iron (Fe).   Not more than 0.0005 per cent.
Lead (Pb).   To pass test (limit about 0.005 per cent).
Substances not precipitated by hydrogen sulfide (as sulfates).   Not more than 0.20 per cent.
Zinc (Zn).   Not more than 0.1 per cent.

TESTS

Assay.   Weigh accurately about 0.45 gram, dissolve in about 100 ml. of water in a 200-ml. volumetric flask, and add 5 ml. of nitric acid and 50.0 ml. of $0.1N$ silver nitrate. Shake vigorously, dilute to volume, mix well, and filter through a dry paper into a dry flask or beaker, rejecting the first 20 ml. of the filtrate. To 100 ml. of the filtrate subsequently collected, add 2 ml. of ferric ammonium sulfate indicator solution, and titrate the excess silver nitrate with $0.1N$ thiocyanate. One milliliter of $0.1N$ silver nitrate corresponds to 0.009165 gram of $CdCl_2$.

Insoluble matter.   Dissolve 20 grams in 150 ml. of water, heat to boiling, and digest in a covered beaker on the steam bath for 1 hour. Filter through a tared filtering crucible, wash thoroughly, and dry at 105°C. The weight of the residue should not exceed 0.0010 gram. Reserve the filtrate for the test for *Sulfate*.

Nitrate and nitrite.

Sample Solution A.   Dissolve 0.3 gram in a 50-ml. centrifuge tube in 3 ml. of water by heating in a boiling water bath. Add 20 ml. of nitrate-free sulfuric acid $(2 + 1)$ and cool in an ice bath. Centrifuge for 10 minutes, decant the solution into a 200-mm. test tube, and dilute to 50 ml. with brucine sulfate reagent solution.

Control Solution B.   Dissolve 0.3 gram in a 50-ml. centrifuge tube in 2 ml. of water and 1 ml. of the standard nitrate solution containing 0.01 mg. of nitrate ion (NO_3) per ml. by heating in a boiling water bath. Add 20 ml. of nitrate-free sulfuric acid $(2 + 1)$ and cool in an ice bath. Centrifuge for 10 minutes, decant the solution into a 200-mm. test tube, and dilute to 50 ml. with brucine sulfate reagent solution.

Blank Solution C. Use 50 ml. of brucine sulfate reagent solution.

Heat the three solutions in a preheated (boiling) water bath for 10 minutes. Cool rapidly in an ice bath to room temperature. Set a spectrophotometer at 410 mμ and, using 1-cm. cells, adjust the instrument to read 0 absorbance with Blank Solution C in the light path, then determine the absorbance of Sample Solution A. Adjust the instrument to read 0 absorbance with Sample Solution A in the light path and determine the absorbance of Control Solution B. The absorbance of Sample Solution A should not exceed that of Control Solution B.

Sulfate. Heat to boiling the filtrate and washings obtained in the test for *Insoluble matter*. Add 1 ml. of hydrochloric acid and 5 ml. of barium chloride reagent solution, digest in a covered beaker on the steam bath for 2 hours, and allow to stand overnight. If a precipitate is formed, filter, wash thoroughly, and ignite. The weight of the precipitate should not be more than 0.0024 gram greater than the weight obtained in a complete blank test.

Ammonium. Dissolve 1 gram in 80 ml. of water and add with stirring 20 ml. of freshly boiled 10 per cent sodium hydroxide reagent solution. After allowing the precipitate to settle, dilute 20 ml. of the clear supernatant liquid to 50 ml., and add 2 ml. of Nessler reagent. Any color should not exceed that produced by 0.01 mg. of ammonium ion (NH_4) in an equal volume of solution containing 4 ml. of the sodium hydroxide solution and 2 ml. of the Nessler reagent.

Copper. Dissolve 2 grams in 20 ml. of water and transfer the solution to a separatory funnel. For the standard add 0.01 mg. of copper ion (Cu) to 20 ml. of water in another separatory funnel. To each solution add 15 ml. of 40 per cent ammonium citrate solution and 1 ml. of 0.1 per cent sodium diethyldithiocarbamate solution and shake well. Add 5 ml. of isopentyl alcohol to each, shake for 1 minute, and allow the layers to separate. Any yellow color in the isopentyl alcohol from the solution of the sample should not exceed that in the isopentyl alcohol from the standard.

Iron. Dissolve 2 grams in 40 ml. of water, add 2 ml. of hydrochloric acid, and dilute to 50 ml. Add 30 to 50 mg. of ammonium persulfate crystals and 3 ml. of ammonium thiocyanate reagent solution. Any red color should not exceed that produced by 0.01 mg. of iron (Fe) in an

equal volume of solution containing the quantities of reagents used in the test.

Lead.   Dissolve 1 gram in 25 ml. of water, add 0.25 ml. of glacial acetic acid, and filter if necessary. Add 2 ml. of 1 per cent potassium chromate solution. Any turbidity or precipitate should not exceed that produced by 0.05 mg. of lead ion (Pb) in an equal volume of solution containing the quantities of reagents used in the test.

Substances not precipitated by hydrogen sulfide.   Dissolve 2 grams in 150 ml. of water containing 15 ml. of approximately $1N$ sulfuric acid. Heat to boiling and pass a rapid stream of hydrogen sulfide through the solution as it cools to room temperature. Filter the solution, but do not wash the precipitate. Add 0.25 ml. of sulfuric acid to 75 ml. of the clear filtrate and evaporate to dryness in a tared dish. Finally, ignite at 800° ± 25°C. for 15 minutes. The weight of the residue should not exceed 0.0020 gram.

Zinc.   Dissolve 1 gram in 50 ml. of dilute hydrochloric acid (2 + 25). For the standard add 1.0 mg. of zinc ion (Zn) to 50 ml. of dilute hydrochloric acid (2 + 25). Transfer the solutions to separatory funnels. To each solution add 25 ml. of ammonium thiocyanate reagent solution and 25 ml. of ether. Shake vigorously, allow the layers to separate, and draw off and reserve the ether. Repeat the extractions three more times. Combine the respective ether extracts, add 10 ml. of 25 per cent sulfuric acid reagent solution to each, and heat on the steam bath until all the ether has evaporated. Add about 100 ml. of water to each, filter, wash thoroughly, and dilute the filtrate plus washings to 1 liter. Adjust the pH of an 8-ml. aliquot of each solution to between 5.0 and 5.5 (using a pH meter) with $0.5N$ sodium acetate solution that has been extracted with dithizone extraction solution before use. Add 1 ml. of $0.1N$ sodium thiosulfate to each, transfer the solutions to separatory funnels, add 5 ml. of dithizone standard solution in carbon tetrachloride, and shake vigorously for about 2 minutes. Draw off the dithizone layers. Repeat with successive portions of dithizone extraction solution until the color of the dithizone solution remains unchanged. Combine the extracts from each and dilute to the smallest uniform volume with dithizone standard solution. Any red color, producing a purplish hue in the extract from the sample, should not exceed that in the extract from the standard. The color intensities may be determined with a spectrophotometer at a wavelength of 535 mμ.

If desired, the monocolor method may be used. Transfer 10 ml. of each carbon tetrachloride extract to separate separatory funnels. Wash the carbon tetrachloride twice with 10-ml. portions of water, discarding the aqueous phase. Then wash the carbon tetrachloride extract with 5-ml. portions of a freshly prepared dilute solution of sodium sulfide (20 ml. of a freshly prepared 1 per cent solution of sodium sulfide diluted to 500 ml. with water) until the aqueous phase remains colorless. Any red color in the carbon tetrachloride extract from the sample should not exceed that in the carbon tetrachloride extract from the standard.

Notes

Cadmium Sulfate, Anhydrous

$CdSO_4$ Formula Wt. 208.46

REQUIREMENTS

Insoluble matter.   Not more than 0.005 per cent.
Loss on drying at 150°C.   Not more than 1 per cent.
Chloride (Cl).   Not more than 0.001 per cent.
Nitrate and nitrite (as NO_3).   Not more than 0.003 per cent.
Arsenic (As).   Not more than 0.0002 per cent.
Copper (Cu).   Not more than 0.002 per cent.
Iron (Fe).   Not more than 0.001 per cent.
Lead (Pb).   Not more than 0.003 per cent.
Substances not precipitated by hydrogen sulfide (as sulfates).   Not more than 0.15 per cent.
Zinc (Zn).   Not more than 0.1 per cent.

TESTS

Insoluble matter.   Dissolve 20 grams in 150 ml. of water, heat to boiling, then digest in a covered beaker on the steam bath for 1 hour. Filter through a tared filtering crucible, wash thoroughly, and dry at 105°C. The weight of the residue should not exceed 0.0010 gram.

Loss on drying at 150°C.   Weigh accurately about 1 gram and dry to constant weight at 150°C. The loss in weight should not be more than 1 per cent of the weight of the sample.

Chloride.   Dissolve 1 gram in 20 ml. of water, filter if necessary through a chloride-free filter, and add 1 ml. of nitric acid and 1 ml. of silver nitrate reagent solution. Any turbidity should not exceed that produced by 0.01 mg. of chloride ion (Cl) in an equal volume of solution containing the quantities of reagents used in the test.

Nitrate and nitrite.

Sample Solution A.   Dissolve 0.5 gram in 3 ml. of water by heating in a boiling water bath. Dilute to 50 ml. with brucine sulfate reagent solution.

Control Solution B.   Dissolve 0.5 gram in 1.5 ml. of water and 1.5 ml. of the standard nitrate solution containing 0.01 mg. of nitrate ion (NO_3) per ml. by heating in a boiling water bath. Dilute to 50 ml. with brucine sulfate reagent solution.

Blank Solution C.   Use 50 ml. of brucine sulfate reagent solution.

Heat the three solutions in a preheated (boiling) water bath for 10 minutes. Cool rapidly in an ice bath to room temperature. Set a spectrophotometer at 410 mμ and, using 1-cm. cells, adjust the instrument to read 0 absorbance with Blank Solution C in the light path, then determine the absorbance of Sample Solution A. Adjust the instrument to read 0 absorbance with Sample Solution A in the light path and determine the absorbance of Control Solution B. The absorbance of Sample Solution A should not exceed that of Control Solution B.

Arsenic. Test 1 gram by the Gutzeit method described on page 11, except that the zinc is to be added in 2-gram portions until the cadmium is all precipitated. The amount of stain should not exceed that produced by 0.002 mg. of arsenic (As).

Copper. Dissolve 0.5 gram in 10 ml. of water and transfer the solution to a separatory funnel. For the standard add 0.01 mg. of copper ion (Cu) to 10 ml. of water in another separatory funnel. To each solution add 10 ml. of 40 per cent ammonium citrate reagent solution and 1 ml. of 0.1 per cent sodium diethyldithiocarbamate reagent solution and shake. Add 5 ml. of isopentyl alcohol, shake for 1 minute, and allow the layers to separate. Any yellow color in the isopentyl alcohol from the solution of the sample should not exceed that in the isopentyl alcohol from the standard.

Iron. Dissolve 1 gram in 30 ml. of water, add 5 ml. of hydrochloric acid, and dilute to 50 ml. Add 30 to 50 mg. of ammonium persulfate crystals and 3 ml. of ammonium thiocyanate reagent solution. Any red color should not exceed that produced by 0.01 mg. of iron (Fe) in an equal volume of solution containing the quantities of reagents used in the test.

Lead. Dissolve 2 grams in 25 ml. of water, add 5 drops of glacial acetic acid, filter if necessary, and add 2 ml. of 1 per cent potassium chromate solution. Any turbidity or precipitate should not exceed that produced by 0.06 mg. of lead ion (Pb) in an equal volume of solution containing the quantities of reagents used in the test.

Substances not precipitated by hydrogen sulfide. Dissolve 2 grams in 150 ml. of water containing 15 ml. of approximately 1N sulfuric acid. Heat to boiling and pass a rapid stream of hydrogen sulfide through the solution as it cools to room temperature. Filter the solution but do not wash the precipitate. Add 0.25 ml. of sulfuric acid to 75 ml. of the clear filtrate and evaporate to dryness in a tared dish. Finally, ignite at 800° ± 25°C. for 15 minutes. The weight of the residue should not exceed 0.0015 gram.

Zinc. Dissolve 1 gram in 50 ml. of dilute hydrochloric acid $(2 + 25)$. For the standard add 1.0 mg. of zinc ion (Zn) to 50 ml. of dilute hydrochloric acid $(2 + 25)$. Transfer the solutions to separatory funnels. To each solution add 25 ml. of ammonium thiocyanate reagent solution and 25 ml. of ether. Shake vigorously, allow the layers to separate, and draw off and reserve the ether. Repeat the extractions three more times. Combine the respective ether extracts, add 10 ml. of 25 per cent sulfuric acid reagent solution to each, and heat on the steam bath until all the ether has evaporated. Add about 100 ml. of water to each, filter, wash thoroughly, and dilute the filtrate plus washings to 1 liter. Adjust the pH of an 8-ml. aliquot of each solution to between 5.0 and 5.5 (using a pH meter) with 0.5 N sodium acetate solution that has been extracted with dithizone extraction solution before use. Add 1 ml. of 0.1 N sodium thiosulfate to each, transfer the solutions to separatory funnels, add 5 ml. of dithizone standard solution in carbon tetrachloride, and shake vigorously for about 2 minutes. Draw off the dithizone layers. Repeat with successive portions of dithizone standard solution until the color of the dithizone solution remains unchanged. Combine the extracts from each and dilute to the smallest uniform volume with dithizone standard solution. Any red color, producing a purplish hue in the extract from the sample, should not exceed that in the extract from the standard. The color intensities may be determined with a spectrophotometer at a wavelength of 535 mμ.

If desired, the monocolor method may be used. Transfer 10 ml. of each carbon tetrachloride extract to separate separatory funnels. Wash the carbon tetrachloride twice with 10-ml. portions of distilled water, discarding the aqueous phase. Then wash the carbon tetrachloride extract with 5-ml. portions of a freshly prepared dilute solution of sodium sulfide (20 ml. of a freshly prepared 1 per cent solution of sodium sulfide diluted to 500 ml. with water) until the aqueous phase remains colorless. Any red color in the carbon tetrachloride extract from the sample should not exceed that in the carbon tetrachloride extract from the standard.

Notes

Cadmium Sulfate, Crystals

$3CdSO_4 \cdot 8H_2O$ Formula Wt. 769.51

REQUIREMENTS

Insoluble matter.   Not more than 0.005 per cent.
Chloride (Cl).   Not more than 0.001 per cent.
Nitrate and nitrite (as NO_3).   Not more than 0.003 per cent.
Arsenic (As).   Not more than 0.0002 per cent.
Copper (Cu).   Not more than 0.002 per cent.
Iron (Fe).   Not more than 0.001 per cent.
Lead (Pb).   Not more than 0.003 per cent.
Substances not precipitated by hydrogen sulfide (as sulfates).   Not more than 0.10 per cent.
Zinc (Zn).   Not more than 0.1 per cent.

TESTS

Insoluble matter.   Dissolve 20 grams in 150 ml. of water, heat to boiling, and digest in a covered beaker on the steam bath for 1 hour. Filter through a tared filtering crucible, wash thoroughly, and dry at 105°C. The weight of the residue should not exceed 0.0010 gram.

Chloride.   Dissolve 1 gram in 20 ml. of water, filter if necessary through a chloride-free filter, and add 1 ml. of nitric acid and 1 ml. of silver nitrate reagent solution. Any turbidity should not exceed that produced by 0.01 mg. of chloride ion (Cl) in an equal volume of solution containing the quantities of reagents used in the test.

Nitrate and nitrite.

Sample Solution A.   Dissolve 0.5 gram in 3 ml. of water by heating in a boiling water bath. Dilute to 50 ml. with brucine sulfate reagent solution.

Control Solution B.   Dissolve 0.5 gram in 1.5 ml. of water and 1.5 ml. of the standard nitrate solution containing 0.01 mg. of nitrate ion (NO_3) per ml. by heating in a boiling water bath. Dilute to 50 ml. with brucine sulfate reagent solution.

Blank Solution C.   Use 50 ml. of brucine sulfate reagent solution.

Heat the three solutions in a preheated (boiling) water bath for 10 minutes. Cool rapidly in an ice bath to room temperature. Set a spectrophotometer at 410 mμ and, using 1-cm. cells, adjust the instrument to read 0 absorbance with Blank Solution C in the light path, then determine the absorbance of Sample Solution A. Adjust the instrument to read 0 absorbance with Sample Solution A in the light path and determine the absorbance of Control Solution B. The absorbance of Sample Solution A should not exceed that of Control Solution B.

Arsenic.   Test 1 gram by the Gutzeit method described on page 11, except that the zinc is to be added in 2-gram portions until the cadmium is all precipitated. The amount of stain should not exceed that produced by 0.002 mg. of arsenic (As).

Copper.   Dissolve 0.5 gram in 10 ml. of water and transfer the solution to a separatory funnel. For the standard add 0.01 mg. of copper ion (Cu) to 10 ml. of water in another separatory funnel. To each solution add 10 ml. of 40 per cent ammonium citrate reagent solution and 1 ml. of 0.1 per cent sodium diethyldithiocarbamate reagent solution and shake. Add 5 ml. of isopentyl alcohol, shake for 1 minute, and allow the layers to separate. Any yellow color in the isopentyl alcohol from the solution of the sample should not exceed that in the isopentyl alcohol from the standard.

Iron.   Dissolve 1 gram in 30 ml. of water, add 5 ml. of hydrochloric acid, and dilute to 50 ml. Add 30 to 50 mg. of ammonium persulfate crystals and 3 ml. of ammonium thiocyanate reagent solution. Any red color should not exceed that produced by 0.01 mg. of iron (Fe) in an equal volume of solution containing the quantities of reagents used in the test.

Lead.   Dissolve 2 grams in 25 ml. of water, add 5 drops of glacial acetic acid, filter if necessary, and add 2 ml. of 1 per cent potassium chromate solution. Any turbidity or precipitate should not exceed that produced by 0.06 mg. of lead ion (Pb) in an equal volume of solution containing the quantities of reagents used in the test.

Substances not precipitated by hydrogen sulfide.   Dissolve 2 grams in 150 ml. of water containing 15 ml. of approximately $1N$ sulfuric acid. Heat to boiling and pass a rapid stream of hydrogen sulfide through the solution as it cools to room temperature. Filter the solution but do not wash the precipitate. Add 0.25 ml. of sulfuric acid to 75 ml. of the clear filtrate and evaporate to dryness in a tared dish. Finally, ignite at 800° ± 25°C. for 15 minutes. The weight of the residue should not exceed 0.0010 gram.

Zinc.   Dissolve 1 gram in 50 ml. of dilute hydrochloric acid (2 + 25). For the standard add 1.0 mg. of zinc ion (Zn) to 50 ml. of dilute hydrochloric acid (2 + 25). Transfer the solutions to separatory funnels. To each solution add 25 ml. of ammonium thiocyanate reagent solution and

25 ml. of ether. Shake vigorously, allow the layers to separate, and draw off and reserve the ether. Repeat the extractions three more times. Combine the respective ether extracts, add 10 ml. of 25 per cent sulfuric acid reagent solution to each, and heat on the steam bath until all the ether has evaporated. Add about 100 ml. of water to each, filter, wash thoroughly, and dilute the filtrate plus washings to 1 liter. Adjust the pH of an 8-ml. aliquot of each solution to between 5.0 and 5.5 (using a pH meter) with 0.5 N sodium acetate solution that has been extracted with dithizone extraction solution before use. Add 1 ml. of 0.1 N sodium thiosulfate to each, transfer the solutions to separatory funnels, add 5 ml. of dithizone standard solution in carbon tetrachloride, and shake vigorously for about 2 minutes. Draw off the dithizone layers. Repeat with successive portions of dithizone standard solution until the color of the dithizone solution remains unchanged. Combine the extracts from each and dilute to the smallest uniform volume with dithizone standard solution. Any red color, producing a purplish hue in the extract from the sample, should not exceed that in the extract from the standard. The color intensities may be determined with a spectrophotometer at a wavelength of 535 mμ.

If desired, the monocolor method may be used. Transfer 10 ml. of each carbon tetrachloride extract to separate separatory funnels. Wash the carbon tetrachloride twice with 10-ml. portions of distilled water, discarding the aqueous phase. Then wash the carbon tetrachloride extract with 5-ml. portions of a freshly prepared dilute solution of sodium sulfide (20 ml. of a freshly prepared 1 per cent solution of sodium sulfide diluted to 500 ml. with water) until the aqueous phase remains colorless. Any red color in the carbon tetrachloride extract from the sample should not exceed that in the carbon tetrachloride extract from the standard.

Notes

Calcium Carbonate

Formula Wt. 100.09$CaCO_3$

REQUIREMENTS

Insoluble in dilute hydrochloric acid. Not more than 0.010 per cent.
Ammonium hydroxide precipitate. Not more than 0.010 per cent.
Alkalinity. To pass test.
Chloride (Cl). Not more than 0.001 per cent.
Oxidizing substances (as NO_3). Not more than 0.005 per cent
Sulfate (SO_4). Not more than 0.010 per cent.
Ammonium (NH_4). Not more than 0.003 per cent.
Barium (Ba). Not more than 0.005 per cent.
Heavy metals (as Pb). Not more than 0.001 per cent.
Iron (Fe). Not more than 0.003 per cent.
Magnesium (Mg). Not more than 0.02 per cent.
Potassium (K). Not more than 0.01 per cent.
Sodium (Na). Not more than 0.10 per cent.
Strontium (Sr). Not more than 0.10 per cent.

TESTS

Insoluble in dilute hydrochloric acid. Add 10 grams to about 100 ml. of water, swirl, slowly and carefully add 20 ml. of hydrochloric acid, and dilute to 150 ml. Heat the solution to boiling, boil gently to expel the carbon dioxide, and digest in a covered beaker on the steam bath for 1 hour. Filter through a tared filtering crucible (reserve the filtrate for the determination of *Ammonium hydroxide precipitate*), wash thoroughly, and dry at 105°C. The weight of the residue should not exceed 0.0010 gram.

Ammonium hydroxide precipitate. Add 0.10 ml. of methyl red indicator solution to the filtrate reserved from the test for *Insoluble in dilute hydrochloric acid* and make slightly alkaline with ammonium hydroxide. Heat the solution to boiling and boil gently for 5 minutes to coagulate the precipitate. If necessary add more ammonium hydroxide to maintain the alkalinity throughout this operation. Filter through a small filter paper and wash with a small amount of hot water. (Reserve this filtrate for the determination of *Sulfate.*) Redissolve the precipitate from the filter paper with hot dilute hydrochloric acid (1 + 3) and wash the filter paper free of acid. Heat the filtrate plus washings, which should amount to about 25 ml., to boiling and boil gently for 1 to 2 minutes. Add 0.05 ml. of methyl red indicator solution, make slightly alkaline with ammonium hydroxide, and again boil gently to coagulate the precipitate. Filter through the same small filter paper, wash thoroughly, and ignite in a tared crucible. The weight of the residue should not exceed 0.0010 gram.

Alkalinity.   Suspend 3 grams in 30 ml. of warm water in a small stoppered flask. Shake for 10 minutes, cool, and filter. To 20 ml. of the filtrate add 0.05 ml. of phenolphthalein indicator solution. If a red color is produced, it should be discharged by 0.05 ml. of 0.1N hydrochloric acid.

Chloride.   Dissolve 1 gram in 10 ml. of water plus 2 ml. of nitric acid, filter if necessary through a small chloride-free filter, wash with hot water, dilute to 20 ml., and add 1 ml. of silver nitrate reagent solution. Any turbidity should not exceed that produced by 0.01 mg. of chloride ion (Cl) in an equal volume of solution containing the quantities of reagents used in the test.

Oxidizing substances.   Place 0.1 gram in a dry beaker. Cool the beaker thoroughly in an ice bath and add 22 ml. of sulfuric acid which has been cooled to ice-bath temperature. Allow the mixture to warm to room temperature and swirl the beaker at intervals to effect gentle dissolution with slow evolution of carbon dioxide. When dissolution is complete, add 3 ml. of diphenylamine reagent solution and digest on the steam bath for 90 minutes. Prepare a standard by evaporating to dryness a solution containing 0.005 mg. of nitrate (0.5 ml. of the nitrate standard solution) and 0.01 gram of sodium carbonate. Treat the residue exactly like the sample. Any color produced in the solution of the sample should not exceed that in the standard.

Sulfate.   Neutralize with hydrochloric acid the first filtrate from the test for *Ammonium hydroxide precipitate* and add an excess of 1 ml. of the acid. Heat to boiling, add 5 ml. of barium chloride reagent solution, digest in a covered beaker on the steam bath for 2 hours, and allow to stand overnight. Filter, wash thoroughly, and ignite. The weight of the precipitate should not be more than 0.0024 gram greater than the weight obtained in a complete blank test. In the blank test the hydrochloric acid equivalent to that used for dissolution of the calcium carbonate should be nearly all evaporated before addition of the ammonium hydroxide.

Sample Solution A for the determination of Ammonium, Heavy metals, Iron, Magnesium, Potassium, Sodium, and Strontium.   Cautiously dissolve 20 grams in 100 ml. of dilute hydrochloric acid (1 + 1) and evaporate on the steam bath to dryness or a moist residue. Dissolve the residue in about 100 ml. of water, filter, and dilute to 200 ml. (1 ml. = 0.1 gram).

Ammonium. Dilute 10 ml. (1-gram sample) of Sample Solution A to 80 ml., add 20 ml. of 10 per cent sodium hydroxide reagent solution, stopper, mix well, and allow to stand for 1 hour. Decant 50 ml. through a filtering crucible which has been washed with 10 per cent sodium hydroxide solution, and add to the filtrate 2 ml. of Nessler reagent. Any color should not exceed that produced by 0.015 mg. of ammonium ion (NH_4) in an equal volume of solution containing the quantities of reagents used in the test.

Barium. For the sample dissolve 3 grams in 15 ml. of water and sufficient nitric acid (about 3.5 ml.) to effect dissolution. For the control dissolve 1 gram in 15 ml. of water and sufficient nitric acid (about 1.5 ml.) to effect dissolution and add 0.1 mg. of barium ion (Ba). Heat each solution to boiling, boil gently for 5 minutes, cool, filter if necessary, and dilute to 23 ml. Add 2 ml. of potassium dichromate reagent solution and neutralize with ammonium hydroxide until the orange color is just dissipated and the yellow color persists. To each solution slowly add, with constant stirring, 25 ml. of methanol. Any turbidity in the solution of the sample should not exceed that in the control.

Heavy metals. For the sample use a 30-ml. aliquot (3-gram sample) of Sample Solution A. For the control add 0.02 mg. of lead ion (Pb) to a 10-ml. aliquot (1-gram sample) of Sample Solution A and dilute to 30 ml. Adjust the pH of the control and sample solutions to between 3 and 4 (using a pH meter) with $1N$ acetic acid or ammonium hydroxide (10 per cent NH_3), dilute to 40 ml., and mix. Add 10 ml. of freshly prepared hydrogen sulfide water to each and mix. Any color in the solution of the sample should not exceed that in the control.

Iron. To 3.3 ml. (0.33-gram sample) of Sample Solution A add 2 ml. of hydrochloric acid and dilute to 50 ml. Add 30 to 50 mg. of ammonium persulfate crystals and 3 ml. of ammonium thiocyanate reagent solution. Any red color should not exceed that produced by 0.01 mg. of iron (Fe) in an equal volume of solution containing the quantities of reagents used in the test.

Magnesium. Dilute 5 ml. (0.5-gram sample) of Sample Solution A to 20 ml. For the control add 0.05 mg. of magnesium ion (Mg) to 2.5 ml. (0.25-gram sample) of Sample Solution A and dilute to 20 ml. To each solution add 0.15 ml. of a 0.1 per cent aqueous solution of Titan yellow (Clayton yellow) and 2 ml. of approximately $1N$ sodium hydroxide. Mix, let stand for 10 minutes, and shake well. The color in the solution representing the sample should not exceed that in the control.

Potassium.   Determine the potassium by the flame photometric method described on page 14. (It is necessary to use the oxyhydrogen flame.)

Sample Solution A-1.   To a 10-ml. aliquot (1-gram sample) of Sample Solution A add 5 ml. of hydrochloric acid and 1 gram of dibasic ammonium phosphate, and dilute to 100 ml. with water.

Control Solution B.   To another 10-ml. aliquot of Sample Solution A add 0.10 mg. of potassium ion (K), 5 ml. of hydrochloric acid, and 1 gram of dibasic ammonium phosphate, and dilute to 100 ml. with water.

Observe the emission of Control Solution B at the 767-mμ potassium line. Observe the emission of Sample Solution A-1 at the 767-mμ potassium line and at a wavelength of 750 mμ. The difference (D_1) between the intensities observed at 767 mμ and 750 mμ should not exceed the difference (D_2) observed at 767 mμ between Sample Solution A-1 and Control Solution B.

Sodium.   Determine the sodium by the flame photometric method described on page 14.

Sample Solution A-1.   To a 5-ml. aliquot (0.5-gram sample) of Sample Solution A add 5 ml. of hydrochloric acid and 0.5 gram of (low sodium) dibasic ammonium phosphate, and dilute to 500 ml. with water.

Control Solution B.   To another 5-ml. aliquot of Sample Solution A add 0.50 mg. of sodium ion (Na), 5 ml. of hydrochloric acid, and 0.5 gram of (low sodium) dibasic ammonium phosphate, and dilute to 500 ml. with water.

Observe the emission of Control Solution B at the 589-mμ sodium line. Observe the emission of Sample Solution A-1 at the 589-mμ sodium line and at wavelengths of 586 mμ and 592 mμ. To estimate the background emission at 589 mμ interpolate between the intensities at 586 mμ and 592 mμ. The difference (D_1) between the interpolated background emission and the intensity observed for Sample Solution A-1 should not exceed the difference (D_2) observed at 589 mμ between Sample Solution A-1 and Control Solution B.

Strontium.   Determine the strontium by the flame photometric method described on page 14.

Sample Solution A-1.   To a 10-ml. aliquot (1-gram sample) of Sample Solution A add 1 ml. of hydrochloric acid, and dilute to 100 ml. with water.

Control Solution B. To another 10-ml. aliquot of Sample Solution A add 1.0 mg. of strontium ion (Sr) and 1 ml. of hydrochloric acid, and dilute to 100 ml. with water.

Observe the emission of Control Solution B at the 460.7-mμ strontium line. Observe the emission of Sample Solution A-1 at the 460.7-mμ strontium line and at a wavelength of 458.7 mμ. The difference (D_1) between the intensities observed for Sample Solution A-1 at 460.7 mμ and 458.7 mμ should not exceed the difference (D_2) observed at 460.7 mμ between Sample Solution A-1 and Control Solution B.

Notes

Calcium Carbonate, Low in Alkalies

$CaCO_3$ Formula Wt. 100.09

REQUIREMENTS

Insoluble in dilute hydrochloric acid.   Not more than 0.010 per cent.
Ammonium hydroxide precipitate.   Not more than 0.010 per cent.
Chloride (Cl).   Not more than 0.001 per cent.
Sulfate (SO_4).   Not more than 0.010 per cent.
Barium (Ba).   Not more than 0.01 per cent.
Heavy metals (as Pb).   Not more than 0.001 per cent.
Iron (Fe).   Not more than 0.002 per cent.
Magnesium (Mg).   Not more than 0.01 per cent.
Potassium (K).   Not more than 0.01 per cent.
Sodium (Na).   Not more than 0.01 per cent.
Strontium (Sr).   Not more than 0.10 per cent.

TESTS

Insoluble in dilute hydrochloric acid.   Add 10 grams to about 100 ml. of water, swirl, slowly and carefully add 20 ml. of hydrochloric acid, and dilute to 150 ml. Heat the solution to boiling, boil gently to expel the carbon dioxide, and digest in a covered beaker on the steam bath for 1 hour. Filter through a tared filtering crucible (reserve the filtrate for the determination of *Ammonium hydroxide precipitate*), wash thoroughly and dry at 105°C. The weight of the residue should not exceed 0.0010 gram.

Ammonium hydroxide precipitate.   Add 0.10 ml. of methyl red indicator solution to the filtrate reserved from the test for *Insoluble in dilute hydrochloric acid* and make slightly alkaline with ammonium hydroxide. Heat the solution to boiling and boil gently for 5 minutes to coagulate the precipitate. If necessary, add more ammonium hydroxide to maintain the alkalinity throughout this operation. Filter through a small filter paper and wash with a small amount of hot water. (Reserve this filtrate for the determination of *Sulfate*.) Redissolve the precipitate from the filter paper with hot dilute hydrochloric acid (1 + 3) and wash the filter paper free of acid. Heat the filtrate plus washings, which should amount to about 25 ml., to boiling and boil gently for 1 to 2 minutes. Add 0.05 ml. of methyl red indicator solution, make slightly alkaline with ammonium hydroxide, and again boil gently to coagulate the precipitate. Filter through the same small filter paper, wash thoroughly, and ignite in a tared crucible. The weight of the residue should not exceed 0.0010 gram.

Chloride. Dissolve 1 gram in 10 ml. of water plus 2 ml. of nitric acid, filter if necessary through a small chloride-free filter, wash with hot water, dilute to 20 ml., and add 1 ml. of silver nitrate reagent solution. Any turbidity should not exceed that produced by 0.01 mg. of chloride ion (Cl) in an equal volume of solution containing the quantities of reagents used in the test.

Sulfate. Neutralize with hydrochloric acid the first filtrate from the test for *Ammonium hydroxide precipitate* and add an excess of 1 ml. of the acid. Heat to boiling, add 5 ml. of barium chloride reagent solution, digest in a covered beaker on the steam bath for 2 hours, and allow to stand overnight. Filter, wash thoroughly, and ignite. The weight of the precipitate should not be more than 0.0024 gram greater than the weight obtained in a complete blank test. In the blank test the hydrochloric acid equivalent to that used for dissolution of the calcium carbonate should be nearly all evaporated before addition of the ammonium hydroxide.

Barium. For the sample dissolve 2 grams in 15 ml. of water and sufficient nitric acid (about 2.5 ml.) to effect dissolution. For the control dissolve 1 gram in 15 ml. of water and sufficient nitric acid (about 1.5 ml.) to effect dissolution and add 0.10 mg. of barium ion (Ba). Heat each to boiling, boil gently for 5 minutes, cool, filter if necessary, and dilute to 23 ml. Add 2 ml. of potassium dichromate reagent solution and neutralize with ammonium hydroxide until the orange color is just dissipated and the yellow color persists. To each solution slowly add, with constant stirring, 25 ml. of methanol. Any turbidity in the solution of the sample should not exceed that in the control.

Sample Solution A for the determination of Heavy metals, Iron, Magnesium, Potassium, Sodium, and Strontium. Cautiously dissolve 20 grams in 100 ml. of dilute hydrochloric acid (1 + 1) and evaporate on the steam bath to dryness or a moist residue. Dissolve the residue in about 100 ml. of water, filter, and dilute to 200 ml. (1 ml. = 0.1 gram).

Heavy metals. For the sample use a 30-ml. aliquot (3-gram sample) of Sample Solution A. For the control add 0.02 mg. of lead ion (Pb) to a 10-ml. aliquot (1-gram sample) of Sample Solution A and dilute to 30 ml. Adjust the pH of the control and sample solutions to between 3 and 4 (using a pH meter) with $1N$ acetic acid or ammonium hydroxide (10 per cent NH_3), dilute to 40 ml., and mix. Add 10 ml. of freshly prepared hydrogen sulfide water to each and mix. Any color in the solution of the sample should not exceed that in the control.

Iron. To 5 ml. (0.5-gram sample) of Sample Solution A add 2 ml. of hydrochloric acid and dilute to 50 ml. Add 30 to 50 mg. of ammonium persulfate crystals and 3 ml. of ammonium thiocyanate reagent solution. Any red color should not exceed that produced by 0.01 mg. of iron (Fe) in an equal volume of solution containing the quantities of reagents used in the test.

Magnesium. Dilute 7.5 ml. (0.75-gram sample) of Sample Solution A to 20 ml. For the control add 0.05 mg. of magnesium ion (Mg) to 2.5 ml. (0.25-gram sample) of Sample Solution A and dilute to 20 ml. To each solution add 0.15 ml. of a 0.1 per cent aqueous solution of Titan yellow (Clayton yellow) and 2 ml. of approximately $1N$ sodium hydroxide. Mix, let stand for 10 minutes, and shake well. The color in the solution representing the sample should not exceed that in the control.

Potassium. Determine the potassium by the flame photometric method described on page 14. (It is necessary to use the oxyhydrogen flame.)

Sample Solution A-1. To a 10-ml. aliquot (1-gram sample) of Sample Solution A add 5 ml. of hydrochloric acid and 1 gram of dibasic ammonium phosphate, and dilute to 100 ml. with water.

Control Solution B. To another 10-ml. aliquot of Sample Solution A add 0.10 mg. of potassium ion (K), 5 ml. of hydrochloric acid, and 1 gram of dibasic ammonium phosphate, and dilute to 100 ml. with water.

Observe the emission of Control Solution B at the 767-mμ potassium line. Observe the emission of Sample Solution A-1 at the 767-mμ potassium line and at a wavelength of 750 mμ. The difference (D_1) between the intensities observed at 767 mμ and 750 mμ should not exceed the difference (D_2) observed at 767 mμ between Sample Solution A-1 and Control Solution B.

Sodium. Determine the sodium by the flame photometric method described on page 14.

Sample Solution A-1. To a 10-ml. aliquot (1-gram sample) of Sample Solution A add 5 ml. of hydrochloric acid and 1 gram of (low sodium) dibasic ammonium phosphate, and dilute to 100 ml. with water.

Control Solution B. To another 10-ml. aliquot of Sample Solution A add 0.10 mg. of sodium ion (Na), 5 ml. of hydrochloric acid, and 1 gram of (low sodium) dibasic ammonium phosphate, and dilute to 100 ml. with water.

Observe the emission of Control Solution B at the 589-mμ sodium line. Observe the emission of Sample Solution A-1 at 589 mμ and at a wavelength of 580 mμ. The difference (D_1) between the intensities observed for Sample Solution A-1 at 580 mμ and 589 mμ should not exceed the difference (D_2) observed at 589 mμ between Sample Solution A-1 and Control Solution B.

Strontium.   Determine the strontium by the flame photometric method described on page 14.

Sample Solution A-1.   To a 10-ml. aliquot (1-gram sample) of Sample Solution A add 1 ml. of hydrochloric acid and dilute to 100 ml. with water.

Control Solution B.   To another 10-ml. aliquot of Sample Solution A add 1.0 mg. of strontium ion (Sr) and 1 ml. of hydrochloric acid and dilute to 100 ml. with water.

Observe the emission of Control Solution B at the 460.7-mμ strontium line. Observe the emission of Sample Solution A-1 at the 460.7-mμ strontium line and at a wavelength of 458.7 mμ. The difference (D_1) between the intensities observed for Sample Solution A-1 at 460.7 mμ and 458.7 mμ should not exceed the difference (D_2) observed at 460.7 mμ between Sample Solution A-1 and Control Solution B.

Notes

Calcium Carbonate, Chelometric Standard

$CaCO_3$ Formula Wt. 100.09

REQUIREMENTS

Assay.   Not less than 99.95 nor more than 100.05 per cent $CaCO_3$.
Insoluble in dilute hydrochloric acid.   Not more than 0.010 per cent.
Ammonium hydroxide precipitate.   Not more than 0.010 per cent.
Chloride (Cl).   Not more than 0.001 per cent.
Sulfate (SO_4).   Not more than 0.010 per cent.
Barium (Ba).   Not more than 0.01 per cent.
Heavy metals (as Pb).   Not more than 0.001 per cent.
Iron (Fe).   Not more than 0.002 per cent.
Magnesium (Mg).   Not more than 0.01 per cent.
Potassium (K).   Not more than 0.01 per cent.
Sodium (Na).   Not more than 0.01 per cent.
Strontium (Sr).   Not more than 0.10 per cent.

TESTS

Assay.   Weigh 1 gram to the nearest 1 mg. and transfer to a small conical weighing bottle of the type used for weighing primary standards. Dry in an oven at 300°C. for 3 hours, cool in a desiccator for 2 hours, and weigh accurately into a 600-ml. beaker. Add 10 ml. of water, cover the beaker, and add cautiously 6.7 ml. of hydrochloric acid. Dilute to 200 ml., heat to incipient boiling, stir, and add slowly a hot solution prepared as follows: dissolve 5.0 grams of ammonium oxalate in 50 ml. of water, filter, and heat to incipient boiling. Add 0.25 ml. of methyl red indicator solution and then dilute ammonium hydroxide $(1 + 1)$, drop-wise with rapid stirring, until the color changes to a distinct yellow (pH about 6). Approximately 10 minutes should be required for the neutralization. Wash down the sides of the beaker, cover, and allow to stand at room temperature for 2 hours.

   Decant the solution through a weighed sintered porcelain filter crucible (fine porosity), transfer the precipitate quantitatively to the filter with the aid of a "policeman" and an ice cold wash solution of 0.1 per cent ammonium oxalate, and wash 8 to 10 times with approximately 7-ml. portions of the ice cold solution. Dry the precipitate at 115°C. for 1 to 2 hours and ignite at 490° ± 5°C. for 4 hours in a muffle furnace fitted with an iron-constantan thermocouple. The thermocouple potential should be measured with a potentiometer having a 16 to 64 millivolt scale and a dial for compensating the reference junction potential. To check the maximum temperature attained, place a few crystals of lead chloride ($PbCl_2$) in a porcelain crucible in the muffle furnace. Lead chloride (melting point, 501°C.) should remain unmelted throughout the ignition. Cool for 1.5 hours or longer in a desiccator, weigh, and repeat the ignition for 4-hour periods until the weight is constant. Three or more such ignitions may be required.

Transfer the precipitate to a mortar, lightly crush to remove all lumps, and transfer to a weighed platinum crucible, avoiding packing. Weigh the crucible and contents, ignite again at 490° ± 5° for 3 hours, cool for 1 hour, and weigh. Repeat the ignition for 3-hour periods until constant weight is attained. Transfer the precipitate to a 150-ml. beaker, add 20 ml. of water and 5 ml. of hydrochloric acid, stir vigorously, and filter on a weighed sintered glass crucible (fine porosity). Wash 10 times with 10-ml. portions of water, heat at 110° to 120°C. for 3 hours, cool for 1.5 hours or more, and weigh. The weight obtained on the first ignition is slightly high, presumably as a result of some form of carbon formed as a by-product during ignition. The necessary correction is obtained by adding the loss on re-ignition to the weight of the acid insoluble residue. Subtract the total correction in mg. from the weight of the precipitate obtained in the first ignition. The purity by assay may then be calculated as follows:

$$\%CaCO_3 = \frac{\text{Corrected wt. of precipitate} \times 100}{\text{Wt. of sample}}$$

Insoluble in dilute hydrochloric acid and other tests except *Assay* are the same as for **Calcium Carbonate, Low in Alkalies,** page 143.

Notes

Calcium Chloride, Anhydrous

(For drying)

$CaCl_2$ Formula Wt. 110.99

REQUIREMENTS

Assay.   Not less than 96 per cent $CaCl_2$.
Alkalinity.   Not more than 0.020 per cent as $Ca(OH)_2$.
Magnesium and alkali salts (as sulfates).   Not more than 2.0 per cent.

TESTS

Assay.   Weigh accurately about 2 grams, dissolve in water in a 200-ml. volumetric flask, and dilute to volume with water. Transfer a 25.0-ml. aliquot to a second 200-ml. volumetric flask, and dilute with 100 ml. of dilute nitric acid $(1 + 49)$. Add, slowly and with constant agitation, 50.0 ml. of $0.1N$ silver nitrate, dilute to volume with water, and mix well. Filter through a dry filter into a dry flask, rejecting the first 30 ml. of the filtrate. To 100 ml. of the subsequent filtrate add 2 ml. of ferric ammonium sulfate indicator solution, and titrate the excess silver nitrate with $0.1N$ thiocyanate solution. One milliliter of $0.1N$ silver nitrate corresponds to 0.005549 gram of $CaCl_2$.

Alkalinity.   Dissolve 5 grams in 50 ml. of water and add 0.10 ml. of phenolphthalein indicator solution. If any pink color is produced, it should be discharged by not more than 0.30 ml. of $0.1N$ hydrochloric acid.

Magnesium and alkali salts.   To 1 gram in 100 ml. of water add 5 ml. of hydrochloric acid and a few drops of methyl red indicator solution and heat to boiling. Add dropwise with stirring 100 ml. of warm ammonium oxalate reagent solution. Heat the solution at 70° to 80°C. and add dropwise 10 per cent ammonium hydroxide until the solution is just alkaline to methyl red. Dilute to 250 ml. and allow the solution to stand without further heating for 1 hour. Filter and to 125 ml. of the filtrate add 0.5 ml. of sulfuric acid, evaporate to about 30 ml., and cool. Add 25 ml. of nitric acid and evaporate to dryness on the steam bath. Dissolve the residue in a few milliliters of water, filter through a small filter paper, and wash. Transfer the filtrate and washings to a small tared dish. Evaporate to dryness, ignite gently to volatilize the excess acids and salts, and finally ignite at 800° ± 25°C. for 15 minutes. The weight of the residue should not exceed 0.0100 gram.

Calcium Chloride Dihydrate

$CaCl_2 \cdot 2H_2O$ Formula Wt. 147.02

REQUIREMENTS

Assay.   Not less than 74 nor more than 78 per cent $CaCl_2$.
Insoluble and ammonium hydroxide precipitate.   Not more than 0.010 per cent.
pH of a 5 per cent solution.   From 4.5 to 8.5 at 25°C.
Oxidizing substances (as NO_3).   Not more than 0.003 per cent.
Sulfate (SO_4).   Not more than 0.010 per cent.
Ammonium (NH_4).   Not more than 0.005 per cent.
Barium (Ba).   Not more than 0.005 per cent.
Heavy metals (as Pb).   Not more than 0.0005 per cent.
Iron (Fe).   Not more than 0.001 per cent.
Magnesium (Mg).   Not more than 0.005 per cent.
Potassium (K).   Not more than 0.01 per cent.
Sodium (Na).   Not more than 0.02 per cent.
Strontium (Sr).   Not more than 0.1 per cent.

TESTS

Assay.   Weigh accurately about 2 grams, dissolve in water in a 200-ml. volumetric flask, and dilute to volume with water. Transfer a 25.0-ml. aliquot to a second 200-ml. volumetric flask, and dilute with 100 ml. of dilute nitric acid $(1 + 49)$. Add, slowly and with constant agitation, 50.0 ml. of 0.1N silver nitrate, dilute to volume with water, and mix well. Filter through a dry filter into a dry flask, rejecting the first 30 ml. of the filtrate. To 100 ml. of the subsequent filtrate add 2 ml. of ferric ammonium sulfate indicator solution, and titrate the excess silver nitrate with 0.1N thiocyanate solution. One milliliter of 0.1N silver nitrate corresponds to 0.005549 gram of $CaCl_2$.

Insoluble and ammonium hydroxide precipitate.   Dissolve 10 grams in 100 ml. of water and heat to boiling. Add 0.10 ml. of methyl red indicator solution, make slightly alkaline with ammonium hydroxide (free from carbonate), and boil for 5 minutes. Filter through a small paper and wash with a little hot water. Retain the filtrate for the test for *Sulfate*. Redissolve the precipitate with hot dilute hydrochloric acid $(1 + 3)$, wash the paper free of acid, boil the solution (which should amount to about 30 ml.) for 1 to 2 minutes, add 0.05 ml. of methyl red indicator solution, make slightly alkaline with ammonium hydroxide, and again boil gently to coagulate the precipitate. Filter through the same paper, wash thoroughly, and ignite. The weight of the residue should not exceed 0.0010 gram.

pH of a 5 per cent solution. Dissolve 10 grams in 200 ml. of carbon dioxide- and ammonia-free water. Determine the pH by the method described on page 18. The pH should be from 4.5 to 8.5 at 25°C. The pH of a 5 per cent solution of pure calcium chloride dihydrate would be 6.6 at 25°C.

Oxidizing substances. Place 0.2 gram in a dry beaker. Cool the beaker thoroughly in an ice bath and add 22 ml. of sulfuric acid that has been cooled to ice-bath temperature. Allow the mixture to warm to room temperature and swirl the beaker at intervals to effect gentle dissolution with slow evolution of hydrogen chloride. When dissolution is complete, add 3 ml. of diphenylamine reagent solution and digest on the steam bath for 90 minutes. Prepare a standard by evaporating to dryness a solution containing 0.006 mg. of nitrate (0.6 ml. of the nitrate standard solution) and 0.01 gram of sodium carbonate. Treat the residue exactly like the sample. Any color produced in the solution of the sample should not exceed that in the standard.

Sulfate. Neutralize with hydrochloric acid the filtrate from the test for *Insoluble and ammonium hydroxide precipitate* and add an excess of 1 ml. of the acid. Heat to boiling, add 5 ml. of barium chloride reagent solution, digest in a covered beaker on the steam bath for 2 hours, and allow to stand overnight. Filter, wash thoroughly, and ignite. The weight of the precipitate should not be more than 0.0024 gram greater than the weight obtained in a complete blank test.

Sample Solution A for determining Ammonium, Barium, Heavy metals, Iron, Magnesium, Potassium, Sodium, and Strontium. Dissolve 50 grams in about 200 ml. of water, filter if necessary, and dilute to 250 ml. in a volumetric flask (1 ml. = 0.2 gram).

Ammonium. Dilute 10 ml. (2-gram sample) of Sample Solution A to 45 ml. and add 15 ml. of 10 per cent sodium hydroxide reagent solution. Filter through a filtering crucible previously washed with 10 per cent sodium hydroxide reagent solution. Dilute 6 ml. of the filtrate to 50 ml. and add 2 ml. of Nessler reagent. Any color should not exceed that produced by 0.01 mg. of ammonium ion (NH_4) in an equal volume of solution containing 1.5 ml. of 10 per cent sodium hydroxide reagent solution and 2 ml. of Nessler reagent.

Barium. For the sample add 2 grams of sodium acetate and 0.05 ml. of acetic acid to 15 ml. (3-gram sample) of Sample Solution A. For the control add 2 grams of sodium acetate, 0.05 ml. of acetic acid, and 0.10 mg. of barium ion (Ba) to 5 ml. (1-gram sample) of Sample Solution A and dilute to 15 ml. To each solution add 2 ml. of potassium dichromate reagent solution and allow to stand for 15 minutes. Any turbidity in the solution of the sample should not exceed that in the control.

Heavy metals. For the sample use a 30-ml. aliquot of Sample Solution A (6-gram sample). For the control add 0.02 mg. of lead ion (Pb) to a 10-ml. aliquot of Sample Solution A (2-gram sample) and dilute to 30 ml. Adjust the pH of the control and sample solutions to between 3 and 4 (using a pH meter) with 1N acetic acid or ammonium hydroxide (10 per cent NH_3), dilute to 40 ml., and mix. Add 10 ml. of freshly prepared hydrogen sulfide water to each and mix. Any color in the solution of the sample should not exceed that in the control.

Iron. To 5 ml. of Sample Solution A (1-gram sample) add 2 ml. of hydrochloric acid, dilute to 50 ml., and add 30 to 50 mg. of ammonium persulfate crystals and 3 ml. of ammonium thiocyanate reagent solution. Any red color should not exceed that produced by 0.01 mg. of iron (Fe) in an equal volume of solution containing the quantities of reagents used in the test.

Magnesium. Dilute 7.5 ml. (1.5-gram sample) of Sample Solution A to 20 ml. For the control add 0.05 mg. of magnesium ion to 2.5 ml. (0.5-gram sample) of Sample Solution A and dilute to 20 ml. To each solution add 0.15 ml. of a 0.1 per cent aqueous solution of Titan yellow (Clayton yellow) and 2 ml. of approximately 1N sodium hydroxide. Mix, let stand for 10 minutes, and shake well. The color in the solution representing the sample should not exceed that in the control.

Potassium. Determine the potassium by the flame photometric method described on page 14. (It is necessary to use the oxyhydrogen flame.)

Sample Solution A-1. To a 5-ml. aliquot (1-gram sample) of Sample Solution A add 5 ml. of hydrochloric acid and 1 gram of dibasic ammonium phosphate, and dilute to 100 ml. with water.

Control Solution B. To another 5-ml. aliquot of Sample Solution A add 0.10 mg. of potassium ion (K), 5 ml. of hydrochloric acid, and 1 gram of dibasic ammonium phosphate, and dilute to 100 ml. with water.

Observe the emission of Control Solution B at the 767-mμ potassium line. Observe the emission of Sample Solution A-1 at the 767-mμ potassium line and at a wavelength of 750 mμ. The difference (D_1) between the intensities observed at 767 mμ and 750 mμ should not exceed the difference (D_2) observed at 767 mμ between Sample Solution A-1 and Control Solution B.

Sodium.   Determine the sodium by the flame photometric method described on page 14.

Sample Solution A-1.   To a 5-ml. aliquot (1-gram sample) of Sample Solution A add 5 ml. of hydrochloric acid and 1 gram of (low sodium) dibasic ammonium phosphate, and dilute to 250 ml. with water.

Control Solution B.   To another 5-ml. aliquot of Sample Solution A add 0.20 mg. of sodium ion (Na), 5 ml. of hydrochloric acid, and 1 gram of (low sodium) dibasic ammonium phosphate, and dilute to 250 ml. with water.

Observe the emission of Control Solution B at the 589-mμ sodium line. Observe the emission of Sample Solution A-1 at the 589-mμ sodium line and at wavelengths of 586 mμ and 592 mμ. To estimate the background emission at 589 mμ interpolate between the intensities at 586 mμ and 592 mμ. The difference (D_1) between the interpolated background emission and the intensity observed for Sample Solution A-1 should not exceed the difference (D_2) observed at 589 mμ between Sample Solution A-1 and Control Solution B.

Strontium.   Determine the strontium by the flame photometric method described on page 14.

Sample Solution A-1.   To a 5-ml. aliquot (1-gram sample) of Sample Solution A add 1 ml. of hydrochloric acid and dilute to 100 ml. with water.

Control Solution B.   To another 5-ml. aliquot of Sample Solution A add 1.0 mg. of strontium ion (Sr) and 1 ml. of hydrochloric acid, and dilute to 100 ml. with water.

Observe the emission of Control Solution B at the 460.7-mμ strontium line. Observe the emission of Sample Solution A-1 at the 460.7-mμ strontium line and at a wavelength of 458.7-mμ. The difference (D_1) between the intensities observed for Sample Solution A-1 at 460.7 mμ and 458.7 mμ should not exceed the difference (D_2) observed at 460.7 mμ between Sample Solution A-1 and Control Solution B.

Notes

Carbon Disulfide

CS$_2$ Formula Wt. 76.14

Note. Carbon disulfide should be supplied and stored in amber glass containers and protected from direct sunlight.

REQUIREMENTS

Color (APHA). Not more than 10.
Boiling range. 1 ml. to 95 ml., not more than 0.5°C.; 95 ml. to dryness, not more than 0.5°C.
Residue after evaporation. Not more than 0.002 per cent.
Foreign sulfides and dissolved sulfur. To pass test.
Sulfite and sulfate. To pass test (limit about 0.002 per cent SO$_2$).
Water (H$_2$O). Not more than 0.05 per cent.

TESTS

Color (APHA). For the color standard dilute a 2-ml. aliquot of platinum-cobalt stock solution (APHA No. 500) to 100 ml. with water. Compare this solution (APHA No. 10) with 100 ml. of the carbon disulfide in 100-ml. Nessler tubes, viewed vertically over a white background.

Boiling range. Distill 100 ml. by the method described on page 12, immersing the bulb of the distilling flask in water heated to about 60°C., and keeping the level of the liquid in the flask above the level of the water in the bath throughout the test. The difference between the temperatures when 1 ml. and 95 ml. have distilled should not exceed 0.5°C., and the difference between the temperatures when 95 ml. have distilled and when the dry point is reached should not exceed 0.5°C. The boiling point of pure carbon disulfide is 46.3°C. at 760-mm. mercury pressure.

Residue after evaporation. Evaporate 40 ml. (50 grams) to dryness in a tared dish at 50° to 60°C. The residue should not have a disagreeable odor and, when dried at 60°C. for 1 hour, should not weigh more than 0.0010 gram.

Foreign sulfides and dissolved sulfur. Shake 2 ml. in a dry test tube with a globule of clean bright mercury for 2 minutes. The mercury should remain bright.

Sulfite and sulfate. Shake 10 ml. with 10 ml. of water in a separatory funnel for 5 minutes; separate and discard the carbon disulfide. To the aqueous layer add 0.05 ml. of 0.1N iodine solution. A yellow or violet color should be produced. Add to the solution 1 ml. of barium chloride reagent solution. No turbidity should be produced in 15 minutes.

Water. Place 25 ml. of methanol in a dry titration flask and add Karl Fischer reagent to a visually or electrometrically determined end point. Add 20 ml. (25 grams) of the sample, taking care to protect the sample and contents of the flask from moisture. Stir vigorously and titrate with Karl Fischer reagent to the same end point. Calculate the water content from the titer and volume of Karl Fisher reagent consumed by the sample.

Notes

Carbon Tetrachloride

CCl$_4$ Formula Wt. 153.82

REQUIREMENTS

Color (APHA). Not more than 10.

Density (grams per ml.) at 25°C. Not less than 1.583 nor more than 1.585.

Boiling range. 1 ml. to 95 ml., not more than 0.5°C.; 95 ml. to dryness, not more than 0.5°C.

Residue after evaporation. Not more than 0.001 per cent.

Acidity. To pass test.

Free chlorine (Cl). To pass test.

Sulfur compounds (as S). To pass test (limit about 0.005 per cent).

Iodine-consuming substances. To pass test.

Substances darkened by sulfuric acid. To pass test.

Suitability for use in dithizone tests. To pass test.

TESTS

Color (APHA). For the color standard dilute a 2-ml. aliquot of platinum-cobalt stock solution (APHA No. 500) to 100 ml. with water. Compare this solution (APHA No. 10) with 100 ml. of the carbon tetrachloride in 100-ml. Nessler tubes, viewed vertically over a white background.

Boiling range. Distill 100 ml. by the method described on page 12. The difference between the temperatures when 1 ml. and 95 ml. have distilled should not exceed 0.5°C., and the difference in temperatures when 95 ml. have distilled and the dry point is reached should not exceed 0.5°C. The boiling point of pure carbon tetrachloride at 760-mm. mercury pressure is 76.7°C.

Residue after evaporation. Evaporate 63 ml. (100 grams) to dryness in a tared dish on the steam bath and dry the residue at 105°C. for 30 minutes. The weight of the residue should not exceed 0.0010 gram.

Acidity. Shake 13 ml. (20 grams) with 20 ml. of carbon dioxide-free water for 5 minutes, separate, and discard the carbon tetrachloride. To 10 ml. of the aqueous layer add 0.05 ml. of phenolphthalein indicator solution and 0.05 ml. of 0.1N sodium hydroxide. A pink color should be produced.

Free chlorine. Shake 10 ml. for 2 minutes with 10 ml. of water to which 0.10 ml. of 10 per cent potassium iodide reagent solution has been added, and allow to separate. The lower layer should not show a violet tint.

Sulfur compounds. To 3 ml. in an Erlenmeyer flask add 30 ml. of approximately $0.5N$ potassium hydroxide in methanol and boil the mixture gently for 30 minutes under a reflux condenser. Detach the condenser, dilute with 50 ml. of water, and heat on the steam bath till the carbon tetrachloride and methanol are evaporated. Add 50 ml. of saturated bromine water and heat for 15 minutes longer. Transfer the solution to a beaker, neutralize with dilute hydrochloric acid $(1 + 4)$; if alkaline, add an excess of 1 ml. of hydrochloric acid, and concentrate to a volume of 100 ml. Filter if necessary, heat the filtrate to boiling, add 5 ml. of barium chloride reagent solution, digest in a covered beaker on the steam bath for 2 hours, and allow to stand overnight. If a precipitate is formed, filter, wash thoroughly, and ignite. The weight of the precipitate should not be more than 0.0018 gram greater than the weight obtained in a complete blank test.

Iodine-consuming substances. To 25 ml. add 0.05 ml. of $0.1N$ iodine solution, shake well, and allow to stand for 30 minutes. The violet color of the iodine should not be entirely discharged.

Substances darkened by sulfuric acid. To 40 ml. in a glass-stoppered separatory funnel that has been rinsed with sulfuric acid add 5 ml. of sulfuric acid and shake vigorously for 5 minutes. Allow to separate completely and transfer the acid to a comparison tube. The acid should have no more color than a color standard of the following composition: 0.1 ml. of cobaltous chloride solution (5.95 grams of $CoCl_2 \cdot 6H_2O$ and 2.5 ml. of hydrochloric acid in 100 ml.), 0.4 ml. of ferric chloride solution (4.50 grams of $FeCl_3 \cdot 6H_2O$ and 2.5 ml. of hydrochloric acid in 100 ml.), 0.1 ml. of cupric sulfate solution (6.24 grams of $CuSO_4 \cdot 5H_2O$ and 2.5 ml. of hydrochloric acid in 100 ml.), and 4.4 ml. of water.

Suitability for use in dithizone tests.

Solution A. Dissolve 4 mg. of dithizone in 200 ml. of the sample of carbon tetrachloride.

A. Alkaline extractions. To 50 ml. of a 5 per cent solution of sodium hydroxide in a 200-ml. glass-stoppered flask add 0.025 mg. of cadmium ion (Cd) and 25 ml. of Solution A, shake, and allow to stand for 10 minutes. The color after standing 10 minutes should be identical in hue and intensity with that in a similar, freshly prepared solution.

B. Acid extractions. Dilute 25 ml. of Solution A with the carbon tetrachloride to 100 ml. and transfer 25-ml. aliquots of this diluted solution to each of two 200-ml. glass-stoppered flasks. Add 25 ml. of $0.1N$ hydrochloric acid to one flask and 25 ml. of water to the other flask and shake

each intermittently for 10 minutes. The green color in the carbon tetrachloride layers should be identical. Add 0.5 mg. of mercury ion (Hg)
to the flask to which 0.1N hydrochloric acid was added, shake, and allow
to stand for 10 minutes. The orange color should be identical in hue and
intensity with that in a similar, freshly prepared solution which is allowed
to stand for only 1 minute instead of 10 minutes. Since mercury dithizonate is slightly light-sensitive, both flasks should be shaken for 15 seconds
before final comparison is made.

Note. Dithizone is extremely sensitive to various metal ions. Therefore, the distilled water, 0.1N hydrochloric acid, and the 5 per cent solution of sodium hydroxide used must be absolutely free of metal ions
that react with dithizone. In case of doubt, the solutions before use
must be freed of such metals by shaking with portions of chloroform-
dithizone solution until the color of the dithizone remains unchanged.

Notes

Carbon Tetrachloride

(Suitable for use in ultraviolet spectrophotometry)

CCl$_4$ Formula Wt. 153.82

REQUIREMENTS

Absorbance. To pass test.

Density (grams per ml.) at 25°C. Not less than 1.583 nor more than 1.585.

Boiling range. 1 ml. to 95 ml., not more than 0.5°C.; 95 ml. to dryness, not more than 0.5°C.

Residue after evaporation. Not more than 0.001 per cent.

Acidity. To pass test.

Free chlorine (Cl). To pass test.

Sulfur compounds (as S). To pass test (limit about 0.005 per cent).

Iodine-consuming substances. To pass test.

Substances darkened by sulfuric acid. To pass test.

Suitability for use in dithizone tests. To pass test.

TESTS

Absorbance. Determine the absorbance of the sample in a 1.00-cm. cell throughout the range of 265 mμ to 400 mμ, against water in a similar matched cell set at zero absorbance as the reference liquid. The absorbance should not exceed 1.00 at 265 mμ, 0.35 at 270 mμ, 0.10 at 280 mμ, 0.05 at 290 mμ, 0.02 at 300 mμ, and 0.01 at 330 mμ to 400 mμ. The spectral absorbance curve recorded through the wavelengths indicated should be smooth throughout the prescribed range and should not show any extraneous impurity peaks within this range.

Other tests are the same as for **Carbon Tetrachloride,** page 156, except *Color (APHA)*, which is superseded by the *Absorbance* test.

Notes

Ceric Ammonium Nitrate

$(NH_4)_2Ce(NO_3)_6$ Formula Wt. 548.23

REQUIREMENTS

Assay.   Not less than 99 per cent $(NH_4)_2Ce(NO_3)_6$.
Insoluble in dilute sulfuric acid.   Not more than 0.05 per cent.
Chloride (Cl).   Not more than 0.01 per cent.
Phosphate (PO$_4$).   Not more than 0.02 per cent.
Iron (Fe).   Not more than 0.005 per cent.

TESTS

Assay.   Weigh accurately about 2.5 grams, previously dried for 24 hours at 85°C., dissolve in 10 ml. of dilute sulfuric acid $(1 + 9)$, and add 40 ml. of water. Add 1,10-phenanthroline ferrous sulfate indicator solution* and titrate with standard ferrous sulfate solution.** One milliliter of 0.1N ferrous sulfate corresponds to 0.0548 gram of $(NH_4)_2Ce(NO_3)_6$.

> *** 1,10-Phenanthroline Ferrous Sulfate Indicator Solution.** Dissolve 0.070 gram of clear crystals of ferrous sulfate in 10 ml. of water, and then dissolve 0.15 gram of 1,10-phenanthroline in this solution.

> **** Standard Ferrous Sulfate Solution, 0.1N.** Dissolve 2.8 grams of clear crystals of ferrous sulfate in 90 ml. of freshly boiled and cooled water, and add sulfuric acid to make 100 ml. Standardize the solution with 0.1N potassium permanganate. The solution must be freshly prepared and standardized.

Insoluble in dilute sulfuric acid.   To 5 grams add 10 ml. of sulfuric acid, stir, then cautiously add 90 ml. of water to dissolve. Heat to boiling and digest in a covered beaker on the steam bath for 1 hour. Filter through a tared filtering crucible, wash thoroughly, and dry at 105°C. The weight of the residue should not exceed 0.0025 gram.

Chloride.   Dissolve 0.1 gram in 10 ml. of water, filter if necessary through a small chloride-free filter, and add 1 ml. of nitric acid and 1 ml. of silver nitrate reagent solution. Any turbidity should not exceed that produced by 0.01 mg. of chloride ion (Cl) in an equal volume of solution containing the quantities of reagents used in the test. The comparison is best made by superimposing a tube containing 0.1 gram of sample in 12 ml. of water over the tube containing the standard turbidity and placing a tube containing 12 ml. of water below the tube containing the sample and added reagents. Both turbidities are thus viewed through the same depth and color of solution. The comparison tubes may be machine-made vials, long style, of about 20-ml. capacity.

Phosphate.   Dissolve 0.25 gram in 30 ml. of dilute sulfuric acid $(1 + 9)$, add hydrogen peroxide until the solution just turns colorless, then boil to destroy excess peroxide. Cool and dilute to 50 ml. Dilute a 10-ml. aliquot to 60 ml. and adjust the pH to 2 to 3 (pH paper) with ammonium hydroxide. (**Note.** This neutralization must be made with care to avoid formation of a permanent precipitate which would vitiate the test. If this happens, discard the solution and start with another 10-ml. aliquot.) Add 0.5 gram of ammonium molybdate and adjust the pH to 1.8 (using a pH meter) with dilute hydrochloric acid $(1 + 9)$. Heat the solution to boiling and cool to room temperature. Dilute to 90 ml. and add 10 ml. of hydrochloric acid. Transfer to a separatory funnel, add 35 ml. of ether, shake vigorously, and allow the layers to separate. Draw off and discard the aqueous layer. Wash the ether layer twice with 10-ml. portions of dilute hydrochloric acid $(1 + 9)$, drawing off and discarding the aqueous layer each time. Add 0.2 ml. of a 2 per cent solution of stannous chloride in hydrochloric acid. If the solution is cloudy, shake it with a small amount of dilute hydrochloric acid $(1 + 9)$ to clear it. Any blue color should not exceed that produced by 0.01 mg. of phosphate ion (PO_4) in 10 ml. of dilute sulfuric acid $(3 + 47)$ treated exactly like the 10-ml. aliquot of the sample. If the ether solutions are turbid, wash them with 10 ml. of dilute hydrochloric acid $(1 + 9)$.

Iron.   Dissolve 1 gram in 30 ml. of dilute sulfuric acid $(1 + 9)$ and add a 3 per cent solution of hydrogen peroxide, dropwise, until the yellow color disappears. For the standard add 0.05 mg. of iron (Fe) to 30 ml. of dilute sulfuric acid $(1 + 9)$ and the same quantity of 3 per cent solution of hydrogen peroxide added to the sample. Add ammonium hydroxide to each solution until the pH is 1 to 3 and cool to room temperature. Adjust the pH of each to 3.5 (glass electrode) and dilute to 50 ml. To a 10-ml. aliquot of each add 6 ml. of 10 per cent hydroxylamine hydrochloride reagent solution and 4 ml. of 1,10-phenanthroline reagent solution. Any red color produced in the solution of the sample should not exceed that in the standard. Compare 1 hour after adding the reagents to the sample and standard solutions.

Chloroform

CHCl$_3$ Formula Wt. 119.38

Note. Chloroform should be supplied and stored in amber glass containers and protected from direct sunlight.

Reagent chloroform contains about 0.75 per cent of alcohol as a stabilizer.

REQUIREMENTS

Color (APHA). Not more than 10.

Density (grams per ml.) at 25°C. Not less than 1.471 nor more than 1.474.

Residue after evaporation. Not more than 0.001 per cent.

Acetone and aldehyde. To pass test [limit about 0.005 per cent as (CH$_3$)$_2$CO].

Acid and chloride. To pass test.

Free chlorine (Cl). To pass test.

Lead (Pb). Not more than 0.000005 per cent.

Substances darkened by sulfuric acid. To pass test.

Suitability for use in dithizone tests. To pass test.

TESTS

Color (APHA). For the color standard dilute a 2-ml. aliquot of platinum-cobalt stock solution (APHA No. 500) to 100 ml. with water. Compare this solution (APHA No. 10) with 100 ml. of the chloroform in 100-ml. Nessler tubes, viewed vertically over a white background.

Residue after evaporation. Evaporate 67 ml. (100 grams) to dryness in a tared dish on the steam bath and dry the residue at 105°C. for 30 minutes. The weight of the residue should not exceed 0.0010 gram.

Acetone and aldehyde. Shake 15 ml. with 20 ml. of ammonia-free water for 5 minutes in a separatory funnel. Allow the layers to separate and transfer 10 ml. of the aqueous layer to a 125-ml. glass-stoppered flask containing 40 ml. of ammonia-free water. Adjust and maintain the temperature of this solution at 25° ± 1°C. Add 5 ml. of Nessler reagent solution and allow to stand for 5 minutes. No turbidity or precipitate should develop.

Acid and chloride. Shake 17 ml. (25 grams) with 25 ml. of water for 5 minutes, allow the liquids to separate, and draw off the aqueous phase. Add a small piece of blue litmus paper to 10 ml. of the aqueous phase. The blue litmus paper should not change color. Add 0.25 ml. of silver nitrate reagent solution to another 10 ml. of the aqueous phase. No turbidity should be produced in this solution.

Free chlorine. Gently shake 10 ml. for 2 minutes with 10 ml. of water to which have been added 0.10 ml. of starch indicator solution and 0.10 ml. of 10 per cent potassium iodide reagent solution, and allow to separate. The lower layer should not be colored.

Lead. For the solution of the sample transfer 27 ml. (40 grams) of the sample to a separatory funnel, add 20 ml. of dilute nitric acid (1 + 99), and shake vigorously for 1 minute. Allow the phases to separate, draw off and discard the chloroform phase, and use the aqueous phase for the solution of the sample. For the standard prepare a solution containing 0.002 mg. of lead ion (Pb) in 20 ml. of dilute nitric acid (1 + 99) in another separatory funnel. To each solution add 4 ml. of ammonium cyanide, lead-free, reagent solution (**Caution.** *Do this in a well-ventilated hood*) and 5 ml. of dithizone standard solution in chloroform, and shake vigorously for one-half minute. Allow the phases to separate, draw off the dithizone-chloroform phase into clean dry comparison tubes, and compare the colors using a white background. The purplish hue in the solution of the sample due to any red lead dithizonate present should not exceed that in the standard.

> **Note.** When making this test, all glassware must be carefully cleaned and thoroughly rinsed with warm dilute nitric acid (1 +1) to remove any adsorbed lead, and finally rinsed with distilled water. All glassware used in the preparation and storage of reagents and in performing the test must be made of lead-free glass.

Substances darkened by sulfuric acid. To 40 ml. in a separatory funnel add 5 ml. of sulfuric acid, shake the mixture vigorously for 5 minutes, and allow the liquids to separate completely. The chloroform layer should be colorless. The acid layer should have no more color than 5 ml. of a color standard of the following composition: 0.4 ml. of cobaltous chloride solution (5.95 grams of $CoCl_2 \cdot 6H_2O$ and 2.5 ml. of hydrochloric acid in 100 ml.), 1.6 ml. of ferric chloride solution (4.50 grams of $FeCl_3 \cdot 6H_2O$ and 2.5 ml. of hydrochloric acid in 100 ml.), 0.4 ml. of cupric sulfate solution (6.24 grams of $CuSO_4 \cdot 5H_2O$ and 2.5 ml. of hydrochloric acid in 100 ml.), and 17.6 ml. of water.

Suitability for use in dithizone tests.

Solution A. Dissolve 4 mg. of dithizone in 200 ml. of chloroform.

A. Alkaline extractions. To 50 ml. of a 5 per cent solution of sodium hydroxide in a 200-ml. glass-stoppered flask add 0.025 mg. of cadmium ion (Cd) and 25 ml. of Solution A, shake, and allow to stand for 10 minutes. The color after standing 10 minutes should be identical in hue and intensity with that in a similar, freshly prepared solution.

B. Acid extractions. Dilute 25 ml. of Solution A with the chloroform to 100 ml. and transfer 25-ml. aliquots of this diluted solution to each of two 200-ml. glass-stoppered flasks. Add 25 ml. of 0.1N hydrochloric acid to one flask and 25 ml. of water to the other flask and shake each intermittently for 10 minutes. The green color in the chloroform layers should be identical. Add 0.5 mg. of mercury ion (Hg) to the flask to which 0.1N hydrochloric acid was added, shake, and allow to stand for 10 minutes. The orange color should be identical in hue and intensity with that in a similar freshly prepared solution which is allowed to stand for only 1 minute instead of 10 minutes. Since mercury dithizonate is slightly light-sensitive, both flasks should be shaken for about 15 seconds before final comparison is made.

> **Note.** Dithizone is extremely sensitive to various metal ions. Therefore, the distilled water, 0.1N hydrochloric acid, and the 5 per cent solution of sodium hydroxide must be absolutely free of metal ions that react with dithizone. In case of doubt, the solutions before use must be freed of such metals by shaking with portions of a chloroform-dithizone solution until the color of the dithizone remains unchanged.

Notes

Chloroform

(Suitable for use in ultraviolet spectrophotometry)

CHCl$_3$ Formula Wt. 119.38

REQUIREMENTS

Absorbance.   To pass test.

Density (grams per ml.) at 25°C.   Not less than 1.471 nor more than 1.474.

Residue after evaporation.   Not more than 0.001 per cent.

Acetone and aldehyde.   To pass test [limit about 0.005 per cent as $(CH_3)_2CO$].

Acid and chloride.   To pass test.

Free chlorine (Cl).   To pass test.

Lead (Pb).   Not more than 0.000005 per cent.

Substances darkened by sulfuric acid.   To pass test.

Suitability for use in dithizone tests.   To pass test.

TESTS

Absorbance.   Determine the absorbance of the sample in a 1.00-cm. cell throughout the range of 245 mμ to 400 mμ, against water in a similar matched cell set at zero absorbance as the reference liquid. The absorbance should not exceed 1.00 at 245 mμ, 0.25 at 255 mμ, 0.15 at 260 mμ, 0.05 at 270 mμ, and 0.01 at 290 mμ to 400 mμ. The spectral absorbance curve recorded through the wavelengths indicated should be smooth throughout the prescribed range and should not show any extraneous impurity peaks within this range.

Other tests are the same as for **Chloroform,** page 162, except *Color (APHA)*, which is superseded by the *Absorbance* test.

Notes

Chloroplatinic Acid

Platinic Chloride

$H_2PtCl_6 \cdot 6H_2O$ Formula Wt. 517.92

REQUIREMENTS

Solubility in alcohol.   To pass test.
Assay.   Not less than 37.50 per cent Pt.
Alkali and other salts (as sulfates).   Not more than 0.05 per cent.
Suitability for potassium determinations.   To pass test.

TESTS

Solubility in alcohol.   Dissolve 1 gram in 10 ml. of alcohol and allow to stand, with occasional stirring, for 15 minutes. The solution should contain no more than traces of insoluble matter.

Assay.   Using precautions to prevent absorption of moisture, weigh accurately about 1 gram, and transfer to a tared platinum dish of about 100-ml. capacity. Dissolve in 80 ml. of water and add 2 ml. of sulfuric acid. Cover the dish with a split watch glass and electrolyze the solution for 4 hours at a current of 0.4 ampere and a temperature of 55° to 60°C., using a rotating platinum anode and the platinum dish as the cathode. Wash the cover several times during the electrolysis. When the electrolysis is complete, transfer the solution to a second tared platinum dish, and reserve for the *Alkali and other salts* test. Rinse the platinum dish and deposited platinum with water, dry, and ignite at 600°C. for 5 minutes. The weight of the deposit should not be less than 37.50 per cent of the sample weight.

Alkali and other salts.   Evaporate the solution retained from the *Assay* in a tared dish and ignite at 800° ± 25°C. for 30 minutes. The weight of the residue should not exceed 0.0005 gram.

Suitability for potassium determinations.   Dissolve 7.456 grams of potassium chloride, previously dried at 105°C., in water and dilute to a volume of 1 liter. To a 10-ml. aliquot of this solution add 0.100 to 0.110 gram of sodium chloride and dilute to 100 ml. Heat on the steam bath and add between 0.90 and 1.00 gram of the chloroplatinic acid crystals dissolved in about 1 ml. of water. Evaporate to substantial dryness on the steam bath (the residue may be slightly moist). Add 10 ml. of 80 per cent alcohol (85 ml. of alcohol and 15 ml. of water); break up any lumps with a stirring rod and decant through a small filtering crucible.

Leach with five additional successive 10-ml. portions of the 80 per cent alcohol and pour through the same filter. Allow the alcohol to evaporate from the crucible and from the residue in the beaker. Dissolve the precipitate from the crucible with hot water and add the solution to the residue in the beaker. When all the salt is dissolved, transfer the solution to a tared evaporating dish and dry at 105°C. for 1 hour. The weight of the residue should not be less than 0.2425 gram nor more than 0.2440 gram.

Notes

Chromium Potassium Sulfate

$CrK(SO_4)_2 \cdot 12H_2O$ Formula Wt. 499.41

REQUIREMENTS

    Insoluble matter.   Not more than 0.010 per cent.
    Chloride (Cl).   To pass test (limit about 0.002 per cent).
    Aluminum (Al).   Not more than 0.02 per cent.
    Ammonium (NH_4).   Not more than 0.010 per cent.
    Heavy metals (as Pb).   Not more than 0.01 per cent.
    Iron (Fe).   Not more than 0.01 per cent.

TESTS

Insoluble matter.   Dissolve 10 grams in 100 ml. of water, heat to boiling, then digest in a covered beaker on the steam bath for 1 hour. Filter through a tared filtering crucible, wash thoroughly, and dry at 105°C. The weight of the residue should not exceed 0.0010 gram.

Chloride.   Dissolve 1 gram in 10 ml. of water, heat the solution to boiling, and add 2 ml. of ammonium hydroxide to the hot, constantly stirred solution. Boil gently to expel excess ammonia, filter through a small chloride-free filter, wash with hot water until the volume of filtrate and washings is about 45 ml., dilute to 50 ml., and mix. To a 25-ml. aliquot of this solution add 1.5 ml. of nitric acid and 1 ml. of silver nitrate reagent solution. Any turbidity should not exceed that produced by 0.01 mg. of chloride ion (Cl) in an equal volume of solution containing the quantities of reagents used in the test.

Aluminum.   Dissolve 4 grams in 100 ml. of water. Add 20 ml. of 10 per cent sodium hydroxide reagent solution and 10 ml. of hydrogen peroxide. When the reaction ceases, heat to boiling and boil for 15 minutes. Filter and wash with a small quantity of hot water. Reserve the precipitate for the determination of *Iron.* Adjust the pH of the filtrate to 5.0 (using a pH meter) with hydrochloric acid and dilute to 200 ml. For the solution of the sample dilute a 25-ml. aliquot to 100 ml. For the control add 0.05 mg. of aluminum ion (Al) to another 12.5-ml. aliquot and dilute to 100 ml. To each solution add 0.2 ml. of a 5 per cent solution of cupferron. Any turbidity in the solution of the sample should not exceed that in the control.

Ammonium.   Dissolve 1 gram in 80 ml. of water in a flask connected through a spray trap to a condenser, the end of which dips beneath the surface of 10 ml. of 0.1N hydrochloric acid. Add to the flask 20 ml. of freshly boiled 10 per cent sodium hydroxide reagent solution, distill 35 to 40 ml., and dilute the cooled distillate to 50 ml. To 5 ml. of the distillate add 1 ml. of the freshly boiled sodium hydroxide solution, dilute to 50 ml., and add 2 ml. of Nessler reagent. Any color should not exceed that produced by 0.01 mg. of ammonium ion (NH_4) in an equal volume of solution containing 1 ml. of the sodium hydroxide solution and 2 ml. of Nessler reagent.

Heavy metals. Dissolve 1 gram of the sample and 30 mg. of mercuric chloride in 40 ml. of water. Add 15 ml. of hydrogen sulfide water, stir, and allow to stand for 30 minutes. Filter and wash thoroughly with hydrogen sulfide water containing 1 per cent of potassium sulfate. Ignite the precipitate at low temperature in a small porcelain dish in a well ventilated hood to char the paper, then at 525° ± 25°C. for 30 minutes. To the residue add 1 ml. of hydrochloric acid, 1 ml. of nitric acid, and about 30 mg. of sodium carbonate, and evaporate to dryness on the steam bath. Dissolve the residue in about 20 ml. of water and dilute to 100 ml. For the sample dilute a 20-ml. aliquot of this solution to 25 ml. For the standard dilute a solution containing 0.02 mg. of lead ion (Pb) to 25 ml. Adjust the pH of the standard and sample solutions to between 3 and 4 (using a pH meter) with $1N$ acetic acid or ammonium hydroxide (10 per cent NH_3), dilute to 40 ml., and mix. Add 10 ml. of freshly prepared hydrogen sulfide water to each and mix. Any color in the solution of the sample should not exceed that in the standard.

Iron. Wash with hot water the residue remaining on the filter in the test for *Aluminum* until the washings are colorless. Dissolve the residue from the filter with 5 ml. of dilute hydrochloric acid $(1 + 1)$ and wash the filter paper with hot water. Cool, dilute to 80 ml., and mix. To 2 ml. of the solution add 2 ml. of hydrochloric acid, dilute to 50 ml., and add 30 to 50 mg. of ammonium persulfate crystals and 3 ml. of ammonium thiocyanate reagent solution. Any red color should not exceed that produced by 0.01 mg. of iron (Fe) in an equal volume of solution containing the quantities of reagents used in the test.

Notes

Chromium Trioxide

CrO_3 Formula Wt. 99.99

Caution. Chromium Trioxide should not be brought into intimate contact with organic substances or other reducing agents, as serious explosions are likely to result.

REQUIREMENTS

Assay.   Not less than 98 per cent CrO_3.
Insoluble matter.   Not more than 0.010 per cent.
Chloride (Cl).   Not more than 0.005 per cent.
Nitrate (NO_3).   Not more than 0.05 per cent.
Sulfate (SO_4).   Not more than 0.005 per cent.
Sodium (Na).   Not more than 0.20 per cent.
Iron, aluminum, barium.   Not more than 0.03 per cent.

TESTS

Assay.   Weigh accurately about 5 grams, transfer to a 1-liter volumetric flask, dissolve in water, and dilute to volume. Mix the solution thoroughly, transfer a 25.0-ml. aliquot to a glass-stoppered flask, and dilute with 100 ml. of water. Add 5 ml. of dilute sulfuric acid $(1 + 1)$ and 3 grams of potassium iodide, and allow to stand in the dark for 15 minutes. Dilute with 100 ml. of water and titrate the liberated iodine with $0.1N$ sodium thiosulfate, adding starch indicator solution near the end point. Correct for a complete blank test. One milliliter of $0.1N$ sodium thiosulfate corresponds to 0.003333 gram of CrO_3.

Insoluble matter.   Dissolve 10 grams in 100 ml. of water, heat to boiling, and digest in a covered beaker on the steam bath for 1 hour. Filter through a tared filtering crucible, wash thoroughly, and dry at 105°C. The weight of the residue should not exceed 0.0010 gram.

Chloride.   Dissolve 1 gram in water, filter if necessary through a chloride-free filter, and dilute to 50 ml. To 10-ml. of this solution add 1.5 ml. of ammonium hydroxide and 1 ml. of silver nitrate reagent solution, mix, and add 2 ml. of nitric acid. Any turbidity should not exceed that produced in a standard containing 1 ml. of ammonium hydroxide, 1 ml. of silver nitrate reagent solution, 2 ml. of nitric acid, and 0.01 mg. of added chloride ion (Cl). The comparison is best made by superimposing a tube containing 10 ml. of the sample solution, 1.5 ml. of ammonium hydroxide, and 2 ml. of nitric acid over the tube containing the standard turbidity, and placing a similar tube containing 11 ml. of water, 1 ml. of ammonium hydroxide, and 2 ml. of nitric acid below the tube containing the sample and added reagents. Both turbidities are thus viewed through the same depth and color of solution. The comparison tubes may be machine-made vials, long style, of about 20-ml. capacity.

Nitrate. Dissolve 1.0 gram in 100 ml. of water. To a 10-ml. aliquot add 10 per cent sodium hydroxide reagent solution until the color of the solution just turns to light yellow, then add 0.15 ml. of glacial acetic acid to change the color to orange. Slowly add this solution to a solution of 0.5 gram of lead acetate dissolved in 30 ml. of water. Warm to about 50°C., digest for 15 minutes with occasional stirring, and dilute to 100 ml. Allow the precipitate to settle and decant about 40 ml. through a filter. *This solution must be clear and colorless.* (**Note.** Two filter papers may be required to obtain a clear, colorless filtrate. Use a Nessler tube to check.)

Sample Solution A. To 20 ml. of the filtrate add 10 per cent sodium hydroxide reagent solution until it is slightly alkaline and evaporate to 5 ml. Transfer to a centrifuge tube and dilute to 50 ml. with brucine sulfate reagent solution.

Control Solution B. To 20 ml. of the filtrate add 1 ml. of the standard nitrate solution containing 0.01 mg. of nitrate ion (NO_3) per ml. Add 10 per cent sodium hydroxide reagent solution until it is alkaline and evaporate to 5 ml. Transfer to a centrifuge tube and dilute to 50 ml. with brucine sulfate reagent solution.

Blank Solution C. Dissolve 0.1 gram of lead acetate in 5 ml. of water, transfer to a centrifuge tube, and dilute to 50 ml. with brucine sulfate reagent solution.

Heat the three solutions in a preheated (boiling) water bath for 10 minutes. Cool rapidly in an ice bath to room temperature, centrifuge for 10 minutes, and decant the clear solutions. Set a spectrophotometer at 410 mμ and, using 1-cm. cells, adjust the instrument to read 0 absorbance with Blank Solution C in the light path, then determine the absorbance of Sample Solution A. Adjust the instrument to read 0 absorbance with Sample Solution A in the light path and determine the absorbance of Control Solution B. The absorbance of Sample Solution A should not exceed that of Control Solution B.

Sulfate. Dissolve 10 grams in 350 ml. of water and add 5 grams of sodium carbonate. Heat to boiling and add 35 ml. of a solution containing 1 gram of barium chloride and 2 ml. of hydrochloric acid in 100 ml. of solution. Digest in a covered beaker on the steam bath for 2 hours and allow to stand overnight. If a precipitate is formed, filter, wash thoroughly, and ignite. Fuse the ignited precipitate with 1 gram of sodium carbonate. Extract the fused mass with water and filter out the insoluble residue. Add 5 ml. of hydrochloric acid to the filtrate, dilute to about 200 ml., heat to boiling, and add 10 ml. of alcohol. Digest on the steam bath until the reduction of chromate is complete, as indicated by the change to a clear green or colorless solution. Neutralize the solution with ammonium hydroxide and add 2 ml. of hydrochloric acid. Heat to boiling and add 10 ml. of barium chloride reagent solution. Digest in a covered beaker on the steam bath for 2 hours and allow to stand overnight. Filter, wash thoroughly, and ignite. The weight of the precipitate should not be more than 0.0012 gram greater than the weight obtained in a complete blank test.

Sodium. Determine the sodium by the flame photometric method described on page 14. Dissolve 10 grams in 80 ml. of water and digest in a covered beaker on the steam bath for 20 minutes. Cool and dilute to 100 ml. with water.

Sample Solution A. Dilute a 10-ml. aliquot of this solution to 100 ml. with water.

Control Solution B. Add 2.0 mg. of sodium ion (Na) to another 10-ml. aliquot of the same solution and dilute to 100 ml. with water.

Observe the emission of Control Solution B at the 589-mμ sodium line. Observe the emission of Sample Solution A at the 589-mμ sodium line and at a wavelength of 580 mμ. The difference (D_1) between the intensities observed for Sample Solution A at 580 mμ and 589 mμ should not exceed the difference (D_2) observed at 589 mμ between Sample Solution A and Control Solution B.

Iron, aluminum, barium. Dissolve 5 grams in 100 ml. of water, and add 10 ml. of ammonium hydroxide and 1 ml. of 30 per cent hydrogen peroxide. Heat the solution to boiling and boil gently for 5 minutes. Cool, filter, and wash the precipitate with water. Dissolve the precipitate in warm dilute hydrochloric acid (1 + 1), catching the filtrate in the original beaker. Dilute the filtrate to about 30 ml., adjust to pH 7 with ammonium hydroxide, and add 0.5 ml. of 30 per cent hydrogen peroxide. Heat the solution to boiling and boil gently for 5 minutes. Cool, filter, and ignite. The weight of the residue should not exceed 0.0015 gram.

Citric Acid, Anhydrous

HOCOCH$_2$C(OH)(COOH)CH$_2$COOH   Formula Wt. 192.13

REQUIREMENTS

Assay.   Not less than 99.5 per cent H$_3$C$_6$H$_5$O$_7$.
Insoluble matter.   Not more than 0.005 per cent.
Residue after ignition.   Not more than 0.020 per cent.
Chloride (Cl).   Not more than 0.001 per cent.
Oxalate (C$_2$O$_4$).   To pass test (limit about 0.05 per cent).
Phosphate (PO$_4$).   Not more than 0.001 per cent.
Sulfate (SO$_4$).   Not more than 0.002 per cent.
Heavy metals (as Pb).   Not more than 0.0002 per cent.
Iron (Fe).   Not more than 0.0003 per cent.
Substances carbonizable by hot sulfuric acid (tartrates, etc.).   To pass test.

TESTS

Assay.   Accurately weigh from 2.56 to 2.88 grams, dissolve in about 40 ml. of water, and add 0.10 ml. of phenolphthalein indicator solution. Titrate with 1N sodium hydroxide to a pink color that persists for 5 minutes. One milliliter of 1N sodium hydroxide corresponds to 0.06404 gram of HOCOCH$_2$C(OH)(COOH)CH$_2$COOH.

Insoluble matter.   Dissolve 20 grams in 150 ml. of water, heat to boiling, and digest in a covered beaker on the steam bath for 1 hour. Filter through a tared filtering crucible, wash thoroughly, and dry at 105°C. The weight of the residue should not exceed 0.0010 gram.

Residue after ignition.   Gently ignite 5 grams in a tared crucible or dish until charred. Cool, moisten the char with 2 ml. of sulfuric acid, and ignite again slowly until all carbon and excess sulfuric acid have been volatilized. Finally, ignite at 800° ± 25°C. for 15 minutes. The weight of the residue should not exceed 0.0010 gram.

Chloride.   Dissolve 1.0 gram in 20 ml. of water, filter if necessary through a chloride-free filter, and add 1 ml. of nitric acid and 1 ml. of silver nitrate reagent solution. Any turbidity should not exceed that produced by 0.01 mg. of chloride ion (Cl) in an equal volume of solution containing the quantities of reagents used in the test.

Oxalate.   Dissolve 5 grams in 25 ml. of water and add 2 ml. of 10 per cent calcium acetate solution. No turbidity or precipitate should appear after standing 4 hours.

Phosphate. To 4 grams in a 150-ml. beaker add 0.2 ml. of ammonium vanadate solution* and 10 ml. of nitric acid. Digest in a covered beaker on the steam bath until reaction ceases, rinse and remove the watch glass, and evaporate to dryness. Add another 10 ml. of nitric acid, repeat the digestion and evaporation, and dissolve the residue by warming with about 10 ml. of water and 0.05 ml. of nitric acid. Cool and transfer to a 50-ml. Nessler tube. Dilute to about 25 ml. and add in order, mixing between each addition, 5 ml. of nitric acid $(1 + 2)$, 5 ml. of ammonium vanadate solution,* and 5 ml. of ammonium molybdate solution.* Dilute to 50 ml. Any yellow color should not exceed that produced by 0.04 mg. of phosphate ion (PO_4) taken through the entire procedure with the sample. Compare 5 minutes after adding the ammonium molybdate to the sample and standard solutions.**

 * Reagents. 1. Ammonium Vanadate Solution. Dissolve 2.5 grams of ammonium vanadate, NH_4VO_3, in 500 ml. of boiling water, cool, and add 20 ml. of nitric acid. Cool, dilute to 1 liter, and store in a polyethylene bottle.

 2. Ammonium Molybdate Solution. Dissolve 50 grams of ammonium molybdate, $(NH_4)_6Mo_7O_{24}\cdot4H_2O$, in 1 liter of water and store in a polyethylene bottle.

 ** If results are near the limit, the absorbance may be measured at 460 mμ, in 5-cm. cells, using a suitable spectrophotometer. The absorbance of the sample should not exceed that of the standard.

Sulfate. To 3 grams add 0.2 to 0.5 mg. of ammonium vanadate and 10 ml. of nitric acid. Digest in a covered beaker on the steam bath until the reaction ceases, remove the cover, and evaporate to dryness. Add 10 ml. of nitric acid and repeat the digestion and evaporation. Add 5 ml. of dilute hydrochloric acid $(1 + 1)$ and evaporate to dryness. Dissolve the residue in 4 ml. of water plus 1 ml. of dilute hydrochloric acid $(1 + 19)$, filter if necessary through a small filter, wash with two 2-ml. portions of water, and dilute to 10 ml. Add 1 ml. of barium chloride reagent solution. Any turbidity should not exceed that produced by 0.06 mg. of sulfate ion (SO_4) treated in the same manner as the sample. Compare 10 minutes after adding the barium chloride to the sample and standard solutions.

Heavy metals. Dissolve 1.5 grams in 10 ml. of water, adjust the pH to 9 to 10 (using a pH meter) with ammonium hydroxide, and dilute to 15 ml. Prepare a control containing 0.003 mg. of lead ion (Pb) and the amount of ammonium hydroxide required to neutralize the sample and evaporate it to dryness on the steam bath. Moisten the residue from the control with 0.1 ml. of nitric acid, dissolve in 5 ml. of water, and add 5 ml. of ammonium citrate (lead-free) reagent solution. Adjust the pH to 9 to 10 (using a pH meter) with ammonium hydroxide and dilute to 15 ml. Transfer the sample solution and the control solution to separatory funnels, add to each 5 ml. of dithizone standard solution in chloroform, and shake vigorously for 2 minutes. Allow the layers to separate, draw off the dithizone-chloroform layers into clean, dry comparison tubes, and dilute to 10 ml. with chloroform. Any red color, producing a purplish hue in the chloroform from the sample solution, should not exceed that in the chloroform from the control.

Iron.   Dissolve 5 grams in about 40 ml. of water plus 2 ml. of hydrochloric acid, dilute to 50 ml., and add 30 to 50 mg. of ammonium persulfate crystals and 3 ml. of ammonium thiocyanate reagent solution. Any red color should not exceed that produced by 0.015 mg. of iron (Fe) in an equal volume of solution containing the quantities of reagents used in the test.

Substances carbonizable by hot sulfuric acid.   Carefully powder about 1 gram of the sample, taking precautions to prevent contamination during the powdering. Mix 0.30 gram with 10 ml. of sulfuric acid in a test tube previously rinsed with the acid. Heat the mixture at 110°C. (in a brine bath) for 30 minutes, keeping the test tube covered during the heating. Any color should not exceed that produced in a color standard of the following composition: 1 part of cobaltous chloride solution (5.95 grams of $CoCl_2 \cdot 6H_2O$ and 2.5 ml. of hydrochloric acid in 100 ml.), 2.4 parts of ferric chloride solution (4.5 grams of $FeCl_3 \cdot 6H_2O$ and 2.5 ml. of hydrochloric acid in 100 ml.), 0.4 part of cupric sulfate solution (6.24 grams of $CuSO_4 \cdot 5H_2O$ and 2.5 ml. of hydrochloric acid in 100 ml.), and 6.2 parts of water.

Notes

Citric Acid, Monohydrate

HOCOCH$_2$C(OH)(COOH)CH$_2$COOH·H$_2$O   Formula Wt. 210.14

REQUIREMENTS

Insoluble matter.   Not more than 0.005 per cent.
Residue after ignition.   Not more than 0.020 per cent.
Chloride (Cl).   Not more than 0.001 per cent.
Oxalate (C$_2$O$_4$).   To pass test (limit about 0.05 per cent).
Phosphate (PO$_4$).   Not more than 0.001 per cent.
Sulfate (SO$_4$).   Not more than 0.002 per cent.
Heavy metals (as Pb).   Not more than 0.0002 per cent.
Iron (Fe).   Not more than 0.0003 per cent.
Substances carbonizable by hot sulfuric acid (tartrates, etc.).   To pass
test.

TESTS

Insoluble matter.   Dissolve 20 grams in 150 ml. of water, heat to boiling, and digest in a covered beaker on the steam bath for 1 hour. Filter through a tared filtering crucible, wash thoroughly, and dry at 105°C. The weight of the residue should not exceed 0.0010 gram.

Residue after ignition.   Gently ignite 5 grams in a tared crucible or dish until charred. Cool, moisten the char with 2 ml. of sulfuric acid, and ignite again slowly until all carbon and excess sulfuric acid have been volatilized. Finally, ignite at 800° ± 25°C. for 15 minutes. The weight of the residue should not exceed 0.0010 gram.

Chloride.   Dissolve 1.0 gram in 20 ml. of water, filter if necessary through a chloride-free filter, and add 1 ml. of nitric acid and 1 ml. of silver nitrate reagent solution. Any turbidity should not exceed that produced by 0.01 mg. of chloride ion (Cl) in an equal volume of solution containing the quantities of reagents used in the test.

Oxalate.   Dissolve 5 grams in 25 ml. of water and add 2 ml. of 10 per cent calcium acetate solution. No turbidity or precipitate should appear after standing 4 hours.

Phosphate.   To 4 grams in a 150-ml. beaker add 0.2 ml. of ammonium vanadate solution* and 10 ml. of nitric acid. Digest in a covered beaker on the steam bath until reaction ceases, rinse and remove the watch glass, and evaporate to dryness. Add another 10 ml. of nitric acid, repeat the digestion and evaporation, and dissolve the residue by warming with about 10 ml. of water and 0.05 ml. of nitric acid. Cool and transfer to a 50-ml. Nessler tube. Dilute to about 25 ml. and add in order, mixing be-

Instructions: Cut along all dotted lines and tip slips into book, large slip at page 1, bottom slip at page 644.

....

ERRATA
REAGENT CHEMICALS, 4th Edition

Page 219 **Dioxane**

Under **Carbonyl,** change the sentence following **Sample Solution A** to: "Transfer 1.6 ml. of the sample to a 200-ml. volumetric flask."

In the next paragraph, change the last sentence to: "The standards correspond to 0.025 per cent, 0.05 per cent, and 0.10 per cent, respectively."

Page 439 **Potassium Chloride**

Correct misprinted letter:
  Bold face **Blank Solution B** should read **Blank Solution C.**

Page 505 **Sodium Acetate**

Insert omission under **Heavy metals.** Second sentence, end of third line, after "solution."
  Insert "and dilute to 25 ml."

Page 511 **Sodium Bismuthate**

In the 3rd paragraph, next to last line, change "standard oxalic acid" to "standard sodium oxalate."

In the formula for calculating "oxidizing efficiency," the factor, 0.0110, should be 0.00110.

Page 530 **Sodium Chloride**

Insert omission under **Chlorate and nitrate.** Last paragraph, third sentence should read:
  "Set a spectrophotometer at 410 mμ and, using 1-cm. cells, adjust . . ."

....

Page 644 **Zinc Sulfate**

Cut off paragraph below and tip onto page 644 to complete the tests for this reagent:

....

Substances not precipitated by ammonium sulfide. Dissolve 2 grams in 148 ml. of water and pass hydrogen sulfide through the solution until practically all the zinc is precipitated. Add 2 ml. of ammonium hydroxide, pass hydrogen sulfide for 2 or 3 minutes longer, and filter without washing. If the first filtrate is not clear, pass it through the filter a second time. Evaporate 75 ml. of the filtrate nearly to dryness in a tared dish, add 0.50 ml. of sulfuric acid, evaporate, ignite carefully until the ammonium salts are volatilized, and finally ignite at 800° ± 25°C. for 15 minutes. The weight of the residue should not exceed 0.0020 gram.

tween each addition, 5 ml. of nitric acid $(1 + 2)$, 5 ml. of ammonium vanadate solution,* and 5 ml. of ammonium molybdate solution.* Dilute to 50 ml. Any yellow color should not exceed that produced by 0.04 mg. of phosphate ion (PO_4) taken through the entire procedure with the sample. Compare 5 minutes after adding the ammonium molybdate to the sample and standard solutions.**

* **Reagents 1. Ammonium Vanadate Solution.** Dissolve 2.5 grams of ammonium vanadate, NH_4VO_3, in 500 ml. of boiling water, cool, and add 20 ml. of nitric acid. Cool, dilute to 1 liter, and store in a polyethylene bottle.

2. Ammonium Molybdate Solution. Dissolve 50 grams of ammonium molybdate, $(NH_4)_6Mo_7O_{24} \cdot 4H_2O$, in 1 liter of water and store in a polyethylene bottle.

** If results are near the limit, the absorbance may be measured at 460 mμ, in 5-cm. cells, using a suitable spectrophotometer. The absorbance of the sample should not exceed that of the standard.

Sulfate. To 3 grams add 0.2 to 0.5 mg. of ammonium vanadate and 10 ml. of nitric acid. Digest in a covered beaker on the steam bath until the reaction ceases, remove the cover, and evaporate to dryness. Add 10 ml. of nitric acid and repeat the digestion and evaporation. Add 5 ml. of dilute hydrochloric acid $(1 + 1)$ and evaporate to dryness. Dissolve the residue in 4 ml. of water plus 1 ml. of dilute hydrochloric acid $(1 + 19)$, filter if necessary through a small filter, wash with two 2-ml. portions of water, and dilute to 10 ml. Add 1 ml. of barium chloride reagent solution. Any turbidity should not exceed that produced by 0.06 mg. of sulfate ion (SO_4) treated in the same manner as the sample. Compare 10 minutes after adding the barium chloride to the sample and standard solutions.

Heavy metals. Dissolve 1.5 grams in 10 ml. of water, adjust the pH to 9 to 10 (using a pH meter) with ammonium hydroxide, and dilute to 15 ml. Prepare a control containing 0.003 mg. of lead ion (Pb) and the amount of ammonium hydroxide required to neutralize the sample and evaporate it to dryness on the steam bath. Moisten the residue from the control with 0.1 ml. of nitric acid, dissolve in 5 ml. of water, and add 5 ml. of ammonium citrate (lead-free) reagent solution. Adjust the pH to 9 to 10 (using a pH meter) with ammonium hydroxide and dilute to 15 ml. Transfer the sample solution and the control solution to separatory funnels, add to each 5 ml. of dithizone standard solution in chloroform, and shake vigorously for 2 minutes. Allow the layers to separate, draw off the dithizone-chloroform layers into clean, dry comparison tubes, and dilute to 10 ml. with chloroform. Any red color, producing a purplish hue in the chloroform from the sample solution, should not exceed that in the chloroform from the control.

Iron. Dissolve 5 grams in about 40 ml. of water plus 2 ml. of hydrochloric acid, dilute to 50 ml., and add 30 to 50 mg. of ammonium persulfate crystals and 3 ml. of ammonium thiocyanate reagent solution. Any red color should not exceed that produced by 0.015 mg. of iron (Fe) in an equal volume of solution containing the quantities of reagents used in the test.

Substances carbonizable by hot sulfuric acid. Carefully powder about 1 gram of the sample, taking precautions to prevent contamination during the powdering. Mix 0.30 gram with 10 ml. of sulfuric acid in a test tube previously rinsed with the acid. Heat the mixture at 110°C. (in a brine bath) for 30 minutes, keeping the test tube covered during the heating. Any color should not exceed that produced in a color standard of the following composition: 1 part of cobaltous chloride solution (5.95 grams of $CoCl_2 \cdot 6H_2O$ and 2.5 ml. of hydrochloric acid in 100 ml.), 2.4 parts of ferric chloride solution (4.5 grams of $FeCl_3 \cdot 6H_2O$ and 2.5 ml. of hydrochloric acid in 100 ml.), 0.4 part of cupric sulfate solution (6.24 grams of $CuSO_4 \cdot 5H_2O$ and 2.5 ml. of hydrochloric acid in 100 ml.), and 6.2 parts of water.

Notes

Cobalt Chloride

$CoCl_2 \cdot 6H_2O$ Formula Wt. 237.93

REQUIREMENTS

Insoluble matter.   Not more than 0.010 per cent.
Nitrate (NO_3).   Not more than 0.01 per cent.
Sulfate (SO_4).   Not more than 0.010 per cent.
Ammonium (NH_4).   Not more than 0.005 per cent.
Copper (Cu).   Not more than 0.002 per cent.
Iron (Fe).   Not more than 0.005 per cent.
Nickel (Ni).   Not more than 0.10 per cent.
Zinc (Zn).   Not more than 0.03 per cent.
Substances not precipitated by ammonium sulfide (as sulfates).   Not more than 0.25 per cent.

TESTS

Insoluble matter.   Dissolve 10 grams in 100 ml. of water, heat to boiling, and digest in a covered beaker on the steam bath for 1 hour. Filter through a tared filtering crucible, retaining the filtrate without the washings for the test for *Sulfate*. Wash thoroughly and dry at 105°C. The weight of the residue should not exceed 0.0010 gram.

Nitrate.   Dissolve 1 gram in 10 ml. of water. Add this solution in small portions and with constant stirring to 10 ml. of 10 per cent sodium hydroxide reagent solution. Digest in a covered beaker on the steam bath for 15 minutes. Cool, dilute to 20 ml., and filter.

Sample Solution A.   To 4 ml. of the above filtrate add 6 ml. of water. Dilute to 50 ml. with brucine sulfate reagent solution.

Control Solution B.   To 4 ml. of the above filtrate add 4 ml. of water and 2 ml. of the standard nitrate solution containing 0.01 mg. of nitrate ion per ml. Dilute to 50 ml. with brucine sulfate reagent solution.

Blank Solution C.   Use 50 ml. of brucine sulfate reagent solution.

Heat the three solutions in a preheated (boiling) water bath for 10 minutes. Cool rapidly in an ice bath to room temperature. Set a spectrophotometer at 410 mμ and, using 1-cm. cells, adjust the instrument to read 0 absorbance with Blank Solution C in the light path, then determine the absorbance of Sample Solution A. Adjust the instrument to read 0 absorbance with Sample Solution A in the light path and determine the absorbance of Control Solution B. The absorbance of Sample Solution A should not exceed that of Control Solution B.

Sulfate. To the filtrate obtained in the test for *Insoluble matter* add 1 ml. of hydrochloric acid and heat to boiling. Add 10 ml. of barium chloride reagent solution, digest in a covered beaker on the steam bath for 2 hours, and allow to stand overnight. If a precipitate is formed, filter, wash thoroughly, and ignite. The weight of the precipitate should not be more than 0.0024 gram greater than the weight obtained in a complete blank test.

Ammonium. Dissolve 1 gram in 50 ml. of water in a flask connected through a spray trap to a condenser, the end of which dips beneath the surface of 10 ml. of 0.1N hydrochloric acid. Add to the contents of the flask 10 ml. of freshly boiled 10 per cent sodium hydroxide reagent solution. Distill over about 35 ml. and dilute the distillate to 50 ml. To 10 ml. of this solution add 40 ml. of water, 1 ml. of 10 per cent sodium hydroxide reagent solution, and 2 ml. of Nessler reagent. Any color should not exceed that produced when a quantity of an ammonium salt containing 0.05 mg. of ammonium ion (NH_4) is treated exactly like the 1-gram sample, including distillation.

Copper. Dissolve 3 grams in 50 ml. of dilute hydrochloric acid (1 + 25). Prepare a standard containing 0.06 mg. of copper ion (Cu) in 50 ml. of dilute hydrochloric acid (1 + 25). To each solution add 2 ml. of a 1 per cent solution of mercuric chloride and saturate with hydrogen sulfide. Filter through a small filter paper and wash with hydrogen sulfide water until the washings are colorless. Ignite the filters in porcelain crucibles in a well-ventilated hood. Avoid a temperature above 500°C., which might cause fusion of the copper into the glaze of the dish. Dissolve the residues by warming with 1 ml. of dilute nitric acid (1 + 1), dilute to 10 ml., and filter if necessary. To each solution add 5 ml. of a 10 per cent solution of ammonium acetate, 2 ml. of an 8 per cent solution of ammonium thiocyanate, 2 ml. of glacial acetic acid, 0.5 ml. of pyridine, and 10 ml. of chloroform. Shake well, cool in ice water, and allow the layers to separate. Any greenish yellow color in the chloroform layer from the solution of the sample should not exceed that in the chloroform layer from the standard.

Iron. Dissolve 1 gram in 20 ml. of water and add 1 gram of ammonium chloride and enough ammonium hydroxide to dissolve the precipitate first formed. Heat gently to coagulate the precipitate, filter, and wash 2 or 3 times with 2.5 per cent ammonia (NH_3) reagent solution. Dissolve the precipitate from the filter with 5 ml. of hot dilute hydrochloric acid (1 + 1), wash, and dilute to a volume of 30 ml. Heat and repeat the precipitation with ammonium hydroxide. Filter and wash with dilute ammonium hydroxide $(1 + 9)$ until the filtrate is colorless. Dissolve the precipitate in 5 ml. of hot dilute hydrochloric acid $(1 + 1)$, wash thoroughly, cool the filtrate, and dilute to 50 ml. To 10 ml. of this solution add 2 ml. of hydrochloric acid and dilute to 50 ml. Add 30 to 50 mg. of ammonium persulfate crystals and 3 ml. of ammonium thiocyanate reagent solution. Any red color should not exceed that produced by 0.01 mg. of iron (Fe) in an equal volume of solution containing the quantities of reagents used in the test.

Nickel.   Dissolve 1 gram in 25 ml. of water and add 10 ml. of 20 per cent sodium cyanide solution. If the precipitate first formed does not redissolve, add enough more sodium cyanide to dissolve it. Add 0.5 ml. of 30 per cent hydrogen peroxide and evaporate to dryness on the steam bath. Dissolve in 50 ml. of water, filter if necessary, and add 0.1 gram of solid dimethylglyoxime and 5 ml. of 37 per cent formaldehyde solution. Allow to stand for 1 hour, filter, and wash with water. Dissolve the nickel dimethylglyoxime on the filter with 10 ml. of dilute hydrochloric acid $(1 + 1)$ and dilute the solution and washings to 100 ml. Dilute 3 ml. of the solution to 85 ml., add ammonium hydroxide to make the solution slightly alkaline (pH 8), and add 5 ml. of bromine water, 5 ml. of 1 per cent dimethylglyoxime solution in alcohol, and 5 ml. of 10 per cent sodium hydroxide reagent solution. Any red color should not exceed that produced by 0.03 mg. of nickel (Ni) in an equal volume of solution containing the quantities of reagents used in the test.

Zinc.   Dissolve 1 gram in 20 ml. of water. Add this solution to 40 ml. of 5 per cent sodium hydroxide reagent solution which has been heated. Heat the resulting mixture to boiling and boil gently for 10 minutes. Cool to room temperature, dilute with water to 100 ml., and filter. Acidify 10 ml. of the filtrate with hydrochloric acid and evaporate to dryness on the steam bath. Moisten the residue with 0.05 to 0.10 ml. of hydrochloric acid, dissolve in water, and dilute to 20 ml. Transfer 10 ml. of this solution to a small separatory funnel. Prepare a standard containing 0.015 mg. of zinc ion (Zn) in 10 ml. of water in a second separatory funnel. To each add 5 ml. of acetate buffer solution (65 grams of sodium acetate and 35 ml. of acetic acid in a volume of 250 ml.) and 1 ml. of a 25 per cent solution of sodium thiosulfate. Mix well and, if necessary, adjust the pH to 4.5 to 4.7 (using a pH meter) with more of the acetate buffer. Add 5 ml. of dithizone standard solution in carbon tetrachloride, shake well for 2 minutes, and draw off the carbon tetrachloride layers. Repeat the extraction with 5-ml. portions of the dithizone standard solution until the last portion remains unchanged in color after shaking for 2 minutes. Combine the extracts and dilute with dithizone standard solution to a definite volume. Transfer 10 ml. of each solution to separatory funnels. Wash with 5-ml. portions of 0.1 per cent sodium sulfide wash solution until the last portion of the wash solution remains colorless. Any pink color in the carbon tetrachloride extract from the sample should not exceed that in the extract from the standard.

Substances not precipitated by ammonium sulfide. Dissolve 2 grams in 20 ml. of water. Add 1 gram of ammonium chloride and 5 ml. of ammonium hydroxide, dilute to 90 ml., and pass in hydrogen sulfide until all the cobalt is precipitated. Add sufficient water to make the total volume 100 ml., mix well, and filter. Evaporate 50 ml. of the clear filtrate nearly to dryness in a tared dish. Cool, add 0.05 ml. of sulfuric acid, and ignite carefully to volatilize the excess salts and acids. Finally, ignite at $800° \pm 25°$C. for 15 minutes. The weight of the residue should not exceed 0.0025 gram.

Notes

Cobalt Nitrate

Co(NO$_3$)$_2$·6H$_2$O   Formula Wt. 291.04

REQUIREMENTS

Insoluble matter.   Not more than 0.010 per cent.
Chloride (Cl).   Not more than 0.002 per cent.
Sulfate (SO$_4$).   Not more than 0.005 per cent.
Ammonium (NH$_4$).   Not more than 0.20 per cent.
Copper (Cu).   Not more than 0.002 per cent.
Iron (Fe).   Not more than 0.001 per cent.
Nickel (Ni).   Not more than 0.15 per cent.
Substances not precipitated by ammonium sulfide (as sulfates).   Not more than 0.25 per cent.

TESTS

Insoluble matter.   Dissolve 10 grams in 100 ml. of water, heat to boiling, and digest in a covered beaker on the steam bath for 1 hour. Filter through a tared filtering crucible, wash thoroughly, and dry at 105°C. The weight of the residue should not exceed 0.0010 gram.

Chloride.   Dissolve 0.5 gram in 15 ml. of water plus 1 ml. of nitric acid, filter if necessary through a small chloride-free filter, and add 1 ml. of silver nitrate reagent solution. Any turbidity should not exceed that produced by 0.01 mg. of chloride ion (Cl) in an equal volume of solution containing the quantities of reagents used in the test. The comparison is best made by superimposing a tube containing 0.5 gram of sample in 17 ml. of water over the tube containing the standard turbidity and placing a tube containing 17 ml. of water below the tube containing the sample and added reagents. Both turbidities are thus viewed through the same depth and color of solution. The comparison tubes may be machine-made vials, long style, of about 20-ml. capacity.

Sulfate.   Dissolve 10 grams in 40 ml. of dilute hydrochloric acid (1 + 1) and evaporate to dryness on the steam bath. Dissolve the residue in 30 ml. of dilute hydrochloric acid (1 + 1) and again evaporate to dryness. Dissolve the residue in 100 ml. of water plus 1 ml. of hydrochloric acid and filter. Heat the filtrate to boiling, add 10 ml. of barium chloride reagent solution, digest in a covered beaker on the steam bath for 2 hours, and allow to stand overnight. If a precipitate is formed, filter, wash thoroughly, and ignite. The weight of the precipitate should not be more than 0.0012 gram greater than the weight obtained in a complete blank test.

Ammonium. Dissolve 1 gram in 50 ml. of water in a flask connected through a spray trap to a condenser, the end of which dips beneath the surface of 10 ml. of 0.1N hydrochloric acid. Add to the contents of the flask 10 ml. of freshly boiled 10 per cent sodium hydroxide reagent solution. Distill over about 45 ml. and dilute the distillate to 100 ml. To 5 ml. of this solution add 45 ml. of water, 1 ml. of 10 per cent sodium hydroxide reagent solution, and 2 ml. of Nessler reagent. Any color should not exceed that produced when a quantity of an ammonium salt containing 2.0 mg. of ammonium ion (NH_4) is treated exactly like the 1-gram sample.

Copper. Dissolve 5 grams in 130 ml. of dilute hydrochloric acid (1 + 25). Prepare a standard containing 0.1 mg. of copper ion (Cu) in 130 ml. of dilute hydrochloric acid (1 + 25). To each solution add 2 ml. of a 1 per cent solution of mercuric chloride and saturate with hydrogen sulfide. Filter through small filters and wash with hydrogen sulfide water until the washings are colorless. Ignite the filters and precipitates in porcelain in a well-ventilated hood. Avoid a temperature above 500°C., which might cause fusion of copper into the glaze of the dish. Dissolve the residues by warming with 0.5 ml. of nitric acid and a few drops of water. Dilute to 10 ml., filter if necessary, and add 5 ml. of a 10 per cent solution of ammonium acetate, 2 ml. of an 8 per cent solution of ammonium thiocyanate, 2 ml. of glacial acetic acid, 0.5 ml. of pyridine, and 10 ml. of chloroform. Shake well, cool in ice water, and allow to separate. The greenish yellow color in the chloroform layer from the solution of the sample should not exceed that in the standard.

Iron. Dissolve 1 gram in 20 ml. of water and add 1 gram of ammonium chloride and enough ammonium hydroxide to dissolve the precipitate first formed. Boil gently for 5 minutes. Filter and wash 2 or 3 times with dilute ammonium hydroxide (1 + 9). Dissolve the precipitate on the filter with 5 ml. of hot dilute hydrochloric acid (1 + 1) and wash to a volume of 30 ml. Heat and repeat the precipitation with ammonium hydroxide. Filter and wash with 2.5 per cent ammonium hydroxide until the washings are colorless. Dissolve the precipitate in 5 ml. of hot dilute hydrochloric acid (1 + 1), wash thoroughly, cool the filtrate, and dilute to 50 ml. Add 30 to 50 mg. of ammonium persulfate crystals and 3 ml. of ammonium thiocyanate reagent solution. Any red color should not exceed that produced by 0.01 mg. of iron (Fe) in an equal volume of solution containing the quantities of reagents used in the test.

Nickel. Dissolve 1 gram in 25 ml. of water and add 10 ml. of 20 per cent sodium cyanide solution. If the precipitate first formed does not redissolve, add enough more sodium cyanide to effect solution. Add 0.5 ml. of 30 per cent hydrogen peroxide and evaporate to dryness on the steam bath. Dissolve in 50 ml. of water, filter if necessary, and add 0.1 gram of solid dimethylglyoxime and 5 ml. of 37 per cent formaldehyde solution. Allow to stand for 1 hour, filter, and wash with water. Dissolve the nickel dimethylglyoxime on the filter with 10 ml. of dilute hydrochloric acid (1 + 1) and dilute the solution and washings to 100 ml. Dilute 2 ml. of the solution to 85 ml., add ammonium hydroxide to make the solution slightly alkaline (pH 8), and add 5 ml. of bromine water, 5 ml. of 1 per cent dimethylglyoxime in alcohol, and 5 ml. of 10 per cent sodium hydroxide reagent solution. Any red color should not exceed that produced by 0.03 mg. of nickel ion (Ni) in an equal volume of solution containing the quantities of reagents used in the test.

Substances not precipitated by ammonium sulfide. Dissolve 2 grams in 20 ml. of water, add 1 gram of ammonium chloride and 5 ml. of ammonium hydroxide, dilute to 90 ml., and pass in hydrogen sulfide until all the cobalt is precipitated. Add sufficient water to make the total volume 100 ml., mix well, and filter. Evaporate 50 ml. of the filtrate nearly to dryness in a tared dish. Cool, add 0.05 ml. of sulfuric acid, and ignite to volatilize the excess salts and acids. Finally, ignite at 800° ± 25°C. for 15 minutes. The weight of the residue should not exceed 0.0025 gram.

Notes

Copper

Cu

Atomic Wt. 63.546

REQUIREMENTS

Assay.   Not less than 99.90 per cent Cu.
Insoluble in dilute nitric acid.   Not more than 0.020 per cent.
Antimony and tin (as Sn).   Not more than 0.01 per cent.
Arsenic (As).   Not more than 0.0005 per cent.
Iron (Fe).   Not more than 0.005 per cent.
Lead (Pb).   Not more than 0.005 per cent.
Manganese (Mn).   Not more than 0.001 per cent.
Phosphorus (P).   Not more than 0.001 per cent.
Silver (Ag).   To pass test (limit about 0.002 per cent).

TESTS

Assay.   Accurately weigh from 5.0050 to 5.0070 grams of the sample and transfer this weighed sample to a tall-form lipless beaker provided with a close-fitting cover glass. Add 42 ml. of a solution which contains 10 ml. of sulfuric acid plus 7 ml. of nitric acid and 25 ml. of water, cover, and allow to stand until the active reactions have subsided. Heat at 80° to 90°C. until the copper is completely dissolved and brown nitrous fumes are completely expelled. Wash down the cover glass and the sides of the beaker and dilute the solution sufficiently with water so that it will cover a cathode cylinder. Insert a tared cathode and an anode and electrolyze at a current density of about 0.6 ampere per sq. dm. for about 16 hours. If electrolysis of the copper is not completed, as indicated by copper plating on a new surface of the cathode stem when the level of the solution is raised, continue the electrolysis until all the copper is deposited. When all of the copper is deposited, slowly lower the beaker, without interrupting the current, and wash the electrodes continuously with a stream of water from a wash bottle while removing the beaker. Reserve this solution for preparing Sample Solution A. Rinse the electrodes by raising and lowering a beaker of water around them. Remove the beaker of rinse water, discontinue the current, and remove the electrodes. Wash the cathode in acetone and dry it in an oven at 110°C. for 3 to 5 minutes. Cool, weigh, and calculate the percentage of copper from the weight of the deposit. This value may have to be corrected for a small amount of undeposited copper as determined in preparing Sample Solution A.

Sample Solution A.   Place the anode in a 150-ml. beaker and add 10 ml. of dilute nitric acid $(1 + 1)$ containing 0.20 ml. of alcohol. Heat for 5 minutes on the steam bath, rotating the anode so that any deposit is dissolved in the dilute nitric acid. Remove the anode and wash it with a stream of water. Add this solution and washings to the electrolyte from which the copper was deposited. Evaporate the electrolyte to fumes of sulfur trioxide and continue until the volume is reduced to approximately 5 ml. Cool, add 50 ml. of water, cool, and transfer the solution to a 100-ml. volumetric flask. Dilute to 100 ml. and mix (1 ml. = 0.05 gram).

To 20 ml. of Sample Solution A (1-gram sample) add an excess of ammonium hydroxide. If the presence of copper is indicated by a blue color, determine the amount colorimetrically, calculate the amount in Sample Solution A, and add to the amount determined electrolytically. Retain the remainder of Sample Solution A for succeeding tests.

Insoluble in dilute nitric acid. Dissolve 30 grams in 200 ml. of dilute nitric acid (1 + 1) and dilute to 225 ml. Filter through a tared filtering crucible, and reserve the filtrate separate from the washings (Sample Solution B). Wash thoroughly with hot water and dry at 105°C. The weight of the insoluble residue should not exceed 0.0060 gram. Retain Sample Solution B for the *Silver* test.

Antimony and tin. Dissolve 4 grams in 35 ml. of dilute nitric acid (1 + 1) in a 150-ml. beaker and evaporate to 6 to 10 ml. Dilute to 30 ml. with water and digest on the steam bath for 15 minutes. Any insoluble residue should not be greater than that obtained when a control solution containing 0.4 mg. of tin ion (Sn) dissolved in 35 ml. of dilute nitric acid (1 + 1) is treated exactly like the 4 grams of the sample.

Arsenic. Dissolve 0.5 gram in 10 ml. of dilute nitric acid (1 + 1). When dissolution is complete, cool, add 5 ml. of arsenic-free sulfuric acid, and evaporate to fumes of sulfur trioxide. Cautiously add 5 ml. of water and again evaporate to fumes of sulfur trioxide. Cautiously dilute with 25 ml. of water and test for arsenic by the Gutzeit method (page 11). Any stain should not be greater than the stain produced by 0.0025 mg. of arsenic (As) and the residue from evaporation of 10 ml. of the dilute nitric acid.

Iron. Dissolve 1 gram in 10 ml. of dilute nitric acid (1 + 1) and boil until free of brown oxides of nitrogen. Dilute to 20 ml., and pour slowly, with constant stirring, into a mixture of 10 ml. of ammonium hydroxide and 20 ml. of water. Digest on the steam bath to coagulate any precipitate. Filter and wash with water containing 2.5 per cent ammonia until the washings are colorless. Dissolve the precipitate on the filter paper in 20 ml. of dilute hydrochloric acid (1 + 1) and dilute to 50 ml. Dilute

10 ml. of the solution to 50 ml. and add 30 to 50 mg. of ammonium per-sulfate crystals and 3 ml. of ammonium thiocyanate reagent solution. Any red color should not exceed that produced by 0.01 mg. of iron (Fe) in an equal volume of solution containing the quantities of reagents used in the test.

Lead.   Dilute 1 ml. of Sample Solution A (0.05-gram sample) to 20 ml. Prepare a standard containing 0.0025 mg. of lead ion (Pb) in 20 ml. To each solution in a separatory funnel add 4 ml. of ammonia-cyanide, lead-free, reagent solution (**Caution.** *Use hood*) and 5 ml. of dithizone stand-ard solution in chloroform, and shake for half a minute. Drain the dithi-zone extracts into clean, dry comparison tubes and observe the color over a white background. The color in the sample solution should be of no deeper shade of violet than in the standard.

Manganese.   To 20 ml. of Sample Solution A (1-gram sample) add 8 ml. of dilute sulfuric acid (1 + 1). For the standard add 0.01 mg. of manganese ion (Mn) to 25 ml. of dilute sulfuric acid (1 + 4). To each solution add 10 ml. of nitric acid and 5 ml. of phosphoric acid, dilute to 50 ml., transfer to a 150-ml. beaker, and heat to boiling. Boil gently for 5 minutes, cool slightly, and add 0.25 gram of potassium periodate. Again boil gently for 5 minutes, cool, and dilute to 50 ml. Any pink color in the solution of the sample should not exceed that in the stand-ard.

To make the color comparison with a photometer, transfer suitable portions of the solution of the sample to two absorption cells. To one cell add 0.10 ml. of mercurous nitrate solution [5 grams of mercurous nitrate dissolved in 100 ml. of dilute nitric acid (1 + 9) and filtered, if necessary]. Use this cell as the 100 per cent transmittancy blank and measure the transmittancy of the solution in the other cell. Compare the transmittancy with that of the manganese standard, the measurements being made at approximately 520 mμ.

Phosphorus.   Dilute 10 ml. of Sample Solution A (0.5-gram sample) to 25 ml., add 1 ml. of ammonium molybdate reagent solution and 1 ml. of *p*-methylaminophenol sulfate reagent solution, and allow to stand at room temperature for 2 hours. Any blue color should not exceed that produced by 1.5 ml. of phosphate standard solution (0.005 mg. of P) in 25 ml. of approximately 0.5N sulfuric acid when treated with the re-agents used with the 25-ml. dilution of the 10 ml. of Sample Solution A.

Silver.   Dilute 7.5 ml. of Sample Solution B to 30 ml. and add 1 ml. of dilute hydrochloric acid (1 + 3). No turbidity should be produced.

Cupferron

Ammonium Salt of Nitrosophenylhydroxylamine

$C_6H_5N \cdot NO \cdot ONH_4$ Formula Wt. 155.16

Note. Packages of this reagent usually contain a lump or a small cloth-wrapped package of ammonium carbonate as a preservative.

REQUIREMENTS

Appearance. To pass test.
Solubility in water. To pass test.
Residue after ignition. Not more than 0.050 per cent.
Suitability for precipitation of iron, etc. To pass test.

TESTS

Appearance. The material should consist of crystalline flakes, white to light buff in color. It should be free flowing and contain no tarry matter.

Solubility in water. Dissolve 5 grams in 100 ml. of water. The solution should be practically clear and have no more than a pale yellow color.

Residue after ignition. Decompose 5 grams in a tared platinum dish by means of an infrared lamp placed above the sample. Cool, moisten the residue with 1 ml. of sulfuric acid, and heat gently to remove the sulfuric acid. Finally, ignite at 800° ± 25°C. for 15 minutes. The weight of the residue should not exceed 0.0025 gram.

Suitability for precipitation of iron, etc. Accurately weigh about 3 grams, dissolve in water, and dilute to 100 ml. Prepare a ferric chloride solution containing approximately 0.000826 gram of iron (Fe) per ml. [Dissolve about 4 grams of ferric chloride hexahydrate in 1 liter of dilute hydrochloric acid (1 + 99).] To 40 ml. of the iron solution add 20 ml. of hydrochloric acid and 75 ml. of water. Cool in an ice bath for about 15 minutes and add, from a buret, with constant stirring, 14.0 ml. of the cupferron solution. Allow to stand for 15 minutes at room temperature and filter. (The addition of a small amount of filter paper pulp to the solution prior to filtration aids in obtaining a clear filtrate.) To the filtrate add 2 ml. of the cupferron solution. No further precipitate of the brown iron compound should form. (A colorless precipitate of the acid form of the reagent may appear.)

Cupric Acetate

$(CH_3COO)_2Cu \cdot H_2O$ Formula Wt. 199.65

REQUIREMENTS

Insoluble matter. Not more than 0.010 per cent.
Chloride (Cl). Not more than 0.003 per cent.
Sulfate (SO_4). Not more than 0.010 per cent.
Substances not precipitated by hydrogen sulfide (as sulfates). Not more than 0.20 per cent.
Iron (Fe). Not more than 0.002 per cent.
Ammonium sulfide metals other than iron. To pass test (limit about 0.01 per cent as Ni).

TESTS

Insoluble matter. Dissolve 10 grams in 150 ml. of water containing 1 ml. of glacial acetic acid, heat to boiling, and digest in a covered beaker on the steam bath for 1 hour. Filter through a tared filtering crucible, and reserve the filtrate without the washings for the *Sulfate* test. Wash thoroughly, rejecting the washings, and dry the residue at 105°C. The weight of the residue should not exceed 0.0010 gram.

Chloride. Dissolve 0.5 gram in 15 ml. of water, filter if necessary through a small chloride-free filter, and add 1 ml. of nitric acid and 1 ml. of silver nitrate reagent solution. Any turbidity should not exceed that produced by 0.015 mg. of chloride ion (Cl) in an equal volume of solution containing the quantities of reagents used in the test. The comparison is best made by superimposing a tube containing 0.5 gram of sample in 17 ml. of water over the tube containing the standard turbidity and placing a tube containing 17 ml. of water below the tube containing the sample and added reagents. Both turbidities are thus viewed through the same depth and color of solution. The comparison tubes may be machine-made vials, long style, of about 20-ml. capacity.

Sulfate. To the filtrate from the test for *Insoluble matter* add 5 ml. of glacial acetic acid, heat to boiling, add 5 ml. of barium chloride reagent solution, digest in a covered beaker on the steam bath for 2 hours, and allow to stand overnight. If any precipitate is formed, filter, wash thoroughly, and ignite. The weight of the precipitate should not be more than 0.0025 gram greater than the weight of the precipitate obtained in a complete blank test.

Substances not precipitated by hydrogen sulfide. Dissolve 5 grams in about 200 ml. of water. Add 2 ml. of sulfuric acid, heat to about 70°C., and pass hydrogen sulfide through the solution until the copper is completely precipitated. Dilute to 250 ml., mix, allow to settle, and filter without washing. Evaporate 200 ml. of the filtrate to dryness in a tared dish and ignite the residue at 800° ± 25°C. for 15 minutes. The weight of the residue should not exceed 0.0080 gram. Reserve the residue for preparing Sample Solution A.

Sample Solution A.   To the residue obtained in the preceding test add 3 ml. of dilute hydrochloric acid (1 + 1) and 0.10 ml. of nitric acid, cover with a watch glass, and digest on the steam bath for 15 to 20 minutes. Remove the watch glass and evaporate to dryness. Dissolve in 1 ml. of hydrochloric acid and dilute to 40 ml. (1 ml. = 0.1 gram).

Iron.   To 5 ml. of Sample Solution A (0.5-gram sample) add 2 ml. of hydrochloric acid, dilute to 50 ml., and add 30 to 50 mg. of ammonium persulfate crystals and 3 ml. of ammonium thiocyanate reagent solution. Any red color should not exceed that produced by 0.01 mg. of iron (Fe) in an equal volume of solution containing the quantities of reagents used in the test.

Ammonium sulfide metals other than iron.   To 10 ml. of Sample Solution A (1-gram sample) add a slight excess of ammonium hydroxide, boil for 1 minute, filter, and wash with a small quantity of hot water. Dilute the filtrate and washings to 25 ml. Adjust the pH of 5 ml. of this solution to 7 (using a pH meter) with dilute hydrochloric acid (1 + 19), and dilute to 20 ml. Add 0.10 ml. of ammonium hydroxide and 1 ml. of hydrogen sulfide water. Any darkening of the solution should not be greater than is produced by 0.02 mg. of nickel ion (Ni) in an equal volume of solution containing the quantities of reagents used in the test.

Notes

Cupric Ammonium Chloride

$CuCl_2 \cdot 2NH_4Cl \cdot 2H_2O$ Formula Wt. 277.46

REQUIREMENTS

Insoluble matter. Not more than 0.005 per cent.
Free acid. To pass test.
Nitrate (NO_3). To pass test (limit about 0.005 per cent).
Sulfate (SO_4). Not more than 0.010 per cent.
Substances not precipitated by hydrogen sulfide (as sulfates). Not more than 0.15 per cent.
Iron (Fe). Not more than 0.005 per cent.

TESTS

Insoluble matter. Dissolve 20 grams in 200 ml. of water, heat to boiling, and digest in a covered beaker on the steam bath for 1 hour. Filter through a tared filtering crucible, wash thoroughly, and dry at 105°C. The weight of the residue should not exceed 0.0010 gram. Retain the filtrate for the test for *Sulfate*.

Free acid. Dissolve 4 grams in 100 ml. of water and add 0.20 ml. of methyl orange indicator solution. Divide the solution into two equal portions. Upon adding 0.2 ml. of 0.1N sodium hydroxide to one portion the purplish color should disappear.

Nitrate. To 2 grams in 10 ml. of water, in an Erlenmeyer flask, add 10 ml. of 20 per cent sodium hydroxide solution. Bring the solution to a boil and boil to remove all ammonia, constantly rotating the flask over a small flame to avoid bumping. Filter and add to the cooled filtrate 0.10 ml. of indigo carmine reagent solution and 10 ml. of sulfuric acid. The blue color should persist at least 5 minutes.

Sulfate. To the filtrate from the test for *Insoluble matter* add 2 ml. of hydrochloric acid, heat to boiling, add 10 ml. of barium chloride reagent solution, digest in a covered beaker on the steam bath for 2 hours, and allow to stand overnight. If a precipitate is formed, filter, wash thoroughly, and ignite. The weight of the precipitate should not be more than 0.0050 gram greater than the weight obtained in a complete blank test.

Substances not precipitated by hydrogen sulfide. Dissolve 2 grams in 100 ml. of water. Add 1 ml. of sulfuric acid, heat to about 70°C., and pass hydrogen sulfide through the solution until the copper is completely precipitated. Allow the precipitate to settle and filter without washing.

Evaporate 50 ml. of the filtrate to dryness in a tared dish and ignite at 800° ± 25°C. for 15 minutes. The weight of the residue should not exceed 0.0015 gram.

Iron. To the residue obtained in the preceding test add 3 ml. of dilute hydrochloric acid (1 +1), cover with a watch glass, and digest on the steam bath for 15 to 20 minutes. Remove the watch glass and evaporate to dryness. Dissolve the residue in 1 ml. of hydrochloric acid and dilute to 50 ml. To 10 ml. of the solution add 2 ml. of hydrochloric acid and dilute to 50 ml. Add 30 to 50 mg. of ammonium persulfate crystals and 3 ml. of ammonium thiocyanate reagent solution. Any red color should not exceed that produced by 0.01 mg. of iron (Fe) in an equal volume of solution containing the quantities of reagents used in the test.

Notes

Cupric Nitrate

Cu(NO$_3$)$_2$·3H$_2$O   Formula Wt. 241.60

REQUIREMENTS

Insoluble matter.   Not more than 0.010 per cent.
Chloride (Cl).   Not more than 0.002 per cent.
Sulfate (SO$_4$).   Not more than 0.010 per cent.
Substances not precipitated by hydrogen sulfide (as sulfates).   Not more than 0.05 per cent.
Lead (Pb).   Not more than 0.001 per cent.
Iron (Fe).   Not more than 0.005 per cent.
Ammonium sulfide metals other than iron.   To pass test (limit about 0.01 per cent as Ni).

TESTS

Insoluble matter.   Dissolve 10 grams in 100 ml. of dilute nitric acid (1 + 200), heat to boiling, and digest in a covered beaker on the steam bath for 1 hour. Filter through a tared filtering crucible, wash thoroughly, and dry at 105°C. The weight of the residue should not exceed 0.0010 gram.

Chloride.   Dissolve 0.5 gram in 15 ml. of dilute nitric acid (1 + 15), filter if necessary through a small chloride-free filter, and add 1 ml. of silver nitrate reagent solution. Any turbidity should not exceed that produced by 0.01 mg. of chloride ion (Cl) in an equal volume of solution containing the quantities of reagents used in the test. The comparison is best made by superimposing a tube containing 0.5 gram of sample in 17 ml. of water over the tube containing the standard turbidity and placing a tube containing 17 ml. of water below the tube containing the sample and added reagents. Both turbidities are thus viewed through the same depth and color of solution. The comparison tubes may be machine-made vials, long style, of about 20-ml. capacity.

Sulfate.   Dissolve 5 grams in 15 ml. of hot dilute hydrochloric acid (2 + 1) and evaporate to dryness on the steam bath. Dissolve the residue in about 15 ml. of hot dilute hydrochloric acid (2 + 1), and again evaporate to dryness. Dissolve the residue in 100 ml. of dilute hydrochloric acid (1 + 99) and filter. Heat to boiling, add 5 ml. of barium chloride reagent solution, digest in a covered beaker on the steam bath for 2 hours, and allow to stand overnight. If a precipitate is formed, filter, wash thoroughly, and ignite. The weight of the precipitate should not be more than 0.0012 gram greater than the weight obtained in a complete blank test.

Substances not precipitated by hydrogen sulfide. Dissolve 4 grams in about 190 ml. of dilute sulfuric acid (1 + 95), heat to about 70°C., and pass in hydrogen sulfide until all the copper is precipitated. Dilute to 200 ml. and filter. Evaporate 150 ml. of the filtrate to dryness in a tared dish and ignite. The weight of the residue should not exceed 0.0015 gram. Reserve the residue for the preparation of Sample Solution A.

Lead. *In a well ventilated hood* dissolve 1.5 grams in 50 ml. of dilute nitric acid (1 + 99) in a glass-stoppered cylinder. Prepare a control containing 0.5 gram of sample and 0.01 mg. of lead ion (Pb) in 50 ml. of dilute nitric acid (1 + 99) in a glass-stoppered cylinder. To each solution add 2 ml. of hydroxylamine hydrochloride reagent solution for dithizone test. Add ammonium hydroxide *dropwise* until a permanent precipitate forms, shaking well after the addition of each drop. Add 5 ml. of ammonium citrate reagent solution and 25 ml. of potassium cyanide reagent solution. Cool in ice water for 15 minutes. To each add 3 ml. of dithizone standard reagent solution in chloroform, shake for 2 minutes, and allow the layers to separate. Any pink color of the chloroform layer from the solution of the sample should not exceed that of the chloroform layer from the control.

> **Sample Solution A.** To the residue obtained in the test for *Substances not precipitated by hydrogen sulfide* add 3 ml. of dilute hydrochloric acid (1 + 1) and 0.15 ml. of nitric acid, cover with a watch glass, and digest on the steam bath for 15 to 20 minutes. Remove the watch glass and evaporate to dryness. Dissolve the residue in 1 ml. of hydrochloric acid and dilute to 30 ml. (1 ml. = 0.1 gram).

Iron. To 2 ml. of Sample Solution A (0.2-gram sample) add 2 ml. of hydrochloric acid, dilute to 50 ml., and add 30 to 50 mg. of ammonium persulfate crystals and 3 ml. of ammonium thiocyanate reagent solution. Any red color should not exceed that produced by 0.01 mg. of iron (Fe) in an equal volume of solution containing the quantities of reagents used in the test.

Ammonium sulfide metals other than iron. To 10 ml. of Sample Solution A (1-gram sample) add a slight excess of ammonium hydroxide, boil for 1 minute, filter, and wash with a small quantity of hot water. Dilute the filtrate and washings to 25 ml. Adjust the pH of 5 ml. of this solution to 7 (using a pH meter) with dilute hydrochloric acid (1 +19), and dilute to 20 ml. Add 0.10 ml. of ammonium hydroxide and 1 ml. of hydrogen sulfide water. Any color should not exceed that produced by 0.02 mg. of nickel ion (Ni) in an equal volume of solution containing the quantities of reagents used in the test.

Cupric Oxide, Powdered

CuO   Formula Wt. 79.55

REQUIREMENTS

    Insoluble in dilute hydrochloric acid.   Not more than 0.02 per cent.
    Carbon compounds (as C).   Not more than 0.01 per cent.
    Chloride (Cl).   Not more than 0.005 per cent.
    Nitrogen compounds (as N).   Not more than 0.002 per cent.
    Sulfur compounds (as SO_4).   Not more than 0.02 per cent.
    Free alkali.   To pass test.
    Substances not precipitated by hydrogen sulfide (as sulfates).   Not more than 0.20 per cent.
    Ammonium hydroxide precipitate.   Not more than 0.10 per cent.

TESTS

Insoluble in dilute hydrochloric acid. Dissolve 5 grams by warming on the steam bath with 30 ml. of dilute hydrochloric acid (2 + 1). Dilute with about 100 ml. of water, heat to boiling, and digest in a covered beaker on the steam bath for 1 hour. Filter through a tared filtering crucible, wash thoroughly, and dry at 105°C. The weight of the dried residue should not exceed 0.0010 gram.

Carbon compounds. Ignite 1.2 grams in a stream of carbon dioxide–free air or oxygen, and pass the effluent gases into 20 ml. of dilute ammonium hydroxide (2.5 per cent NH_3) plus 2 ml. of water. Prepare a standard of 20 ml. of the dilute ammonium hydroxide and 1.06 mg. of sodium carbonate (Na_2CO_3) (0.12 mg. of C). Add 2 ml. of barium chloride reagent solution to each and compare promptly. Any turbidity in the solution of the sample should not exceed that in the standard.

Chloride. Shake 1 gram with 25 ml. of dilute nitric acid (1 + 3) for 10 minutes, filter through a chloride-free filter and dilute to 50 ml. (Sample Solution A). To 10 ml. of Sample Solution A add 5 ml. of water and 1 ml. of silver nitrate reagent solution. Any turbidity should not exceed that produced by 0.01 mg. of chloride ion (Cl) in an equal volume of solution containing 1 ml. of nitric acid and 1 ml. of silver nitrate reagent solution. The comparison is best made by superimposing a tube containing 10 ml. of Sample Solution A and 6 ml. of water over the tube containing the standard turbidity and placing a tube containing 16 ml. of water below the tube containing the sample turbidity. Both turbidities are thus viewed through the same depth and color of solution.

The comparison tubes may be machine-made vials, long-style, of about 20-ml. capacity.

Nitrogen compounds. Suspend 3 grams in 30 ml. of freshly boiled 10 per cent sodium hydroxide reagent solution, add 0.5 gram of aluminum wire, and allow to stand for 1 hour in a flask which is connected through a spray trap to a condenser, the end of which dips beneath the surface of 10 ml. of 0.1N hydrochloric acid. Add 70 ml. of water to the flask and slowly distill a volume of 60 ml. To 10 ml. of the well mixed distillate add 1 ml. of 10 per cent sodium hydroxide reagent solution, dilute to 50 ml., and add 2 ml. of Nessler reagent. Any color should not exceed that produced when a quantity of an ammonium salt containing 0.06 mg. of nitrogen (N) is treated exactly like the sample.

Sulfur compounds. Dissolve 5 grams in 25 ml. of dilute aqua regia (1 volume of nitric acid plus 4 volumes of hydrochloric acid plus 6 volumes of water) and evaporate to dryness. Dissolve the residue in 100 ml. of dilute hydrochloric acid (1 + 99) and filter. Heat to boiling, add 5 ml. of barium chloride reagent solution, digest in a covered beaker on the steam bath for 2 hours, and allow to stand overnight. If a precipitate is formed, filter, wash thoroughly, and ignite. The weight of the precipitate should not be more than 0.0024 gram greater than the weight obtained in a complete blank test.

Free alkali. Boil gently 3 grams with 30 ml. of water in a flask for 10 minutes. Allow to cool, add water to restore the original volume, mix well, and allow to settle. Decant 20 ml. of the liquid and add 0.10 ml. of phenolphthalein indicator solution. No red color should be produced.

Substances not precipitated by hydrogen sulfide. Dissolve 4 grams by heating with 30 ml. of dilute hydrochloric acid (2 + 1) and dilute to 150 ml. Heat to 70°C., pass in hydrogen sulfide to precipitate the copper completely, and filter, without washing. Evaporate 75 ml. of the filtrate to near dryness in a tared dish. Cool, add 0.25 ml. of sulfuric acid, and heat gently to volatilize the excess acids. Finally, ignite at 800° ± 25°C. for 15 minutes. The weight of the residue should not exceed 0.0040 gram. Reserve the residue.

Ammonium hydroxide precipitate. To the residue obtained in the preceding test add 5 ml. of dilute hydrochloric acid (1 + 1), cover with a watch glass, and digest on the steam bath for 15 to 20 minutes. Dilute with 10 ml. of water, filter through a small filter, wash with two 2-ml. portions of water, dilute to 20 ml., and add a slight excess of ammonium hydroxide. Heat to coagulate the precipitate, filter, wash, and ignite. The weight of the residue should not exceed 0.0020 gram.

Notes

Cupric Oxide, Wire

REQUIREMENTS

Carbon compounds (as C).   Not more than 0.002 per cent.
Nitrogen compounds (as N).   Not more than 0.002 per cent.
Sulfur compounds (as SO_4).   Not more than 0.012 per cent.

TESTS

Carbon compounds.   Ignite 6 grams in a stream of carbon dioxide-free air or oxygen and pass the effluent gases into 20 ml. of dilute ammonium hydroxide (2.5 per cent NH_3) plus 2 ml. of water. Prepare a standard of 20 ml. of the dilute ammonium hydroxide and 1.06 mg. of sodium carbonate (Na_2CO_3) (0.12 mg. of C). Add 2 ml. of barium chloride reagent solution to each and compare promptly. Any turbidity in the solution representing the sample should not exceed that in the standard.

Nitrogen compounds.   Suspend 3 grams in 30 ml. of freshly boiled 10 per cent sodium hydroxide reagent solution in a flask connected through a spray trap to a condenser, the end of which dips beneath the surface of 10 ml. of 0.1N hydrochloric acid. Add to the flask 0.5 gram of aluminum wire, allow to stand for 1 hour, add 70 ml. of water, and slowly distill 60 ml. To 10 ml. of the well mixed distillate add 1 ml. of 10 per cent sodium hydroxide reagent solution, dilute to 50 ml., and add 2 ml. of Nessler reagent. Any color should not exceed that obtained when a quantity of an ammonium salt containing 0.06 mg. of nitrogen (N) is treated exactly like the sample.

Sulfur compounds.   Dissolve 5 grams in 25 ml. of dilute aqua regia (1 volume of nitric acid plus 4 volumes of hydrochloric acid plus 6 volumes of water) and evaporate to dryness. Dissolve the residue in 100 ml. of dilute hydrochloric acid (1 +99) and filter. Heat to boiling, add 5 ml. of barium chloride reagent solution, digest in a covered beaker on the steam bath for 2 hours, and allow to stand overnight. Filter, wash thoroughly, and ignite. The weight of the precipitate should not be more than 0.0015 gram greater than the weight obtained in a complete blank test.

Notes

Cupric Sulfate

$CuSO_4 \cdot 5H_2O$ Formula Wt. 249.68

REQUIREMENTS

Insoluble matter.   Not more than 0.005 per cent.
Chloride (Cl).   Not more than 0.001 per cent.
Nitrogen compounds (as N).   Not more than 0.001 per cent.
Substances not precipitated by hydrogen sulfide (as sulfates).   Not more than 0.10 per cent.
Iron (Fe).   Not more than 0.003 per cent.
Ammonium sulfide metals other than iron.   To pass test (limit about 0.005 per cent as Ni).

TESTS

Insoluble matter.   Dissolve 20 grams in 200 ml. of dilute sulfuric acid $(1 + 40)$, heat to boiling, and digest in a covered beaker on the steam bath for 1 hour. Filter through a tared filtering crucible, wash thoroughly, and dry at 105°C. The weight of the residue should not exceed 0.0010 gram.

Chloride.   Dissolve 1 gram in 15 ml. of water, filter if necessary through a small chloride-free filter, and add 1 ml. of nitric acid and 1 ml. of silver nitrate reagent solution. Any turbidity should not exceed that produced by 0.01 mg. of chloride ion (Cl) in an equal volume of solution containing the quantities of reagents used in the test. The comparison is best made by superimposing a tube containing 1 gram of the sample in 17 ml. of water over the tube containing the standard turbidity and placing a tube containing 17 ml. of water below the tube containing the sample and added reagents. Both turbidities are thus viewed through the same depth and color of solution. The comparison tubes may be machine-made vials, long style, of about 20-ml. capacity.

Nitrogen compounds.   To 2 grams in a flask connected through a spray trap to a condenser, the end of which dips beneath the surface of 10 ml. of 0.1N hydrochloric acid, add 30 ml. of freshly boiled 10 per cent sodium hydroxide reagent solution and 0.5 gram of aluminum wire in small pieces. Allow to stand for 1 hour, add 70 ml. of water, and slowly distill about 35 ml. To the distillate add 1 ml. of 10 per cent sodium hydroxide reagent solution, dilute to 50 ml., and add 2 ml. of Nessler reagent. Any color should not exceed that produced when a quantity of an ammonium salt containing 0.02 mg. of nitrogen (N) is treated exactly like the sample.

Substances not precipitated by hydrogen sulfide. Dissolve 5 grams in 200 ml. of dilute sulfuric acid (1 + 99), heat to about 70°C., and pass hydrogen sulfide through the solution until the copper is completely precipitated. Dilute to 250 ml., mix, allow to settle, and filter without washing. Evaporate 200 ml. of the filtrate to dryness in a tared dish and ignite at 800° ± 25°C. for 15 minutes. The weight of the residue should not exceed 0.0040 gram. Reserve the residue for preparing Sample Solution A.

Sample Solution A. To the residue from the test for *Substances not precipitated by hydrogen sulfide* add 3 ml. of dilute hydrochloric acid (1 + 1) and 0.10 ml. of nitric acid, cover with a watch glass, and digest on the steam bath for 15 to 20 minutes. Remove the watch glass and evaporate to dryness. Dissolve the residue in 1 ml. of hydrochloric acid and dilute to 60 ml. (1 ml. = 0.067 gram).

Iron. Dilute 5 ml. of Sample Solution A (0.34-gram sample) to 50 ml. and add 2 ml. of hydrochloric acid, 30 to 50 mg. of ammonium persulfate crystals, and 3 ml. of ammonium thiocyanate reagent solution. Any red color should not exceed that produced by 0.01 mg. of iron (Fe) in an equal volume of solution containing the quantities of reagents used in the test.

Ammonium sulfide metals other than iron. To a 12-ml. aliquot (0.8-gram sample) of Sample Solution A add a slight excess of ammonium hydroxide, boil for 1 minute, filter, and wash with a small quantity of hot water. Dilute the filtrate and washings to 40 ml. Exactly neutralize 20 ml. of this solution with dilute hydrochloric acid (1 + 9), using an external indicator, and add 0.10 ml. of ammonium hydroxide and 1 ml. of hydrogen sulfide water. Any color should not exceed that produced by 0.02 mg. of nickel ion (Ni) in an equal volume of solution containing the quantities of reagents used in the test.

Notes

Cuprous Chloride

CuCl

Formula Wt. 99.00

REQUIREMENTS

Assay. Not less than 90 per cent CuCl.
Insoluble in acid. Not more than 0.020 per cent.
Sulfate (SO_4). Not more than 0.10 per cent.
Arsenic (As). Not more than 0.001 per cent.
Substances not precipitated by hydrogen sulfide (as sulfates). Not more than 0.20 per cent.
Iron (Fe). Not more than 0.005 per cent.

TESTS

Assay. Dissolve 0.5 gram in the cold in 30 ml. of ferric ammonium sulfate solution made by dissolving 10 grams of ferric ammonium sulfate in 100 ml. of 20 per cent hydrochloric acid reagent solution. Add 5 ml. of phosphoric acid, dilute with 200 ml. of water, and titrate with 0.1N potassium permanganate. The solution should be prepared and titrated in a flask in which the air is replaced with carbon dioxide. A stream of carbon dioxide should be passed through the flask during the titration. One milliliter of 0.1N permanganate corresponds to 0.009900 gram of CuCl.

Insoluble in acid. Heat 5 grams with 50 ml. of dilute hydrochloric acid $(1 + 1)$ and add nitric acid in small portions until the sample is dissolved. Dilute with 50 ml. of water. If insoluble matter is present, filter through a tared filtering crucible, wash thoroughly, and dry at 105°C. The weight of the residue should not exceed 0.0010 gram.

Sample Solution A. Dilute to 200 ml. the combined filtrate and washings from the test for *Insoluble in acid* (1 ml. = 0.025 gram).

Sulfate. Evaporate 80 ml. of Sample Solution A (2-gram sample) to dryness on the water bath. Dissolve the residue with 2 ml. of hydrochloric acid and dilute to 100 ml. Heat to boiling, add 5 ml. of barium chloride reagent solution, digest in a covered beaker on the steam bath for 2 hours, and allow to stand overnight. If a precipitate is formed, filter, wash thoroughly, and ignite. The weight of the precipitate should not be more than 0.0049 gram greater than the weight obtained in a complete blank test.

Arsenic. Add 10 grams to 40 ml. of hydrochloric acid in a 250-ml. distilling flask and distill, receiving the distillate in a 250-ml. Erlenmeyer flask containing 30 ml. of water which is kept cool in an ice bath. When the volume distilled over is about 25 ml., add 20 ml. more of hydrochloric acid and again distill until the volume in the distilling flask is about 15 ml. Dilute the distillate to 250 ml., mix, and take 5 ml. for determination of the arsenic by the Gutzeit method (page 11). The amount of stain should not exceed that produced by 0.002 mg. of arsenic (As).

Substances not precipitated by hydrogen sulfide. Dilute 80 ml. of Sample Solution A (2-gram sample) with 20 ml. of water, heat to about 70°C., and pass in hydrogen sulfide to precipitate the copper. Filter without washing. To 50 ml. of the filtrate (1-gram sample) add 0.25 ml. of sulfuric acid, evaporate to dryness in a weighed dish, and ignite at 800° ± 25°C. for 15 minutes. Reserve the remaining filtrate for the determination of *Iron*. The weight of the residue should not exceed 0.0020 gram.

Iron. Evaporate 10 ml. (0.2-gram sample) of the filtrate reserved from the test for *Substances not precipitated by hydrogen sulfide* to dryness. Dissolve the residue in 50 ml. of dilute hydrochloric acid (1 + 25) and filter if not clear. Add 30 to 50 mg. of ammonium persulfate crystals and 3 ml. of ammonium thiocyanate reagent solution. Any red color should not exceed that produced by 0.01 mg. of iron (Fe) in an equal volume of solution containing the quantities of reagents used in the test.

Notes

Cyclohexane

$CH_2(CH_2)_4CH_2$ Formula Wt. 84.16

REQUIREMENTS

Appearance. Clear.
Color (APHA). Not more than 10.
Odor. Characteristic solvent odor.
Density (grams per ml.) at 25°C. Not less than 0.772 nor more than 0.776.
Boiling range. 1 ml. to 95 ml., not more than 1°C.; 95 ml. to dryness, not more than 1°C.
Residue after evaporation. Not more than 0.002 per cent.
Substances darkened by sulfuric acid. To pass test.
Water (H_2O). Not more than 0.02 per cent.

TESTS

Color (APHA). For the color standard dilute a 2-ml. aliquot of platinum-cobalt stock solution (APHA No. 500) to 100 ml. with water. Compare this solution (APHA No. 10) with 100 ml. of the cyclohexane in 100-ml. Nessler tubes, viewed vertically over a white background.

Boiling range. Distill 100 ml. by the method described on page 12. The difference between the temperatures when 1 ml. and 95 ml. have distilled should not exceed 1°C., and the difference in temperatures when 95 ml. have distilled and the dry point is reached should not exceed 1°C. The boiling point of pure cyclohexane at 760-mm. mercury pressure is 80.7°C.

Residue after evaporation. Evaporate 129 ml. (100 grams) to dryness in a tared dish on the steam bath and dry the residue at 105°C. for 30 minutes. The weight of the residue should not exceed 0.0020 gram.

Substances darkened by sulfuric acid. Shake 25 ml. with 15 ml. of sulfuric acid for 15 to 20 seconds and allow to separate. Neither the cyclohexane nor the acid should be darkened.

Water. Place 25 ml. of methanol in a dry titration flask and add Karl Fischer reagent to a visually or electrometrically determined end point. Add 20 ml. (15.6 grams) of the sample, taking care to protect the sample and contents of the flask from moisture. Stir vigorously and titrate with Karl Fischer reagent to the same end point. Calculate the water content of the sample from the titer and volume of Karl Fischer reagent consumed by the sample.

Cyclohexane

(Suitable for use in ultraviolet spectrophotometry)

$CH_2(CH_2)_4CH_2$ Formula Wt. 84.16

REQUIREMENTS

Absorbance. To pass test.
Appearance. Clear.
Odor. Characteristic solvent odor.
Density (grams per ml.) at 25°C. Not less than 0.772 nor more than 0.776.
Boiling range. 1 ml. to 95 ml., not more than 1°C.; 95 ml. to dryness, not more than 1°C.
Residue after evaporation. Not more than 0.002 per cent.
Substances darkened by sulfuric acid. To pass test.
Water (H_2O). Not more than 0.02 per cent.

TESTS

Absorbance. Determine the absorbance of the sample in a 1.00-cm. cell throughout the range of 210 mμ to 400 mμ, against water in a similar matched cell set at zero absorbance as the reference liquid. The absorbance should not exceed 1.00 at 210 mμ, 0.50 at 220 mμ, 0.20 at 230 mμ, 0.08 at 240 mμ, 0.03 at 250 mμ, 0.02 at 260 mμ, and 0.01 at 300 mμ to 400 mμ. The spectral absorbance curve recorded through the wavelengths indicated should be smooth throughout the prescribed range and should not show any extraneous impurity peaks within this range.

Other tests are the same as for **Cyclohexane,** page 204, except *Color* (*APHA*), which is superseded by the *Absorbance* test.

Notes

1,2-Dichloroethane

CH₂ClCH₂Cl

Formula Wt. 98.96

REQUIREMENTS

Appearance. Clear.
Color (APHA). Not more than 10.
Odor. Resembling odor of chloroform.
Density (grams per ml.) at 25°C. Not less than 1.241 nor more than 1.251.
Boiling range. 1 ml. to 95 ml., not more than 1.5°C.
Residue after evaporation. Not more than 0.002 per cent.
Acidity (as HCl). Not more than 0.001 per cent.
Water (H₂O). Not more than 0.03 per cent.

TESTS

Color (APHA). For the color standard dilute a 2-ml. aliquot of platinum-cobalt stock solution (APHA No. 500) to 100 ml. with water. Compare this solution (APHA No. 10) with 100 ml. of the 1,2-dichloroethane in 100-ml. Nessler tubes, viewed vertically over a white background.

Boiling range. Distill 100 ml. by the method described on page 12. The difference between the temperatures when 1 ml. and 95 ml. have distilled should not exceed 1.5°C. The boiling point of pure 1,2-dichloroethane at 760-mm. mercury pressure is 83.5°C.

Residue after evaporation. Evaporate 82 ml. (100 grams) to dryness in a tared dish on the steam bath and dry the residue at 105°C. for 30 minutes. The weight of the residue should not exceed 0.0020 gram.

Acidity. To 25 ml. of alcohol in a 100-ml. glass-stoppered flask, add 0.10 ml. of phenolphthalein indicator solution and 0.01N sodium hydroxide until a faint pink color persists after shaking for 30 seconds. Add 25 ml. (31 grams) of sample, mix well, and titrate with 0.01N sodium hydroxide until the pink color is restored. Not more than 0.85 ml. of 0.01N sodium hydroxide should be required.

Note. Special care should be taken during the addition of the sample and titration to avoid contamination from carbon dioxide.

Water. Place 25 ml. of methanol in a dry titration flask and add Karl Fischer reagent to a visually or electrometrically determined end point. Add 25 ml. (31 grams) of the sample, taking care to protect the sample and contents of the flask from moisture. Stir vigorously and titrate with Karl Fischer reagent to the same end point. Calculate the water content of the sample from the titer and volume of Karl Fischer reagent consumed by the sample.

Notes

1,2-Dichloroethane

(Suitable for use in ultraviolet spectrophotometry)

CH$_2$ClCH$_2$Cl   Formula Wt. 98.96

REQUIREMENTS

Absorbance.   To pass test.
Appearance.   Clear.
Odor.   Resembling odor of chloroform.
Density (grams per ml.) at 25°C.   Not less than 1.241 nor more than 1.251.
Boiling range.   1 ml. to 95 ml., not more than 1.5°C.
Residue after evaporation.   Not more than 0.002 per cent.
Acidity (as HCl).   Not more than 0.001 per cent.
Water (H$_2$O).   Not more than 0.03 per cent.

TESTS

Absorbance.   Determine the absorbance of the sample in a 1.00-cm. cell throughout the range of 226 mμ to 400 mμ, against water in a similar matched cell set at zero absorbance as the reference liquid. The absorbance should not exceed 1.00 at 226 mμ, 0.50 at 230 mμ, 0.20 at 235 mμ, 0.10 at 240 mμ, 0.05 at 245 mμ, 0.02 at 250 mμ, and 0.01 at 255 mμ to 400 mμ. The spectral absorbance curve recorded through the wavelengths indicated should be smooth throughout the prescribed range and should not show any extraneous impurity peaks within this range.

Other tests are the same as for **1,2-Dichloroethane,** page 206, except *Color (APHA)*, which is superseded by the *Absorbance* test.

Notes

2,6-Dichloroindophenol Sodium Salt

O:C$_6$H$_2$Cl$_2$:NC$_6$H$_4$ONa   Formula Wt. 290.08

REQUIREMENTS

Loss on drying at 120°C.   Not more than 12 per cent.
Interfering dyes.   To pass test.

TESTS

Loss on drying at 120°C.   Weigh accurately about 1 gram and dry at
120°C. to constant weight. The loss in weight should not be more than
12 per cent.

Interfering dyes.

Solution A.   Dissolve 50 mg. of the sample and 42 mg. of sodium bicarbonate in water and dilute to 200 ml. Filter through a dry filter,
rejecting the first 20 ml. of the filtrate.

Solution B.   Dissolve 50 mg. of ascorbic acid in 50 ml. of a solution
composed of 1.5 grams of metaphosphoric acid plus 4 ml. of glacial
acetic acid and dilute to 50 ml. with water.

To 15 ml. of Solution A add 2.5 ml. of Solution B. The mixture should
become colorless.

Notes

Dichloromethane

Methylene Chloride

CH_2Cl_2 Formula Wt. 84.93

REQUIREMENTS

Appearance. Clear.

Color (APHA). Not more than 10.

Density (grams per ml.) at 25°C. Not less than 1.315 nor more than 1.321.

Boiling range. 1 ml. to 95 ml., not more than 0.5°C.; 95 ml. to dryness, not more than 1.0°C.

Residue after evaporation. Not more than 0.002 per cent.

Acidity (as HCl). Not more than 0.001 per cent.

Water (H_2O). Not more than 0.02 per cent.

Free halogens. To pass test.

Foreign odor. To pass test.

TESTS

Color (APHA). For the color standard dilute a 2-ml. aliquot of platinum-cobalt stock solution (APHA No. 500) to 100 ml. with water. Compare this solution (APHA No. 10) with 100 ml. of the dichloromethane in 100-ml. Nessler tubes, viewed vertically over a white background.

Boiling range. Distill 100 ml. by the method described on page 12. The difference between the temperatures when 1 ml. and 95 ml. have distilled should not exceed 0.5°C., and the difference in temperatures when 95 ml. have distilled and when the dry point is reached should not exceed 1.0°C. The boiling point of pure dichloromethane at 760-mm. mercury pressure is 39.8°C.

Residue after evaporation. Evaporate 76 ml. (100 grams) in a tared dish on the steam bath and dry the residue at 105°C. for 30 minutes. The weight of the residue should not exceed 0.0020 gram.

Acidity.

Note. Great care should be taken in the test during the addition of the sample and the titration to avoid contamination from carbon dioxide.

To 25 ml. of alcohol in a 100-ml. glass-stoppered flask, add 0.10 ml. of phenolphthalein indicator solution and 0.01N sodium hydroxide solution until a pink color persists for at least 30 seconds after vigorous shaking. Add 25 ml. (33 grams) of sample from a pipet and mix thoroughly with the neutralized alcohol. If no pink color remains, titrate with 0.01N sodium hydroxide to the end point where the pink color persists for at least 30 seconds. Not more than 0.90 ml. of 0.01N sodium hydroxide should be required.

Water. Place 25 ml. of methanol in a dry titration flask and add Karl Fischer reagent to a visually or electrometrically determined end point. Add 25 ml. (33 grams) of the sample, taking care to protect the sample and contents of the flask from moisture. Stir vigorously and titrate with Karl Fischer reagent to the same end point. Calculate the water content of the sample from the titer and volume of Karl Fischer reagent consumed by the sample.

Free halogens. Shake vigorously 10 ml. for 2 minutes with 10 ml. of 10 per cent potassium iodide reagent solution and 1 ml. of starch indicator solution. A blue coloration should not be present in the water layer.

Foreign odor. Allow 10 ml. to evaporate spontaneously in a dry evaporating dish to a volume of about 1 ml. No foreign odor should be perceptible. Transfer this residue to a piece of clean, odorless, absorbent paper. No foreign odor should be perceptible when the last traces of dichloromethane evaporate from the paper.

Notes

Dichloromethane

Methylene Chloride

(Suitable for use in ultraviolet spectrophotometry)

CH_2Cl_2 Formula Wt. 84.93

REQUIREMENTS

Absorbance. To pass test.

Density (grams per ml.) at 25°C. Not less than 1.315 nor more than 1.321.

Boiling range. 1 ml. to 95 ml., not more than 0.5°C.; 95 ml. to dryness, not more than 1.0°C.

Residue after evaporation. Not more than 0.002 per cent.

Acidity (as HCl). Not more than 0.001 per cent.

Water (H_2O). Not more than 0.02 per cent.

Free halogens. To pass test.

Foreign odor. To pass test.

TESTS

Absorbance. Determine the absorbance of the sample in a 1.00-cm. cell throughout the range of 235 mμ to 400 mμ, against water in a similar matched cell set at zero absorbance as the reference liquid. The absorbance should not exceed 1.00 at 235 mμ, 0.35 at 240 mμ, 0.10 at 250 mμ, 0.04 at 260 mμ, and 0.01 at 340 mμ to 400 mμ. The spectral absorbance curve recorded through the wavelengths indicated should be smooth throughout the prescribed range and should not show any extraneous impurity peaks within this range.

Other tests are the same as for **Dichloromethane,** page 209, except *Color (APHA)*, which is superseded by the *Absorbance* test.

Notes

N,N-Dimethylformamide

HCON(CH₃)₂   Formula Wt. 73.10

REQUIREMENTS

Appearance. Clear.
Color (APHA). Not more than 15.
Density (grams per ml.) at 25°C. Not less than 0.942 nor more than 0.946.
Boiling range. 1 ml. to 95 ml., not more than 1.0°C.; 95 ml. to dryness, not more than 1.0°C.
Residue after evaporation. Not more than 0.005 per cent.
Neutrality. To pass tests.
Water (H₂O). Not more than 0.15 per cent.

TESTS

Color (APHA). For the color standard dilute a 3-ml. aliquot of platinum-cobalt stock solution (APHA No. 500) to 100 ml. with water. Compare this solution (APHA No. 15) with 100 ml. of the N,N-dimethylformamide in 100-ml. Nessler tubes, viewed vertically over a white background.

Boiling range. Distill 100 ml. by the method described on page 12. The difference between the temperatures when 1 ml. and 95 ml. have distilled should not exceed 1.0°C., and the difference in temperatures when 95 ml. have distilled and when the dry point is reached should not exceed 1.0°C. The boiling point of pure N,N-dimethylformamide at 760-mm. mercury pressure is 153°C.

Residue after evaporation. Evaporate 21 ml. (20 grams) to dryness in a tared dish on the steam bath and dry the residue at 105°C. for 30 minutes. The weight of the residue should not exceed 0.0010 gram.

Neutrality.

Note. Take care to minimize exposure of the sample to the atmosphere because of rapid absorption of carbon dioxide. Flush the flask with nitrogen during the titrations.

Test A. Mix 10.6 ml. (10 grams) with 25 ml. of carbon dioxide-free water in a glass-stoppered flask and add 0.05 ml. of methyl red indicator solution. If the solution becomes yellow, titrate with 0.1N hydrochloric acid until a red color appears. Not more than 0.3 ml. of the hydrochloric acid solution should be required.

Test B. Quickly add 20 ml. of the sample from a graduated cylinder to a 125-ml. conical flask. Add 0.10 ml. of thymol blue indicator solution.* The color of the solution should be yellow. Titrate with 0.1N sodium methoxide solution** to a blue end point. Not more than 0.10 ml. should be consumed in the titration.

*Thymol Blue Indicator Solution.** Dissolve 0.3 gram of thymol blue in 100 ml. of dry methanol.

Sodium Methoxide in Methanol, 0.1N. Dissolve 5.40 grams of sodium methylate in dry methanol and dilute to 1 liter in a volumetric flask. Standardize by titrating 40 ml. of 0.1N sulfuric acid, using thymol blue indicator.

Water. Place 25 ml. of methanol in a dry titration flask and add Karl Fischer reagent to a visually or electrometrically determined end point. Add 25 ml. (23.6 grams) of the sample, taking care to protect the sample and contents of the flask from moisture. Stir vigorously and titrate with Karl Fischer reagent to the same end point. Calculate the water content of the sample from the titer and volume of Karl Fischer reagent consumed by the sample.

Notes

N,N-Dimethylformamide

(Suitable for use in ultraviolet spectrophotometry)

HCON(CH₃)₂   Formula Wt. 73.10

REQUIREMENTS

Absorbance. To pass test.

Appearance. Clear.

Density (grams per ml.) at 25°C. Not less than 0.942 nor more than 0.946.

Boiling range. 1 ml. to 95 ml., not more than 1.0°C.; 95 ml. to dryness, not more than 1.0°C.

Residue after evaporation. Not more than 0.005 per cent.

Neutrality. To pass tests.

Water (H₂O). Not more than 0.15 per cent.

TESTS

Absorbance. Determine the absorbance of the sample in a 1.00-cm. cell throughout the range of 270 mμ to 400 mμ, against water in a similar matched cell set at zero absorbance as the reference liquid. The absorbance should not exceed 1.00 at 270 mμ, 0.30 at 275 mμ, 0.10 at 295 mμ, 0.05 at 310 mμ, and 0.01 at 340 mμ to 400 mμ. The spectral absorbance curve recorded through the wavelengths indicated should be smooth throughout the prescribed range and should not show any extraneous impurity peaks within this range.

Other tests are the same as for **N,N-Dimethylformamide,** page 213, except *Color (APHA),* which is superseded by the *Absorbance* test.

Notes

Dimethylglyoxime

CH₃C:NOHC:NOHCH₃   Formula Wt. 116.12

REQUIREMENTS

> **Melting point.** About 240°C.
> **Insoluble in alcohol.** Not more than 0.05 per cent.
> **Residue after ignition.** Not more than 0.05 per cent.
> **Suitability for nickel determination.** To pass test.

TESTS

Insoluble in alcohol. Gently boil 2 grams with 100 ml. of alcohol under a reflux condenser until no more dissolves. Filter through a tared filtering crucible, wash with 50 ml. of alcohol in small portions, and dry at 105°C. The weight of the residue should not exceed 0.0010 gram.

Residue after ignition. Ignite 2 grams in a tared crucible or dish at a temperature just high enough to burn off all the carbonaceous matter. Cool, moisten the residue with 0.05 ml. of sulfuric acid, and gently ignite again to remove the sulfuric acid. Finally, ignite at 800° ± 25°C. for 15 minutes. The weight of the residue should not exceed 0.0010 gram.

Suitability for nickel determination. Dissolve 0.665 gram of nickel sulfate hexahydrate ($NiSO_4 \cdot 6H_2O$) in water and dilute to 50 ml. Dilute 20 ml. of this solution to 100 ml., heat to boiling, and add 0.25 gram of the dimethylglyoxime in 25 ml. of alcohol. Add dilute ammonium hydroxide $(1 + 4)$ dropwise until the solution is alkaline to litmus, cool, and filter. To the filtrate add 1 ml. of the nickel sulfate solution and heat to boiling. A substantial precipitate of nickel dimethylglyoxime should appear.

Notes

Dioxane

1,4-Dioxane

$CH_2CH_2OCH_2CH_2O$ Formula Wt. 88.11

Caution. *Dioxane tends to form explosive peroxides, especially when anhydrous. It should not be allowed to evaporate to dryness unless the absence of peroxides has been shown.*

Note. Dioxane usually contains a stabilizer. If a stabilizer is present, its identity and quantity must be stated on the label.

REQUIREMENTS

Peroxide (as H_2O_2). Not more than 0.005 per cent.
Freezing point. Not below 11.0°C.
Residue after evaporation. Not more than 0.005 per cent.
Neutrality. To pass test.
Carbonyl (as $>C=O$). Not more than 0.05 per cent.
Water (H_2O). Not more than 0.05 per cent.

TESTS

Peroxide. To 29 ml. (30 grams) of the dioxane add 2 ml. of 0.1 per cent ammonium vanadate solution.* For the control add 2.5 ml. of standard hydrogen peroxide** and 2 ml. of 0.1 per cent ammonium vanadate solution to 14.5 ml. (15 grams) of the dioxane. Any color in the solution of the sample should not exceed that in the control.

*Ammonium Vanadate Solution.** Prepare a stock solution by dissolving 1 gram of ammonium vanadate, NH_4VO_3, in 100 ml. of 10 per cent sulfuric acid. Keep stoppered when not in use. Dilute 10 ml. of the stock solution to 100 ml. with water (0.1 per cent NH_4VO_3).

Standard Hydrogen Peroxide (0.30 mg. H_2O_2 in 1 ml.). Transfer 1.0 ml. of reagent hydrogen peroxide (30 per cent) to a 100-ml. volumetric flask, dilute to volume with water, and mix thoroughly. Determine the concentration of hydrogen peroxide in mg. per ml. of solution by the method of *Assay* for **Hydrogen Peroxide** described on page 290. Transfer an aliquot of the solution containing 30.0 mg. to a 100-ml. volumetric flask, dilute to volume with water, and mix.

Caution. *If peroxide is present, do not make the test for Residue after evaporation.*

Residue after evaporation. Evaporate 19 ml. (20 grams) to dryness in a tared platinum dish on the steam bath, and dry the residue at 105°C. for 30 minutes. The weight of the residue should not exceed 0.0010 gram.

Freezing point.

Apparatus. The sample container is a test tube (25 × 100 mm.) supported by a cork in a water-tight, glass cylinder (50 × 110 mm.). The cylinder is mounted in a water bath which provides at least a 37-mm. layer of water surrounding the sides and bottom of the cylinder. An accurate thermometer with 0.1°C.-subdivisions is centered in the test tube and a thermometer with 1°C.-subdivisions is mounted in the water bath. The stirrer, about 30 cm. long, is a wire having a loop at the bottom.

Pour sufficient sample into the test tube to make a 50-mm. column. Assemble the apparatus with the bulb of the 0.1°-thermometer immersed halfway between the top and bottom of the sample in the test tube. Fill the water bath with a mixture of ice and water to within 12 mm. of the top, and adjust the temperature to 0°C. by the addition of more ice, if necessary. Stir the sample continuously during the test by moving the wire loop up and down throughout the entire depth of the sample at a regular rate of 20 cycles per minute. Record the reading of the 0.1°-thermometer every 30 seconds. Anticipate that the temperature will fall gradually at first, then become constant for 1 or 2 minutes at the freezing point, and finally fall gradually again. The freezing point is the average of 4 consecutive readings that lie within a range of 0.2°C.

Neutrality. Pour 50 ml. of the sample from a graduated cylinder into a 125-ml. Erlenmeyer flask and add 0.10 ml. of methyl violet indicator solution.** The color of the solution should be violet. Titrate with 0.1N perchloric acid in dioxane* to a bluish green end point. Not more than 0.10 ml. of 0.1N perchloric acid should be consumed.

*Perchloric Acid in Dioxane, 0.1N. Mix 8.5 ml. of perchloric acid with sufficient dioxane to make 1 liter. Standardize the solution as follows: weigh accurately about 0.7 gram of potassium hydrogen phthalate, previously dried at 105°C. for 2 hours, and dissolve in 50 ml. of glacial acetic acid in a 250-ml. flask. Add 0.10 ml. of methyl violet indicator solution** and titrate with the perchloric acid solution to a bluish green end point. Correct for the blank and calculate the normality of the acid. One milliliter of 0.1N perchloric acid corresponds to 0.02042 gram of potassium hydrogen phthalate.

****Methyl Violet Indicator Solution.** Dissolve 100 mg. of methyl violet (C.I. No. 42535, Basic Violet 1) in 10 ml. of glacial acetic acid.

Carbonyl.

Sample Solution A. Transfer 10.0 ml. of the sample to a 100-ml. volumetric flask, dilute to volume with carbonyl-free methanol, and mix well.

Add 2.0 ml. of Sample Solution A to a 25-ml. glass-stoppered graduated cylinder. Prepare a series of standards containing 0.004 mg., 0.008 mg., and 0.016 mg. of carbonyl (as $>C{=}O$) in 2.0-ml. aliquots, respectively.** Add 2.0 ml. of 2,4-dinitrophenylhydrazine solution* to each, stopper, mix thoroughly, and allow to stand at room temperature for 30 minutes. Add 10.0 ml. of pyridine stabilizer* and 2.0 ml. of potassium hydroxide methanol solution,* mix, and let stand for 10 minutes. Compare any color in the solution of the sample with the series of standards and estimate the per cent carbonyl (as $>C{=}O$). The standards correspond to 0.002 per cent, 0.004 per cent, and 0.008 per cent, respectively.

*Reagents. 1. Carbonyl-free methanol.** To 2 liters of anhydrous reagent methanol add 10 grams of 2,4-dinitrophenylhydrazine and 0.5 ml. of hydrochloric acid. Reflux for 2 hours, distill, and reject the first 50 ml. of distillate.

Note. The methanol should be stirred magnetically to avoid bumping. Stored in a tightly stoppered bottle, the methanol will remain carbonyl-free indefinitely. Prepare all of the methanol used in the foregoing analysis in this manner.

2. Pyridine. Redistill and store over reagent grade potassium hydroxide.

3. Pyridine stabilizer. Dilute 80 ml. of the pyridine to 100 ml. with water.

4. 2,4-Dinitrophenylhydrazine solution. Suspend 50 mg. of reagent grade 2,4-dinitrophenylhydrazine in 25 ml. of carbonyl-free methanol, add 2 ml. of hydrochloric acid, and dilute to 50 ml. with water. Prepare fresh solution every 2 weeks.

5. Potassium hydroxide methanol solution. Mix 15.0 ml. of 33 per cent potassium hydroxide solution with 50 ml. of carbonyl-free methanol. Prepare fresh solution every 2 weeks.

****Standard Carbonyl Solution.** Accurately measure 1.05 ml. of acetone (400 mg. of carbonyl as $>C{=}O$) into a 100-ml. volumetric flask containing 50 ml. of carbonyl-free methanol. Dilute to volume with carbonyl-free methanol and mix thoroughly. Dilute a 1.0-ml. aliquot of this solution to 100 ml. in a volumetric flask with carbonyl-free methanol and mix (Stock Solution). Transfer 5.0 ml., 10.0 ml., and 20.0 ml. of the Stock Solution to separate 100-ml. volumetric flasks, dilute to volume with carbonyl-free methanol, and mix. Each 2.0-ml. aliquot of the final dilutions contains 0.004 mg., 0.008 mg., and 0.016 mg. of carbonyl (as $>C{=}O$), respectively.

Water. Place 25 ml. of methanol in a dry titration flask and add Karl Fischer reagent to a visually or electrometrically determined end point. Add 20 ml. (20.7 grams) of the sample, taking care to protect the sample and contents of the flask from moisture. Stir vigorously and titrate with Karl Fischer reagent to the same end point. Calculate the water content of the sample from the titer and volume of Karl Fischer reagent consumed by the sample.

Notes

Diphenylamine

$(C_6H_5)_2NH$ Formula Wt. 169.23

Note. This reagent discolors on exposure to light.

REQUIREMENTS

Melting point. Not below 52.5°C. nor above 54.0°C.
Solubility in alcohol. To pass test.
Residue after ignition. Not more than 0.030 per cent.
Nitrate (NO_3). To pass test.
Sensitivity to nitrate. To pass test.

TESTS

Solubility in alcohol. Dissolve 1 gram in 50 ml. of alcohol. The solution should be clear and colorless.

Residue after ignition. Gently ignite 4 grams in a tared crucible or dish until charred. Cool, moisten the char with 2 ml. of sulfuric acid, and ignite again slowly until all carbon and excess sulfuric acid have been volatilized. Finally, ignite at 800° ± 25°C. for 15 minutes. The weight of the residue should not exceed 0.0012 gram.

Nitrate. To 20 ml. of water add 60 ml. of sulfuric acid, adjust the temperature to about 60°C., and add 0.5 ml. of hydrochloric acid and 0.0100 gram of the sample. No blue color should be produced in 5 minutes. Retain the solution for the test for *Sensitivity to nitrate*.

Sensitivity to nitrate. To 8 ml. of the solution retained from the test for *Nitrate* add 0.01 mg. of nitrate ion (NO_3) and allow to stand at 60°C. for 5 minutes. A blue color should be produced.

Notes

Diphenylaminesulfonic Acid Sodium Salt
Sodium Diphenylaminesulfonate

$C_6H_5NHC_6H_4SO_3Na$ Formula Wt. 271.27

REQUIREMENTS

Sensitivity as indicator. To pass test.

TESTS

Sensitivity as indicator. Dissolve 0.15 gram in 100 ml. of water. To 25 ml. of water in a 50-ml. test tube, add 10 ml. of $4N$ sulfuric acid, 5 ml. of phosphoric acid, 0.05 ml. of $0.01N$ ferrous ammonium sulfate, and 0.05 ml. of the sample solution. The addition of 0.10 ml. of $0.01N$ potassium dichromate should produce a violet color. The color should be completely discharged by the addition of 0.10 ml. of $0.01N$ ferrous ammonium sulfate.

Notes

Dithizone

Phenylazothioformic Acid 2-Phenylhydrazide
Diphenylthiocarbazone

$C_6H_5NHNHCSN:NC_6H_5$ 　　　　　　　　　　　Formula Wt. 256.33

REQUIREMENTS

Assay. Not less than 85 per cent.
Residue after ignition. Not more than 0.3 per cent.
Heavy metals (as Pb). Not more than 0.002 per cent.
Ratio of absorbances. Not less than 1.55.

TESTS

Assay. Weigh accurately 10.0 mg., transfer to a 100-ml. volumetric flask, dissolve in about 75 ml. of carbon tetrachloride, and dilute to volume with carbon tetrachloride. Dilute 5 ml. of this solution to 100.0 ml. with carbon tetrachloride, and determine the absorbance ($-\log_{10} T$) of this solution in 1.00-cm. cells at 620 mμ, using carbon tetrachloride as the blank. Reserve the remainder of the solution for determining the *Ratio of absorbances*. Determine the molar absorptivity by dividing the absorbance by 1.95×10^{-5} (the molar concentration of the dithizone) and calculate the assay value as follows:

$$\frac{\text{Molar absorptivity at 620 m}\mu}{34,600} \times 100 = \text{per cent dithizone}$$

Residue after ignition. Gently ignite 1 gram in a tared crucible or dish until charred. Cool, moisten the char with 1 ml. of nitric acid and 1 ml. of sulfuric acid, and ignite again slowly until all carbon and excess sulfuric acid have been volatilized. Finally, ignite at $800° \pm 25°C$. for 15 minutes. The weight of the residue should not exceed 0.0030 gram. Retain the residue for the test for *Heavy metals*.

Heavy metals. Digest the residue obtained in the preceding test with 10 ml. of ammonium acetate solution (10 grams in 100 ml.) in a covered crucible on the steam bath for 30 minutes. Filter, wash with 10 ml. of water, add 2 ml. of 1N hydrochloric acid to the combined filtrate and washings, and dilute to 25 ml. For the standard use a solution containing 0.02 mg. of lead ion (Pb), add 10 ml. of ammonium acetate solution and 2 ml. of 1N hydrochloric acid, and dilute to 25 ml. Adjust the pH of the standard and sample solutions to between 3 and 4 (using a pH meter) with 1N acetic acid or ammonium hydroxide (10 per cent NH_3), dilute to 40 ml., and mix. Add 10 ml. of freshly prepared hydrogen sulfide water to each and mix. Any color in the solution of the sample should not exceed that in the standard.

Ratio of absorbances. Determine the molar absorptivity at 450 mμ of the solution prepared in the test for *Assay*, using the method described in the test. The ratio of the value at 620 mμ to that at 450 mμ should not be less than 1.55.

Notes

Ethyl Acetate

$CH_3COOCH_2CH_3$ Formula Wt. 88.11

REQUIREMENTS

Color (APHA). Not more than 10.

Density (gram per ml.) at 25°C. Not less than 0.893 nor more than 0.895.

Boiling range. 1 ml. to 95 ml., not more than 0.5°C.; 95 ml. to dryness, not more than 0.5°C.

Residue after evaporation. Not more than 0.003 per cent.

Water (H_2O). Not more than 0.20 per cent.

Acidity (as CH_3COOH). Not more than 0.005 per cent.

Foreign esters. To pass test.

Substances darkened by sulfuric acid. To pass test.

TESTS

Color (APHA). For the color standard dilute a 2-ml. aliquot of platinum-cobalt stock solution (APHA No. 500) to 100 ml. with water. Compare this solution (APHA No. 10) with 100 ml. of the ethyl acetate in 100-ml. Nessler tubes, viewed vertically over a white background.

Boiling range. Distill 100 ml. by the method described on page 12. The difference between the temperatures when 1 ml. and 95 ml. have distilled should not exceed 0.5°C., and the difference between the temperatures when 95 ml. have distilled and when the dry point is reached should not exceed 0.5°C. The boiling point of pure ethyl acetate at 760-mm. mercury pressure is 77.1°C.

Residue after evaporation. Evaporate 45 ml. (40 grams) to dryness in a tared dish on the steam bath and dry the residue at 105°C. for 30 minutes. The weight of the residue should not exceed 0.0012 gram.

Water. Place 25 ml. of methanol in a dry titration flask and add Karl Fischer reagent to a visually or electrometrically determined end point. Add 10 ml. (9 grams) of the sample, taking care to protect the contents of the flask from moisture. Stir vigorously and titrate with Karl Fischer reagent to the same end point. Calculate the water content of the sample from the titer and volume of Karl Fischer reagent consumed by the sample.

Acidity. To 10 ml. of alcohol add 0.10 ml. of phenolphthalein indicator solution, and neutralize with 0.02N sodium hydroxide. Add 10 ml. of the sample, mix gently, and titrate with 0.02N sodium hydroxide until the pink color persists for 15 seconds. Not more than 0.40 ml. should be required.

Foreign esters.   Evaporate 5 ml. from clean, odorless filter paper. The final odor should not be different in character from that observed at the beginning of the test.

Substances darkened by sulfuric acid.   Superimpose 5 ml. of ethyl acetate upon 5 ml. of sulfuric acid. No dark coloration should be produced at the zone of contact.

Notes

Ethyl Acetate

(Suitable for use in ultraviolet spectrophotometry)

CH₃COOCH₂CH₃   Formula Wt. 88.11

REQUIREMENTS

Absorbance. To pass test.

Density (gram per ml.) at 25°C. Not less than 0.893 nor more than 0.895.

Boiling range. 1 ml. to 95 ml., not more than 0.5°C.; 95 ml. to dryness, not more than 0.5°C.

Residue after evaporation. Not more than 0.003 per cent.

Water (H₂O). Not more than 0.20 per cent.

Acidity (as CH₃COOH). Not more than 0.005 per cent.

Foreign esters. To pass test.

Substances darkened by sulfuric acid. To pass test.

TESTS

Absorbance. Determine the absorbance of the sample in a 1.00-cm. cell throughout the range of 255 mμ to 400 mμ, against water in a similar matched cell set at zero absorbance as the reference liquid. The absorbance should not exceed 1.00 at 255 mμ, 0.50 at 257 mμ, 0.10 at 263 mμ, 0.05 at 275 mμ, and 0.01 at 330 mμ to 400 mμ. The spectral absorbance curve recorded through the wavelengths indicated should be smooth throughout the prescribed range and should not show any extraneous impurity peaks within this range.

Other tests are the same as for **Ethyl Acetate,** page 225, except *Color (APHA),* which is superseded by the *Absorbance* test.

Notes

Ethyl Alcohol

Ethanol

CH₃CH₂OH

Formula Wt. 46.07

REQUIREMENTS

Assay. Not less than 95 per cent by volume.
Color (APHA). Not more than 10.
Solubility in water. To pass test.
Residue after evaporation. Not more than 0.001 per cent.
Acetone, isopropyl alcohol. To pass test (limit about 0.001 per cent acetone, 0.003 per cent isopropyl alcohol).
Acidity (as CH₃COOH). Not more than 0.003 per cent.
Alkalinity (as NH₃). Not more than 0.0003 per cent.
Fusel oil. To pass test.
Methanol (CH₃OH). To pass test (limit about 0.1 per cent).
Substances darkened by sulfuric acid. To pass test.
Substances reducing permanganate. To pass test.

TESTS

Assay. The density at 25°C. should not exceed 0.807 gram per ml.

Color (APHA). For the color standard dilute a 2-ml. aliquot of platinum-cobalt stock solution (APHA No. 500) to 100 ml. with water. Compare this solution (APHA No. 10) with 100 ml. of the ethyl alcohol in 100-ml. Nessler tubes, viewed vertically over a white background.

Solubility in water. Mix 15 ml. with 45 ml. of water and allow to stand for 1 hour. The mixture should be as clear as an equal volume of water.

Residue after evaporation. Evaporate 124 ml. (100 grams) to dryness in a tared dish on the steam bath and dry the residue at 105°C. for 30 minutes. The weight of the residue should not exceed 0.0010 gram.

Acetone, isopropyl alcohol. Dilute 1 ml. with 1 ml. of water. Add 1 ml. of a saturated solution of disodium hydrogen phosphate and 3 ml. of a saturated solution of potassium permanganate. Warm the mixture to 45° to 50°C. and allow to stand until the permanganate color is discharged. Add 3 ml. of 10 per cent sodium hydroxide reagent solution and filter, without washing, through glass or asbestos. Prepare a control containing 1 ml. of the saturated solution of disodium hydrogen phosphate, 3 ml. of 10 per cent sodium hydroxide reagent solution, and 0.008 mg. of acetone in 9 ml. To each solution add 1 ml. of 1 per cent furfural reagent solution, and allow to stand for 10 minutes. To 1 ml. of each solution add

3 ml. of hydrochloric acid. Any pink color produced in the solution of the sample should not exceed that in the control.

Acidity.   Add 10 ml. to 25 ml. of water in a glass-stoppered flask and add 0.5 ml. of phenolphthalein indicator solution. Add 0.02N sodium hydroxide until a slight pink color persists after shaking for 30 seconds. Add 25 ml. of the sample, mix well, and titrate with 0.02N sodium hydroxide until the pink color is restored. Not more than 0.50 ml. of the hydroxide solution should be required.

Alkalinity.   Dilute 25 ml. with 25 ml. of water and add 0.05 ml. of methyl red indicator solution. Not more than 0.20 ml. of 0.02N sulfuric acid should be required to produce a pink color.

Fusel oil.   Mix 10 ml. with 5 ml. of water plus 1 ml. of glycerol and allow to evaporate spontaneously from a piece of clean blotting paper. When the last traces of alcohol leave the paper, no disagreeable odor should be perceptible.

Methanol.   Dilute 5 ml. with water to 100 ml. To 1 ml. of the solution add 0.2 ml. of dilute phosphoric acid (1 + 9) and 0.25 ml. of a 5 per cent potassium permanganate solution. Allow to stand for 15 minutes, add 0.3 ml. of 10 per cent sodium bisulfite solution, and shake until colorless. Add slowly 5 ml. of ice-cold 80 per cent sulfuric acid (3 volumes of acid plus 1 volume of water), keeping the mixture cool during the addition. Add 0.1 ml. of a 1 per cent aqueous solution of chromotropic acid, mix, and digest on the steam bath for 20 minutes. Any violet color should not exceed that produced by 0.04 mg. of methanol in 1 ml. of water treated in the same way as the 1 ml. of the diluted sample.

Substances darkened by sulfuric acid.   Cool 10 ml. of sulfuric acid, contained in a small Erlenmeyer flask, to 10°C. and add dropwise, with constant agitation, 10 ml. of the sample, meanwhile keeping the temperature of the mixture below 20°C. The resulting solution should have no more color than either of the two liquids before mixing.

Substances reducing permanganate.   Cool 20 ml. to 15°C., add 0.1 ml. of 0.1N potassium permanganate, and allow to stand at 15°C. for 5 minutes. The pink color should not be entirely discharged.

Notes

Ethyl Alcohol

Ethanol

(Suitable for use in ultraviolet spectrophotometry)

CH_3CH_2OH Formula Wt. 46.07

REQUIREMENTS

Absorbance. To pass test.

Assay. Not less than 95 per cent by volume.

Solubility in water. To pass test.

Residue after evaporation. Not more than 0.001 per cent.

Acetone, isopropyl alcohol. To pass test (limit about 0.001 per cent acetone, 0.003 per cent isopropyl alcohol).

Acidity (as CH_3COOH). Not more than 0.003 per cent.

Alkalinity (as NH_3). Not more than 0.0003 per cent.

Fusel oil. To pass test.

Methanol (CH_3OH). To pass test (limit about 0.1 per cent).

Substances darkened by sulfuric acid. To pass test.

Substances reducing permanganate. To pass test.

TESTS

Absorbance. Determine the absorbance of the sample in a 1.00-cm. cell, throughout the range of 210 mμ to 400 mμ, against water in a similar matched cell set at zero absorbance as the reference liquid. The absorbance should not exceed 0.40 at 210 mμ, 0.25 at 220 mμ, 0.15 at 230 mμ, 0.05 at 240 mμ, and 0.01 at 270 mμ to 400 mμ. The spectral absorbance curve recorded through the wavelengths indicated should be smooth throughout the prescribed range and should not show any extraneous impurity peaks within this range.

Other tests are the same as for **Ethyl Alcohol,** page 228, except *Color (APHA)*, which is superseded by the *Absorbance* test.

Notes

Ethyl Alcohol, Absolute
Ethanol, Absolute

CH_3CH_2OH Formula Wt. 46.07

REQUIREMENTS

Assay. Not less than 99.5 per cent CH_3CH_2OH by volume (about 99.2 per cent by weight).

Water (H_2O). Not more than 0.20 per cent.

Color (APHA). Not more than 10.

Solubility in water. To pass test.

Residue after evaporation. Not more than 0.001 per cent.

Acetone, isopropyl alcohol. To pass test (limit about 0.001 per cent acetone, 0.003 per cent isopropyl alcohol).

Acidity (as CH_3COOH). Not more than 0.003 per cent.

Alkalinity (as NH_3). Not more than 0.0003 per cent.

Fusel oil. To pass test.

Methanol (CH_3OH). To pass test (limit about 0.1 per cent).

Substances darkened by sulfuric acid. To pass test.

Substances reducing permanganate. To pass test.

TESTS

Assay. The density at 25°C. should not exceed 0.7876 gram per ml.

Water. Place 25 ml. of methanol in a dry titration flask and add Karl Fischer reagent to a visually or electrometrically determined end point. Add 20 ml. (14.8 grams) of the sample, taking care to protect the sample and contents of the flask from moisture. Stir vigorously and titrate with Karl Fischer reagent to the same end point. Calculate the water content of the sample from the titer and volume of Karl Fischer reagent consumed by the sample.

Color (APHA) and other tests are the same as for **Ethyl Alcohol**, page 228.

Notes

Ethyl Ether

Diethyl Ether

$(CH_3CH_2)_2O$ Formula Wt. 74.12

Caution. Ethyl ether tends to form explosive peroxides, especially when anhydrous. It should not be allowed to evaporate to dryness unless the absence of peroxides has been shown. The presence of water or appropriate reducing agents lessens peroxide formation.

Note. Ethyl ether normally contains about 2 per cent of alcohol and 0.5 per cent of water as stabilizers.

REQUIREMENTS

Color (APHA). Not more than 10.
Density (gram per ml.) at 25°C. Between 0.710 and 0.712.
Peroxide (as H_2O_2). Not more than 0.0001 per cent.
Residue after evaporation. Not more than 0.0010 per cent.
Acidity (as CH_3COOH). Not more than 0.0010 per cent.
Carbonyl (as $>C{=}O$). Not more than 0.001 per cent.
Substances darkened by sulfuric acid. To pass test.
Foreign odor. To pass test.

TESTS

Color (APHA). For the color standard dilute a 2-ml. aliquot of platinum-cobalt stock solution (APHA No. 500) to 100 ml. with water. Compare this solution (APHA No. 10) with 100 ml. of the ethyl ether in 100-ml. Nessler tubes, viewed vertically over a white background.

Peroxide. To 420 ml. (300 grams) in a separatory funnel add 9.0 ml. of ammonium vanadate solution.* Shake for 3 minutes and allow to separate. Drain the lower layer into a 25-ml. glass-stoppered graduated cylinder, dilute to 10.0 ml. with 10 per cent sulfuric acid, and mix. Any orange color should not exceed that produced by 0.30 mg. of hydrogen peroxide (1-ml. aliquot of standard hydrogen peroxide solution)** and 9.0 ml. of ammonium vanadate solution.

* **Ammonium Vanadate Solution.** Dissolve 1.0 gram of ammonium vanadate, NH_4VO_3, in 100 ml. of 10 per cent sulfuric acid.

** **Standard Hydrogen Peroxide** (0.30 mg. H_2O_2 in 1 ml.). Transfer 1.0 ml. of reagent hydrogen peroxide (30 per cent) to a 100-ml. volumetric flask, dilute to the mark with water, and mix thoroughly. Determine the concentration of hydrogen peroxide in mg. per ml. of solution by the method of *Assay* for **Hydrogen Peroxide** described on page 290. Transfer an aliquot of the solution containing 30.0 mg. to a 100-ml. volumetric flask, dilute to the mark with 10 per cent sulfuric acid, and mix.

Note. Fresh ethyl ether should meet this test, but after storage for several months peroxide may be formed.

Caution. If peroxide is present, do not make the test for Residue after evaporation.

Residue after evaporation. Evaporate 141 ml. (100 grams) to dryness in a tared dish and dry the residue at 105°C. for 30 minutes. The weight of the residue should not exceed 0.0010 gram.

Acidity.

Note. Great care should be taken in the test during the addition of the sample and the titration to avoid contamination from carbon dioxide.

To 10 ml. of water in a glass-stoppered flask, add 0.10 ml. of bromothymol blue indicator solution and 0.01N sodium hydroxide until a blue color persists after vigorous shaking. Add 25 ml. of sample from a pipet and shake briskly to mix the two layers. If no blue color remains, titrate with 0.01N sodium hydroxide until the blue color is restored and persists for several minutes. Not more than 0.30 ml. of 0.01N sodium hydroxide should be required.

Carbonyl. To 2.0 ml. in a 25-ml. glass-stoppered graduated cylinder, add 2.0 ml. of carbonyl-free methanol.* Prepare a series of standards containing 0.0035 mg., 0.0070 mg., and 0.014 mg. of carbonyl (as >C=O) in 4.0-ml. aliquots, respectively.** Add 2.0 ml. of 2,4-dinitrophenylhydrazine solution* to each, stopper, mix thoroughly, and allow to stand at room temperature for 30 minutes. Remove the stoppers, place the cylinders in a hot water bath at 50° to 55°C., and boil off the ether with the aid of a stream of nitrogen. Remove the cylinders from the water bath, cool to room temperature, add 10.0 ml. of pyridine stabilizer* and 2.0 ml. of potassium hydroxide methanol solution* to each, mix thoroughly, and allow to stand 10 minutes. Compare any color in the solution of the sample to the series of standards and estimate the per cent carbonyl (as >C=O). The standards correspond to 0.00025 per cent, 0.0005 per cent, and 0.001 per cent, respectively.

* **Reagents. 1. Carbonyl-free methanol.** To 2 liters of anhydrous reagent methanol add 10 grams of 2,4-dinitrophenylhydrazine and 0.5

ml. of hydrochloric acid. Reflux for two hours, distill, and reject the first 50 ml. of distillate.

Note. The methanol should be stirred magnetically to avoid bumping. Stored in a tightly stoppered bottle, the methanol will remain carbonyl-free indefinitely. Prepare all of the methanol used in the foregoing analysis in this manner.

2. Pyridine. Redistill and store over reagent grade potassium hydroxide.

3. Pyridine stabilizer. Dilute 80 ml. of the pyridine to 100 ml. with water.

4. 2,4-Dinitrophenylhydrazine solution. Suspend 50 mg. of reagent grade 2,4-dinitrophenylhydrazine in 25 ml. of carbonyl-free methanol, add 2 ml. of concentrated hydrochloric acid, and dilute to 50 ml. with water. Prepare fresh solution every 2 weeks.

5. Potassium hydroxide methanol solution. Mix 15.0 ml. of 33 per cent potassium hydroxide solution with 50 ml. of carbonyl-free methanol. Prepare fresh solution every 2 weeks.

** Standard Carbonyl Solution. Accurately measure 0.92 ml. of acetone (350 mg. of carbonyl as $>C=O$) into a 100 ml. of volumetric flask containing 50 ml. of carbonyl-free methanol. Dilute to the mark with carbonyl-free methanol and mix thoroughly. Dilute a 1.00-ml. aliquot of this solution to 100 ml. in a volumetric flask with carbonyl-free methanol and mix (Stock Solution). Transfer 5.0 ml., 10.0 ml., and 20.0 ml. of the Stock Solution to separate 200-ml. volumetric flasks, dilute to the mark with carbonyl-free methanol, and mix. Each 4.0-ml. aliquot of the final dilutions contains 0.0035 mg., 0.0070 mg., and 0.014 mg. of carbonyl (as $>C=O$), respectively.

Substances darkened by sulfuric acid. Cool 10 ml. of sulfuric acid to about 10°C. and add dropwise with gentle stirring 10 ml. of the ethyl ether. Any color should not exceed that produced in a color standard of the following composition: 0.4 ml. of cobaltous chloride solution (5.95 grams of $CoCl_2 \cdot 6H_2O$ and 2.5 ml. of hydrochloric acid in 100 ml.), 0.6 ml. of ferric chloride solution (4.50 grams of $FeCl_3 \cdot 6H_2O$ and 2.5 ml. of hydrochloric acid in 100 ml.), 0.6 ml. of cupric sulfate solution (6.24 grams of $CuSO_4 \cdot 5H_2O$ and 2.5 ml. of hydrochloric acid in 100 ml.), and 18.4 ml. of water.

Foreign odor. Allow 10 ml. to evaporate spontaneously to a volume of about 1 ml. in a dry evaporating dish. No foreign odor should be perceptible. Transfer this residue to a piece of clean, odorless absorbent paper. No foreign odor should be perceptible when the last traces of ether evaporate from the paper.

Notes

Ethyl Ether, Anhydrous

Diethyl Ether, Anhydrous

$(CH_3CH_2)_2O$ Formula Wt. 74.12

Caution. Ethyl ether tends to form explosive peroxides, especially when anhydrous. It should not be allowed to evaporate to dryness or near dryness unless the absence of peroxides has been shown. The formation of peroxides is more rapid in ethyl ether kept in containers that have been opened and partly emptied. Some ethyl ether may contain a stabilizer. If it does, the amount and type should be marked on the label.

REQUIREMENTS

Color (APHA). Not more than 10.
Density (gram per ml.) at 25°C. Not above 0.7079.
Peroxide (as H_2O_2). Not more than 0.0001 per cent.
Residue after evaporation. Not more than 0.0010 per cent.
Acidity (as CH_3COOH). Not more than 0.0010 per cent.
Carbonyl (as $>C{=}O$). Not more than 0.001 per cent.
Substances darkened by sulfuric acid. To pass test.
Foreign odor. To pass test.
Alcohol (CH_3CH_2OH). To pass test (limit about 0.05 per cent).
Water (H_2O). Not more than 0.01 per cent.

TESTS

Color (APHA). For the color standard dilute a 2-ml. aliquot of platinum-cobalt stock solution (APHA No. 500) to 100 ml. with water. Compare this solution (APHA No. 10) with 100 ml. of the ethyl ether in 100-ml. Nessler tubes, viewed vertically over a white background.

Peroxide. To 420 ml. (300 grams) in a separatory funnel add 9.0 ml. of ammonium vanadate solution.* Shake for 3 minutes and allow to separate. Drain the lower layer into a 25-ml. glass-stoppered graduated cylinder, dilute to 10.0 ml. with 10 per cent sulfuric acid, and mix. Any orange color should not exceed that produced by 0.30 mg. of hydrogen peroxide (1-ml. aliquot of standard hydrogen peroxide solution)** and 9.0 ml. of ammonium vanadate solution.

* **Ammonium Vanadate Solution.** Dissolve 1.0 gram of ammonium vanadate, NH_4VO_3, in 100 ml. of 10 per cent sulfuric acid.

** **Standard Hydrogen Peroxide** (0.30 mg. H_2O_2 in 1 ml.).   Transfer 1.0 ml. of reagent hydrogen peroxide (30 per cent) to a 100-ml. volumetric flask, dilute to the mark with water, and mix thoroughly. Determine the concentration of hydrogen peroxide in mg. per ml. of solution by the method of *Assay* for **Hydrogen Peroxide** described on page 290. Transfer an aliquot of the solution containing 30.0 mg. to a 100-ml. volumetric flask, dilute to the mark with 10 per cent sulfuric acid, and mix.

Note.   Fresh ethyl ether should meet this test, but after storage for several months peroxide may be formed.

Caution.   If peroxide is present, do not make the test for Residue after evaporation.

Residue after evaporation.   Evaporate 141 ml. (100 grams) to dryness in a tared dish and dry the residue at 105°C. for 30 minutes. The weight of the residue should not exceed 0.0010 gram.

Acidity.

Note.   Great care should be taken in the test during the addition of the sample and the titration to avoid contamination from carbon dioxide.

To 10 ml. of water in a glass-stoppered flask, add 0.10 ml. of bromothymol blue indicator solution and $0.01N$ sodium hydroxide until a blue color persists after vigorous shaking. Add 25 ml. of sample from a pipet and shake briskly to mix the two layers. If no blue color remains, titrate with $0.01N$ sodium hydroxide until the blue color is restored and persists for several minutes. Not more than 0.30 ml. of $0.01N$ sodium hydroxide should be required.

Carbonyl.   To 2.0 ml. in a 25-ml. glass-stoppered graduated cylinder, add 2.0 ml. of carbonyl-free methanol.* Prepare a series of standards containing 0.0035 mg., 0.0070 mg., and 0.014 mg. of carbonyl (as >C=O) in 4.0-ml. aliquots, respectively.** Add 2.0 ml. of 2,4-dinitrophenylhydrazine solution* to each, stopper, mix thoroughly, and allow to stand at room temperature for 30 minutes. Remove the stoppers, place the cylinders in a hot water bath at 50° to 55°C., and boil off the ether with the aid of a stream of nitrogen. Remove the cylinders from the water bath, cool to room temperature, add 10.0 ml. of pyridine stabilizer* and 2.0 ml. of potassium hydroxide methanol solution* to each, mix thoroughly, and allow to stand 10 minutes. Compare any color in the solution of the sample to the series of standards and estimate the per cent carbonyl (as $>C=O$). The standards correspond to 0.00025 per cent, 0.0005 per cent, and 0.001 per cent, respectively.

* **Reagents. 1. Carbonyl-free methanol.** To 2 liters of anhydrous reagent methanol add 10 grams of 2,4-dinitrophenylhydrazine and 0.5 ml. of hydrochloric acid. Reflux for two hours, distill, and reject the first 50 ml. of distillate.

> **Note.** The methanol should be stirred magnetically to avoid bumping. Stored in a tightly stoppered bottle, the methanol will remain carbonyl-free indefinitely. Prepare all of the methanol used in the foregoing analysis in this manner.

2. Pyridine. Redistill and store over reagent grade potassium hydroxide.

3. Pyridine stabilizer. Dilute 80 ml. of the pyridine to 100 ml. with water.

4. 2,4-Dinitrophenylhydrazine solution. Suspend 50 mg. of reagent grade 2,4-dinitrophenylhydrazine in 25 ml. of carbonyl-free methanol, add 2 ml. of concentrated hydrochloric acid, and dilute to 50 ml. with water. Prepare fresh solution every 2 weeks.

5. Potassium hydroxide methanol solution. Mix 15.0 ml. of 33 per cent potassium hydroxide solution with 50 ml. of carbonyl-free methanol. Prepare fresh solution every 2 weeks.

** **Standard Carbonyl Solution.** Accurately measure 0.92 ml. of acetone (350 mg. of carbonyl as $>C=O$) into a 100-ml. volumetric flask containing 50 ml. of carbonyl-free methanol. Dilute to the mark with carbonyl-free methanol and mix thoroughly. Dilute a 1.00-ml. aliquot of this solution to 100 ml. in a volumetric flask with carbonyl-free methanol and mix (Stock Solution). Transfer 5.0 ml., 10.0 ml., and 20.0 ml. of the Stock Solution to separate 200-ml. volumetric flasks, dilute to the mark with carbonyl-free methanol, and mix. Each 4.0-ml. aliquot of the final dilutions contains 0.0035 mg., 0.0070 mg., and 0.014 mg. of carbonyl (as $>C=O$), respectively.

Substances darkened by sulfuric acid. Cool 10 ml. of sulfuric acid to about 10°C. and add dropwise with gentle stirring 10 ml. of the ethyl ether. Any color should not exceed that produced in a color standard of the following composition: 0.4 ml. of cobaltous chloride solution (5.95 grams of $CoCl_2 \cdot 6H_2O$ and 2.5 ml. of hydrochloric acid in 100 ml.), 0.6

ml. of ferric chloride solution (4.50 grams of $FeCl_3 \cdot 6H_2O$ and 2.5 ml. of hydrochloric acid in 100 ml.), 0.6 ml. of cupric sulfate solution (6.24 grams of $CuSO_4 \cdot 5H_2O$ and 2.5 ml. of hydrochloric acid in 100 ml.), and 18.4 ml. of water.

Foreign odor. Allow 10 ml. to evaporate spontaneously to a volume of about 1 ml. in a dry evaporating dish. No foreign odor should be perceptible. Transfer this residue to a piece of clean, odorless absorbent paper. No foreign odor should be perceptible when the last traces of ether evaporate from the paper.

Alcohol. Transfer 100 ml. to a separatory funnel and shake with five successive portions, 20 ml., 10 ml., 10 ml., 5 ml., and 5 ml., respectively, of distilled water at about 25°C. Shake each portion for 2 minutes and separate the water layer carefully. Finally, pour the combined water extract from one flask to another six times to assure minimum contamination with ether. Transfer 1 ml. of the water extract with a pipet to a comparison tube and add 4 ml. of water. For a standard take 5 ml. of a solution of 0.2 ml. of absolute alcohol in a liter of water. Add 10 ml. of nitrochromic acid reagent to each solution, mix, and allow to stand for 1 hour. At the end of this time the color of the sample solution should show no more change from yellow to green or blue than is shown by the standard. The test and the standard must be kept at the same temperature.

Nitrochromic acid reagent. Mix 1 volume of 5 per cent potassium chromate solution with 133 volumes of water and 66 volumes of colorless nitric acid. This reagent should not be used if more than 1 month old.

Water. Place 25 ml. of methanol in a dry titration flask and add Karl Fischer reagent to a visually or electrometrically determined end point. Add 20 ml. (14.2 grams) of the sample, taking care to protect the sample and contents of the flask from moisture. Stir vigorously and titrate with Karl Fischer reagent to the same end point. Calculate the water content of the sample from the titer and volume of Karl Fischer reagent consumed by the sample.

Notes

(Ethylenedinitrilo)tetraacetic Acid

Ethylenediaminetetraacetic Acid

$(HOCOCH_2)_2NCH_2CH_2N(CH_2COOH)_2$ Formula Wt. 292.25

REQUIREMENTS

Assay. Not less than 99.4 nor more than 100.6 per cent $C_{10}H_{16}N_2O_8$.
Insoluble in dilute ammonium hydroxide. Not more than 0.005 per cent.
Residue after ignition. Not more than 0.20 per cent.
Nitrilotriacetic acid $[(HOCOCH_2)_3N]$. Not more than 0.1 per cent.
Heavy metals (as Pb). Not more than 0.001 per cent.
Iron (Fe). Not more than 0.005 per cent.

TESTS

Assay. Transfer about 4 grams of the sample, accurately weighed, into a 250-ml. volumetric flask, dissolve in 25 ml. of 1N sodium hydroxide, dilute to volume, and mix. To about 200 mg., accurately weighed, of chelometric standard calcium carbonate in a 400-ml. beaker, add 10 ml. of water and swirl to form a slurry. Cover the beaker with a watch glass, add 2 ml. of dilute hydrochloric acid (10 per cent HCl) from a pipet inserted between the lip of the beaker and the edge of the watch glass, and swirl the contents of the beaker to dissolve the calcium carbonate. Wash down the sides of the beaker, the outer surface of the pipet, and the watch glass, and dilute to about 100 ml. While stirring the standard solution, preferably with a magnetic stirrer, add about 30 ml. of the sample solution from a 50-ml. buret. Add 15 ml. of 1N sodium hydroxide solution and 300 mg. of hydroxy naphthol blue indicator, and continue the titration with the sample solution to a blue end point.

$$\text{Per cent } C_{10}H_{16}N_2O_8 = \frac{W_{CaCO_3} \times 7.300 \times 10^4}{V \times W_{EDTA}}$$

where:

W_{CaCO_3} = weight, in grams, of $CaCO_3$

V = total volume, in ml., of sample solution consumed in the titration

W_{EDTA} = weight, in grams, of EDTA used to prepare the sample solution

Insoluble in dilute ammonium hydroxide. To 20 grams add 190 ml. of water and 0.10 ml. of methyl red indicator solution. Slowly add ammonium hydroxide, keeping the solution acidic, until all the sample is dissolved. Warm if necessary. Heat to boiling and digest in a covered beaker on the steam bath for 1 hour. Filter through a tared filtering crucible, wash thoroughly, and dry at 105°C. The weight of the residue should not exceed 0.0010 gram.

Residue after ignition. Gently ignite 3 grams in a tared crucible or dish until charred. Cool, moisten the char with 1 ml. of sulfuric acid, and ignite again slowly until all carbon and excess sulfuric acid have been volatilized. Finally, ignite at $800 \pm 25°C$. for 15 minutes. The weight of the residue should not exceed 0.0060 gram.

Nitrilotriacetic acid. For a stock solution transfer 10 grams of the sample to a 100-ml. volumetric flask. Dissolve in 87 ml. of potassium hydroxide solution (100 grams KOH per liter), dilute to volume, and mix.

Sample Solution A. Dilute a 10-ml. aliquot of the stock solution to 100 ml. in a volumetric flask.

Control Solution B. Add 1 ml. (10 mg.) of the nitrilotriacetic acid standard* to a 10-ml. aliquot of the stock solution and dilute to 100 ml. in a volumetric flask.

Transfer a 20-ml. aliquot of Sample Solution A to a 150-ml. beaker and a 20-ml. aliquot of Control Solution B to a second 150-ml. beaker. Add to each beaker 1 ml. of potassium hydroxide solution (100 grams KOH per liter) and 2 ml. of ammonium nitrate solution (100 grams NH_4NO_3 per liter). Add approximately 0.05 gram of Eriochrome Black T indicator* and titrate with an aqueous cadmium nitrate solution [30 grams $Cd(NO_3)_2 \cdot 4H_2O$ per liter] to a red end point.

Sample Solution C. Transfer a 20-ml. aliquot of Sample Solution A to a 100-ml. volumetric flask.

Control Solution D. Transfer a 20-ml. aliquot of Control Solution B to a 100-ml. volumetric flask.

Add to each flask a volume of the cadmium nitrate solution equal to the volume determined by the titration plus 0.05 ml. in excess. Add 1.5 ml. of potassium hydroxide solution (100 grams KOH per liter), 10 ml. of ammonium nitrate solution (100 grams NH_4NO_3 per liter), and 0.5 ml. of a 0.1 per cent solution of methyl red in alcohol. Dilute each solution to 100 ml. and mix.

Transfer a portion of Control Solution D to an H-type polarographic cell equipped with a saturated calomel electrode (SCE) and deaerate with nitrogen for 10 minutes. Record the polarogram from −0.6 to −1.2 volts (vs. SCE) at a sensitivity of 0.006 microampere per millimeter. Repeat with Sample Solution C. The diffusion current in Sample Solution C should not exceed 0.1 times the difference in diffusion current between Control Solution D and Sample Solution C.

*Reagents. 1. Nitrilotriacetic Acid Standard. Transfer 1 gram of nitrilotriacetic acid, $(HOCOCH_2)_3N$, to a 100-ml. volumetric flask. Dissolve in 10 ml. of potassium hydroxide solution (100 grams KOH per liter) and dilute to volume with water (1 ml. = 10 mg.).

2. Eriochrome Black T Indicator. Grind 0.2 gram of Eriochrome Black T to a fine powder with 20 grams of potassium chloride.

Sample Solution A. Char 3 grams thoroughly and heat in an oven at 500°C. until most of the carbon is volatilized. Cool, add 0.15 ml. of nitric acid, and heat at 500°C. until all of the carbon is volatilized. Dissolve the residue in 2 ml. of dilute hydrochloric acid (1 + 1), digest in a covered dish on the steam bath for 10 minutes, remove the cover, and evaporate to dryness. Dissolve in 1 ml. of 1N acetic acid and 20 ml. of hot water, digest for 5 minutes, cool, and dilute to 30 ml. (1 ml. = 0.1 gram).

Heavy metals. Dilute a 20-ml. aliquot of Sample Solution A (2-gram sample) to 25 ml. For the standard dilute a solution containing 0.02 mg. of lead ion (Pb) to 25 ml. Adjust the pH of the standard and sample solutions to between 3 and 4 (using a pH meter) with 1N acetic acid or ammonium hydroxide (10 per cent NH_3), dilute to 40 ml., and mix. Add 10 ml. of freshly prepared hydrogen sulfide water to each and mix. Any color in the solution of the sample should not exceed that in the standard.

Iron. To 2 ml. of Sample Solution A (0.2-gram sample) add 2 ml. of hydrochloric acid and dilute to 50 ml. Add 30 to 50 mg. of ammonium persulfate crystals and 3 ml. of ammonium thiocyanate reagent solution. Any red color should not exceed that produced by 0.01 mg. of iron (Fe) in an equal volume of solution containing the quantities of reagents used in the test.

Notes

(Ethylenedinitrilo)tetraacetic Acid Disodium Salt

Ethylenediaminetetraacetic Acid Disodium Salt

$HOCOCH_2(NaOCOCH_2)NCH_2CH_2N(CH_2COONa)$
$CH_2COOH \cdot 2H_2O$ Formula Wt. 372.24

REQUIREMENTS

Assay. Not less than 99.0 nor more than 101.0 per cent $C_{10}H_{14}N_2O_8$-$Na_2 \cdot 2H_2O$.

Insoluble matter. Not more than 0.005 per cent.

pH of a 5 per cent solution. From 4.0 to 6.0 at 25°C.

Nitrilotriacetic acid [$(HOCOCH_2)_3N$]. Not more than 0.1 per cent.

Heavy metals (as Pb). Not more than 0.005 per cent.

Iron (Fe). Not more than 0.010 per cent.

TESTS

Assay. Transfer about 5 grams of the sample, accurately weighed, into a 250-ml. volumetric flask, dissolve in water, dilute to volume, and mix. To about 200 mg., accurately weighed, of chelometric standard calcium carbonate in a 400-ml. beaker, add 10 ml. of water and swirl to form a slurry. Cover the beaker with a watch glass, add 2 ml. of dilute hydrochloric acid (10 per cent HCl) from a pipet inserted between the lip of the beaker and the edge of the watch glass, and swirl the contents of the beaker to dissolve the calcium carbonate. Wash down the sides of the beaker, the outer surface of the pipet, and the watch glass, and dilute to about 100 ml. While stirring the standard solution, preferably with a magnetic stirrer, add about 30 ml. of the sample solution from a 50-ml. buret. Add 15 ml. of 1N sodium hydroxide solution and 300 mg. of hydroxy naphthol blue indicator, and continue the titration with the sample solution to a blue end point.

$$\text{Per cent } C_{10}H_{14}N_2O_8Na_2 \cdot 2H_2O = \frac{W_{CaCO_3} \times 9.298 \times 10^4}{V \times W_{sample}}$$

where,

W_{CaCO_3} = weight, in grams, of $CaCO_3$

V = total volume, in ml., of sample solution consumed in the titration

W_{sample} = weight, in grams, of sample used to prepare the sample solution

Insoluble matter. Dissolve 20 grams in 200 ml. of hot water, heat to boiling, and digest in a covered beaker on the steam bath for 1 hour.

Filter through a tared filtering crucible, wash thoroughly, and dry at 105°C. The weight of the residue should not exceed 0.0010 gram.

pH of a 5 per cent solution. Dissolve 5 grams in carbon dioxide- and ammonia-free water and dilute to 100 ml. Determine the pH by the method described on page 18. The pH should be from 4.0 to 6.0 at 25°C.

Nitrilotriacetic acid. For a stock solution transfer 10 grams of the sample to a 100-ml. volumetric flask. Dissolve in 40 ml. of potassium hydroxide solution (100 grams KOH per liter), dilute to volume, and mix.

Sample Solution A. Dilute a 10-ml. aliquot of the stock solution to 100 ml. in a volumetric flask.

Control Solution B. Add 1 ml. (10 mg.) of the nitrilotriacetic acid standard* to a 10-ml. aliquot of the stock solution and dilute to 100 ml. in a volumetric flask.

Transfer a 20-ml. aliquot of Sample Solution A to a 150-ml. beaker and a 20-ml. aliquot of Control Solution B to a second 150-ml. beaker. Add to each beaker 1 ml. of potassium hydroxide solution (100 grams KOH per liter) and 2 ml. of ammonium nitrate solution (100 grams NH_4NO_3 per liter). Add approximately 0.05 gram of Eriochrome Black T indicator* and titrate with an aqueous cadmium nitrate solution [30 grams $Cd(NO_3)_2 \cdot 4H_2O$ per liter] to a red end point.

Sample Solution C. Transfer a 20-ml. aliquot of Sample Solution A to a 100-ml. volumetric flask.

Control Solution D. Transfer a 20-ml. aliquot of Control Solution B to a 100-ml. volumetric flask.

Add to each flask a volume of the cadmium nitrate solution equal to the volume determined by the titration plus 0.05 ml. in excess. Add 1.5 ml. of potassium hydroxide solution (100 grams KOH per liter), 10 ml. of ammonium nitrate solution (100 grams NH_4NO_3 per liter), and 0.5 ml. of a 0.1 per cent solution of methyl red in alcohol. Dilute each solution to 100 ml. and mix.

Transfer a portion of Control Solution D to an H-type polarographic cell equipped with a saturated calomel electrode (SCE) and deaerate with nitrogen for 10 minutes. Record the polarogram from −0.6 to −1.2 volts (vs. SCE) at a sensitivity of 0.006 microampere per millimeter. Repeat with Sample Solution C. The diffusion current in Sample Solution C should not exceed 0.1 times the difference in diffusion current between Control Solution D and Sample Solution C.

*Reagents. 1. Nitrilotriacetic Acid Standard. Transfer 1 gram of nitrilotriacetic acid, $(HOCOCH_2)_3N$, to a 100-ml. volumetric flask. Dissolve in 10 ml. of potassium hydroxide solution (100 grams KOH per liter) and dilute to volume with water (1 ml. = 10 mg.).

2. Eriochrome Black T Indicator. Grind 0.2 gram of Eriochrome Black T to a fine powder with 20 grams of potassium chloride.

Sample Solution A. To 1 gram add 1 ml. of sulfuric acid, heat cautiously until the sample is charred, and ignite in an oven at 500°C. until most of the carbon is volatilized. Cool, add 1 ml. of nitric acid, heat until the acid is evaporated, and ignite again at 500°C. until all of the carbon is volatilized. Cool, add 4 ml. of dilute hydrochloric acid (1 + 1), digest on the steam bath for 10 minutes, and evaporate to dryness. Add 10 ml. of 10 per cent ammonium acetate solution and digest on the steam bath for 30 minutes. Filter, wash thoroughly, and dilute to 50 ml. (1 ml. = 0.02 gram).

Heavy metals. For the sample dilute a 20-ml. aliquot of Sample Solution A (0.4-gram sample) to 25 ml. For the standard dilute a solution containing 0.02 mg. of lead ion (Pb) to 25 ml. Adjust the pH of the standard and sample solutions to between 3 and 4 (using a pH meter) with $1N$ acetic acid or ammonium hydroxide (10 per cent NH_3), dilute to 40 ml., and mix. Add 10 ml. of freshly prepared hydrogen sulfide water to each and mix. Any color in the solution of the sample should not exceed that in the standard.

Iron. To 5 ml. of Sample Solution A (0.1-gram sample) add 2 ml. of hydrochloric acid and dilute to 50 ml. Add 30 to 50 mg. of ammonium persulfate crystals and 3 ml. of ammonium thiocyanate reagent solution. Any red color should not exceed that produced by 0.01 mg. of iron (Fe) in an equal volume of solution and containing the quantities of reagents used in the test.

Notes

Ferric Ammonium Sulfate

$FeNH_4(SO_4)_2 \cdot 12H_2O$ Formula Wt. 482.19

REQUIREMENTS

Appearance.   Pale violet crystals.
Insoluble matter.   Not more than 0.010 per cent.
Chloride (Cl).   To pass test (limit about 0.001 per cent).
Nitrate (NO_3).   To pass test (limit about 0.01 per cent).
Copper (Cu).   Not more than 0.003 per cent.
Ferrous iron (Fe^{++}).   To pass test (limit about 0.001 per cent).
Substances not precipitated by ammonium hydroxide.   Not more than 0.05 per cent.
Zinc (Zn).   Not more than 0.003 per cent.

TESTS

Insoluble matter.   Dissolve 10 grams in 100 ml. of dilute hydrochloric acid $(1 + 99)$ and digest in a covered beaker on the steam bath for 1 hour. Filter through a tared filtering crucible, wash thoroughly, and dry at 105°C. The weight of the residue should not exceed 0.0010 gram.

Chloride.   Dissolve 4 grams in 40 ml. of dilute nitric acid $(1 + 9)$, filter if necessary through a chloride-free filter, and dilute to 60 ml. For the sample use a 30-ml. aliquot of the solution. For the control add 0.01 mg. of chloride ion (Cl) and 1 ml. of nitric acid to a 15-ml. aliquot of the solution and dilute to 30 ml. To each solution add 1 ml. of silver nitrate reagent solution. Any turbidity in the solution of the sample should not exceed that in the control.

Nitrate.   Dissolve 2.0 grams in 1.0 ml. of water by swirling in a test tube. Add 10 ml. of dilute ammonium hydroxide $(1 + 1)$, mix well, and filter through a dry filter paper. Do not wash the precipitate.

Sample Solution A.   Add 1.0 ml. of the filtrate to 2.0 ml. of water, dilute to 50 ml. with brucine sulfate reagent solution, and mix.

Control Solution B.   Add 1.0 ml. of the filtrate to 2.0 ml. of the standard nitrate solution containing 0.01 mg. of nitrate ion (NO_3) per ml., dilute to 50 ml. with brucine sulfate reagent solution, and mix.

Blank Solution C.   Use 50 ml. of brucine sulfate reagent solution.

Heat the three solutions in a preheated (boiling) water bath for 10 minutes. Cool rapidly in an ice bath to room temperature. Set a spectrophotometer at 410 mμ and, using 1-cm. cells, adjust the instrument to read 0 absorbance with Blank Solution C in the light path, then determine the absorbance of Sample Solution A. Adjust the instrument to read 0 absorbance with Sample Solution A in the light path and determine the absorbance of Control Solution B. The absorbance of Sample Solution A should not exceed that of Control Solution B.

Copper. Dissolve 2 grams in 100 ml. of water. For the sample use 10 ml. (0.2-gram sample) of this solution. For the standard add 0.006 mg. of copper ion (Cu) and 0.006 mg. of zinc ion (Zn) to 10 ml. of water. Transfer the solutions to separatory funnels and to each add 50 ml. of a 10 per cent solution of ammonium tartrate in dilute ammonium hydroxide (1 + 9). (The solution of ammonium tartrate in dilute ammonium hydroxide should be purified by extracting with small portions of dithizone extraction solution in chloroform.) Add 10 ml. of dithizone standard solution in chloroform to each separatory funnel, shake vigorously for 2 minutes, and allow to separate. Draw off the dithizone solution, and repeat the extraction with 10-ml. portions of dithizone standard solution in chloroform until the color of the last portion remains unchanged after shaking for 2 minutes. Combine the dithizone extracts in a separatory funnel, add 15 ml. of dilute hydrochloric acid (1 + 250) to each chloroform solution, shake vigorously for 2 minutes, and allow the phases to separate. Draw off the chloroform, and wash it again with 15 ml. of the dilute hydrochloric acid (1 + 250). Combine these acid washings with the previous corresponding acid washings, and reserve each solution for the determination of *Zinc*. Combine the chloroform extracts, and dilute with chloroform to a definite volume. Any red color, producing a purplish hue in the chloroform from the sample solution, should not exceed that in the chloroform from the standard.

Ferrous iron. Dissolve 1 gram in a mixture of 20 ml. of water and 1 ml. of hydrochloric acid and add 0.05 ml. of a freshly prepared 5 per cent solution of potassium ferricyanide. No blue or green color should be produced in 1 minute.

Substances not precipitated by ammonium hydroxide. Dissolve 2 grams in 50 ml. of water. Heat to boiling and pour *slowly with constant stirring* into 20 ml. of dilute ammonium hydroxide (1 + 4). Filter while hot and wash with hot water until the filtrate measures 100 ml. Evaporate the filtrate to dryness in a tared dish and ignite at 800° ± 25°C. for 15 minutes. The weight of the residue should not exceed 0.0010 gram.

Zinc. Adjust the pH of the acid extracts reserved from the test for *Copper* to between 5.0 and 5.5 (using a pH meter) with 0.5N sodium acetate solution that has been extracted with dithizone extraction solution before use. Add 1 ml. of 0.1N sodium thiosulfate and 5 ml. of dithizone standard solution in carbon tetrachloride. Shake vigorously for 2 minutes and allow the phases to separate. Draw off the carbon tetrachloride and repeat the extraction with another 5-ml. portion of dithizone standard solution in carbon tetrachloride. Combine the respective carbon tetrachloride extracts and dilute to 25 ml. with carbon tetrachloride. Any red color, producing a purplish hue in the carbon tetrachloride from the solution of the sample, should not exceed that in the carbon tetrachloride from the standard.

Notes

Ferric Chloride

FeCl$_3$·6H$_2$O   Formula Wt. 270.30

REQUIREMENTS

Insoluble matter. Not more than 0.010 per cent.
Nitrate (NO$_3$). To pass test (limit about 0.01 per cent).
Phosphorus Compounds (as PO$_4$). Not more than 0.010 per cent.
Sulfate (SO$_4$). Not more than 0.01 per cent.
Arsenic (As). Not more than 0.002 per cent.
Copper (Cu). Not more than 0.003 per cent.
Ferrous iron (Fe^{++}). To pass test (limit about 0.002 per cent).
Substances not precipitated by ammonium hydroxide (as sulfates). Not more than 0.10 per cent.
Zinc (Zn). Not more than 0.003 per cent.

TESTS

Insoluble matter. Dissolve 10 grams in 50 ml. of dilute hydrochloric acid (1 + 49), heat to boiling, and digest in a covered beaker on the steam bath for 1 hour. Filter through a tared filtering crucible, wash with warm dilute hydrochloric acid (1 + 99) until the washings are free of iron, and dry at 105°C. The weight of the residue should not exceed 0.0010 gram.

Sample Solution A for the determination of Nitrate, Sulfate, and Substances not precipitated by ammonium hydroxide. Dissolve 10 grams in 75 ml. of water, heat to boiling, and pour *slowly with constant stirring* into 200 ml. of dilute ammonium hydroxide (1 + 3). Filter through a folded filter while still hot, wash with hot water until the volume of the filtrate plus washings measures 300 ml., and thoroughly mix the solution (1 ml. = 0.033 gram).

Nitrate.

Sample Solution A-1. Add 42 ml. of brucine sulfate reagent solution and 2 ml. of water to 6 ml. of Sample Solution A (0.2-gram sample).

Control Solution B. Add 42 ml. of brucine sulfate reagent solution and 2 ml. of the standard nitrate solution containing 0.01 mg. of nitrate ion (NO$_3$) per ml. to 6 ml. of Sample Solution A.

Blank Solution C. Add 42 ml. of brucine sulfate reagent solution to 8 ml. of water.

Heat the three solutions in a preheated (boiling) water bath for 10 minutes. Cool rapidly in an ice bath to room temperature. Set a spectrophotometer at 410 mμ and, using 1-cm. cells, adjust the instrument to read 0 absorbance with Blank Solution C in the light path, then determine the absorbance of Sample Solution A-1. Adjust the instrument to read 0 absorbance with Sample Solution A-1 in the light path and determine the absorbance of Control Solution B. The absorbance of Sample Solution A-1 should not exceed that of Control Solution B.

Phosphorus compounds.   Dissolve 5 grams in 40 ml. of dilute nitric acid (1 + 1) and evaporate on the steam bath to a sirupy residue. Dissolve the residue in about 80 ml. of water, dilute to 100 ml., and dilute a 20-ml. aliquot of this solution to 100 ml. For the test dilute a 10-ml. aliquot (0.1-gram sample) to 70 ml. Prepare a standard containing 0.01 mg. of phosphate ion (PO$_4$) in 70 ml. of water. To each solution add 5 ml. of ammonium molybdate solution (5 grams in 50 ml.) and adjust the pH to 1.8 (using a pH meter) by adding dilute hydrochloric acid (1 + 1) or dilute ammonium hydroxide (1 + 1). Cautiously heat the solutions to boiling but do not boil, and cool to room temperature. If a precipitate forms, it will dissolve when the solution is acidified in the next step. To each solution add 10 ml. of hydrochloric acid and dilute each to 100 ml. Transfer the solutions to separatory funnels, add 35 ml. of ether to each, shake vigorously, and allow to separate. Draw off and discard the aqueous phases. Wash the ether phases twice with 10-ml. portions of dilute hydrochloric acid (1 + 9), discarding the washings each time. To the washed ether phases add 10 ml. of dilute hydrochloric acid (1 + 9) to which has just been added 0.2 ml. of a freshly prepared 2 per cent solution of stannous chloride in hydrochloric acid. Shake the solutions and allow the phases to separate. Any blue color in the ether phase from the solution of the sample should not exceed that in the ether phase from the standard.

Sulfate.   Evaporate 120 ml. of Sample Solution A (4-gram sample) to 100 ml., add 1 ml. of hydrochloric acid, and heat to boiling. Add 5 ml. of barium chloride reagent solution, digest in a covered beaker on the steam bath for 2 hours, and allow to stand overnight. If a precipitate is formed, filter, wash thoroughly, and ignite. The weight of the precipitate should not be more than 0.0010 gram greater than the weight obtained in a complete blank test.

Arsenic.   Dissolve 1 gram in water and dilute to 100 ml. Determine the arsenic in 10 ml. of this solution by the Gutzeit method (page 11), omitting the addition of the potassium iodide solution. The stain should not exceed that produced by 0.002 mg. of arsenic (As).

Copper. Dissolve 2 grams in 100 ml. of water. For the sample use 10 ml. (0.2-gram sample) of this solution. For the standard add 0.006 mg. of copper ion (Cu) and 0.006 mg. of zinc ion (Zn) to 10 ml. of water. Transfer the solutions to separatory funnels and to each add 50 ml. of a 10 per cent solution of ammonium tartrate in dilute ammonium hydroxide (1 + 9). (The solution of ammonium tartrate in dilute ammonium hydroxide should be purified by extracting with small portions of dithizone extraction solution in chloroform.) Add 10 ml. of dithizone standard solution in chloroform to each separatory funnel, shake vigorously for 2 minutes, and allow to separate. Draw off the dithizone solution, and repeat the extraction with 10-ml. portions of dithizone standard solution in chloroform until the color of the last portion remains unchanged after shaking for 2 minutes. Combine the dithizone extracts in a separatory funnel, add 15 ml. of dilute hydrochloric acid (1 + 250) to each chloroform solution, shake vigorously for 2 minutes, and allow the phases to separate. Draw off the chloroform, and wash it again with 15 ml. of the dilute hydrochloric acid (1 + 250). Combine these acid washings with the previous corresponding acid washings, and reserve each solution for the determination of *Zinc*. Combine the chloroform extracts, and dilute with chloroform to a definite volume. Any red color, producing a purplish hue in the chloroform from the sample solution, should not exceed that in the chloroform from the standard.

Ferrous iron. Dissolve 0.5 gram in 20 ml. of dilute hydrochloric acid (1 + 19) and add 0.05 ml. of a freshly prepared 5 per cent solution of potassium ferricyanide. No blue color should be produced in 1 minute.

Substances not precipitated by ammonium hydroxide. To 30 ml. of Sample Solution A (1-gram sample) add 0.50 ml. of sulfuric acid, evaporate in a tared dish or crucible, ignite cautiously until ammonium salts are volatilized, and finally ignite at 800° ± 25°C. for 15 minutes. The weight of the residue should not exceed 0.0010 gram.

Zinc. Adjust the pH of the acid extracts reserved from the test for *Copper* to between 5.0 and 5.5 (using a pH meter) with 0.5N sodium acetate solution that has been extracted with dithizone extraction solution before use. Add 1 ml. of 0.1N sodium thiosulfate and 5 ml. of dithizone standard solution in carbon tetrachloride. Shake vigorously for 2 minutes and allow the phases to separate. Draw off the carbon tetrachloride and repeat the extraction with another 5-ml. portion of dithizone standard solution in carbon tetrachloride. Combine the respective carbon tetra-chloride extracts and dilute to 25 ml. with carbon tetrachloride. Any red color, producing a purplish hue in the carbon tetrachloride from the solution of the sample, should not exceed that in the carbon tetrachloride from the standard.

Notes

Ferric Nitrate

$Fe(NO_3)_3 \cdot 9H_2O$ Formula Wt. 404.00

REQUIREMENTS

Insoluble matter.   Not more than 0.005 per cent.
Chloride (Cl).   Not more than 0.0005 per cent.
Sulfate (SO$_4$).   Not more than 0.010 per cent.
Substances not precipitated by ammonium hydroxide (as sulfates).
    Not more than 0.10 per cent.

TESTS

Insoluble matter.   Dissolve 20 grams in 200 ml. of dilute nitric acid (1 + 99), heat to boiling, and digest in a covered beaker on the steam bath for 1 hour. Filter through a tared filtering crucible, wash thoroughly, and dry at 105°C. The weight of the residue should not exceed 0.0010 gram.

Chloride.   Dissolve 2 grams in 20 ml. of water, filter if necessary through a chloride-free filter, and add 1 ml. of nitric acid plus 1 ml. of phosphoric acid and 1 ml. of silver nitrate reagent solution. Any turbidity should not exceed that produced by 0.01 mg. of chloride ion (Cl) in an equal volume of solution containing the quantities of reagents used in the test.

> **Sample Solution A.**   Dissolve 5 grams in 70 ml. of water, heat to boiling, and pour *slowly with constant stirring* into 100 ml. of dilute ammonium hydroxide (1 + 6). Filter through a folded filter while still hot and wash with hot water until the filtrate (Sample Solution A) measures 250 ml. Mix thoroughly (1 ml. = 0.02 gram).

Sulfate.   To 25 ml. (0.5-gram sample) of Sample Solution A add 5 ml. of hydrochloric acid and 10 ml. of nitric acid. For the standard add 0.05 mg. of sulfate ion (SO$_4$) and 1.5 ml. of ammonium hydroxide to 25 ml. of water and add 5 ml. of hydrochloric acid and 10 ml. of nitric acid. Digest each solution in a covered beaker on the steam bath until reaction ceases, uncover, and evaporate to dryness. Dissolve the residues in 4 ml. of water plus 1 ml. of dilute hydrochloric acid (1 + 19), filter if necessary through a small filter, wash with two 2-ml. portions of water, and dilute to 10 ml. To each solution add 1 ml. of barium chloride reagent solution. Any turbidity in the solution of the sample should not exceed that in the standard. Compare 10 minutes after adding the barium chloride to the sample and standard solutions.

Substances not precipitated by ammonium hydroxide. Evaporate 50 ml. of Sample Solution A to dryness in a tared dish and add 0.50 ml. of sulfuric acid. Heat carefully to volatilize the ammonium salts and excess sulfuric acid, and finally ignite at $800° \pm 25°C$. for 15 minutes. The weight of the residue should not exceed 0.0010 gram.

Notes

Ferrous Ammonium Sulfate

Fe(NH$_4$)$_2$(SO$_4$)$_2 \cdot$6H$_2$O   Formula Wt. 392.14

REQUIREMENTS

Insoluble matter. Not more than 0.010 per cent.
Phosphate (PO$_4$). Not more than 0.003 per cent.
Copper (Cu). Not more than 0.003 per cent.
Ferric iron (Fe^{+3}). Not more than 0.01 per cent.
Manganese (Mn). Not more than 0.010 per cent.
Substances not precipitated by ammonium hydroxide. Not more than
    0.050 per cent.
Zinc (Zn). Not more than 0.003 per cent.

TESTS

Insoluble matter. Dissolve 10 grams in 100 ml. of freshly boiled dilute
sulfuric acid (1 + 99), heat to boiling, and digest in a covered beaker
on the steam bath for 1 hour. Filter through a tared filtering crucible,
wash thoroughly, and dry at 105°C. The weight of the residue should
not exceed 0.0010 gram.

Phosphate. Dissolve 1 gram in 10 ml. of water and add 2 ml. of nitric
acid. Boil to oxidize the iron and expel the excess gases. Dilute to 90 ml.
Dilute a 30-ml. aliquot to 80 ml., add 5 ml. of ammonium molybdate
solution (5 grams in 50 ml.), and adjust the pH to 1.8 (using a pH meter) with dilute ammonium hydroxide (1 + 1). Prepare a standard containing 0.01 mg. of phosphate ion (PO$_4$), the residue from evaporation
of the amount of ammonium hydroxide used in adjusting the pH of
the sample, and 5 ml. of the ammonium molybdate solution in 85 ml.
Adjust the pH to 1.8 (using a pH meter) with dilute hydrochloric acid
(1 + 9). Cautiously heat the solutions to boiling, but do not boil, and
cool to room temperature. If a precipitate forms, it will dissolve when
acidified in the next operation. Add 10 ml. of hydrochloric acid and
dilute to 100 ml. Transfer the solutions to separatory funnels, add 35 ml.
of ether to each, shake vigorously, and allow to separate. Draw off and
discard the aqueous phase. Wash the ether phase twice with 10-ml. portions of dilute hydrochloric acid (1 + 9), discarding the washings each
time. Add 10 ml. of dilute hydrochloric acid (1 + 9) to which has just
been added 0.2 ml. of a freshly prepared 2 per cent solution of stannous
chloride in hydrochloric acid, shake, and allow to separate. Any blue
color in the ether extract from the sample should not exceed that in the
ether extract from the standard.

ACS SPECIFICATIONS   **255**

Copper. Dissolve 2 grams in 25 ml. of dilute nitric acid $(1 + 4)$. Boil to oxidize the iron and expel the excess gases. Cool and dilute to 100 ml. For the sample use 10 ml. (0.2-gram sample) of this solution. For the standard add 0.006 mg. of copper ion (Cu) and 0.006 mg. of zinc ion (Zn) to 10 ml. of water. Transfer the solutions to separatory funnels, and to each add 50 ml. of a 10 per cent solution of ammonium tartrate in dilute ammonium hydroxide $(1 + 9)$. (The solution of ammonium tartrate in dilute ammonium hydroxide should be purified by extracting with small portions of dithizone extraction solution in chloroform.) Add 10 ml. of dithizone standard solution in chloroform to each separatory funnel, shake vigorously for 2 minutes, and allow to separate. Draw off the dithizone solution, and repeat the extraction with 10-ml. portions of dithizone standard solution in chloroform until the color of the last portion remains unchanged after shaking for 2 minutes. Combine the dithizone extracts in a separatory funnel, add 15 ml. of dilute hydrochloric acid $(1 + 250)$ to each chloroform solution, shake vigorously for 2 minutes, and allow the phases to separate. Draw off the chloroform, and wash it again with 15 ml. of the dilute hydrochloric acid $(1 + 250)$. Combine these acid washings with the previous corresponding acid washings, and reserve each solution for the determination of *Zinc*. Combine the chloroform extracts, and dilute with chloroform to a definite volume. The red color, producing a purplish hue in the chloroform from the sample solution, should not exceed that in the chloroform from the standard.

Ferric iron. Place 0.2 gram of the sample and 0.5 gram of sodium bicarbonate in a dry 125-ml. glass-stoppered Erlenmeyer flask. For the control place 0.1 gram of the sample and 0.5 gram of sodium bicarbonate in a similar flask. To each flask add 94 ml. of a freshly boiled and cooled solution of dilute sulfuric acid $(1 + 25)$ and loosely stopper the flasks until effervescence stops. To the control add 0.01 mg. of ferric ion (Fe^{+3}). Add 6 ml. of ammonium thiocyanate reagent solution to each flask. Any red color in the solution of the sample should not exceed that in the control.

Manganese. Dissolve 0.1 gram in 35 ml. of water and add 10 ml. of nitric acid, 5 ml. of sulfuric acid, and 5 ml. of phosphoric acid. Prepare a standard containing 0.01 mg. of manganese ion (Mn) in a solution of equal volume containing the same quantities of acids used to dissolve the sample. Heat the solutions to boiling and boil gently for 5 minutes. Cool the solutions, add 0.25 gram of potassium periodate to each, again boil for 5 minutes, and cool. Any color in the solution of the sample should not exceed that in the standard.

Substances not precipitated by ammonium hydroxide. Dissolve 2 grams in 25 ml. of dilute nitric acid $(1 + 4)$ and boil gently to oxidize the iron. Pour the solution slowly with constant stirring into 50 ml. of dilute ammonium hydroxide $(1 + 4)$. Filter, wash moderately with hot water, and evaporate the solution to dryness in a tared dish. Heat gently to volatilize the excess ammonium salts and finally ignite at $800° \pm 25°$C. for 15 minutes. The weight of the residue should not exceed 0.0010 gram.

Zinc. Adjust the pH of the acid extracts reserved from the test for *Copper* to between 5.0 and 5.5 (using a pH meter) with $0.5N$ sodium acetate solution that has been extracted with dithizone extraction solution before use. Add 1 ml. of $0.1N$ sodium thiosulfate and 5 ml. of dithizone standard solution in carbon tetrachloride. Shake vigorously for 2 minutes and allow the phases to separate. Draw off the carbon tetrachloride and repeat the extraction with another 5-ml. portion of dithizone standard solution in carbon tetrachloride. Combine the respective carbon tetrachloride extracts and dilute to 25 ml. with carbon tetrachloride. The red color, producing a purplish hue in the carbon tetrachloride from the solution of the sample, should not exceed that in the carbon tetrachloride from the standard.

Notes

Ferrous Sulfate

$FeSO_4 \cdot 7H_2O$ Formula Wt. 278.02

REQUIREMENTS

Insoluble matter.   Not more than 0.010 per cent.
Chloride (Cl).   To pass test (limit about 0.001 per cent).
Phosphate (PO_4).   Not more than 0.001 per cent.
Copper (Cu).   Not more than 0.005 per cent.
Ferric iron (Fe^{+3}).   Not more than 0.05 per cent.
Manganese (Mn).   Not more than 0.05 per cent.
Substances not precipitated by ammonium hydroxide.   Not more than 0.05 per cent.
Zinc (Zn).   Not more than 0.005 per cent.

TESTS

Insoluble matter.   Dissolve 10 grams in 100 ml. of freshly boiled dilute sulfuric acid (1 + 99), heat to boiling, and digest in a covered beaker on the steam bath for 1 hour. Filter through a tared filtering crucible, wash thoroughly, and dry at 105°C. The weight of the residue should not exceed 0.0010 gram.

Chloride.   Dissolve 1 gram in 10 ml. of water and add slowly 2 ml. of nitric acid. After the evolution of nitrogen oxides has ceased, dilute to 15 ml., filter if necessary through a small chloride-free filter, and add 1 ml. of silver nitrate reagent solution. Any turbidity should not exceed that produced by 0.01 mg. of chloride ion (Cl) in an equal volume of solution containing the quantities of reagents used in the test. The comparison is best made by superimposing a tube containing 1 gram of sample and 2 ml. of nitric acid in 14 ml. of water over the tube containing the standard turbidity and placing a tube containing 16 ml. of water below the tube containing the sample and added reagents. Both turbidities are thus viewed through the same depth and color of solution. The comparison tubes may be machine-made vials, long style, of about 20-ml. capacity.

Phosphate.   Dissolve 1 gram in 10 ml. of dilute nitric acid (1 + 5) and boil to expel the excess gases. Dilute the solution to 80 ml., add 5 ml. of ammonium molybdate solution (5 grams in 50 ml.), and adjust the pH to 1.8 (using a pH meter) with dilute ammonium hydroxide (1 + 1). Prepare a standard containing 0.01 mg. of phosphate ion (PO_4), the residue from evaporation of the amount of ammonium hydroxide used in adjusting the pH of the sample, and 5 ml. of the ammonium molybdate solution in 85 ml. Adjust the pH to 1.8 (using a pH meter) with dilute hydrochloric acid (1 + 9). Cautiously heat the solutions to boiling, but do not boil, and cool to room temperature. If a precipitate forms, it will dissolve when acidified in the next operation. Add 10 ml. of hydrochloric acid and dilute to 100 ml. Transfer the solutions to separatory funnels, add 35 ml. of ether to each, shake vigorously, and allow to separate. Draw off and discard the aqueous phase. Wash the ether phase twice with 10-ml. portions of dilute hydrochloric acid (1 + 9), discarding the washings each time. Add 10 ml. of dilute hydrochloric acid (1 + 9) to which has just been added 0.2 ml. of a freshly prepared 2 per cent solution of stannous chloride in hydrochloric acid, shake, and allow to separate. Any blue color in the ether extract from the sample should not exceed that in the ether extract from the standard.

Copper. Dissolve 1.2 grams in 25 ml. of dilute nitric acid (1 + 4). Boil to oxidize the iron and expel the excess gases. Cool and dilute to 100 ml. For the sample use 10 ml. (0.12-gram sample) of this solution. For the standard add 0.006 mg. of copper ion (Cu) and 0.006 mg. of zinc ion (Zn) to 10 ml. of water. Transfer the solutions to separatory funnels, and to each add 50 ml. of a 10 per cent solution of ammonium tartrate in dilute ammonium hydroxide (1 + 9). (The solution of ammonium tartrate in dilute ammonium hydroxide should be purified by extracting with a small portion of dithizone extraction solution in chloroform.) Add 10 ml. of dithizone standard solution in chloroform to each separatory funnel, shake vigorously for 2 minutes, and allow to separate. Draw off the dithizone solution, and repeat the extraction with 10-ml. portions of dithizone standard solution in chloroform until the color of the last portion remains unchanged after shaking for 2 minutes. Combine the dithizone extracts in a separatory funnel, add 15 ml. of dilute hydrochloric acid (1 + 250) to each chloroform solution, shake vigorously for 2 minutes, and allow the phases to separate. Draw off the chloroform, and wash it again with 15 ml. of the dilute hydrochloric acid (1 + 250). Combine these acid washings with the previous corresponding acid washings, and reserve each solution for the determination of *Zinc*. Combine the chloroform extracts, and dilute with chloroform to a definite volume. The red color, producing a purplish hue in the chloroform from the sample solution, should not exceed that in the chloroform from the standard.

Ferric iron. Place 0.2 gram of the sample and 0.5 gram of sodium bicarbonate in a dry 125-ml. glass-stoppered Erlenmeyer flask. For the control place 0.1 gram of the sample and 0.5 gram of sodium bicarbonate in a similar flask. To each flask add 94 ml. of a freshly boiled and cooled solution of dilute sulfuric acid (1 + 25) and loosely stopper the flasks until effervescence stops. To the control add 0.05 mg. of ferric ion (Fe^{+3}). Add 6 ml. of ammonium thiocyanate reagent solution to each flask. Any red color in the solution of the sample should not exceed that in the control.

Manganese. Dissolve 0.1 gram in 35 ml. of water and add 10 ml. of nitric acid, 5 ml. of sulfuric acid, and 5 ml. of phosphoric acid. Prepare a standard containing 0.05 mg. of manganese ion (Mn) in a solution of equal volume containing the same quantities of acids used to dissolve the sample. Heat the solutions to boiling and boil gently for 5 minutes. Cool the solutions, add 0.25 gram of potassium periodate to each, again boil for 5 minutes, and cool. Any color in the solution of the sample should not exceed that in the standard.

Substances not precipitated by ammonium hydroxide. Dissolve 2 grams in 25 ml. of dilute nitric acid (1 + 4) and boil gently to oxidize the iron. Pour the solution slowly with constant stirring into 50 ml. of dilute ammonium hydroxide (1 + 4). Filter, wash moderately with hot water, and evaporate the solution to dryness in a tared dish. Heat gently to volatilize the excess ammonium salts and finally ignite at 800° ± 25°C. for 15 minutes. The weight of the residue should not exceed 0.0010 gram.

Zinc. Adjust the pH of the acid extracts reserved from the test for *Copper* to between 5.0 and 5.5 (using a pH meter) with 0.5N sodium acetate solution that has been extracted with dithizone extraction solution before use. Add 1 ml. of 0.1N sodium thiosulfate and 5 ml. of dithizone standard solution in carbon tetrachloride. Shake vigorously for 2 minutes and allow the phases to separate. Draw off the carbon tetrachloride and repeat the extraction with another 5-ml. portion of dithizone standard solution in carbon tetrachloride. Combine the respective carbon tetrachloride extracts and dilute to 25 ml. with carbon tetrachloride. The red color, producing a purplish hue in the carbon tetrachloride from the solution of the sample, should not exceed that in the carbon tetrachloride from the standard.

Notes

Formaldehyde Solution

(With stabilizer)

HCHO   Formula Wt. 30.03

Note. This reagent contains 10 to 15 per cent of methanol as a stabilizer.

REQUIREMENTS

Assay. Not less than 36.0 nor more than 38.0 per cent HCHO.
Color (APHA). Not more than 10.
Residue after ignition. Not more than 0.005 per cent.
Acidity (as HCOOH). Not more than 0.03 per cent.
Chloride (Cl). Not more than 0.0005 per cent.
Sulfate (SO$_4$). Not more than 0.002 per cent.
Heavy metals (as Pb). Not more than 0.0005 per cent.
Iron (Fe). Not more than 0.0005 per cent.

TESTS

Assay. Tare a small glass-stoppered flask or weighing bottle containing 15 ml. of water. Quickly add about 3 ml. of the sample, stopper, and weigh accurately. Add this solution carefully to 50.0 ml. of 1N sodium hydroxide, and then add slowly 50 ml. of 3 per cent hydrogen peroxide, previously neutralized to bromothymol blue. Cover with a small funnel and heat on the steam bath for 15 minutes, shaking occasionally with a gentle rotary motion. Cool to room temperature in cold water, rinse the funnel and walls of the flask with water, add 0.20 ml. of bromothymol blue indicator solution, and titrate with 1N sulfuric acid to a bluish-green end point. Determine the quantity of 1N sulfuric acid required in a complete blank test. The difference in quantities of sulfuric acid used is equivalent to the sodium hydroxide neutralized by the formic acid corresponding to the formaldehyde in the sample, correction being made for any significant amount of acid in the 3-ml. sample of formaldehyde. One milliliter of 1N sulfuric acid corresponds to 0.03003 gram of HCHO.

Color (APHA). For the color standard dilute a 2-ml. aliquot of platinum-cobalt stock solution (APHA No. 500) to 100 ml. with water. Compare this solution (APHA No. 10) with 100 ml. of the formaldehyde solution in 100-ml. Nessler tubes, viewed vertically over a white background.

Residue after ignition. Evaporate 20 ml. (20 grams) to dryness in a tared dish on the steam bath, add 0.05 ml. of sulfuric acid to the residue, and ignite gently to volatilize the excess sulfuric acid. Finally, ignite at $800° \pm 25°$C. for 15 minutes. The weight of the residue should not exceed 0.0010 gram.

Acidity. To 10 ml. in a flask containing 20 ml. of water, add 0.15 ml. of bromothymol blue indicator solution, and titrate with $0.1N$ sodium hydroxide. One milliliter of $0.1N$ sodium hydroxide corresponds to 0.004603 gram of HCOOH.

Chloride. Dilute 2 ml. with 20 ml. of water, filter if necessary through a chloride-free filter, and add 1 ml. of nitric acid and 1 ml. of silver nitrate reagent solution. Any turbidity should not exceed that produced by 0.01 mg. of chloride ion (Cl) in an equal volume of solution containing the quantities of reagents used in the test.

Sulfate. Dilute 3 ml. to 10 ml. Add 1 ml. of dilute hydrochloric acid $(1 + 19)$ and 1 ml. of barium chloride reagent solution. Any turbidity should not exceed that produced by 0.06 mg. of sulfate ion (SO_4) in an equal volume of solution containing the quantities of reagents used in the test. Compare 10 minutes after adding the barium chloride to the sample and standard solutions.

Heavy metals. To 4 ml. add about 10 mg. of sodium carbonate, evaporate to dryness, and heat gently to volatilize any organic matter. Dissolve the residue in about 20 ml. of water and dilute to 25 ml. For the standard dilute a solution containing 0.02 mg. of lead ion (Pb) to 25 ml. Adjust the pH of the standard and sample solutions to between 3 and 4 (using a pH meter) with $1N$ acetic acid or ammonium hydroxide (10 per cent NH_3), dilute to 40 ml., and mix. Add 10 ml. of freshly prepared hydrogen sulfide water to each and mix. Any color in the solution of the sample should not exceed that in the standard.

Iron. Dilute 2 ml. to 15 ml. Add 6 ml. of hydroxylamine hydrochloride reagent solution and 4 ml. of 1,10-phenanthroline reagent solution. Adjust the pH to approximately 5 with ammonium hydroxide. Any color should not exceed that produced by 0.01 mg. of iron (Fe) in an equal volume of solution containing the quantities of reagents used in the test. Compare 1 hour after adding the reagents to the sample and standard solutions.

Formic Acid, 98 Per Cent

HCOOH   Formula Wt. 46.03

Caution.   Slow decomposition of this reagent may produce pressure in the bottle. Loosen cap occasionally to vent the gas.

REQUIREMENTS

Assay.   Not less than 98 per cent HCOOH.
Color (APHA).   Not more than 15.
Dilution test.   To pass test.
Residue after evaporation.   Not more than 0.003 per cent.
Acetic acid (CH₃COOH).   Not more than 0.4 per cent.
Ammonium (NH₄).   Not more than 0.005 per cent.
Chloride (Cl).   To pass test (limit about 0.001 per cent).
Sulfate (SO₄).   Not more than 0.003 per cent.
Sulfite (SO₃).   To pass test.
Heavy metals (as Pb).   Not more than 0.001 per cent.
Iron (Fe).   Not more than 0.001 per cent.

TESTS

Assay.   Tare a small glass-stoppered Erlenmeyer flask containing 15 ml. of water. Quickly introduce 1.0 to 1.5 ml. of the sample and weigh. Dilute to about 50 ml. and titrate with $1N$ sodium hydroxide, using phenolphthalein indicator. One milliliter of $1N$ sodium hydroxide corresponds to 0.04603 gram of HCOOH.

Color (APHA).   For the color standard dilute a 3-ml. aliquot of platinum-cobalt stock solution (APHA No. 500) to 100 ml. with water. Compare this solution (APHA No. 15) with 100 ml. of the formic acid in 100-ml. Nessler tubes, viewed vertically over a white background.

Dilution test.   Dilute 1 volume of the acid with 3 volumes of water. No turbidity should be observed within 1 hour.

Residue after evaporation.   Evaporate 42 ml. (50 grams) to dryness in a tared dish on the steam bath and dry the residue at 105°C. for 30 minutes. The weight of the residue should not exceed 0.0015 gram.

Acetic acid.   Dilute 1 ml. to 100 ml. To 50 ml. of this solution in a 250-ml. boiling flask add 5 grams of yellow mercuric oxide. Boil the solution under total reflux for 2 hours, stirring the mixture continuously. Cool, filter, and wash the residue with about 25 ml. of water. Add 0.10 ml. of phenolphthalein indicator solution to the combined filtrate and washings and titrate with $0.02N$ sodium hydroxide. Not more than 2.0

ml. of the 0.02N sodium hydroxide should be required to produce a pink color.

Ammonium. Dilute 8.3 ml. (10 grams) to 100 ml. To 2.0 ml. of this solution add 5 ml. of 10 per cent sodium hydroxide solution, dilute to 50 ml., and add 2 ml. of Nessler reagent. Any color should not exceed that produced by 0.01 mg. of ammonium ion (NH_4) in an equal volume of solution containing the quantities of reagents used in the test.

Chloride. Dilute 1 ml. to 20 ml., filter if necessary through a chloride-free filter and add 1 ml. of nitric acid and 1 ml. of silver nitrate reagent solution. Any turbidity should not exceed that produced by 0.012 mg. of chloride ion (Cl) in an equal volume of solution containing the quantities of reagents used in the test.

Sulfate. To 2 ml. add about 10 mg. of sodium carbonate, evaporate to dryness, and dissolve the residue in 4 ml. of water plus 1 ml. of dilute hydrochloric acid (1 + 19). Filter if necessary through a small filter, wash with two 2-ml. portions of water, and dilute to 15 ml. To 10 ml. of this solution add 1 ml. of barium chloride reagent solution. Any turbidity should not exceed that produced by 0.048 mg. of sulfate ion (SO_4) in an equal volume of solution containing the quantities of reagents used in the test. Compare 10 minutes after adding the barium chloride to the sample and standard solutions.

Sulfite. Dilute 25 ml. with 25 ml. of water and add 0.1 ml. of 0.1N iodine solution. The mixture should retain a distinct yellow color.

Heavy metals. To 1.6 ml. (2 grams) in a beaker add about 10 mg. of sodium carbonate and evaporate to dryness on the steam bath. Dissolve the residue in about 20 ml. of water and dilute to 25 ml. For the standard dilute a solution containing 0.02 mg. of lead ion (Pb) to 25 ml. Adjust the pH of the standard and sample solutions to between 3 and 4 (using a pH meter) with 1N acetic acid or ammonium hydroxide (10 per cent NH_3), dilute to 40 ml., and mix. Add 10 ml. of freshly prepared hydrogen sulfide water to each and mix. Any color in the solution of the sample should not exceed that in the standard.

Iron. To 5 ml. (6 grams) in a beaker add about 10 mg. of sodium carbonate and evaporate to dryness. Dissolve in 6 ml. of hydrochloric acid and dilute to 60 ml. Dilute 10 ml. of the solution to 50 ml. and add 30 to 50 mg. of ammonium persulfate crystals and 3 ml. of ammonium thiocyanate reagent solution. Any red color should not exceed that produced by 0.01 mg. of iron (Fe) in an equal volume of solution containing the quantities of reagents used in the test.

Formic Acid, 88 Per Cent

HCOOH   Formula Wt. 46.03

REQUIREMENTS

Assay.   Not less than 88 per cent HCOOH.
Color (APHA).   Not more than 15.
Dilution test.   To pass test.
Residue after evaporation.   Not more than 0.002 per cent.
Acetic acid (CH_3COOH).   Not more than 0.4 per cent.
Ammonium (NH_4).   Not more than 0.005 per cent.
Chloride (Cl).   To pass test (limit about 0.001 per cent).
Sulfate (SO_4).   Not more than 0.002 per cent.
Sulfite (SO_3).   To pass test.
Heavy metals (as Pb).   Not more than 0.0005 per cent.
Iron (Fe).   Not more than 0.0005 per cent.

TESTS

Assay.   Tare a small glass-stoppered Erlenmeyer flask containing 15 ml. of water. Quickly introduce 1.0 to 1.5 ml. of the sample and weigh. Dilute to about 50 ml. and titrate with $1N$ sodium hydroxide, using phenolphthalein indicator. One milliliter of $1N$ sodium hydroxide corresponds to 0.04603 gram of HCOOH.

Color (APHA).   For the color standard dilute a 3-ml. aliquot of platinum-cobalt stock solution (APHA No. 500) to 100 ml. with water. Compare this solution (APHA No. 15) with 100 ml. of the formic acid in 100-ml. Nessler tubes, viewed vertically over a white background.

Dilution test.   Dilute 1 volume of the acid with 3 volumes of water. No turbidity should be observed within 1 hour.

Residue after evaporation.   Evaporate 42 ml. (50 grams) to dryness in a tared dish on the steam bath and dry the residue at 105°C. for 30 minutes. The weight of the residue should not exceed 0.0010 gram.

Acetic acid.   Dilute 1 ml. to 100 ml. To 50 ml. of this solution in a 250-ml. boiling flask add 5 grams of yellow mercuric oxide. Boil the solution under total reflux for 2 hours, stirring the mixture continuously. Cool, filter, and wash the residue with about 25 ml. of water. Add 0.10 ml. of phenolphthalein indicator solution to the combined filtrate and washings and titrate with $0.02N$ sodium hydroxide. Not more than 2.0 ml. of the $0.02N$ sodium hydroxide should be required to produce a pink color.

Ammonium. Dilute 8.3 ml. (10 grams) to 100 ml. To 2.0 ml. of this solution add 5 ml. of 10 per cent sodium hydroxide solution, dilute to 50 ml., and add 2 ml. of Nessler reagent. Any color should not exceed that produced by 0.01 mg. of ammonium ion (NH_4) in an equal volume of solution containing the quantities of reagents used in the test.

Chloride. Dilute 1 ml. to 20 ml., filter if necessary through a chloride-free filter, and add 1 ml. of nitric acid and 1 ml. of silver nitrate reagent solution. Any turbidity should not exceed that produced by 0.012 mg. of chloride ion (Cl) in an equal volume of solution containing the quantities of reagents used in the test.

Sulfate. To 2 ml. add about 10 mg. of sodium carbonate, evaporate to dryness, and dissolve the residue in 4 ml. of water plus 1 ml. of dilute hydrochloric acid (1 + 19). Filter if necessary through a small filter, wash with two 2-ml. portions of water, dilute to 10 ml., and add 1 ml. of barium chloride reagent solution. Any turbidity should not exceed that produced by 0.048 mg. of sulfate ion (SO_4) in an equal volume of solution containing the quantities of reagents used in the test. Compare 10 minutes after adding the barium chloride to the sample and standard solutions.

Sulfite. Dilute 25 ml. with 25 ml. of water and add 0.1 ml. of 0.1N iodine solution. The mixture should retain a distinct yellow color.

Heavy metals. To 3.3 ml. (4 grams) in a beaker add about 10 mg. of sodium carbonate and evaporate to dryness on the steam bath. Dissolve the residue in about 20 ml. of water and dilute to 25 ml. For the standard dilute a solution containing 0.02 mg. of lead ion (Pb) to 25 ml. Adjust the pH of the standard and sample solutions to between 3 and 4 (using a pH meter) with 1N acetic acid or ammonium hydroxide (10 per cent NH_3), dilute to 40 ml., and mix. Add 10 ml. of freshly prepared hydrogen sulfide water to each and mix. Any color in the solution of the sample should not exceed that in the standard.

Iron. To 5 ml. (6 grams) in a beaker add about 10 mg. of sodium carbonate and evaporate to dryness. Dissolve in 6 ml. of hydrochloric acid and dilute to 60 ml. Dilute 20 ml. of the solution to 50 ml. and add 30 to 50 mg. of ammonium persulfate crystals and 3 ml. of ammonium thiocyanate reagent solution. Any red color should not exceed that produced by 0.01 mg. of iron (Fe) in an equal volume of solution containing the quantities of reagents used in the test.

D-Glucose, Anhydrous

Dextrose, Anhydrous

CH$_2$OH(CHOH)$_4$CHO   Formula Wt. 180.16

REQUIREMENTS

Specific rotation [α]$_D^{25°}$.   Not less than +52.5° nor more than +53.0°.
Insoluble matter.   Not more than 0.005 per cent.
Loss on drying at 105°C.   Not more than 0.20 per cent.
Residue after ignition.   Not more than 0.020 per cent.
Acidity (as CH$_3$COOH).   Not more than 0.015 per cent.
Chloride (Cl).   Not more than 0.010 per cent.
Sulfate and sulfite (as SO$_4$).   Not more than 0.005 per cent.
Starch.   To pass test.
Arsenic (As).   Not more than 0.00004 per cent.
Heavy metals (as Pb).   Not more than 0.0005 per cent.
Iron (Fe).   Not more than 0.0005 per cent.

TESTS

Specific rotation.   Weigh accurately about 10 grams and dissolve in 90 ml. of water in a 100-ml. volumetric flask. Add 0.2 ml. of ammonium hydroxide and dilute to volume at 25°C. Observe the optical rotation in a polarimeter at 25°C. using sodium light, and calculate the specific rotation. It should not be less than +52.5° nor more than +53.0°.

Insoluble matter.   Dissolve 20 grams in 150 ml. of water, heat to boiling, and digest in a covered beaker on the steam bath for 1 hour. Filter through a tared filtering crucible, wash thoroughly, and dry at 105°C. The weight of the residue should not exceed 0.0010 gram.

Loss on drying.   Weigh accurately about 1 gram and dry at 105°C. for 6 hours. The loss in weight should not exceed 0.20 per cent.

Residue after ignition.   Gently ignite 5 grams in a tared crucible or dish until charred. Cool, moisten the char with 2 ml. of sulfuric acid, and ignite again slowly until all carbon and excess sulfuric acid have been volatilized. Finally, ignite at 800° ± 25°C. for 15 minutes. The weight of the residue should not exceed 0.0010 gram.

Acidity.   To 100 ml. of carbon dioxide-free water add 0.10 ml. of phenolphthalein indicator solution and 0.02N sodium hydroxide until a pink color is produced. Dissolve 10 grams of the sample in this solution and titrate with 0.02N sodium hydroxide to the same end point. Not more than 1.25 ml. should be required.

Chloride. Dissolve 0.5 gram in 50 ml. of water, and filter if necessary through a chloride-free filter. Dilute 10 ml. of the solution to 25 ml. and add 1 ml. of nitric acid and 1 ml. of silver nitrate reagent solution. Any turbidity should not exceed that produced by 0.01 mg. of chloride ion (Cl) in an equal volume of solution containing the quantities of reagents used in the test.

Sulfate and sulfite. Dissolve 1 gram in 10 ml. of water. Add 1 ml. of bromine water and boil. Cool and add 1 ml. of dilute hydrochloric acid (1 + 19) and 1 ml. of barium chloride reagent solution. Any turbidity should not exceed that produced by 0.05 mg. of sulfate ion (SO_4) in an equal volume of solution containing the quantities of hydrochloric acid and barium chloride used in the test. Compare 10 minutes after adding the barium chloride to the sample and standard solutions.

Starch. Dissolve 1 gram in 10 ml. of water and add 0.05 ml. of 0.1N iodine solution. No blue color should appear.

Arsenic. Determine the arsenic in 5 grams by the Gutzeit method (page 11). The amount of stain should not exceed that produced by 0.002 mg. of arsenic (As).

Heavy metals. Dissolve 6 grams in about 20 ml. of water and dilute to 30 ml. For the control add 0.02 mg. of lead ion (Pb) to a 5-ml. aliquot of the solution and dilute to 25 ml. For the sample use the remaining 25-ml. portion. Adjust the pH of the control and sample solutions to between 3 and 4 (using a pH meter) with 1N acetic acid or ammonium hydroxide (10 per cent NH_3), dilute to 40 ml., and mix. Add 10 ml. of freshly prepared hydrogen sulfide water to each and mix. Any color in the solution of the sample should not exceed that in the control.

Iron. Dissolve 2 grams in 40 ml. of water, add 2 ml. of hydrochloric acid, and dilute to 50 ml. Add 30 to 50 mg. of ammonium persulfate crystals and 3 ml. of ammonium thiocyanate reagent solution. Any red color should not exceed that produced by 0.01 mg. of iron (Fe) in an equal volume of solution containing the quantities of reagents used in the test.

Notes

Glycerol

CH$_2$OHCHOHCH$_2$OH   Formula Wt. 92.10

REQUIREMENTS

Assay. Not less than 95 per cent by volume.
Color. To pass test.
Residue after ignition. Not more than 0.005 per cent.
Neutrality. To pass test.
Chloride (Cl). Not more than 0.0005 per cent.
Sulfate (SO$_4$). To pass test (limit about 0.001 per cent).
Fatty acid esters. To pass test (limit about 0.05 per cent as butyric acid).
Silver-reducing substances. To pass test.
Substances darkened by sulfuric acid. To pass test.
Heavy metals (as Pb). Not more than 0.0002 per cent.

TESTS

Assay. The density at 25°C. determined with a pycnometer should not be less than 1.245 grams per ml.

Color. The color of a 50-ml. sample in a 50-ml. Nessler tube when viewed downward against a white background should not exceed the color of a standard made by diluting 0.3 ml. of ferric chloride color solution* to 50 ml. in a matching Nessler tube.

Residue after ignition. Heat 20 grams in a tared open dish, ignite the vapors, and when the glycerol has been entirely consumed, ignite at 800° ± 25°C. for 15 minutes. The weight of the residue should not exceed 0.0010 gram.

Neutrality. A 10 per cent aqueous solution of glycerol should not affect the color of either red or blue litmus paper in 1 minute.

Chloride. Dilute 2 grams to 20 ml. with water, filter if necessary through a chloride-free filter, and add 1 ml. of nitric acid and 1 ml. of silver nitrate reagent solution. Any turbidity should not exceed that produced by 0.01 mg. of chloride ion (Cl) in an equal volume of solution containing the quantities of reagents used in the test.

Sulfate. Dilute 8 ml. (10 grams) with 25 ml. of water, and add 1 ml. of 0.1N hydrochloric acid and 2 ml. of barium chloride reagent solution. Any turbidity should not exceed that produced by 0.10 mg. of sulfate ion (SO$_4$) in an equal volume of solution containing the quantities of re-agents used in the test. Compare 20 minutes after adding the barium chloride to the sample and standard solutions.

Fatty acid esters. To 40 grams in a 250-ml. Erlenmeyer flask add 50 ml. of hot, freshly boiled water. Add 10.0 ml. of 0.1N sodium hydroxide, cover with a loosely fitting pear-shaped bulb, and digest on the steam bath for 45 minutes. Cool and titrate the excess alkali with 0.1N hydrochloric acid, using 0.15 ml. of bromothymol blue indicator solution and titrating to a bluish green end point. Run a blank with 50 ml. of the same water and 10.0 ml. of 0.1N sodium hydroxide solution, heating for the same length of time and titrating to the same end point. The difference between the volumes of acid used in the titration of the blank and of the sample should be less than 2.3 ml.

Silver-reducing substances. Dilute 5 ml. (6 grams) with 2.5 ml. of water, add 2.5 ml. of ammonium hydroxide (10 per cent NH_3), and heat to 60°C. Add 0.5 ml. of silver nitrate reagent solution and allow to stand at 60°C. for 5 minutes, protected from light. Any color should not exceed that produced in a standard containing 0.02 mg. of lead ion (Pb) in 2.5 ml. of water to which are added 2.5 ml. of ammonium hydroxide (10 per cent NH_3) and 5 ml. of hydrogen sulfide water.

Substances darkened by sulfuric acid. Vigorously shake 5 ml. of glycerol with 5 ml. of 94.5 to 95.5 per cent sulfuric acid in a glass-stoppered 25-ml. cylinder for 1 minute and allow the liquid to stand for 1 hour. The liquid should not be darker than a standard made up of 0.4 ml. of cobaltous chloride color solution, 3.0 ml. of ferric chloride color solution, and 6.6 ml. of water.*

Heavy metals. Dilute 10 ml. (12 grams) to 36 ml. with water. For the control add 0.02 mg. of lead ion (Pb) to a 3-ml. aliquot of the solution and dilute to 33 ml. For the sample use the remaining 33-ml. portion. Adjust the pH of the control and sample solutions to between 3 and 4 (using a pH meter) with 1N acetic acid or ammonium hydroxide (10 per cent NH_3), dilute to 40 ml., and mix. Add 10 ml. of freshly prepared hydrogen sulfide water to each and mix. Any color in the solution of the sample should not exceed that in the control. Compare 15 minutes after adding the hydrogen sulfide water to the control and sample solutions.

*Note. **Ferric Chloride Color Solution.** Dissolve ferric chloride in a mixture of 25 volumes of hydrochloric acid and 975 volumes of water and adjust the strength so that the iron content corresponds to 45.0 mg. of $FeCl_3 \cdot 6H_2O$ per ml.

Cobaltous Chloride Color Solution. Dissolve cobaltous chloride in a mixture of 25 volumes of hydrochloric acid and 975 volumes of water and adjust the strength so that the cobalt content corresponds to 59.5 mg. of $CoCl_2 \cdot 6H_2O$ per ml.

Gold Chloride

Chloroauric (III) Acid, Trihydrate

$HAuCl_4 \cdot 3H_2O$ Formula Wt. 393.83

REQUIREMENTS

Insoluble in ether.   Not more than 0.10 per cent.
Assay.   Not less than 49.0 per cent Au.
Alkalies and other metals (as sulfates).   Not more than 0.20 per cent.

TESTS

Insoluble in ether. Weigh accurately about 1 gram. Add 10 ml. of ether, allow to stand for 10 minutes, with occasional stirring, filter through a tared filtering crucible of fine porosity, wash with small portions of ether, and dry at 105°C. Retain the filtrate and washings. The weight of the residue should not exceed 0.10 per cent.

Assay. Evaporate the solution from the test for *Insoluble in ether* to dryness or a sirupy residue. Dissolve the residue in 100 ml. of dilute hydrochloric acid (1 + 19), disregarding any undissolved material. Add 10 ml. of sulfurous acid and digest on the steam bath until the precipitate is well coagulated. Filter, wash with dilute hydrochloric acid (1 + 99), and ignite in a tared crucible. Retain the filtrate and washings. The weight of the residue should not be less than 49.0 per cent of the weight of the sample.

Alkalies and other metals (as sulfates). Evaporate the filtrate and washings reserved from the assay, in a tared dish to dryness. Ignite the residue cautiously, and finally ignite at 800° ± 25°C. for 15 minutes. The weight of the residue should not exceed 0.20 per cent.

Notes

Hexanes

Note. This reagent is generally a mixture of several isomers of hexane (C_6H_{14}), predominantly *n*-hexane, and methylcyclopentane (C_6H_{12}).

REQUIREMENTS

    Color (APHA). Not more than 10.
    Density (gram per ml.) at 25°C. Not above 0.687.
    Boiling range. 1 ml. to 95 ml., not more than 4.0°C.
    Residue after evaporation. Not more than 0.001 per cent.
    Acidity (as CH_3COOH). To pass test (limit about 0.002 per cent).
    Sulfur compounds (as S). Not more than 0.005 per cent.
    Thiophene. To pass test.

TESTS

Color (APHA). For the color standard dilute a 2-ml. aliquot of platinum-cobalt stock solution (APHA No. 500) to 100 ml. with water. Compare this solution (APHA No. 10) with 100 ml. of the hexanes in 100-ml. Nessler tubes, viewed vertically over a white background.

Boiling range. Distill 100 ml. by the method described on page 12. The difference between the temperatures when 1 ml. and 95 ml. have distilled should not exceed 4.0°C. The boiling point of the pure *n*-hexane at 760-mm. mercury pressure is 68.7°C.

Residue after evaporation. Evaporate 145 ml. (100 grams) to dryness in a tared dish on the steam bath and dry the residue at 105°C. for 30 minutes. The weight of the residue should not exceed 0.0010 gram.

Acidity. To 44 ml. (30 grams) in a separatory funnel, add 50 ml. of water and shake vigorously for 2 minutes. Allow the layers to separate, draw off the aqueous layer, and add 0.05 ml. of phenolphthalein indicator solution to the aqueous layer. Not more than 0.10 ml. of 0.1N sodium hydroxide should be required to produce a pink color.

Sulfur compounds. To 30 ml. of 0.5N potassium hydroxide in methanol in an Erlenmeyer flask, add 8 ml. (5.5 grams) of the sample, and boil the mixture gently for 30 minutes under a reflux condenser, avoiding the use of a rubber stopper or connection. Detach the condenser, dilute with 50 ml. of water, and heat on the steam bath until the hexanes and methanol are evaporated. Add 50 ml. of saturated bromine water, heat for 15 minutes longer, and transfer to a beaker. Neutralize with dilute hydrochloric acid $(1 + 3)$, add an excess of 1 ml. of the acid, evaporate to about 50 ml., and filter if necessary. Heat the filtrate to boiling, add 5 ml. of barium chloride reagent solution, digest in a covered beaker on the steam bath for 2 hours, and allow to stand overnight. If a precipitate is formed, filter, wash thoroughly, and ignite. The weight of the precipitate should not be more than 0.0020 gram greater than the weight obtained in a complete blank test.

Thiophene. To 25 ml. in a glass-stoppered flask add 15 ml. of sulfuric acid to which has been added a few milligrams of isatin, shake the mixture for 15 to 20 seconds, and allow to stand for 1 hour. The acid layer should not be colored blue or green.

Notes

Hexanes

(Suitable for use in ultraviolet spectrophotometry)

Note. This reagent is generally a mixture of several isomers of hexane (C_6H_{14}), predominantly *n*-hexane, and methylcyclopentane (C_6H_{12}).

REQUIREMENTS

Absorbance. To pass test.
Density (gram per ml.) at 25°C. Not above 0.687.
Boiling range. 1 ml. to 95 ml., not more than 4.0°C.
Residue after evaporation. Not more than 0.001 per cent.
Acidity (as CH_3COOH). To pass test (limit about 0.002 per cent).
Sulfur compounds (as S). Not more than 0.005 per cent.
Thiophene. To pass test.

TESTS

Absorbance. Determine the absorbance of the sample in a 1.00-cm. cell throughout the range of 210 mμ to 400 mμ, against water in a similar matched cell set at zero absorbance as the reference liquid. The absorbance should not exceed 1.00 at 210 mμ, 0.20 at 220 mμ, 0.10 at 230 mμ, 0.04 at 240 mμ, 0.02 at 250 mμ, and 0.01 at 280 mμ to 400 mμ. The spectral absorbance curve recorded through the wavelengths indicated should be smooth throughout the prescribed range and should not show any extraneous impurity peaks within this range.

Other tests are the same as for **Hexanes,** page 272, except *Color (APHA),* which is superseded by the *Absorbance* test.

Notes

Hydrazine Sulfate

$(NH_2)_2 \cdot H_2SO_4$ Formula Wt. 130.12

REQUIREMENTS

Assay.   Not less than 99.0 per cent $(NH_2)_2 \cdot H_2SO_4$.
Insoluble matter.   Not more than 0.005 per cent.
Residue after ignition.   Not more than 0.050 per cent.
Chloride (Cl).   Not more than 0.005 per cent.
Heavy metals (as Pb).   Not more than 0.002 per cent.
Iron (Fe).   Not more than 0.001 per cent.

TESTS

Assay.   Weigh accurately about 1 gram, dissolve in water, and dilute to 500 ml. in a volumetric flask. To a 50-ml. aliquot add 1 gram of sodium bicarbonate, dissolve the reagent, and add 50.0 ml. of $0.1N$ iodine solution. Titrate the excess iodine with $0.1N$ sodium thiosulfate, adding starch indicator near the end point. One milliliter of $0.1N$ iodine corresponds to 0.003253 gram of $(NH_2)_2 \cdot H_2SO_4$.

Insoluble matter.   Dissolve 20 grams in 300 ml. of water, heat to boiling, and digest in a covered beaker on the steam bath for 1 hour. Filter through a tared filtering crucible, wash thoroughly, and dry at 105°C. The weight of the residue should not exceed 0.0010 gram.

Residue after ignition.   Gently ignite 2 grams in a tared crucible or dish until the sample is nearly all volatilized, cool, moisten the residue with 0.10 ml. of sulfuric acid, and ignite again slowly until the remaining sample and excess sulfuric acid have been volatilized. Finally, ignite at 800° ± 25°C. for 15 minutes. The weight of the residue should not exceed 0.0010 gram. Retain the residue for the test for *Iron*.

Chloride.   Dissolve 1 gram in water, filter if necessary through a chloride-free filter, and dilute to 100 ml. To 20 ml. of the solution add 1 ml. of nitric acid and 1 ml. of silver nitrate reagent solution. Any turbidity should not exceed that produced by 0.01 mg. of chloride ion (Cl) in an equal volume of solution containing the quantities of reagents used in the test.

Heavy metals.   Dissolve 2 grams in 40 ml. of warm water. For the control add 0.02 mg. of lead ion (Pb) to a 10-ml. aliquot of the solution and dilute to 30 ml. Adjust the pH of the control and sample solutions to between 3 and 4 (using a pH meter) with $1N$ acetic acid or ammonium hydroxide (10 per cent NH_3), dilute to 40 ml., and mix. Add 10 ml. of freshly prepared hydrogen sulfide water to each and mix. Any color in the solution of the sample should not exceed that in the control.

Iron. To the *Residue after ignition* add 3 ml. of dilute hydrochloric acid $(1 + 1)$ and 0.10 ml. of nitric acid, cover with a watch glass, and digest on the steam bath for 15 to 20 minutes. Remove the watch glass and evaporate to dryness. Dissolve the residue in a mixture of 4 ml. of hydrochloric acid and 10 ml. of water and dilute to 100 ml. To 50 ml. add 30 to 50 mg. of ammonium persulfate crystals and 3 ml. of ammonium thiocyanate reagent solution. Any red color should not exceed that produced by 0.01 mg. of iron (Fe) in an equal volume of solution containing the quantities of reagents used in the test.

Notes

Hydriodic Acid, 47 Per Cent
(With stabilizer)

HI
Formula Wt. 127.91

Note. To avoid danger of explosions, this acid should be distilled only in an inert atmosphere. The reagent may have a slight yellow color. It contains hypophosphorous acid as a stabilizer.

REQUIREMENTS

Assay.   Not less than 47.0 per cent HI.
Chloride and bromide (as Cl).   Not more than 0.05 per cent.
Sulfate (SO_4).   Not more than 0.005 per cent.
Arsenic (As).   Not more than 0.0005 per cent.
Stabilizer (H_3PO_2).   Not more than 1.5 per cent.
Heavy metals (as Pb).   Not more than 0.001 per cent.
Iron (Fe).   Not more than 0.001 per cent.

TESTS

Assay.   Weigh about 50 ml. of water in a 250-ml. glass-stoppered flask; add about 0.7 ml. of the acid and weigh again. Add 50.0 ml. of 0.1N silver nitrate and shake the mixture well. Then add 5 ml. of nitric acid and heat on the steam bath until the precipitate has acquired a bright yellow color. Cool, and titrate the residual silver nitrate with 0.1N thiocyanate solution, using 2 ml. of ferric ammonium sulfate indicator solution. One milliliter of 0.1N silver nitrate corresponds to 0.01279 gram of HI.

Chloride and bromide.   Dilute 0.67 ml. (1 gram) to 100 ml. in a 250-ml. Erlenmeyer flask. Add 1 ml. of hydrogen peroxide and 1 ml. of phosphoric acid. Heat to boiling and boil gently until all the iodine is expelled and the solution is colorless. Cool, wash down the sides of the flask, and add 0.5 ml. of hydrogen peroxide. If an iodine color develops, boil until the solution is colorless and for 10 minutes longer. If no color develops, boil for 10 minutes. Dilute to 100 ml., take a 2-ml. aliquot, and dilute to 23 ml. Prepare a standard containing 0.01 mg. of chloride ion (Cl) in 23 ml. of water. Add 1 ml. of nitric acid and 1 ml. of silver nitrate reagent solution to each. Any turbidity produced in the solution of the sample should not exceed that in the standard.

Sulfate.   Dilute 6.7 ml. (10 grams) of the acid with 50 ml. of water, neutralize with ammonium hydroxide, and add 1 ml. of hydrochloric acid. Heat to boiling, add 5 ml. of barium chloride reagent solution, digest in a covered beaker on the steam bath for 2 hours, and allow to stand overnight. If a precipitate is formed, filter, wash thoroughly, and ignite. The weight of the precipitate should not be more than 0.0012 gram greater than the weight obtained in a complete blank test.

Arsenic. Dilute 2.7 ml. (4 grams) to 100 ml. To 10 ml. of the solution add 1 ml. of nitric acid and evaporate on the steam bath to expel the iodine. Determine the arsenic in the residue by the Gutzeit method (page 11). The amount of stain should not exceed that produced by 0.002 mg. of arsenic (As).

> **Sample Solution A.** To 3.4 ml. (5 grams) add 10 ml. of water, 7 ml. of nitric acid, and 9 ml. of hydrochloric acid. Evaporate to dryness on the steam bath, dissolve in water, and dilute to 50 ml. (1 ml. = 0.1 gram).

Stabilizer. Dilute 1 ml. of Sample Solution A (0.1-gram sample) to 1 liter. Dilute a 4.8-ml. aliquot to 85 ml. Add 5 ml. of a 10 per cent solution of ammonium molybdate and adjust the pH to 1.8 (using a pH meter) with dilute hydrochloric acid $(1 + 9)$. Heat to boiling and cool to room temperature. Add 10 ml. of hydrochloric acid and transfer to a separatory funnel. Add 35 ml. of ether and shake vigorously. Allow the layers to separate and draw off and discard the aqueous layer. Wash the ether layer twice with 10-ml. portions of dilute hydrochloric acid $(1 + 9)$, drawing off and discarding the aqueous portion each time. Add 10 ml. of dilute hydrochloric acid $(1 + 9)$ to which has just been added 0.2 ml. of a 2 per cent stannous chloride solution in hydrochloric acid and shake. Any blue color in the ether should not exceed that produced by 0.01 mg. of phosphate ion (PO_4) treated exactly like the 4.8-ml. aliquot.

Heavy metals. For the sample dilute a 20-ml. aliquot of Sample Solution A (2-gram sample) to 25 ml. For the standard dilute a solution containing 0.02 mg. of lead ion (Pb) to 25 ml. Adjust the pH of the standard and sample solutions to between 3 and 4 (using a pH meter) with $1N$ acetic acid or ammonium hydroxide (10 per cent NH_3), dilute to 40 ml., and mix. Add 10 ml. of freshly prepared hydrogen sulfide water to each and mix. Any color in the solution of the sample should not exceed that in the standard.

Iron. To 10 ml. of Sample Solution A (1-gram sample) add 2 ml. of hydrochloric acid and dilute to 50 ml. Add 30 to 50 mg. of ammonium persulfate crystals and 3 ml. of ammonium thiocyanate reagent solution.

Any red color should not exceed that produced by 0.01 mg. of iron (Fe) in an equal volume of solution containing the quantities of reagents used in the test.

Notes

Hydrobromic Acid, 48 Per Cent

HBr

Formula Wt. 80.91

REQUIREMENTS

Assay. Not less than 47.0 nor more than 49.0 per cent HBr.
Organic substances. To pass test.
Residue after ignition. Not more than 0.002 per cent.
Chloride (Cl). Not more than 0.05 per cent.
Iodide (I). To pass test (limit about 0.003 per cent).
Phosphate (PO$_4$). Not more than 0.001 per cent.
Sulfate and sulfite (as SO$_4$). Not more than 0.003 per cent.
Arsenic (As). Not more than 0.00005 per cent.
Heavy metals (as Pb). Not more than 0.0005 per cent.
Iron (Fe). Not more than 0.0001 per cent.
Selenium (Se). To pass test (limit about 0.000001 per cent).

TESTS

Assay. Tare a glass-stoppered Erlenmeyer flask containing about 15 ml. of water. Quickly add about 4 ml. of the acid and weigh. Dilute to 50 ml. and titrate with 1N sodium hydroxide, using phenolphthalein indicator. One milliliter of 1N sodium hydroxide corresponds to 0.08091 gram of HBr.

Organic substances. Dilute 25 ml. with 25 ml. of water in a glass-stoppered cylinder, shake well, and note odor. No foreign odor should be observed.

Residue after ignition. To 34 ml. (50 grams) in a tared dish (not platinum) add 0.05 ml. of sulfuric acid, evaporate as far as possible on the steam bath, then heat gently to volatilize the solution. Finally, ignite at 800° ±25°C. for 15 minutes. The weight of the residue should not exceed 0.0010 gram.

Chloride. To 0.67 ml. (1 gram) in a 150-ml. Erlenmeyer flask add 50 ml. of dilute nitric acid (1 + 3) and digest on the steam bath until the solution is colorless. Wash down the sides of the flask with a little water and digest for an additional 15 minutes. Cool, filter if necessary through a chloride-free filter, and dilute to 100 ml. Dilute a 2-ml. portion to 23 ml. Prepare a standard containing 0.01 mg. of chloride ion (Cl) in 23 ml. of water. Add 1 ml. of nitric acid and 1 ml. of silver nitrate reagent solution to each. Any turbidity produced in the solution of the sample should not exceed that in the standard.

Iodide. Dilute 4 ml. (6 grams) with 20 ml. of water. Add 5 ml. of chloroform, 0.2 ml. of 10 per cent ferric chloride solution, and 0.1 ml. of dilute sulfuric acid (1 + 15) and mix gently in a separatory funnel. Draw off the chloroform layer into a comparison tube of about 1.5-cm. diameter. No violet color should be observed on looking down through the chloroform.

Phosphate. Add 5 ml. of nitric acid to 4 ml. (6 grams) of the sample and evaporate to dryness on the steam bath. Dissolve in 75 ml. of approximately $0.5N$ sulfuric acid. To 25 ml. of the solution add 1 ml. of ammonium molybdate reagent solution and 1 ml. of p-methylaminophenol sulfate reagent solution and allow to stand for 2 hours at room temperature. Any blue color should not exceed that produced by 0.02 mg. of phosphate ion (PO_4) in an equal volume of solution containing the quantities of reagents used in the test.

Sulfate and sulfite. Dilute 4 ml. (6 grams) to 60 ml. To 20 ml. of the solution add a slight excess of bromine water and boil to expel the excess bromine. Add 10 to 20 mg. of sodium carbonate and evaporate to dryness on the steam bath. Dissolve the residue in 4 ml. of water plus 1 ml. of dilute hydrochloric acid (1 + 19), filter if necessary through a small filter, wash with two 2-ml. portions of water, and dilute to 10 ml. Add 1 ml. of barium chloride reagent solution. Any turbidity should not exceed that produced by 0.06 mg. of sulfate ion (SO_4) in an equal volume of solution containing the quantities of reagents used in the test. Compare 10 minutes after adding the barium chloride to the sample and standard solutions.

Arsenic. Determine the arsenic in 4 ml. (6 grams) by the Gutzeit method (page 11). The amount of stain should not exceed that produced by 0.003 mg. of arsenic (As).

Heavy metals. To 2.7 ml. (4-gram sample) in a beaker add about 10 mg. of sodium carbonate and evaporate to dryness on the steam bath. Dissolve the residue in about 20 ml. of water and dilute to 25 ml. For the standard dilute a solution containing 0.02 mg. of lead ion (Pb) to 25 ml. Adjust the pH of the standard and sample solutions to between 3 and 4 (using a pH meter) with $1N$ acetic acid or ammonium hydroxide (10 per cent NH_3), dilute to 40 ml., and mix. Add 10 ml. of freshly prepared hydrogen sulfide water to each and mix. Any color in the solution of the sample should not exceed that in the standard.

Iron. To 6.6 ml. (10 grams) add about 10 mg. of sodium carbonate and evaporate to dryness on the steam bath. Dissolve the residue in 2 ml. of hydrochloric acid, dilute to 50 ml., and add 30 to 50 mg. of ammonium persulfate crystals and 3 ml. of ammonium thiocyanate reagent solution. Any red color should not exceed that produced by 0.01 mg. of iron (Fe) in an equal volume of solution containing the quantities of reagents used in the test.

Selenium. Place 100 ml. (150 grams) in an all-glass distilling apparatus, add 2 ml. of bromine, and distill off approximately 25 ml. Dilute the distillate with an equal volume of water and decolorize with sulfurous acid. Add 0.1 gram of hydroxylamine hydrochloride and warm gently on the steam bath for 30 minutes. Cool to room temperature, filter through a white asbestos pad in a small Gooch crucible, without washing, and examine immediately. No pink or red color should be observed on the asbestos pad.

Notes

Hydrochloric Acid

HCl   Formula Wt. 36.46

REQUIREMENTS

Appearance.   Free from suspended matter or sediment.
Assay.   Not less than 36.5 nor more than 38.0 per cent HCl.
Color (APHA).   Not more than 10.
Residue after ignition.   Not more than 0.0005 per cent.
Bromide (Br).   Not more than 0.005 per cent.
Sulfate (SO_4).   Not more than 0.0001 per cent.
Sulfite (SO_3).   Not more than 0.0001 per cent.
Extractable organic substances.   To pass test (not more than about 0.0005 per cent).
Free chlorine (Cl).   To pass test (limit about 0.0001 per cent).
Ammonium (NH_4).   Not more than 0.0003 per cent.
Arsenic (As).   Not more than 0.000001 per cent.
Heavy metals (as Pb).   Not more than 0.0001 per cent.
Iron (Fe).   Not more than 0.00002 per cent.

TESTS

Assay.   Tare a glass-stoppered flask containing about 30 ml. of water. Quickly add about 3 ml. of the sample, stopper, and weigh accurately. Dilute to about 50 ml., add methyl orange indicator solution, and titrate with $1N$ sodium hydroxide. One milliliter of $1N$ sodium hydroxide corresponds to 0.03646 gram of HCl.

Color (APHA).   For the color standard dilute a 2-ml. aliquot of platinum-cobalt stock solution (APHA No. 500) to 100 ml. with water. Compare this solution (APHA No. 10) with 100 ml. of the hydrochloric acid in 100-ml. Nessler tubes, viewed vertically over a white background.

Residue after ignition.   To 170 ml. (200 grams) in a tared platinum dish, add 0.05 ml. of sulfuric acid, evaporate as far as possible on the steam bath, and heat gently to volatilize the excess sulfuric acid. Finally, ignite at $800° \pm 25°C.$ for 15 minutes. The weight of the residue should not exceed 0.0010 gram.

Bromide.   Pipet 1 ml. into 25 ml. of water in a 100-ml. beaker, add 2 ml. of phenolsulfonphthalein indicator solution (0.020 gram of the sodium salt in 100 ml. of water), and titrate with $1N$ sodium hydroxide. Add just sufficient titrant to change the yellow color to red. Transfer the solution to a 100-ml. volumetric flask with about 25 ml. of water. For the standard add identical amounts of indicator and water to 0.06 mg. of bromide ion (Br) in a 100-ml. volumetric flask. To each flask add 5 ml. of acetate buffer solution (68 grams of sodium acetate, $CH_3COONa \cdot 3H_2O$, and 30 ml. of glacial acetic acid per liter) and 2.0 ml. of freshly prepared chloramine-T solution (0.125 gram per 100 ml.). Mix, allow to stand for 20.0 minutes, and add 20 ml. of $0.1N$ sodium thiosulfate solution. Swirl, dilute to volume, and mix. Compare visually or spectrophotometrically at 590 mμ in 1.0-cm. cells. Any blue-violet color in the sample should not exceed that in the standard.

Sulfate. To 42 ml. (50 grams) add about 10 mg. of sodium carbonate, evaporate to dryness, and dissolve the residue in 4 ml. of water plus 1 ml. of dilute hydrochloric acid (1 + 19). Filter through a small filter, wash with two 2-ml. portions of water, and dilute to 10 ml. Add 1 ml. of barium chloride reagent solution. Any turbidity should not exceed that produced by 0.05 mg. of sulfate ion (SO_4) in an equal volume of solution containing the quantities of reagents used in the test. Compare 10 minutes after adding the barium chloride to the sample and standard solutions.

Sulfite. Add 1 ml. of 10 per cent potassium iodide reagent solution, 5 ml. of hydrochloric acid, and 2 ml. of starch indicator solution to 400 ml. of oxygen-free water. Add $0.01N$ iodine until a faint permanent blue color is produced. Add 85 ml. of the sample and titrate with $0.01N$ iodine to the same end point. Not more than 0.25 ml. should be required.

Extractable organic substances. Cool about 110 ml. of the hydrochloric acid in an ice bath. Place 5 ml. of 2,2,4-trimethylpentane and 100 ml. of water in each of two 250-ml. separatory funnels. In a third funnel place 100 ml. of water and 5 ml. of a standard 2,2,4-trimethylpentane solution* containing 6 mg. each of benzene and chlorobenzene, 25 mg. each of 1,2-dichloroethane and DDT**, and 50 mg. of chloroform per 500 ml. To the first funnel add 100 ml. (120 grams) of the cooled sample. To the second and third funnels add 100 ml. of water. Stopper the funnels, shake well, and allow the layers to separate.

Compare the 2,2,4-trimethylpentane layers by gas chromatography, preferably using a programmed temperature column with a hydrogen flame ionization detector. By flame ionization the aromatic compounds can be detected with greater sensitivity than the chlorinated aliphatics. With an electron affinity detector it would be possible to detect the chlorinated aliphatics at lower levels. Any gas chromatographic system which has been demonstrated to give adequate separation and sensitivity may be used, but the following system has given satisfactory results:

Instrument. Perkin Elmer Model 810, F. and M. Model 810, Aerograph

Hy Fi Model 600-D, or equivalent. **Column.** 14 ft. × 0.125 in. stainless steel or glass, packed with 60/80 mesh Chromosorb P containing 20 per cent by weight of Carbowax 20 M and conditioned overnight with the detector disconnected. **Injection port.** Glass or glass insert, 280°C. **Column temperature.** Initial 65°C., final 140°C., programmed at 6°C. per min. **Carrier gas.** Nitrogen with flow rate 40 ml. per min. **Sample.** 1.0 microliter. Attenuation for standard to provide 80 per cent of full scale for benzene peak. **Order of elution.** 2,2,4-Trimethylpentane, carbon tetrachloride (appears as a shoulder on the 2,2,4-trimethyl-pentane peak), benzene, chloroform, 2,2,4-trimethylpentane impurity, 1,2-dichloroethane, chlorobenzene, and dichlorobenzene. For DDT a separate run is made: **Column.** 5 ft. × 0.125 in. stainless steel or glass, packed with 60/80 mesh Chromosorb W containing 5 per cent by weight General Electric silicone gum SE 30, similarly conditioned, operating isothermally at 205°C. **Injection port.** As above. **Carrier gas.** Nitrogen with flow rate 75 ml. per min. **Sample.** 1.0 microliter.

The total area under the impurity peaks from the sample (first funnel) should not exceed that from the blank (second funnel) by more than one-half the area under the peaks from the standard (third funnel), also corrected for the blank.

* **Standard Solution.** Syringe the volumes of liquids cited below into 2,2,4-trimethylpentane, weigh and add the DDT** and dilute to 500 ml. The 2,2,4-trimethylpentane used for both the standard and the analysis should be free from impurities that interfere with the chromatographic analysis.

Substance	Amount in 500 ml. of 2,2,4-trimethylpentane solution		Concentration in p.p.m. for 5 ml. of standard in 100 ml. (120 grams) of HCl
	μl	mg	
Benzene	6.8	6	0.5
Chlorobenzene	5.5	6	0.5
1,2-Dichloroethane	20	25	2.0
Chloroform	34	50	4.0
DDT**		25	2.0
		Total	9.0
		Allowance for CCl$_4$	1.0
		Total	10.0

Half of the above total is 5.0 p.p.m.—that is, 0.0005 per cent.

**1,1,1-Trichloro-2,2-bis(p-chlorophenyl)ethane, dichloro-diphenyl-tri-chloroethane.

Free chlorine. To 50 ml. of the sample add 50 ml. of freshly boiled water and cool. Add 0.1 ml. of 2 per cent potassium iodide solution and 1 ml. of carbon disulfide, and mix. The carbon disulfide should not acquire a pink color within 30 seconds. The potassium iodide should be free from iodate.

Ammonium. Carefully pour 4.2 ml. (5 grams) into 30 ml. of cold water in a flask suitable for ammonia distillation. Cool in ice and cautiously add 20 ml. of 10 per cent sodium hydroxide reagent solution, keeping the temperature low. Cool, add 20 ml. more of the sodium hydroxide solution, and connect the flask through a spray trap to a condenser, the end of which dips beneath the surface of 10 ml. of $0.1N$ hydrochloric acid. Distill over about 35 ml., add to the distillate 2 ml. of 10 per cent sodium hydroxide reagent solution, dilute to 50 ml., and add 2 ml. of Nessler reagent. Any color should not exceed that produced when a quantity of an ammonium salt containing 0.015 mg. of ammonium ion (NH_4) is treated like the sample, starting with a volume of 30 ml. of water to which are added 40 ml. of freshly boiled 10 per cent sodium hydroxide reagent solution.

Arsenic. To 170 ml. (200 grams) add 10 ml. of nitric acid and 5 ml. of sulfuric acid and evaporate to dense fumes. Cool, add cautiously 10 ml. of water, and again evaporate to dense fumes. Determine arsenic in the residue by the Gutzeit method (page 11). The stain should not exceed that produced by 0.002 mg. of arsenic (As).

Heavy metals. To 17 ml. (20 grams) in a 150-ml. beaker, add about 10 mg. of sodium carbonate, and evaporate to dryness on the steam bath. Dissolve the residue in about 20 ml. of water and dilute to 25 ml. For the standard dilute a solution containing 0.02 mg. of lead ion (Pb) to 25 ml. Adjust the pH of the standard and sample solutions to between 3 and 4 (using a pH meter) with $1N$ acetic acid or ammonium hydroxide (10 per cent NH_3), dilute to 40 ml., and mix. Add 10 ml. of freshly prepared hydrogen sulfide water to each and mix. Any color in the solution of the sample should not exceed that in the standard.

Iron. To 42 ml. (50 grams) in a porcelain or glass vessel add about 10 mg. of sodium carbonate and evaporate to dryness on the steam bath. Dissolve in 2 ml. of hydrochloric acid and dilute to 50 ml. Add 30 to 50 mg. of ammonium persulfate crystals and 3 ml. of ammonium thiocyanate reagent solution. Any red color should not exceed that produced by 0.01 mg. of iron (Fe) in an equal volume of solution containing the quantities of reagents used in the test.

Hydrofluoric Acid

HF

Formula Wt. 20.01

REQUIREMENTS

Assay.   Not less than 48.0 nor more than 51.0 per cent HF.
Fluosilicic acid (H_2SiF_6).   Not more than 0.01 per cent.
Residue after ignition.   Not more than 0.0005 per cent.
Chloride (Cl).   Not more than 0.0005 per cent.
Phosphate (PO_4).   Not more than 0.0001 per cent.
Sulfate and sulfite (as SO_4).   Not more than 0.0005 per cent.
Arsenic (As).   Not more than 0.000005 per cent.
Copper (Cu).   Not more than 0.00001 per cent.
Heavy metals (as Pb).   Not more than 0.00005 per cent.
Iron (Fe).   Not more than 0.0001 per cent.

TESTS

Assay.   Tare a covered or stoppered platinum crucible or a suitable plastic container containing about 5 ml. of water. Quickly add from 2.0 to 2.5 ml. of the sample, stopper, and weigh accurately. Dilute to about 50 ml. in a platinum dish, add phenolphthalein indicator solution, and titrate with 1N sodium hydroxide. One milliliter of 1N sodium hydroxide corresponds to 0.02001 gram of HF.

Fluosilicic acid.   Weigh about 33 ml. (37.5 grams) into a large platinum dish. Add 2 grams of potassium chloride and 3 ml. of hydrochloric acid and evaporate to dryness on the steam bath in the hood. Wash down the sides of the dish with a small amount of water, add 3 ml. of hydrochloric acid, and repeat the evaporation. Dissolve the residue in about 100 ml. of water, cool to 0°C., add 0.10 ml. of phenolphthalein indicator solution, and neutralize any free acid with 0.1N sodium hydroxide solution, keeping the temperature of the solution near 0°C. Heat the solution to boiling and titrate with 0.1N sodium hydroxide solution. One milliliter of 0.1N sodium hydroxide corresponds to 0.0036 gram of H_2SiF_6.

Residue after ignition.   To 180 ml. (200 grams) in a tared platinum dish, add 0.05 ml. of sulfuric acid, evaporate as far as possible on the steam bath in the hood, and heat gently to volatilize the excess sulfuric acid. Finally, ignite at 800° ± 25°C. for 15 minutes. The weight of the residue should not exceed 0.0010 gram.

Chloride.   Add 1.8 ml. to 45 ml. of water, filter if necessary through a chloride-free filter, and add 1 ml. of nitric acid and 1 ml. of silver nitrate reagent solution. Any turbidity should not exceed that produced by 0.01

mg. of chloride ion (Cl) in an equal volume of solution containing the quantities of reagents used in the test.

Phosphate. Evaporate 18 ml. (20 grams) to dryness on the steam bath in the hood. Dissolve in 25 ml. of approximately 0.5N sulfuric acid, add 1 ml. of ammonium molybdate reagent solution and 1 ml. of p-methyl-aminophenol sulfate reagent solution, and allow to stand for 2 hours at room temperature. Any blue color should not exceed that produced by 0.02 mg. of phosphate ion (PO_4) in an equal volume of solution containing the quantities of reagents used in the test.

Sulfate and sulfite. To 18 ml. (20 grams) in a platinum or other suitable evaporating dish, add about 10 mg. of sodium carbonate and 1 ml. of 30 per cent hydrogen peroxide. Evaporate to dryness on the steam bath in the hood, wash down the sides of the dish with a small volume of water, and add 3 ml. of perchloric acid. Evaporate to about 1 ml., dilute with about 15 ml. of water, and add 0.10 ml. of phenolphthalein indicator solution. Neutralize with ammonium hydroxide, dilute to 20 ml., and add 2 ml. of dilute hydrochloric acid (1 + 19) and 2 ml. of barium chloride reagent solution. Any turbidity should not exceed that produced by 0.1 mg. of sulfate ion (SO_4) in an equal volume of solution containing the quantities of reagents used in the test. Compare 10 minutes after adding the barium chloride to the sample and standard solutions.

Arsenic. To 68 ml. (80 grams) in a platinum dish, add 0.25 ml. of 2 per cent potassium permanganate solution. Volatilize the hydrofluoric acid on the steam bath in the hood, add 3 ml. of water and 3 ml. of sulfuric acid to the residue, and digest until all traces of stains are removed and in solution. Avoid the evolution of sulfur trioxide fumes. Cool and carefully add more water, if necessary. When all traces of stain are removed, cool, dilute to 25 ml. with water, and add 10 ml. of ferric ammonium sulfate solution.* Add 2 per cent potassium permanganate solution dropwise until the pink color persists, dissolve 1.5 grams of sodium chloride in the solution, and heat just to boiling. Remove the heat, cool to 70° to 80°C., add stannous chloride solution** dropwise until the yellow color of ferric ion just disappears, and then add 0.05 to 0.10 ml. in excess. Cool the solution to 25° ± 2°C. and determine the arsenic by the Gutzeit method (page 11). The amount of stain should not exceed that produced by 0.004 mg. of arsenic (As).

*__Ferric Ammonium Sulfate Solution.__ Dissolve 84 grams of ferric ammonium sulfate, $Fe(NH_4)(SO_4)_2 \cdot 12H_2O$, in water, add 2 ml. of sulfuric acid and 1 gram of sodium chloride, and dilute to 1 liter.

** **Stannous Chloride Solution.** Add 25 ml. of water to 80 grams of stannous chloride in a 250-ml. beaker, slowly add 75 ml. of hydrochloric acid, and stir to dissolve the salt.

Copper

Sample Solution A. To 85 ml. (100 grams) in a platinum dish add 10 mg. of sodium carbonate and evaporate to dryness in the hood. Dissolve the residue in 1 ml. of 1N hydrochloric acid and about 10 ml. of water, add 3.8 ml. of 1 per cent sodium carbonate solution, and dilute to 45 ml. with water. If necessary, adjust the pH between 6.5 and 6.9 (using a pH meter) with 1 per cent sodium carbonate or 1N hydrochloric acid, and dilute to 50 ml.

Transfer 30 ml. of Sample Solution A (60-gram sample) to a separatory funnel. Add 10 ml. of standard dithizone solution in chloroform, shake vigorously, allow the solutions to separate, and draw off the chloroform extract. The red color, producing a purplish hue in the chloroform, should not exceed that produced by 0.006 mg. of copper ion (Cu) treated exactly as the 30 ml. of Sample Solution A.

Heavy metals. To 34 ml. (40 grams) in a platinum dish, add about 10 mg. of sodium carbonate, and evaporate to dryness on the steam bath in the hood. Dissolve the residue in about 20 ml. of water and dilute to 25 ml. For the standard dilute a solution containing 0.02 mg. of lead ion (Pb) to 25 ml. Adjust the pH of the standard and sample solutions to between 3 and 4 (using a pH meter) with 1N acetic acid or ammonium hydroxide (10 per cent NH_3), dilute to 40 ml., and mix. Add 10 ml. of freshly prepared hydrogen sulfide water to each and mix. Any color in the solution of the sample should not exceed that in the standard.

Iron. To 8.7 ml. (10 grams) in a platinum dish, add about 10 mg. of sodium carbonate, and evaporate to dryness on the steam bath in the hood. Add 0.2 ml. of sulfuric acid and ignite gently. Dissolve the residue in 4 ml. of dilute hydrochloric acid (1 + 1), cover, digest for 15 minutes on the steam bath, and dilute to 50 ml. Add 30 to 50 mg. of ammonium persulfate crystals and 3 ml. of ammonium thiocyanate reagent solution. Any red color should not exceed that produced by 0.01 mg. of iron (Fe) in an equal volume of solution containing the quantities of reagents used in the test.

Hydrogen Peroxide

H_2O_2

Formula Wt. 34.01

Note. This reagent should be stored in a cool place in containers with a vent in the stopper. The assay requirement applies to material stored properly for a reasonable time.

REQUIREMENTS

Assay. Not less than 29.0 nor more than 32.0 per cent H_2O_2.
Color (APHA). Not more than 10.
Residue after evaporation. Not more than 0.002 per cent.
Free acid (as H_2SO_4). Not more than 0.003 per cent.
Chloride (Cl). Not more than 0.0003 per cent.
Nitrate (NO_3). Not more than 0.0002 per cent.
Phosphate (PO_4). Not more than 0.0002 per cent.
Sulfate (SO_4). Not more than 0.0005 per cent.
Ammonium (NH_4). Not more than 0.0005 per cent.
Heavy metals (as Pb). Not more than 0.0001 per cent.
Iron (Fe). Not more than 0.00005 per cent.

TESTS

Assay. Weigh accurately about 1 ml. in a tared 100-ml. volumetric flask, dilute to volume with water, and mix thoroughly. To a 20.0-ml. aliquot of this solution add 20 ml. of dilute sulfuric acid $(1 + 15)$ and titrate with 0.1N potassium permanganate. One milliliter of 0.1N potassium permanganate corresponds to 0.001700 gram of H_2O_2.

Color (APHA). For the color standard dilute a 2-ml. aliquot of platinum-cobalt stock solution (APHA No. 500) to 100 ml. with water. Compare this solution (APHA No. 10) with 100 ml. of the hydrogen peroxide in 100-ml. Nessler tubes, viewed vertically over a white background.

Residue after evaporation. Evaporate 45 ml. (50 grams) to dryness in a tared porcelain or silica dish on the steam bath and dry the residue at 105°C. for 30 minutes. The weight of the residue should not exceed 0.0010 gram.

Free acid. Dilute 9 ml. (10 grams) with 90 ml. of carbon dioxide-free water. Add 0.15 ml. of methyl red indicator solution and titrate with 0.02N sodium hydroxide. The volume of sodium hydroxide solution consumed should not be more than 0.3 ml. greater than the volume required for a blank test on 90 ml. of the water used for dilution.

Chloride. Dilute 3 ml. (3.3 grams) with 20 ml. of water, filter if necessary through a chloride-free filter, and add 1 ml. of nitric acid and 1 ml. of silver nitrate reagent solution. Any turbidity should not exceed that produced by 0.01 mg. of chloride ion (Cl) in an equal volume of solution containing the quantities of reagents used in the test.

Nitrate. Add about 10 mg. of sodium carbonate to 4.5 ml. (5 grams) of the sample and evaporate to dryness on the steam bath. Wash down the inside of the container with about 5 ml. of water and again evaporate to dryness. Add 2 ml. of phenoldisulfonic acid reagent solution and heat on the steam bath for 15 minutes. Cool, dilute to 30 ml., and make alkaline with ammonium hydroxide. Any yellow color should not exceed that produced when a solution containing 0.01 mg. of nitrate ion (NO_3) is evaporated to dryness and treated exactly like the sample.

Phosphate. Evaporate 9 ml. (10 grams) to dryness on the steam bath. Dissolve the residue in 25 ml. of approximately 0.5N sulfuric acid, add 1 ml. of ammonium molybdate reagent solution and 1 ml. of p-methyl-aminophenol sulfate reagent solution, and allow to stand for 2 hours at room temperature. Any blue color should not exceed that produced by 0.02 mg. of phosphate ion (PO_4) in an equal volume of solution containing the quantities of reagents used in the test.

Sulfate. Evaporate 9 ml. (10 grams) to dryness on the steam bath, dissolve the residue in 4 ml. of water plus 1 ml. of dilute hydrochloric acid (1 + 19), and filter if necessary through a small filter. Wash with two 2-ml. portions of water, dilute to 10 ml., and add 1 ml. of barium chloride reagent solution. Any turbidity should not exceed that produced by 0.05 mg. of sulfate ion (SO_4) in an equal volume of solution containing the quantities of reagents used in the test. Compare 10 minutes after adding the barium chloride to the sample and standard solutions.

Ammonium. Add 0.1 ml. of sulfuric acid to 1.8 ml. (2 grams) of the sample and evaporate on the steam bath. Dissolve the residue in 45 ml. of water and add 3 ml. of 10 per cent sodium hydroxide reagent solution and 2 ml. of Nessler reagent. Any color should not exceed that produced by 0.01 mg. of ammonium ion (NH_4) in an equal volume of solution containing the quantities of reagents used in the test.

Heavy metals. To 18 ml. (20 grams) in a 100-ml. beaker add about 10 mg. of sodium chloride and evaporate to dryness on the steam bath. Dissolve the residue in about 20 ml. of water and dilute to 25 ml. For the standard dilute a solution containing 0.02 mg. of lead ion (Pb) to 25 ml. Adjust the pH of the standard and sample solutions to between 3 and 4 (using a pH meter) with $1N$ acetic acid or ammonium hydroxide (10 per cent NH_3), dilute to 40 ml., and mix. Add 10 ml. of freshly prepared hydrogen sulfide water to each and mix. Any color in the solution of the sample should not exceed that in the standard.

Iron. To 18 ml. (20 grams) in a 100-ml. beaker, add about 10 mg. of sodium chloride, and evaporate to dryness on the steam bath. Dissolve in 2 ml. of hydrochloric acid and dilute to 50 ml. Add 30 to 50 mg. of ammonium persulfate crystals and 3 ml. of ammonium thiocyanate reagent solution. Any red color should not exceed that produced by 0.01 mg. of iron (Fe) in an equal volume of solution containing the quantities of reagents used in the test.

Notes

Hydroxylamine Hydrochloride

NH$_2$OH·HCl   Formula Wt. 69.49

REQUIREMENTS

Assay.   Not less than 96.0 per cent NH$_2$OH·HCl.
Insoluble in alcohol.   To pass test.
Residue after ignition.   Not more than 0.05 per cent.
Acidity.   To pass test.
Ammonium (NH$_4$).   To pass test (limit about 0.1 per cent).
Sulfur compounds (as SO$_4$).   Not more than 0.005 per cent.
Heavy metals (as Pb).   Not more than 0.0005 per cent.
Iron (Fe).   Not more than 0.0005 per cent.

TESTS

Assay.   Weigh accurately about 1.5 grams, previously dried for 24 hours over sulfuric acid, and transfer to a 250-ml. volumetric flask. Dissolve in oxygen-free water, dilute to volume with oxygen-free water, and take a 20-ml. aliquot of the sample solution. Dissolve 5 grams of ferric ammonium sulfate in 30 ml. of oxygen-free dilute sulfuric acid (1 + 50) and add this solution to the sample solution. Protect the solution from oxygen in the air, boil gently for 5 minutes, and cool. Dilute with 150 ml. of oxygen-free water and titrate with 0.1N potassium permanganate. One milliliter of 0.1N potassium permanganate corresponds to 0.003474 gram of NH$_2$OH·HCl.

Insoluble in alcohol.   Dissolve 1 gram in 25 ml. of alcohol and compare with an equal volume of alcohol. The sample solution should have no more color or turbidity than the alcohol. Retain the solution for the test for *Ammonium*.

Residue after ignition.   Gently ignite 2 grams in a tared crucible or dish. The rate of heating should be such that from 1 to 2 hours is required to volatilize the sample. When nearly all the sample has been volatilized, cool, and moisten the residue with 0.10 ml. of sulfuric acid. Continue the heating until the remainder of the sample and excess sulfuric acid have been volatilized. Finally, ignite at 800° ± 25°C. for 15 minutes. The weight of the residue should not exceed 0.0010 gram. Retain the residue for the test for *Iron*.

Acidity.   Dissolve 10 grams in 50 ml. of water and titrate with 1N sodium hydroxide to the neutral (green) end point of bromophenol blue. Not more than 2.5 ml. of 1N sodium hydroxide should be required.

Ammonium. To the solution obtained in the test for *Insoluble in alcohol* add 1 ml. of a solution of chloroplatinic acid (2.6 grams in 20 ml.). The solution should remain clear for 10 minutes.

Sulfur compounds. Dissolve 2 grams in 10 ml. of water containing 10 mg. of sodium carbonate and add 4 ml. of nitric acid. *Slowly* add 12 ml. of 10 per cent hydrogen peroxide solution (mix 4 ml. of 30 per cent hydrogen peroxide with 8 ml. of water). Digest in a covered beaker until reaction ceases, uncover, and evaporate to dryness on the steam bath. Dissolve the residue in 10 ml. of water, add 2 ml. of dilute hydrochloric acid (1 + 19), filter if necessary, and dilute to 20 ml. To 10 ml. add 1 ml. of barium chloride reagent solution. Any turbidity should not exceed that produced by 0.05 mg. of sulfate ion (SO_4) in an equal volume of solution containing the quantities of reagents used in the test. Compare 10 minutes after adding the barium chloride to the sample and standard solutions.

Heavy metals. Dissolve 6 grams in about 20 ml. of water and dilute to 30 ml. For the control add 0.02 mg. of lead ion (Pb) to a 5-ml. aliquot of the solution and dilute to 25 ml. For the sample use the remaining 25-ml. portion. Adjust the pH of the control and sample solutions to between 3 and 4 (using a pH meter) with $1N$ acetic acid or ammonium hydroxide (10 per cent NH_3), dilute to 40 ml., and mix. Add 10 ml. of freshly prepared hydrogen sulfide water to each and mix. Any color in the solution of the sample should not exceed that in the control.

Iron. To the *Residue after ignition* add 3 ml. of dilute hydrochloric acid (1 + 1), cover the dish, and digest on the steam bath for 15 to 20 minutes. Remove the cover, evaporate to dryness, dissolve in 2 ml. of hydrochloric acid, and dilute to 50 ml. Add 30 to 50 mg. of ammonium persulfate crystals and 3 ml. of ammonium thiocyanate reagent solution. Any red color should not exceed that produced by 0.01 mg. of iron (Fe) in an equal volume of solution containing the quantities of reagents used in the test.

Notes

Hydroxy Naphthol Blue

1-(2-Naphtholazo-3,6-disulfonic acid)-2-naphthol-4-sulfonic acid disodium salt

Note. This compound is deposited on crystals of sodium chloride. The small, blue crystals are freely water-soluble. In the pH range between 12 and 13, the solution of the indicator is reddish pink in the presence of calcium ion and deep blue in the presence of excess (ethylenedinitrilo)tetraacetate.

REQUIREMENT

Suitability for calcium determination.   To pass test.

TEST

Suitability for calcium determination. Dissolve 0.3 gram in 100 ml. of water, add 10 ml. of 1N sodium hydroxide and 1.0 ml. of calcium chloride solution (1 gram in 200 ml.), and dilute to 165 ml. The solution is reddish pink in color. Add 1.0 ml. of 0.05M (ethylenedinitrilo)tetraacetic acid disodium salt. The solution becomes deep blue in color.

Notes

Iodine

I

REQUIREMENTS

Form. Sublimed crystals.
Nonvolatile matter. Not more than 0.010 per cent.
Chlorine and bromine (as Cl). Not more than 0.005 per cent.

TESTS

Nonvolatile matter. Transfer 10 grams to a tared porcelain crucible or dish. Heat on the steam bath until the sample is volatilized. The weight of the residue should not exceed 0.0010 gram.

Chlorine and bromine. Add 1.0 gram to 100 ml. of hot water containing 0.6 gram of hydrazine sulfate in a 250-ml. Erlenmeyer flask. Heat on a steam bath until solution is effected. Cool and neutralize with 1N sodium hydroxide solution, using an external indicator. Add 2 ml. of hydrogen peroxide and 1 ml. of phosphoric acid. Heat to boiling and boil gently until the solution is colorless. Cool, wash down the sides of the flask, and add 0.5 ml. of hydrogen peroxide. If an iodine color develops, boil until the solution is colorless and for 10 minutes longer. If no color develops, boil for 10 minutes. Filter if necessary through a chloride-free filter, dilute to 100 ml., and take a 20-ml. aliquot. For the standard dilute a solution containing 0.01 mg. of chloride ion (Cl) to 20 ml. Add 1 ml. of nitric acid and 1 ml. of silver nitrate reagent solution to each. Any turbidity in the solution of the sample should not exceed that in the standard.

Notes

Iron, Low in Manganese

Fe   Formula Wt. 55.847

REQUIREMENTS

Manganese (Mn).   Not more than 0.002 per cent.

TESTS

Manganese.   To 1.00 gram in a 150-ml. beaker add 25 ml. of water, 10 ml. of nitric acid, 5 ml. of sulfuric acid, and 5 ml. of phosphoric acid. When dissolution is complete, add 0.25 gram of potassium periodate, boil for 5 minutes, and cool. Transfer the oxidized solution to a 50-ml. volumetric flask, dilute to volume with water, and transfer an aliquot to a 1-cm. absorption cell. To the remaining portion add 0.05 ml. of sodium nitrite solution (freshly prepared by dissolving 0.2 gram of sodium nitrite in 10 ml. of water), mix, and transfer to a matching 1-cm. cell. Balance the spectrophotometer at 545 mμ at 100 per cent transmittance with the reduced solution in the light path and read the transmittance of the oxidized solution. The transmittance of the sample solution should be greater than that produced by a standard containing 0.02 mg. of manganese ion (Mn) which has been treated exactly like the sample solution. (For 1-cm. cells the per cent transmittance of the standard is approximately 96.1.)

Notes

Iron Wire

Fe

REQUIREMENTS

Reducing power (as Fe). Not less than 99.90 nor more than 100.00 per cent.

TESTS

Reducing power. Accurately weigh a sample of from 1.1970 to 1.2030 grams and transfer it to a 500-ml. round-bottomed, three-necked flask. Provide one of the necks with a spray trap, another with a stoppered funnel, and the third with a gas-inlet tube. Displace the air in the flask with oxygen-free carbon dioxide (which may be prepared by passing the carbon dioxide gas through a solution of chromous sulfate) and maintain a slow stream of the gas through the flask throughout the entire subsequent operation. Add, through the stoppered funnel, 100 ml. of dilute sulfuric acid $(1 + 5)$ which has been freed of dissolved oxygen by passing carbon dioxide through it. Warm the flask gently until solution is complete. Weigh accurately a quantity of potassium dichromate that weighs 0.150 to 0.152 gram less than the sample. The assay value of the potassium dichromate should be known accurately in terms of a certified dichromate, such as National Bureau of Standards Standard Sample 136. Dissolve the potassium dichromate in 75 ml. of oxygen-free water and transfer the solution to the flask, slowly, with constant mixing, over an interval of about 2 minutes. Use oxygen-free water to rinse the beaker and stoppered funnel. Rinse the spray trap with oxygen-free water. Replace the stoppered funnel with a one-hole stopper to accommodate a buret tip and titrate the remaining ferrous iron with 0.01N ceric sulfate (5 to 10 ml. will be required).

$$\text{Per cent Fe} = \frac{(113.90A + 0.05585B)}{C} + 0.03$$

where A = weight of $K_2Cr_2O_7$
B = milliliters of 0.01N ceric sulfate
C = weight of sample
0.03 = net buoyancy correction for weights taken in air

Notes

Isobutyl Alcohol

2-Methyl-1-propanol

$(CH_3)_2CHCH_2OH$ Formula Wt. 74.12

REQUIREMENTS

Color (APHA).   Not more than 10.
Boiling range.   Not more than 2.0°C.
Residue after evaporation.   Not more than 0.005 per cent.
Solubility in water.   To pass test.
Acidity [as $(CH_3)_2CHCOOH$].   Not more than 0.02 per cent.
Water (H_2O).   Not more than 0.2 per cent.

TESTS

Color (APHA).   For the color standard dilute a 2-ml. aliquot of platinum-cobalt stock solution (APHA No. 500) to 100 ml. with water. Compare this solution (APHA No. 10) with 100 ml. of the isobutyl alcohol in 100-ml. Nessler tubes, viewed vertically over a white background.

Boiling range.   Distill 100 ml. by the method described on page 12. The difference between the temperatures when 1 ml. and 95 ml. have distilled should not exceed 2.0°C. The boiling point of pure isobutyl alcohol at 760-mm. mercury pressure is 107.9°C.

Residue after evaporation.   Evaporate 25 ml. (20 grams) to dryness in a tared dish on the steam bath and dry the residue at 105°C. for 30 minutes. The weight of the residue should not exceed 0.0010 gram.

Solubility in water.   Dilute 1 ml. with 16 ml. of water. The isobutyl alcohol should dissolve completely and the solution should be clear.

Acidity.   To 20 ml. (16 grams) in a glass-stoppered flask, add 20 ml. of water, shake for about 1 minute, and add 0.05 ml. of bromothymol blue indicator solution. A blue color should not be produced (alkalinity). If a yellowish green color is produced, it should be changed to blue by not more than 0.4 ml. of 0.1N sodium hydroxide.

Water.   Place 25 ml. of methanol in a dry titration flask and add Karl Fischer reagent to a visually or electrometrically determined end point. Add 2.0 ml. (1.6 grams) of the sample, taking care to protect the sample and contents of the flask from moisture. Stir vigorously and titrate with Karl Fischer reagent to the same end point. Calculate the water content of the sample from the titer and volume of Karl Fischer reagent consumed by the sample.

Notes

Isobutyl Alcohol

2-Methyl-1-propanol

(Suitable for use in ultraviolet spectrophotometry)

$(CH_3)_2CHCH_2OH$ Formula Wt. 74.12

REQUIREMENTS

Absorbance. To pass test.
Boiling range. Not more than 2.0°C.
Residue after evaporation. Not more than 0.005 per cent.
Solubility in water. To pass test.
Acidity [as $(CH_3)_2CHCOOH$]. Not more than 0.02 per cent.
Water (H_2O). Not more than 0.2 per cent.

TESTS

Absorbance. Determine the absorbance of the sample in a 1.00-cm. cell throughout the range of 230 mμ to 400 mμ, against water in a similar matched cell set at zero absorbance as the reference liquid. The absorbance should not exceed 1.00 at 230 mμ, 0.25 at 240 mμ, 0.07 at 250 mμ, 0.05 at 260 mμ, and 0.01 at 330 mμ to 400 mμ. The spectral absorbance curve recorded through the wavelengths indicated should be smooth throughout the prescribed range and should not show any extraneous impurity peaks within this range.

Other tests are the same as for **Isobutyl Alcohol,** page 299, except *Color* (*APHA*), which is superseded by the *Absorbance* test.

Notes

Isopentyl Alcohol

Isoamyl Alcohol
3-Methyl-1-butanol

$(CH_3)_2CHCH_2CH_2OH$ Formula Wt. 88.15

REQUIREMENTS

Boiling range.   From 128° to 132°C.
Residue after evaporation.   Not more than 0.003 per cent.
Acids and esters (as amyl acetate).   Not more than 0.060 per cent.
Aldehydes.   To pass test.
Substances darkened by sulfuric acid.   To pass test.

TESTS

Boiling range.   Distill 100 ml. by the method described on page 12. The temperatures observed when 1 ml. and 95 ml. have distilled should be between 128° and 132°C. at 760-mm. mercury pressure.

Residue after evaporation.   Evaporate 50 ml. (40 grams) to dryness in a tared dish on the steam bath and dry the residue at 105°C. for 30 minutes. The weight of the residue should not exceed 0.0012 gram.

Acids and esters.   Dilute 20 ml. with 20 ml. of alcohol, add 5.00 ml. of 0.1N sodium hydroxide, and heat gently under a reflux condenser for 10 minutes. Cool, add 0.10 ml. of phenolphthalein indicator solution, and titrate the excess sodium hydroxide with 0.1N hydrochloric acid. The volume of 0.1N sodium hydroxide solution consumed in the test should not be more than 0.75 ml. greater than the volume consumed in a complete blank test.

Aldehydes.   Shake 5 ml. with 5 ml. of 30 per cent potassium hydroxide solution for 5 minutes in a glass-stoppered cylinder and allow to separate. No color should develop in either layer.

Substances darkened by sulfuric acid.   Cool 10 ml. of the sample and 10 ml. of sulfuric acid (94.5 to 95.5 per cent H_2SO_4) to 10°C., mix carefully, and shake for 1 minute. The per cent transmittance determined in a 1-cm. cell at a wavelength of 475 mμ should not be less than 50.

Notes

Isopropyl Alcohol

2-Propanol

$CH_3CHOHCH_3$ Formula Wt. 60.10

REQUIREMENTS

Color (APHA). Not more than 10.

Density (gram per ml.) at 25°C. Not less than 0.781 nor more than 0.783.

Boiling range. 1 ml. to 95 ml., not more than 0.5°C.; 95 ml. to dryness not more than 0.5°C.

Residue after evaporation. Not more than 0.001 per cent.

Solubility in water. To pass test.

Water (H_2O). Not more than 0.20 per cent.

Neutrality. To pass test.

TESTS

Color (APHA). For the color standard dilute a 2-ml. aliquot of platinum-cobalt stock solution (APHA No. 500) to 100 ml. with water. Compare this solution (APHA No. 10) with 100 ml. of the isopropyl alcohol in 100-ml. Nessler tubes, viewed vertically over a white background.

Boiling range. Distill 100 ml. by the method described on page 12. The difference between the temperatures when 1 ml. and 95 ml. have distilled should not exceed 0.5°C., and the difference between the temperatures when 95 ml. have distilled and when the dry point is reached should not exceed 0.5°C. The boiling point of pure isopropyl alcohol at 760-mm. mercury pressure is 82.3°C.

Residue after evaporation. Evaporate 128 ml. (100 grams) to dryness in a tared dish on the steam bath and dry the residue at 105°C. for 30 minutes. The weight of the residue should not exceed 0.0010 gram.

Solubility in water. Mix 10 ml. with 40 ml. of water and allow to stand 1 hour. The solution should be as clear as an equal volume of water.

Water. Place 25 ml. of methanol in a dry titration flask and add Karl Fischer reagent to a visually or electrometrically determined end point. Add 10 ml. (7.8 grams) of the sample, taking care to protect the contents of the flask from moisture. Stir vigorously and titrate with Karl Fischer reagent to the same end point. Calculate the water content of the sample from the titer and volume of Karl Fischer reagent consumed by the sample.

Neutrality. Mix 10 ml. with 10 ml. of carbon dioxide–free water and add 0.10 ml. of bromothymol blue indicator. The solution should be neutral or require not more than 0.10 ml. of $0.01N$ acid or 0.10 ml. of $0.01N$ sodium hydroxide to render it so.

Notes

Isopropyl Alcohol

2-Propanol

(Suitable for use in ultraviolet spectrophotometry)

$CH_3CHOHCH_3$ Formula Wt. 60.10

REQUIREMENTS

Absorbance. To pass test.

Density (gram per ml.) at 25°C. Not less than 0.781 nor more than 0.783.

Boiling range. 1 ml. to 95 ml., not more than 0.5°C.; 95 ml. to dryness not more than 0.5°C.

Residue after evaporation. Not more than 0.001 per cent.

Solubility in water. To pass test.

Water (H_2O). Not more than 0.20 per cent.

Neutrality. To pass test.

TESTS

Absorbance. Determine the absorbance of the sample in a 1.00-cm. cell, throughout the range of 210 mμ to 400 mμ, against water in a similarly matched cell set at zero absorbance as the reference liquid. The absorbance should not exceed 1.00 at 210 mμ, 0.40 at 220 mμ, 0.20 at 230 mμ, 0.10 at 245 mμ, 0.05 at 260 mμ, 0.02 at 300 mμ, and 0.01 at 330 mμ to 400 mμ. The spectral absorbance curve recorded through the wavelengths indicated should be smooth throughout the prescribed range and should not show any extraneous impurity peaks within this range.

Other tests are the same as for **Isopropyl Alcohol,** page 303, except *Color (APHA)*, which is superseded by the *Absorbance* test.

Notes

Lead

Atomic Wt. 207.19

REQUIREMENTS

Antimony and tin (as Sn). To pass test (limit about 0.005 per cent).
Arsenic (As). Not more than 0.0001 per cent.
Bismuth (Bi). Not more than 0.0001 per cent.
Copper (Cu). Not more than 0.0003 per cent.
Iron (Fe). Not more than 0.001 per cent.
Nickel (Ni). Not more than 0.001 per cent.
Silver (Ag). Not more than 0.0002 per cent.

TESTS

Antimony and tin. Dissolve 20 grams in 120 ml. of dilute nitric acid
(1 + 3), warming if necessary to hasten dissolution. Restore the volume
to 120 ml. if necessary, agitate well, and while any insoluble residue is
uniformly dispersed, divide the solution into portions of 30 ml. and 90 ml.
To the 30-ml. portion, as a control, add a solution containing 0.5 mg. of
tin ion (Sn). Evaporate both solutions to moist residues on the steam
bath. Dissolve each residue in 100 ml. of water and digest on the steam
bath for 15 minutes. The amount of turbidity or sediment in the solution
representing the sample should not exceed that in the control.

Sample Solution A. Dissolve 110 grams in 700 ml. of dilute nitric
acid (1 + 3), warming if necessary to hasten dissolution. Cool the solution, transfer to a 1-liter volumetric flask, and cautiously add 66 ml.
of dilute sulfuric acid (1 + 1). Cool, dilute to the mark, and mix.
Allow the precipitate to settle and decant 885 ml. This volume is
equivalent to 100 grams of the sample. Evaporate until dense fumes
of sulfur trioxide appear, but avoid any considerable loss of sulfuric
acid. Cool, carefully add 50 ml. of water, cool again, filter, and wash
slightly. Dilute the filtrate and washings to 100 ml. (1 ml. = 1 gram).

Arsenic. To 3 ml. of Sample Solution A (3-gram sample) add 5 ml. of
sulfuric acid and evaporate to fumes of sulfur trioxide. Cool, wash down
the sides of the beaker, and again evaporate to fumes of sulfur trioxide.
Cool and determine arsenic by the Gutzeit method (page 11). The amount
of stain should not exceed that produced by 0.003 mg. of arsenic (As).

Bismuth. Neutralize 25 ml. of Sample Solution A (25-gram sample)
with ammonium hydroxide and add 5 ml. of dilute nitric acid (1 + 9).
Add 10 ml. of freshly prepared 10 per cent solution of thiourea and mix.

Any yellow color should not exceed that produced by 0.025 mg. of bismuth ion (Bi) in an equal volume of solution containing the quantities of reagents used in the test.

Copper. To 10 ml. of Sample Solution A (10-gram sample) in a separatory funnel add 3 ml. of ammonium citrate reagent solution and adjust the pH to 9.0 to 9.5 with dilute ammonium hydroxide (1 + 1), using 0.10 to 0.15 ml. of thymol blue indicator. Cool, add 1 ml. of a 0.1 per cent solution of sodium diethyldithiocarbamate and 10 ml. of carbon tetrachloride, and shake for 2 minutes. When the layers have separated, draw off the carbon tetrachloride layer into a Nessler or other tube suitable for comparison of the color. There should be no more yellow-brown color than is produced by 0.030 mg. of copper ion (Cu) in an equal volume of aqueous solution treated in the same manner as the solution of the sample.

Iron. To 1 ml. of Sample Solution A (1-gram sample) add 2 ml. of hydrochloric acid and dilute to 50 ml. Add 30 to 50 mg. of ammonium persulfate crystals and 3 ml. of ammonium thiocyanate reagent solution. Any red color should not exceed that produced by 0.010 mg. of iron (Fe) in an equal volume of solution containing the quantities of reagents used in the test.

Nickel. Dilute 10 ml. of Sample Solution A (10-gram sample) to 25 ml. Neutralize with ammonium hydroxide and add 1 ml. of nitric acid, 5 ml. of a 10 per cent solution of citric acid, and 2 ml. of bromine water. Stir and add dilute ammonium hydroxide (1 + 1) until the bromine color is discharged. Add 2 ml. more of the dilute ammonium hydroxide, cool, and add 2 ml. of a 1 per cent solution of dimethylglyoxime in ethyl alcohol. Dilute to 50 ml. and allow to stand for 15 minutes. Any red color should not exceed that produced by 0.10 mg. of nickel ion (Ni) in an equal volume of solution containing the quantities of reagents used in the test.

Silver. To 20 ml. of Sample Solution A (20-gram sample) add 1 ml. of dilute hydrochloric acid (1 + 9). Any turbidity should not exceed that produced by 0.04 mg. of silver ion (Ag) in an equal volume of solution containing 0.5 ml. of sulfuric acid and treated in the same manner as the solution of the sample.

Notes

Lead Acetate

(CH₃COO)₂Pb·3H₂O   Formula Wt. 379.33

REQUIREMENTS

Insoluble matter. Not more than 0.010 per cent.
Chloride (Cl). Not more than 0.0005 per cent.
Nitrate and nitrite (as NO₃). To pass test (limit about 0.005 per cent).
Copper (Cu). Not more than 0.002 per cent.
Substances not precipitated by hydrogen sulfide (as sulfates). Not more than 0.050 per cent.
Iron (Fe). Not more than 0.001 per cent.

TESTS

Insoluble matter. Dissolve 10 grams in 100 ml. of dilute glacial acetic acid (1 + 99) free from carbon dioxide. Filter through a tared filtering crucible, wash thoroughly with water free from carbon dioxide, and dry at 105°C. The weight of the residue should not exceed 0.0010 gram.

Chloride. Dissolve 2 grams in 20 ml. of dilute nitric acid (1 + 19), filter if necessary through a chloride-free filter, and add 1 ml. of silver nitrate reagent solution. Any turbidity should not exceed that produced by 0.01 mg. of chloride ion (Cl) in an equal volume of solution containing the quantities of reagents used in the test.

Nitrate and nitrite.

Sample Solution A. Dissolve 0.2 gram in 1 ml. of water. Add 20 ml. of nitrate-free sulfuric acid (2 + 1), centrifuge, and decant the liquid portion into a 200-mm. test tube. Dilute to 50 ml. with brucine sulfate reagent solution.

Control Solution B. Dissolve 0.2 gram in 1 ml. of the standard nitrate solution containing 0.01 mg. of nitrate ion (NO₃) per ml. Add 20 ml. of nitrate-free sulfuric acid (2 + 1), centrifuge, and decant the liquid portion into a 200-mm. test tube. Dilute to 50 ml. with brucine sulfate reagent solution.

Blank Solution C. Use 50 ml. of brucine sulfate reagent solution.

Heat the three solutions in a preheated (boiling) water bath for 10 minutes. Cool rapidly in an ice bath to room temperature. Set a spectrophotometer at 410 mμ and, using 1-cm. cells, adjust the instrument to read 0 absorbance with Blank Solution C in the light path, then determine the absorbance of Sample Solution A. Adjust the instrument to read

0 absorbance with Sample Solution A in the light path and determine the absorbance of Control Solution B. The absorbance of Sample Solution A should not exceed that of Control Solution B.

Copper.   Dissolve 2.5 grams in 22 ml. of a buffer solution containing 15 ml. of water, 5 ml. of a 10 per cent solution of ammonium acetate, and 2 ml. of acetic acid. For the standard add 0.05 mg. of copper ion (Cu) to 22 ml. of a similar buffer solution. Transfer the solutions to separatory funnels and add to each 0.5 ml. of ammonium thiocyanate reagent solution, 0.5 ml. of pyridine, and 10 ml. of chloroform. Shake vigorously for 1 minute and allow the layers to separate. Any greenish yellow color in the chloroform from the solution of the sample should not exceed that in the chloroform from the standard.

Substances not precipitated by hydrogen sulfide.   Dissolve 4 grams in 100 ml. of dilute acetic acid (1 + 49). Pass hydrogen sulfide through the solution to precipitate lead completely and filter without washing. To 50 ml. of the filtrate (2-gram sample) add 0.25 ml. of sulfuric acid, evaporate to dryness in a tared dish, heat gently to volatilize the excess acids, and finally ignite at 800° ± 25°C. for 15 minutes. The weight of the residue should not exceed 0.0010 gram. Reserve the residue for the test for *Iron*.

Iron.   To the residue obtained in the test for *Substances not precipitated by hydrogen sulfide* add 3 ml. of dilute hydrochloric acid (1 + 1) and 0.10 ml. of nitric acid, cover with a watch glass, and digest on the steam bath for 10 to 15 minutes. Remove the watch glass and evaporate to dryness. Dissolve the residue in 4 ml. of hydrochloric acid and dilute to 100 ml. To 50 ml. of this solution (1-gram sample) add 30 to 50 mg. of ammonium persulfate crystals and 3 ml. of ammonium thiocyanate reagent solution. Any red color should not exceed that produced by 0.01 mg. of iron (Fe) in an equal volume of solution containing the quantities of reagents used in the test.

Notes

Lead Carbonate

Note. This specification applies to both the normal lead carbonate and the basic lead carbonate.

REQUIREMENTS

Insoluble in dilute acetic acid. Not more than 0.020 per cent.
Chloride (Cl). Not more than 0.002 per cent.
Nitrate and nitrite (as NO_3). To pass test (limit about 0.005 per cent).
Substances not precipitated by hydrogen sulfide (as sulfates). Not more than 0.20 per cent.
Iron (Fe). Not more than 0.005 per cent.
Zinc (Zn). Not more than 0.003 per cent.
Cadmium (Cd). Not more than 0.002 per cent.

TESTS

Insoluble in dilute acetic acid. Digest 5 grams on a steam bath for 1 hour in a covered beaker in 50 ml. of water plus 7 ml. of acetic acid. Filter through a tared filtering crucible, wash thoroughly with dilute acetic acid (2 + 98), and dry at 105°C. The weight of the residue should not exceed 0.0010 gram.

Chloride. Dissolve 1 gram in 20 ml. of 10 per cent nitric acid reagent solution, filter if necessary through a chloride-free filter, and dilute to 50 ml. To 25 ml. add 1 ml. of nitric acid and 1 ml. of silver nitrate reagent solution. Any turbidity should not exceed that produced by 0.01 mg. of chloride ion (Cl) in an equal volume of solution containing the quantities of reagents used in the test.

Nitrate and nitrite.

Sample Solution A. Dissolve 0.2 gram in 1 ml. of water and 8 ml. of dilute acetic acid (1 + 7) by heating in a boiling water bath. Add 20 ml. of nitrate-free sulfuric acid (2 + 1), cool, centrifuge, and decant the liquid portion into a 200-mm. test tube. Dilute to 50 ml. with brucine sulfate reagent solution.

Control Solution B. Dissolve 0.2 gram in 8 ml. of dilute acetic acid (1 + 7) and 1 ml. of the standard nitrate solution containing 0.01 mg. of nitrate ion (NO_3) per ml. by heating in a boiling water bath. Add 20 ml. of nitrate-free sulfuric acid (2 + 1), cool, centrifuge, and decant the liquid portion into a 200-mm. test tube. Dilute to 50 ml. with brucine sulfate reagent solution.

Blank Solution C. Use 50 ml. of brucine sulfate reagent solution.

Heat the three solutions in a preheated (boiling) water bath for 10 minutes. Cool rapidly in an ice bath to room temperature. Set a spectrophotometer at 410 mμ and, using 1-cm. cells, adjust the instrument to read 0 absorbance with Blank Solution C in the light path, then determine the absorbance of Sample Solution A. Adjust the instrument to read 0 absorbance with Sample Solution A in the light path and determine the absorbance of Control Solution B. The absorbance of Sample Solution A should not exceed that of Control Solution B.

Substances not precipitated by hydrogen sulfide. Dissolve 2 grams in 25 ml. of dilute nitric acid (3 + 7), heating if necessary. Dilute to 100 ml. and precipitate the lead with hydrogen sulfide. Filter without washing. To 50 ml. of the filtrate add 0.15 ml. of sulfuric acid, evaporate to dryness in a tared dish, and ignite at 800° ± 25°C. for 15 minutes. The weight of the residue should not exceed 0.0020 gram. Retain the residue for the *Iron* test.

Iron. To the residue obtained in the preceding test add 1 ml. of hydrochloric acid and 0.15 ml. of nitric acid and evaporate to dryness. Dissolve in 10 ml. of hydrochloric acid and dilute to 50 ml. Dilute 10 ml. of the solution to 50 ml. and add 30 to 50 mg. of ammonium persulfate crystals and 3 ml. of ammonium thiocyanate reagent solution. Any red color should not exceed that produced by 0.01 mg. of iron (Fe) in an equal volume of solution containing the quantities of reagents used in the test.

Zinc. Dissolve 2 grams in 30 ml. of dilute acetic acid (1 + 9), heating if necessary to obtain complete dissolution. Cool the solution and add 2 ml. of sulfuric acid, slowly with constant stirring, and allow the precipitate to settle. Filter, wash until the filtrate has a volume of about 40 ml., adjust the pH to 4 to 7 (indicator paper) with ammonium hydroxide, and dilute to 50 ml. Prepare a standard containing 0.06 mg. of zinc ion (Zn) and 0.04 mg. of cadmium ion (Cd) in 50 ml. To each solution add 4 ml. of hydrochloric acid and 25 ml. of ammonium thiocyanate reagent solution and transfer to separatory funnels. To each add 25 ml. of ether, shake vigorously, allow the phases to separate, and draw off and reserve the ether phase. Repeat the ether extraction three times. Reserve the aqueous phase for the test for *Cadmium.* Combine the four ether phases obtained from the sample, and combine the four ether phases obtained from the standard. To each of the ether extracts add 10 ml. of 25 per cent sulfuric acid reagent solution, and heat on the steam bath until the ether has evaporated. Dilute each solution to about 60 ml., filter, and dilute to 100 ml. Adjust the pH of a 10-ml. aliquot of each solution to between 5.0 and 5.5 (using a pH meter) with $1N$ sodium acetate solution that has been extracted with dithizone extraction solution before use. Add 1 ml. of $0.1N$ sodium thiosulfate to each, transfer to separatory funnels, add 3 ml. of dithizone standard solution in carbon tetrachloride, and shake vigorously. Allow the phases to separate, and draw off and reserve the carbon tetrachloride phase. Repeat the extraction with small portions of the dithizone standard solution until the color of the dithizone remains unchanged in the carbon tetrachloride phase. Combine the extracts from the solution of the sample, also combine the extracts from the standard, and dilute to the smallest uniform volume with carbon tetrachloride. Transfer 10 ml. of each solution to separate separatory funnels and add 5 ml. of a freshly prepared 0.05 per cent solution of sodium sulfide, shake, and allow to separate. Draw off and discard the aqueous phase. Repeat the washing with the sodium sulfide solution until the aqueous phase remains colorless. Any pink color in the solution of the sample should not exceed that in the standard.

Cadmium.   Dilute the aqueous solutions reserved from the test for *Zinc* to 100 ml. Neutralize 5-ml. aliquots of each solution with 10 per cent sodium hydroxide reagent solution and add an excess of 5 ml. of the sodium hydroxide solution. Add 1 ml. of a 20 per cent solution of potassium sodium tartrate to each and transfer to separatory funnels. Add 5 ml. of dithizone standard solution in carbon tetrachloride to each and shake vigorously for about 1 minute. Draw off the dithizone layers. Repeat the extraction with 5 ml. more of dithizone standard solution. Combine the extracts from the sample; also combine the extracts from the standard. Any pink color, producing a purplish hue in the carbon tetrachloride from the solution of the sample, should not exceed that in the carbon tetrachloride from the standard.

Notes

Lead Chromate

PbCrO₄ Formula Wt. 323.18

REQUIREMENTS

Assay. Not less than 98 per cent PbCrO₄.
Soluble matter. Not more than 0.15 per cent.
Carbon compounds (as C). Not more than 0.01 per cent.

TESTS

Assay. Weigh accurately 0.5 gram of powdered sample and dissolve by warming with 40 ml. of 10 per cent sodium hydroxide reagent solution in a glass-stoppered 250-ml. flask. Add 2 grams of potassium iodide, and when it is dissolved, dilute with 80 ml. of water plus 15 ml. of hydrochloric acid. Allow to stand, protected from light, for 5 minutes. Titrate the liberated iodine with $0.1N$ sodium thiosulfate, adding starch indicator solution toward the end of the titration. One milliliter of $0.1N$ thiosulfate corresponds to 0.01077 gram of PbCrO₄.

Soluble matter. Boil 0.5 gram of the powdered sample for 5 minutes with 100 ml. of dilute acetic acid (1 + 20), stirring well during the heating. Cool and filter. Evaporate 25 ml. of the filtrate to dryness in a tared dish on the steam bath and dry at 105°C. Heat 50 ml. of the filtrate with 2 grams of the powdered sample for 5 minutes at 80° to 90°C., cool, dilute to 50 ml., and filter. Evaporate 25 ml. of this filtrate in a tared dish on the steam bath and dry at 105°C. The difference between the weights of the two residues should not be more than 0.0015 gram.

Carbon compounds. This procedure employs induction heating of the sample and a conductometric measurement of evolved carbon dioxide.*
Transfer 1 gram of sample and one tin capsule to a combustion crucible. Add 1.5 grams each of iron and copper accelerator. Ignite in an induction furnace in a stream of carbon dioxide-free oxygen until combustion is complete. Pass the effluent gas through an approximately 0.1 per cent solution of reagent grade barium hydroxide. Measure the change in conductance, in ohms, using a suitable cell and detection system. Subtract the reading from a blank and calculate the carbon content of the sample from a calibration curve.
Prepare the calibration curve as follows: transfer 0, 10, 25, 75, and 100 microliters of potassium hydrogen phthalate solution (8.5 grams per liter, 1 microliter = 4 micrograms of carbon) to tin capsules. Evaporate the solutions to dryness in the capsules at 80°C. Transfer the capsules to

combustion crucibles, add the accelerators, ignite, and measure the conductance under the same conditions as described above for running the sample. Subtract the reading of the blank from that of each of the standards and plot the calibration curve as ohms versus micrograms of carbon.

*A Leco Carbon Analyzer with accessories has been found satisfactory for the determination.

Notes

Lead Dioxide

PbO$_2$ Formula Wt. 239.19

REQUIREMENTS

Assay.   Not less than 95 per cent PbO$_2$.
Acid-insoluble matter.   Not more than 0.20 per cent.
Carbon compounds (as C).   Not more than 0.04 per cent.
Chloride (Cl).   Not more than 0.002 per cent.
Nitrate (NO$_3$).   Not more than 0.02 per cent.
Sulfate (SO$_4$).   Not more than 0.05 per cent.
Manganese (Mn).   Not more than 0.0005 per cent.
Other hydrogen sulfide metals (as Cu).   To pass test (limit about 0.05 per cent).
Substances not precipitated by hydrogen sulfide.   Not more than 0.50 per cent.

TESTS

Assay.   Weigh accurately 0.56 to 0.58 gram, and add 50.0 ml. of 0.1N arsenious acid, 10 ml. of 1 per cent potassium bromide, and 25 ml. of dilute hydrochloric acid (2 + 1). Stir and crush the lead dioxide and heat to about 50°C. to hasten complete dissolution and reaction. Cool and titrate the excess arsenious acid with 0.1N potassium bromate. The end point may be detected either with methyl orange indicator or potentiometrically. One milliliter of 0.1N arsenious acid corresponds to 0.01196 gram of PbO$_2$.

Acid-insoluble matter.   To 1 gram add 25 ml. of water and 3 ml. of nitric acid. Add carefully with stirring 5 ml. of 30 per cent hydrogen peroxide or more, if needed, to dissolve all the lead dioxide. Filter through a tared filtering crucible, wash thoroughly, and dry at 105°C. The weight of the residue should not exceed 0.0020 gram. Reserve the filtrate for the test for *Substances not precipitated by hydrogen sulfide.*

Carbon compounds.   This procedure employs induction heating of the sample and a conductometric measurement of the evolved carbon dioxide.*
Transfer 1 gram of sample and one tin capsule to a combustion crucible. Add 1.5 grams each of iron and copper accelerator. Ignite in an induction furnace in a stream of carbon dioxide-free oxygen until combustion is complete. Pass the effluent gas through an approximately 0.1 per cent solution of reagent grade barium hydroxide. Measure the change in conductance, in ohms, using a suitable cell and detection

system. Subtract the reading from a blank and calculate the carbon content of the sample from a calibration curve.

Prepare the calibration curve as follows: transfer 0, 10, 25, 75, and 100 microliters of potassium hydrogen phthalate solution (8.5 grams per liter, 1 microliter = 4 micrograms of carbon) to tin capsules. Evaporate the solutions to dryness in the capsules at 80°C. Transfer the capsules to combustion crucibles, add the accelerators, ignite, and measure the conductance under the same conditions as described above for running the sample. Subtract the reading of the blank from that of each of the standards and plot the calibration curve as ohms vs. micrograms of carbon.

*A Leco Carbon Analyzer with accessories has been found satisfactory for the determination.

Chloride. Dissolve 2 grams in 20 ml. of water plus 2 ml. of glacial acetic acid and 2 ml. of 30 per cent hydrogen peroxide. Filter through a chloride-free filter and dilute to 100 ml. To 25 ml. add 1 ml. of nitric acid and 1 ml. of silver nitrate reagent solution. Any turbidity should not exceed that produced by 0.01 mg. of chloride ion (Cl) in an equal volume of solution containing the quantities of reagents used in the test.

Nitrate. Dissolve 0.25 gram in a test tube containing 10 ml. of water, 1 ml. of acetic acid, and 0.5 ml. of 30 per cent hydrogen peroxide. Pass sulfur dioxide through the solution to precipitate the lead, filter, wash with two 2-ml. portions of water, and dilute the filtrate to 20 ml.

Sample Solution A. To 4.0 ml. of the filtrate in a test tube add 1.0 ml. of water, dilute to 50 ml. with brucine sulfate reagent solution, and mix.

Control Solution B. To 4.0 ml. of the filtrate in a test tube add 1.0 ml. of the standard nitrate solution containing 0.01 mg. of nitrate ion (NO_3) per ml., dilute to 50 ml. with brucine sulfate reagent solution, and mix.

Blank Solution C. Use 50 ml. of brucine sulfate reagent solution.

Heat the three solutions in a preheated (boiling) water bath for 10 minutes. Cool rapidly in an ice bath to room temperature. Set a spectrophotometer at 410 mμ and, using 1-cm. cells, adjust the instrument to read 0 absorbance with Blank Solution C in the light path, then determine the absorbance of Sample Solution A. Adjust the instrument to read 0 absorbance with Sample Solution A in the light path and determine the absorbance of Control Solution B. The absorbance of Sample Solution A should not exceed that of Control Solution B.

Sulfate. Decompose 2 grams with 10 ml. of hydrochloric acid and 3 ml. of nitric acid and evaporate to dryness on the steam bath. Add 25 ml. of water and 2 grams of sodium carbonate and digest on the steam bath for several hours, with occasional stirring. Dilute to 100 ml. and filter. Neutralize the filtrate with hydrochloric acid and add an excess of 1 ml. of the acid. Heat to boiling, add 5 ml. of barium chloride reagent solution, digest in a covered beaker on the steam bath for 2 hours, and allow to stand overnight. Filter, wash thoroughly, and ignite. The weight of the precipitate should not be more than 0.0025 gram greater than the weight obtained in a complete blank test.

Manganese. Add 10 grams to 15 ml. of dilute nitric acid $(1 + 1)$. Add carefully, with stirring about 10 ml. of 30 per cent hydrogen peroxide—or more, if necessary—to dissolve all of the lead dioxide. Evaporate nearly to dryness, cool, add 20 ml. of dilute sulfuric acid $(1 + 1)$, and evaporate to dense fumes of sulfur trioxide. Cool, cautiously dilute to 100 ml. with water, allow to settle, and filter. Dilute 20 ml. of the filtrate to 50 ml., add 10 ml. of nitric acid and 5 ml. of phosphoric acid, and boil gently for 5 minutes. Cool slightly, add 0.25 gram of potassium periodate, and again boil gently for 5 minutes. Any pink color should not exceed that produced by 0.01 mg. of manganese ion (Mn) in 50 ml. of dilute sulfuric acid $(1 + 9)$ treated exactly like the 50 ml. of filtrate.

Other hydrogen sulfide metals. Suspend 0.4 gram in 20 ml. of dilute acetic acid $(1 + 19)$ and add 1 ml. of 30 per cent hydrogen peroxide. When dissolution is complete, add 0.3 ml. of sulfuric acid and allow the precipitate to settle. Filter, do not wash the precipitate, and dilute the filtrate to 100 ml. To 10 ml. of the filtrate (0.04-gram sample) add about 10 mg. of sodium carbonate, evaporate to near dryness on a hot plate, add 1 ml. of nitric acid, and evaporate to dryness. Dissolve the residue in about 20 ml. of water and dilute to 25 ml. For the standard dilute a solution containing 0.02 mg. of copper ion (Cu) to 25 ml. Adjust the pH of the standard and sample solutions to between 3 and 4 (using a pH meter) with $1N$ acetic acid or ammonium hydroxide (10 per cent NH_3), dilute to 40 ml., and mix. Add 10 ml. of freshly prepared hydrogen sulfide water to each and mix. Any color in the solution of the sample should not exceed that in the standard.

Substances not precipitated by hydrogen sulfide. Evaporate to dryness the filtrate obtained in the test for *Acid-insoluble matter*. Moisten the residue with 0.2 ml. of hydrochloric acid, dissolve in 100 ml. of water, and pass hydrogen sulfide through the solution until the lead is completely precipitated. Filter, but do not wash. Evaporate 50 ml. of the clear filtrate (0.5-gram sample) to dryness in a tared dish. Heat gently to volatilize the excess salts and acids, and finally ignite at 800° ± 25°C. for 15 minutes. The weight of the residue should not exceed 0.0025 gram.

Notes

Lead Nitrate

Pb(NO₃)₂ $\qquad$ Formula Wt. 331.20

Pb(NO$_3$)$_2$ Formula Wt. 331.20

REQUIREMENTS

Insoluble matter. Not more than 0.005 per cent.
Chloride (Cl). Not more than 0.001 per cent.
Copper (Cu). Not more than 0.002 per cent.
Iron (Fe). Not more than 0.001 per cent.
Substances not precipitated by hydrogen sulfide (as sulfates). Not more than 0.10 per cent.

TESTS

Insoluble matter. Dissolve 20 grams in 200 ml. of dilute nitric acid $(1 + 99)$, heat to boiling, and digest in a covered beaker on the steam bath for 1 hour. Filter through a tared filtering crucible, wash thoroughly, and dry at 105°C. The weight of the residue should not exceed 0.0010 gram.

Chloride. Dissolve 1 gram in 20 ml. of water, filter if necessary through a chloride-free filter, and add 1 ml. of nitric acid and 1 ml. of silver nitrate reagent solution. Any turbidity should not exceed that produced by 0.01 mg. of chloride ion (Cl) in an equal volume of solution containing the quantities of reagents used in the test.

Copper. Dissolve 1 gram in 15 ml. of water and add 5 ml. of a 10 per cent solution of ammonium acetate, 0.5 ml. of ammonium thiocyanate reagent solution, 2 ml. of acetic acid, 0.5 ml. of pyridine, and 10 ml. of chloroform. Shake vigorously and allow to separate. The greenish yellow color in the chloroform layer should not exceed that produced by 0.02 mg. of copper ion (Cu) in an equal volume of solution containing the quantities of reagents used in the test.

Iron. Dissolve 1 gram in 4 ml. of water, add 0.5 ml. of sulfuric acid, evaporate, and heat to dense fumes of sulfur trioxide. Cool, add about 30 ml. of water, cool again, and filter. To the filtrate add 2 ml. of hydrochloric acid and dilute to 50 ml. Add 30 to 50 mg. of ammonium persulfate crystals, and 3 ml. of ammonium thiocyanate reagent solution. Any red color should not exceed that produced by 0.01 mg. of iron (Fe) in an equal volume of solution containing the quantities of reagents used in the test.

Substances not precipitated by hydrogen sulfide. Dissolve 2 grams in 100 ml. of water and pass hydrogen sulfide through the solution until the lead is completely precipitated. Filter but do not wash. To 50 ml. of the filtrate add 0.25 ml. of sulfuric acid, evaporate to dryness in a tared dish, and ignite at $800° \pm 25°C.$ for 15 minutes. The weight of the residue should not exceed 0.0010 gram.

Notes

Lead Subacetate

(For sugar analysis)

REQUIREMENTS

Basic lead (PbO). Not less than 33 per cent.
Loss on drying at 105°C. Not more than 1.5 per cent.
Insoluble in dilute acetic acid. Not more than 0.02 per cent.
Insoluble in water. Not more than 1.0 per cent.
Chloride (Cl). Not more than 0.003 per cent.
Nitrate and nitrite (as NO_3). To pass test (limit about 0.003 per cent).
Copper (Cu). Not more than 0.002 per cent.
Substances not precipitated by hydrogen sulfide (as sulfates). Not more than 0.30 per cent.
Iron (Fe). Not more than 0.002 per cent.

TESTS

Basic lead. Weigh accurately about 5 grams and dissolve in 100 ml. of carbon dioxide–free water in a 500-ml. volumetric flask. Add 50.0 ml. of 1N acetic acid and 100 ml. of carbon dioxide–free 3 per cent solution of sodium oxalate. Mix thoroughly, dilute to volume with carbon dioxide–free water, and allow the precipitate to settle. Titrate 100 ml. of the clear supernatant liquid with 1N sodium hydroxide, using phenolphthalein indicator. Each milliliter of 1N acetic acid consumed is equivalent to 0.1116 gram of PbO.

Loss on drying. Weigh accurately about 0.5 gram in a tared dish or crucible and dry for 2 hours at 105°C. Cool and reweigh. The loss in weight should not exceed 1.5 per cent of the weight of the sample.

Insoluble in dilute acetic acid. Dissolve 5 grams in 100 ml. of dilute acetic acid (1 + 19), warming if necessary to effect complete dissolution. Filter through a tared filtering crucible, wash with dilute acetic acid (1 + 19) until the washings are no longer darkened by hydrogen sulfide, and dry at 105°C. The weight of the residue should not exceed 0.0010 gram.

Insoluble in water. Agitate 1 gram in a small stoppered flask with 50 ml. of carbon dioxide–free water and filter at once through a tared filtering crucible. Wash with carbon dioxide–free water and dry at 105°C. The weight of the residue should not exceed 0.0100 gram.

Chloride. Dissolve 1 gram in 30 ml. of dilute nitric acid (1 + 9), and filter if necessary through a chloride-free filter. To 10 ml. of the filtrate add 10 ml. of water and 1 ml. of silver nitrate reagent solution. Any turbidity should not exceed that produced by 0.01 mg. of chloride ion (Cl) in an equal volume of solution containing the quantities of reagents used in the test.

Nitrate and nitrite.

Sample Solution A. Suspend 0.5 gram in 3 ml. of water. Dilute to 50 ml. with brucine sulfate reagent solution.

Control Solution B. Suspend 0.5 gram in 1.5 ml. of water and 1.5 ml. of the standard nitrate solution containing 0.01 mg. of nitrate ion (NO_3) per ml. Dilute to 50 ml. with brucine sulfate reagent solution.

Blank Solution C. Use 50 ml. of brucine sulfate reagent solution.

Heat Sample Solution A, Control Solution B, and Blank Solution C in a preheated (boiling) water bath until the lead subacetate in A and B is dissolved, then heat for 10 more minutes. Cool rapidly in an ice bath to room temperature, centrifuge Sample Solution A and Control Solution B for 10 minutes, and decant the liquids into 200-mm. test tubes. Set a spectrophotometer at 410 mμ and, using 1-cm. cells, adjust the instrument to read 0 absorbance with Blank Solution C in the light path, then determine the absorbance of Sample Solution A. Adjust the instrument to read 0 absorbance with Sample Solution A in the light path and determine the absorbance of Control Solution B. The absorbance of Sample Solution A should not exceed that of Control Solution B.

Copper. Dissolve 2.5 grams in 22 ml. of a buffer solution containing 15 ml. of water, 5 ml. of a 10 per cent solution of ammonium acetate, and 2 ml. of acetic acid. For the standard add 0.05 mg. of copper ion (Cu) to 22 ml. of a similar buffer solution. Transfer the solutions to separatory funnels and add to each 0.5 ml. of ammonium thiocyanate reagent solution, 0.5 ml. of pyridine, and 10 ml. of chloroform. Shake vigorously for 1 minute and allow the layers to separate. Any greenish yellow color in the chloroform from the solution of the sample should not exceed that in the chloroform from the standard.

Substances not precipitated by hydrogen sulfide. Dissolve 2 grams in 100 ml. of dilute acetic acid (1 + 49). Pass hydrogen sulfide through the solution to precipitate the lead completely and filter without washing. To 50 ml. of the filtrate (1-gram sample) add 0.25 ml. of sulfuric acid, evaporate to dryness in a tared dish, and ignite at 800° ± 25°C. for 15 minutes. The weight of the residue should not exceed 0.0030 gram. Reserve the residue for the test for *Iron*.

Iron.   To the residue obtained in the test for *Substances not precipitated by hydrogen sulfide* add 3 ml. of dilute hydrochloric acid $(1 + 1)$ and 0.10 ml. of nitric acid, cover with a watch glass, and digest on the steam bath for 15 to 20 minutes. Remove the watch glass and evaporate to dryness. Dissolve the residue in 4 ml. of hydrochloric acid and dilute to 100 ml. To 50 ml. add 30 to 50 mg. of ammonium persulfate crystals and 3 ml. of ammonium thiocyanate reagent solution. Any red color should not exceed that produced by 0.01 mg. of iron (Fe) in an equal volume of solution containing the quantities of reagents used in the test.

Notes

Lithium Carbonate

Li$_2$CO$_3$

Formula Wt. 73.89

Note. The formula weight of this reagent is likely to deviate from the value cited above, since the natural distribution of ^{6}Li and ^{7}Li isotopes is often altered in current sources of lithium compounds.

REQUIREMENTS

Assay. Not less than 99 per cent Li$_2$CO$_3$.
Insoluble in dilute hydrochloric acid. Not more than 0.010 per cent.
Chloride (Cl). Not more than 0.005 per cent.
Nitrate (NO$_3$). Not more than 0.0005 per cent.
Sulfur compounds (as SO$_4$). Not more than 0.20 per cent.
Ammonium (NH$_4$). Not more than 0.0005 per cent.
Heavy metals (as Pb). Not more than 0.002 per cent.
Iron (Fe). Not more than 0.002 per cent.
Calcium (Ca). Not more than 0.01 per cent.
Potassium (K). Not more than 0.01 per cent.
Sodium (Na). Not more than 0.1 per cent.

TESTS

Assay. Weigh accurately about 1.3 grams, add 50 ml. of water, and then add cautiously 50.0 ml. of 1N hydrochloric acid. Boil gently to expel carbon dioxide, cool, add 0.15 ml. of methyl red indicator solution, and titrate the excess hydrochloric acid with 1N sodium hydroxide solution. One milliliter of 1N hydrochloric acid corresponds to 0.03694 gram of Li$_2$CO$_3$.

Insoluble in dilute hydrochloric acid. Suspend 10 grams in 75 ml. of water, then add cautiously and slowly 25 ml. of hydrochloric acid. Heat to boiling and digest in a covered beaker on the steam bath for 1 hour. Filter through a tared filtering crucible, wash thoroughly with hot water, and dry at 105°C. The weight of the residue should not exceed 0.0010 gram.

Chloride. Dissolve 2 grams in 25 ml. of dilute nitric acid (1 + 5), filter if necessary through a chloride-free filter, and dilute to 50 ml. Dilute 5 ml. (0.2-gram sample) of the solution to 25 ml. and add 1 ml. of nitric acid and 1 ml. of silver nitrate reagent solution. Any turbidity should not exceed that produced by 0.01 mg. of chloride ion (Cl) in an

equal volume of solution containing the quantities of reagents used in the test.

Nitrate.

Sample Solution A. Add 2.0 grams to 4.0 ml. of water in a test tube. Add brucine sulfate reagent solution, drop by drop, until the sample is completely dissolved. Then dilute to 50 ml. with the same reagent solution and mix.

Control Solution B. Add 2.0 grams to 3.0 ml. of water and 1.0 ml. of the standard nitrate solution containing 0.01 mg. of nitrate ion (NO_3) per ml. Add brucine sulfate reagent solution, drop by drop, until the sample is completely dissolved. Then dilute to 50 ml. with the same reagent solution and mix.

Blank Solution C. Use 50 ml. of brucine sulfate reagent solution.

Heat the three solutions in a preheated (boiling) water bath for 10 minutes. Cool rapidly in an ice bath to room temperature. Set a spectrophotometer at 410 mμ and, using 1-cm. cells, adjust the instrument to read 0 absorbance with Blank Solution C in the light path, then determine the absorbance of Sample Solution A. Adjust the instrument to read 0 absorbance with Sample Solution A in the light path and determine the absorbance of Control Solution B. The absorbance of Sample Solution A should not exceed that of Control Solution B.

Sulfur compounds. Suspend 0.1 gram in 10 ml. of water and cautiously neutralize with dilute hydrochloric acid (1 + 9). Add 0.10 ml. of bromine water and boil gently until the bromine is completely expelled. Add 2 ml. of dilute hydrochloric acid (1 + 19), filter, and dilute to 40 ml. To 10 ml. add 1 ml. of barium chloride reagent solution. Any turbidity should not exceed that produced by 0.05 mg., of sulfate ion (SO_4) in an equal volume of solution containing 1 ml. of dilute hydrochloric acid (1 + 19) and 1 ml. of barium chloride reagent solution. Compare 10 minutes after adding the barium chloride to the sample and standard solutions.

Ammonium. Suspend 2 grams in 50 ml. of water and cautiously add 5 ml. of hydrochloric acid. Transfer the solution to a flask connected through a spray trap to a condenser, the end of which dips beneath the surface of 10 ml. of 0.1N hydrochloric acid. Add 15 ml. of freshly boiled 10 per cent sodium hydroxide reagent solution. Distill about 35 ml., add to the distillate 1 ml. of 10 per cent sodium hydroxide reagent solution, dilute to 50 ml., and add 2 ml. of Nessler reagent. Any color developed should not exceed that produced when 0.01 mg. of ammonium ion (NH_4) is added to the residue obtained from the evaporation of 5 ml. of hydrochloric acid and dissolved in 50 ml. of water and treated exactly like the sample, starting with "transfer the solution to a flask, etc."

Heavy metals. Suspend 1.5 grams in 10 ml. of water and add cautiously 10 ml. of hydrochloric acid. For the control suspend 0.5 gram of the sample in 10 ml. of water containing 0.02 mg. of lead ion (Pb), and add cautiously 10 ml. of hydrochloric acid. Evaporate both solutions to a moist residue on the steam bath. Dissolve each residue in 20 ml. of water and dilute to 25 ml. Adjust the pH of each solution to between 3 and 4 (using a pH meter) with $1N$ acetic acid or ammonium hydroxide (10 per cent NH_3), dilute to 40 ml., and mix. Add 10 ml. of freshly prepared hydrogen sulfide water to each and mix. Any color in the solution of the sample should not exceed that in the control.

Iron. Suspend 0.5 gram in 30 ml. of water and cautiously add 3 ml. of hydrochloric acid. Dilute to 50 ml. and add 30 to 50 mg. of ammonium persulfate crystals and 3 ml. of ammonium thiocyanate reagent solution. Any red color should not exceed that produced by 0.01 mg. of iron (Fe) in an equal volume of solution containing 2 ml. of hydrochloric acid and the quantities of reagents used in the test.

Stock Solution for the flame photometric determination of Calcium, Potassium, and Sodium. Suspend 20 grams in 100 ml. of water, cautiously add 50 ml. of hydrochloric acid, and dilute to 200 ml. (1 ml. = 0.1 gram).

Sample Solution A for the determination of Calcium and Potassium. Dilute a 50-ml. aliquot (5-gram sample) of the Stock Solution to 100 ml.

Control Solution B for the determination of Calcium and Potassium. To another 50-ml. aliquot of the Stock Solution, add 0.5 mg. of calcium ion (Ca) and 0.5 mg. of potassium ion (K), and dilute to 100 ml.

Calcium. Determine the calcium by the flame photometric method described on page 14. Observe the emission of Control Solution B at the 422.7-mμ calcium line. Observe the emission of Sample Solution A at the 422.7-mμ calcium line and at a wavelength of 418 mμ. The difference (D_1) between the intensities observed for Sample Solution A at 418 mμ and 422.7 mμ should not exceed the difference (D_2) observed at 422.7 mμ between Sample Solution A and Control Solution B.

Potassium. Determine the potassium by the flame photometric method described on page 14. Observe the emission of Control Solution B at the 767-mμ potassium line. Observe the emission of Sample Solution A at the 767-mμ potassium line and at a wavelength of 750 mμ. The difference (D_1) between the intensities observed for Sample Solution A at 767 mμ and 750 mμ should not exceed the difference (D_2) observed at 767 mμ between Sample Solution A and Control Solution B.

Sodium. Determine the sodium by the flame photometric method described on page 14.

Sample Solution A. Dilute a 5-ml. aliquot (0.5-gram sample) of the Stock Solution to 100 ml. with water.

Control Solution B. To another 5-ml. aliquot of the Stock Solution, add 0.5 mg. of sodium ion (Na), and dilute to 100 ml. with water.

Observe the emission of Control Solution B at the 589-mμ sodium line. Observe the emission of Sample Solution A at the 589-mμ sodium line and at a wavelength of 580 mμ. The difference (D_1) between the intensities observed for Sample Solution A at 580 mμ and 589 mμ should not exceed the difference (D_2) observed at 589 mμ between Sample Solution A and Control Solution B.

Notes

Litmus Paper

Note. When litmus paper is used in a solution, the length of the piece used should not be more than 0.5 cm. of a strip about 5 × 0.6 cm.

REQUIREMENTS

Ash.   Not more than 0.4 mg. per strip (about 3 sq. cm.).
Phosphate (PO_4).   To pass test.
Rosin acids (for blue paper only).   To pass test.
Sensitivity.   To pass test.

TESTS

Ash.   Carefully ignite 10 strips in a tared crucible, and finally ignite at 800° ± 25°C. for 15 minutes. The weight of the ash should not exceed 0.0040 gram.

Phosphate.   Cut 5 strips into small pieces, mix with 0.5 gram of magnesium nitrate in a porcelain crucible, and ignite. To the ignited residue add 5 ml. of nitric acid and evaporate to dryness. Dissolve in 25 ml. of approximately 0.5N sulfuric acid, add 1 ml. of ammonium molybdate reagent solution and 1 ml. of *p*-methylaminophenol sulfate reagent solution, and allow to stand for 2 hours at room temperature. Any blue color should not exceed that produced by 0.02 mg. of phosphate ion (PO_4) in an equal volume of solution containing the quantities of reagents used in the test.

Rosin acids.   Immerse a strip of blue paper in a solution of 0.10 gram of silver nitrate in 50 ml. of water. The color of the paper should not change in 30 seconds.

Sensitivity.   Drop the pieces from 6 strips of paper into 100 ml. of test solution in a beaker and stir continuously. Blue paper should change color in 45 seconds in 0.0005N acid. Red paper should change color in 30 seconds in 0.0005N alkali.

Notes

Magnesium Acetate

$(CH_3COO)_2Mg \cdot 4H_2O$ Formula Wt. 214.46

REQUIREMENTS

Insoluble matter. Not more than 0.005 per cent.
Chloride (Cl). Not more than 0.001 per cent.
Nitrogen compounds (as N). Not more than 0.001 per cent.
Sulfate (SO$_4$). Not more than 0.005 per cent.
Barium (Ba). Not more than 0.001 per cent.
Calcium (Ca). Not more than 0.01 per cent.
Heavy metals (as Pb). Not more than 0.0005 per cent.
Iron (Fe). Not more than 0.0005 per cent.
Manganese (Mn). Not more than 0.001 per cent.
Potassium (K). Not more than 0.005 per cent.
Sodium (Na). Not more than 0.005 per cent.
Strontium (Sr). Not more than 0.005 per cent.

TESTS

Insoluble matter. Dissolve 20 grams in 200 ml. of dilute acetic acid (1 + 99). Heat to boiling and digest in a covered beaker on the steam bath for 1 hour. Filter through a tared filtering crucible, wash thoroughly, and dry at 105°C. The weight of the residue should not exceed 0.0010 gram. Retain the filtrate, without washings, for the test for *Sulfate*.

Sample Solution A for the determination of Chloride, Nitrogen compounds, and Iron. Dissolve 10 grams in water, filter if necessary through a chloride-free filter, and dilute to 100 ml. (1 ml. = 0.1 gram).

Chloride. Dilute 10 ml. of Sample Solution A (1-gram sample) to 20 ml. and add 1 ml. of nitric acid and 1 ml. of silver nitrate reagent solution. Any turbidity should not exceed that produced by 0.01 mg. of chloride ion (Cl) in an equal volume of solution containing the quantities of reagents used in the test.

Nitrogen compounds. Dilute 10 ml. of Sample Solution A (1-gram sample) to 40 ml. in a flask connected through a spray trap to a condenser, the end of which dips beneath the surface of 10 ml. of 0.1N hydrochloric acid. Add to the flask 10 ml. of freshly boiled 10 per cent sodium hydroxide reagent solution and about 0.5 gram of aluminum wire in small pieces, allow to stand for 1 hour, and slowly distill about 35 ml. To the distillate add 1 ml. of 10 per cent sodium hydroxide reagent solution, dilute to 50 ml., and add 2 ml. of Nessler reagent. Any color should not exceed that produced when a quantity of an ammonium salt containing 0.01 mg. of nitrogen (N) is treated exactly like the 10 ml. of Sample Solution A.

Sulfate. Add 2 ml. of hydrochloric acid to the filtrate, without washings, reserved from the test for *Insoluble matter*. Heat to boiling, add 10 ml. of barium chloride reagent solution, digest on the steam bath for 2 hours, and allow to stand overnight. If a precipitate is formed, filter, wash thoroughly, and ignite. The weight of the precipitate should not be more than 0.0024 gram greater than the weight obtained in a complete blank test.

Barium. Dissolve 6 grams in 25 ml. of dilute nitric acid (1 + 1). For the control dissolve 1 gram in 25 ml. of dilute nitric acid (1 + 1) and add 0.05 mg. of barium ion (Ba). Evaporate each solution on the steam bath to a syrupy consistency and add 20 ml. of water. If the solutions are not clear, add 10 per cent nitric acid until clear. Add 1 ml. of $1N$ acetic acid and 2 ml. of potassium dichromate reagent solution to each, and adjust the pH to 7 (using a pH meter) with ammonium hydroxide (10 per cent NH_3). Add 25 ml. of methanol to each and stir vigorously. Any turbidity in the solution of the sample should not exceed that in the control.

Calcium. Determine the calcium by the flame photometric method described on page 14. Dissolve 10 grams in 50 ml. of dilute hydrochloric acid (1 + 5), digest in a covered beaker on the steam bath for 20 minutes, cool, and dilute to 100 ml.

Sample Solution A. Dilute a 10-ml. aliquot (1-gram sample) of the solution to 100 ml. with water.

Control Solution B. Add 0.10 mg. of calcium ion (Ca) to another 10-ml. aliquot of the solution and dilute to 100 ml. with water.

Observe the emission of Control Solution B at the 422.7-mμ calcium line. Observe the emission of Sample Solution A at the 422.7-mμ calcium line and at a wavelength of 430 mμ. The difference (D_1) between the intensities observed for Sample Solution A at 422.7 mμ and 430 mμ should not exceed the difference (D_2) observed at 422.7 mμ between Sample Solution A and Control Solution B.

Heavy metals. Dissolve 6 grams in about 20 ml. of water and dilute to 30 ml. For the control add 0.02 mg. of lead ion (Pb) to a 5-ml. aliquot of the solution and dilute to 25 ml. For the sample use the remaining 25-ml. portion. Adjust the pH of the control and sample solutions to between 3 and 4 (using a pH meter) with $1N$ acetic acid or ammonium hydroxide (10 per cent NH_3), dilute to 40 ml., and mix. Add 10 ml. of

freshly prepared hydrogen sulfide water to each and mix. Any color in the solution of the sample should not exceed that in the control.

Iron. To 20 ml. of Sample Solution A (2-gram sample) add 2 ml. of hydrochloric acid, dilute to 50 ml., and add 30 to 50 mg. of ammonium persulfate crystals and 3 ml. of ammonium thiocyanate reagent solution. Any red color should not exceed that produced by 0.01 mg. of iron (Fe) in an equal volume of solution containing the quantities of reagents used in the test.

Manganese. Dissolve 5 grams in 20 ml. of water plus 20 ml. of nitric acid and 10 ml. of sulfuric acid. Prepare a standard containing 0.05 mg. of manganese ion (Mn) in 20 ml. of water plus 20 ml. of nitric acid and 10 ml. of sulfuric acid. Evaporate each solution until dense fumes of sulfur trioxide appear, cool, and cautiously add 50 ml. of water plus 20 ml. of nitric acid and 5 ml. of phosphoric acid. Dilute to 100 ml., boil gently for 5 minutes, cool slightly, and add 0.25 gram of potassium periodate to each. Again boil gently for 5 minutes, cool, and dilute to 100 ml. Any pink color in the solution of the sample should not exceed that in the standard.

Potassium. Determine the potassium by the flame photometric method described on page 14.

Sample Solution A. Dissolve 5 grams in water and dilute to 100 ml.

Control Solution B. Dissolve 5 grams in water, add 0.25 mg. of potassium ion (K), and dilute to 100 ml.

Observe the emission of Control Solution B at the 767-mμ potassium line. Observe the emission of Sample Solution A at the 767-mμ potassium line and at a wavelength of 750 mμ. The difference (D_1) between the intensities observed for Sample Solution A at 767 mμ and 750 mμ should not exceed the difference (D_2) observed at 767 mμ between Sample Solution A and Control Solution B.

Sodium. Determine the sodium by the flame photometric method described on page 14.

Sample Solution A. Dissolve 5 grams in water and dilute to 100 ml.

Control Solution B. Dissolve 5 grams in water, add 0.25 mg. of sodium ion (Na), and dilute to 100 ml.

Observe the emission of Control Solution B at the 589-mμ sodium line. Observe the emission of Sample Solution A at the 589-mμ sodium line and at a wavelength of 580 mμ. The difference (D_1) between the intensities observed for Sample Solution A at 589 mμ and 580 mμ should not exceed the difference (D_2) observed at 589 mμ between Sample Solution A and Control Solution B.

Strontium. Determine the strontium by the flame photometric method described on page 14.

Sample Solution A. Dissolve 5 grams in water and dilute to 100 ml.

Control Solution B. Dissolve 5 grams in water, add 0.25 mg. of strontium ion (Sr), and dilute to 100 ml.

Observe the emission of Control Solution B at the 460.7-mμ strontium line. Observe the emission of Sample Solution A at the 460.7-mμ strontium line and at a wavelength of 465 mμ. The difference (D_1) between the intensities observed for Sample Solution A at 460.7 mμ and 465 mμ should not exceed the difference (D_2) observed at 460.7 mμ between Sample Solution A and Control Solution B.

Notes

Magnesium Chloride

MgCl$_2$·6H$_2$O   Formula Wt. 203.30

REQUIREMENTS

Insoluble matter.   Not more than 0.005 per cent.
Nitrate (NO$_3$).   Not more than 0.001 per cent.
Phosphate (PO$_4$).   Not more than 0.0005 per cent.
Sulfate (SO$_4$).   Not more than 0.002 per cent.
Ammonium (NH$_4$).   Not more than 0.002 per cent.
Barium (Ba).   Not more than 0.005 per cent.
Calcium (Ca).   Not more than 0.01 per cent.
Heavy metals (as Pb).   Not more than 0.0005 per cent.
Iron (Fe).   Not more than 0.0005 per cent.
Manganese (Mn).   Not more than 0.0005 per cent.
Potassium (K).   Not more than 0.005 per cent.
Sodium (Na).   Not more than 0.005 per cent.
Strontium (Sr).   Not more than 0.005 per cent.

TESTS

Insoluble matter.   Dissolve 20 grams in 200 ml. of water, heat to boiling, and digest in a covered beaker on the steam bath for 1 hour. Filter through a tared filtering crucible, wash thoroughly, and dry at 105°C. The weight of the residue should not exceed 0.0010 gram. Retain filtrate separate from washings for the test for *Sulfate*.

Nitrate.

Sample Solution A.   Dissolve 1.0 gram in 3 ml. of water by heating in a boiling water bath. Dilute to 50 ml. with brucine sulfate reagent solution.

Control Solution B.   Dissolve 1.0 gram in 2 ml. of water and 1.0 ml. of the standard nitrate solution containing 0.01 mg. of nitrate ion (NO$_3$) per ml. by heating in a boiling water bath. Dilute to 50 ml. with brucine sulfate reagent solution.

Blank Solution C.   Use 50 ml. of brucine sulfate reagent solution.

Heat the three solutions in a preheated (boiling) water bath for 10 minutes. Cool rapidly in an ice bath to room temperature. Set a spectrophotometer at 410 mμ and, using 1-cm. cells, adjust the instrument to read 0 absorbance with Blank Solution C in the light path, then determine the absorbance of Sample Solution A. Adjust the instrument to read 0 absorbance with Sample Solution A in the light path and determine the absorbance of Control Solution B. The absorbance of Sample

Solution A should not exceed that of Control Solution B.

Phosphate.   Dissolve 4 grams in 25 ml. of approximately 0.5N sulfuric acid, add 1 ml. of ammonium molybdate reagent solution and 1 ml. of p-methylaminophenol sulfate reagent solution, and allow to stand at room temperature for 2 hours. Any blue color should not exceed that produced by 0.02 mg. of phosphate ion (PO_4) in an equal volume of solution containing the quantities of reagents used in the test.

Sulfate.   Add 1 ml. of hydrochloric acid to the filtrate, without washings, from the test for *Insoluble matter*. Heat to boiling, add 5 ml. of barium chloride reagent solution, digest in a covered beaker on the steam bath for 2 hours, and allow to stand overnight. If a precipitate is formed, filter, wash thoroughly and ignite. The weight of the precipitate should not be more than 0.0010 gram greater than the weight obtained in a complete blank test.

Ammonium.   Dissolve 1 gram in 90 ml. of water and add 10 ml. of freshly boiled 10 per cent sodium hydroxide reagent solution. Allow to settle, decant 50 ml., and add 2 ml. of Nessler reagent. Any color should not exceed that produced by 0.01 mg. of ammonium ion (NH_4) in an equal volume of solution containing 5 ml. of 10 per cent sodium hydroxide solution and 2 ml. of Nessler reagent.

Barium.   Dissolve 1.5 grams in 20 ml. of water. For the control dissolve 0.5 gram in 15 ml. of water, add 0.05 mg. of barium ion (Ba), and dilute to 20 ml. To each solution add 1 ml. of 1N acetic acid and 2 ml. of potassium dichromate reagent solution. Adjust the pH of the control and sample solutions to 7 (using a pH meter) with ammonium hydroxide (10 per cent NH_3), add 25 ml. of methanol, and stir vigorously. Any turbidity in the solution of the sample should not exceed that in the control.

Calcium.   Determine the calcium by the flame photometric method described on page 14. Dissolve 10 grams in 50 ml. of dilute hydrochloric acid ($1 + 5$), digest in a covered beaker on the steam bath for 20 minutes, cool, and dilute to 100 ml.

   Sample Solution A.   Dilute a 10-ml. aliquot (1-gram sample) of the solution to 100 ml. with water.

   Control Solution B.   Add 0.10 mg. of calcium ion (Ca) to another 10-ml. aliquot of the solution and dilute to 100 ml. with water.

Observe the emission of Control Solution B at the 422.7-mμ calcium line. Observe the emission of Sample Solution A at the 422.7-mμ calcium line and at a wavelength of 430 mμ. The difference (D$_1$) between the intensities observed for Sample Solution A at 422.7 mμ and 430 mμ should not exceed the difference (D$_2$) observed at 422.7 mμ between Sample Solution A and Control Solution B.

Heavy metals. Dissolve 6 grams in about 20 ml. of water and dilute to 30 ml. For the control add 0.02 mg. of lead ion (Pb) to a 5-ml. aliquot of the solution and dilute to 25 ml. For the sample use the remaining 25-ml. portion. Adjust the pH of the control and sample solutions to between 3 and 4 (using a pH meter) with 1N acetic acid or ammonium hydroxide (10 per cent NH$_3$), dilute to 40 ml., and mix. Add 10 ml. of freshly prepared hydrogen sulfide water to each and mix. Any color in the solution of the sample should not exceed that in the control.

Iron. Dissolve 2 grams in 30 ml. of water and 2 ml. of hydrochloric acid, dilute to 50 ml., and add 30 to 50 mg. of ammonium persulfate crystals and 3 ml. of ammonium thiocyanate reagent solution. Any red color should not exceed that produced by 0.01 mg. of iron (Fe) in an equal volume of solution containing the quantities of reagents used in the test.

Manganese. Dissolve 2 grams in 35 ml. of water plus 10 ml. of nitric acid and 5 ml. of sulfuric acid. Prepare a standard containing 0.01 mg. of manganese ion (Mn) in 35 ml. of water plus 10 ml. of nitric acid and 5 ml. of sulfuric acid. Evaporate each solution until dense fumes of sulfur trioxide appear. Cool the solutions, cautiously add 35 ml. of water, 10 ml. of nitric acid, and 5 ml. of phosphoric acid, and boil gently for 5 minutes. Cool, add 0.25 mg. of potassium periodate to each, and again boil gently for 5 minutes. Any pink color in the solution of the sample should not exceed that in the standard.

Potassium. Determine the potassium by the flame photometric method described on page 14.

Sample Solution A. Dissolve 5 grams in water and dilute to 100 ml.

Control Solution B. Dissolve 5 grams in water, add 0.25 mg. of potassium ion (K), and dilute to 100 ml.

Observe the emission of Control Solution B at the 767-mμ potassium line. Observe the emission of Sample Solution A at the 767-mμ potassium line and at a wavelength of 750 mμ. The difference (D$_1$) between the intensities observed for Sample Solution A at 767 mμ and 750 mμ

should not exceed the difference (D_2) observed at 767 mμ between Sample Solution A and Control Solution B.

Sodium.   Determine the sodium by the flame photometric method described on page 14.

Sample Solution A.   Dissolve 5 grams in water and dilute to 100 ml.

Control Solution B.   Dissolve 5 grams in water, add 0.25 mg. of sodium ion (Na), and dilute to 100 ml.

Observe the emission of Control Solution B at the 589-mμ sodium line. Observe the emission of Sample Solution A at the 589-mμ sodium line and at a wavelength of 580 mμ. The difference (D_1) between the intensities observed for Sample Solution A at 589 mμ and 580 mμ should not exceed the difference (D_2) observed at 589 mμ between Sample Solution A and Control Solution B.

Strontium.   Determine the strontium by the flame photometric method described on page 14.

Sample Solution A.   Dissolve 5 grams in water and dilute to 100 ml.

Control Solution B.   Dissolve 5 grams in water, add 0.25 mg. of strontium ion (Sr), and dilute to 100 ml.

Observe the emission of Control Solution B at the 460.7-mμ strontium line. Observe the emission of Sample Solution A at the 460.7-mμ strontium line and at a wavelength of 465 mμ. The difference (D_1) between the intensities observed for Sample Solution A at 460.7 mμ and 465 mμ should not exceed the difference (D_2) observed at 460.7 mμ between Sample Solution A and Control Solution B.

Notes

Magnesium Nitrate

Mg(NO$_3$)$_2 \cdot$ 6H$_2$O   Formula Wt. 256.41

REQUIREMENTS

Insoluble matter. Not more than 0.005 per cent.
pH of a 5 per cent solution. From 5.0 to 8.2 at 25°C.
Chloride (Cl). Not more than 0.001 per cent.
Phosphate (PO$_4$). Not more than 0.0005 per cent.
Sulfate (SO$_4$). Not more than 0.005 per cent.
Ammonium (NH$_4$). Not more than 0.003 per cent.
Barium (Ba). Not more than 0.005 per cent.
Calcium (Ca). Not more than 0.01 per cent.
Heavy metals (as Pb). Not more than 0.0005 per cent.
Iron (Fe). Not more than 0.0005 per cent.
Manganese (Mn). Not more than 0.0005 per cent.
Potassium (K). Not more than 0.005 per cent.
Sodium (Na). Not more than 0.005 per cent.
Strontium (Sr). Not more than 0.005 per cent.

TESTS

Insoluble matter. Dissolve 20 grams in 200 ml. of water, heat to boiling, and digest in a covered beaker on the steam bath for 1 hour. Filter through a tared filtering crucible, wash thoroughly with hot water, and dry at 105°C. The weight of the residue should not exceed 0.0010 gram.

pH of a 5 per cent solution. Dissolve 10 grams in 200 ml. of carbon dioxide- and ammonia-free water. Determine the pH by the method described on page 18. The pH should be from 5.0 to 8.2 at 25°C. The pH of a 5 per cent solution of pure magnesium nitrate would be 6.6 at 25°C.

Chloride. Dissolve 1 gram in 20 ml. of water, filter if necessary through a chloride-free filter, and add 1 ml. of nitric acid and 1 ml. of silver nitrate reagent solution. Any turbidity should not exceed that produced by 0.01 mg. of chloride ion (Cl) in an equal volume of solution containing the quantities of reagents used in the test.

Phosphate. Dissolve 4 grams in 25 ml. of approximately 0.5N sulfuric acid, add 1 ml. of ammonium molybdate reagent solution and 1 ml. of p-methylaminophenol sulfate reagent solution, and allow to stand at room temperature for 2 hours. Any blue color should not exceed that produced by 0.02 mg. of phosphate ion (PO$_4$) in an equal volume of solution containing the quantities of reagents used in the test.

Sulfate. Dissolve 10 grams in 100 ml. of dilute hydrochloric acid (1 + 1) and evaporate to dryness on the steam bath. Add 50 ml. of dilute hydrochloric acid (1 + 1), evaporate again to dryness, and heat for 1 hour at 120°C. Dissolve the residue in 100 ml. of dilute hydrochloric acid (1 + 99) and filter. Heat the filtrate to boiling, add 5 ml. of barium chloride reagent solution, digest in a covered beaker on the steam bath for 2 hours, and allow to stand overnight. Filter, wash thoroughly, and ignite in a tared crucible. The weight of the precipitate should not be more than 0.0012 gram greater than the weight obtained in a complete blank test.

Ammonium. Dissolve 1 gram in 100 ml. of water, add 10 ml. of freshly boiled 10 per cent sodium hydroxide reagent solution, and dilute to 150 ml. Allow the precipitate to settle. Filter through a sintered-glass or porous porcelain filter. To 50 ml. of the filtrate, add 2 ml. of Nessler reagent solution. Any color should not exceed that produced by 0.01 mg. of ammonium ion (NH_4) in an equal volume of solution containing the quantities of reagents used in the test.

Barium. Dissolve 1.5 grams in 20 ml. of water. For the control dissolve 0.5 gram in 15 ml. of water, add 0.05 mg. of barium ion (Ba), and dilute to 20 ml. To each solution add 1 ml. of $1N$ acetic acid and 2 ml. of potassium dichromate reagent solution. Adjust the pH of the control and sample solutions to 7 (using a pH meter) with ammonium hydroxide (10 per cent NH_3), add 25 ml. of methanol, and stir vigorously. Any turbidity in the solution of the sample should not exceed that in the control.

Calcium. Determine the calcium by the flame photometric method described on page 14. Dissolve 10 grams in 50 ml. of dilute hydrochloric acid (1 + 5), digest in a covered beaker on the steam bath for 20 minutes, cool, and dilute to 100 ml.

Sample Solution A. Dilute a 10-ml. aliquot (1-gram sample) of the solution to 100 ml. with water.

Control Solution B. Add 0.10 mg. of calcium ion (Ca) to another 10-ml. aliquot of the solution and dilute to 100 ml. with water.

Observe the emission of Control Solution B at the 422.7-mμ calcium line. Observe the emission of Sample Solution A at the 422.7-mμ calcium line and at a wavelength of 430 mμ. The difference (D_1) between the intensities observed for Sample Solution A at 422.7 mμ and 430 mμ should not exceed the difference (D_2) observed at 422.7 mμ between Sample Solution A and Control Solution B.

Heavy metals. Dissolve 6 grams in about 20 ml. of water and dilute to 30 ml. For the control add 0.02 mg. of lead ion (Pb) to a 5-ml. aliquot of the solution and dilute to 25 ml. For the sample use the remaining 25-ml. portion. Adjust the pH of the control and sample solutions to between 3 and 4 (using a pH meter) with 1N acetic acid or ammonium hydroxide (10 per cent NH_3), dilute to 40 ml., and mix. Add 10 ml. of freshly prepared hydrogen sulfide water to each and mix. Any color in the solution of the sample should not exceed that in the control.

Iron. Dissolve 2 grams in 50 ml. of water, and add 2 ml. of hydrochloric acid, 30 to 50 mg. of ammonium persulfate crystals, and 3 ml. of ammonium thiocyanate reagent solution. Any red color should not exceed that produced by 0.01 mg. of iron (Fe) in an equal volume of solution containing the quantities of reagents used in the test.

Manganese. Dissolve 5 grams in 50 ml. of water plus 20 ml. of nitric acid, 10 ml. of sulfuric acid, and 5 ml. of phosphoric acid. Prepare a standard containing 0.025 mg. of manganese ion (Mn) in 50 ml. of water plus 20 ml. of nitric acid, 10 ml. of sulfuric acid, and 5 ml. of phosphoric acid. Dilute each solution to 100 ml., heat to boiling, and boil gently for 5 minutes. Cool slightly, add 0.25 gram of potassium periodate to each, and again boil gently for 5 minutes. Any pink color in the solution of the sample should not exceed that in the standard.

Potassium. Determine the potassium by the flame photometric method described on page 14.

Sample Solution A. Dissolve 5 grams in water and dilute to 100 ml.

Control Solution B. Dissolve 5 grams in water, add 0.25 mg. of potassium ion (K), and dilute to 100 ml.

Observe the emission of Control Solution B at the 767-mμ potassium line. Observe the emission of Sample Solution A at the 767-mμ potassium line and at a wavelength of 750 mμ. The difference (D_1) between the intensities observed for Sample Solution A at 767 mμ and 750 mμ should not exceed the difference (D_2) observed at 767 mμ between Sample Solution A and Control Solution B.

Sodium. Determine the sodium by the flame photometric method described on page 14.

Sample Solution A. Dissolve 5 grams in water and dilute to 100 ml.

Control Solution B. Dissolve 5 grams in water, add 0.25 mg. of sodium ion (Na), and dilute to 100 ml.

Observe the emission of Control Solution B at the 589-mμ sodium line. Observe the emission of Sample Solution A at the 589-mμ sodium line and at a wavelength of 580 mμ. The difference (D_1) between the intensities observed for Sample Solution A at 589 mμ and 580 mμ should not exceed the difference (D_2) observed at 589 mμ between Sample Solution A and Control Solution B.

Strontium. Determine strontium by the flame photometric method described on page 14.

Sample Solution A. Dissolve 5 grams in water and dilute to 100 ml.

Control Solution B. Dissolve 5 grams in water, add 0.25 mg. of strontium ion (Sr), and dilute to 100 ml.

Observe the emission of Control Solution B at the 460.7-mμ strontium line. Observe the emission of Sample Solution A at the 460.7-mμ strontium line and at a wavelength of 465 mμ. The difference (D_1) between the intensities observed for Sample Solution A at 460.7 mμ and 465 mμ should not exceed the difference (D_2) observed at 460.7 mμ between Sample Solution A and Control Solution B.

Notes

Magnesium Oxide

MgO   Formula Wt. 40.30

REQUIREMENTS

Insoluble in dilute hydrochloric acid.   Not more than 0.020 per cent.
Soluble in water.   Not more than 0.40 per cent.
Loss on ignition.   Not more than 2.0 per cent.
Ammonium hydroxide precipitate.   Not more than 0.020 per cent.
Chloride (Cl).   Not more than 0.010 per cent.
Nitrate (NO_3).   Not more than 0.005 per cent.
Sulfate and sulfite (as SO_4).   Not more than 0.02 per cent.
Barium (Ba).   Not more than 0.005 per cent.
Calcium (Ca).   Not more than 0.05 per cent.
Heavy metals (as Pb).   Not more than 0.003 per cent.
Iron (Fe).   Not more than 0.01 per cent.
Manganese (Mn).   Not more than 0.0005 per cent.
Potassium (K).   Not more than 0.005 per cent.
Sodium (Na).   Not more than 0.5 per cent.
Strontium (Sr).   Not more than 0.005 per cent.

TESTS

Insoluble in dilute hydrochloric acid.   Dissolve 5 grams in 125 ml. of dilute hydrochloric acid $(1 + 4)$, heat to boiling, and boil gently for 5 minutes. Digest the solution in a covered beaker on the steam bath for 1 hour. Filter through a tared filtering crucible, wash thoroughly, and dry at 105°C. The weight of the residue should not exceed 0.0010 gram. Retain the filtrate for the determination of *Ammonium hydroxide precipitate.*

Soluble in water.   Suspend 2 grams in 50 ml. of water, heat to boiling, and filter while hot. Evaporate 25 ml. of the clear filtrate to dryness in a tared dish. Moisten the residue with 0.10 ml. of sulfuric acid, ignite gently to remove the excess acid, and finally ignite at 800° ± 25°C. for 15 minutes. The weight of the residue should not exceed 0.0040 gram.

Loss on ignition.   Weigh accurately about 0.25 gram in a tared covered platinum crucible. Ignite at 800° ± 25°C. for 15 minutes. Cool and reweigh. The loss in weight should not exceed 2.0 per cent of the weight of the sample.

Ammonium hydroxide precipitate.   To the filtrate from the determination of *Insoluble in dilute hydrochloric acid* add ammonium hydroxide until neutral to methyl red and add an excess of 1 ml. Boil the solution for 5 minutes, allow to cool, and filter. Dissolve the precipitate on the

ACS SPECIFICATIONS

filter with 5 ml. of hot dilute hydrochloric acid $(1 + 1)$ and wash to a volume of 25 ml. Add ammonium hydroxide until neutral to methyl red, add an excess of 0.5 ml., and boil for 5 minutes. Filter through the same filter, wash with hot water, and ignite. The weight of the residue should not exceed 0.0010 gram.

Chloride. Dissolve 0.1 gram in 10 ml. of dilute nitric acid $(1 + 9)$ and dilute to 25 ml. with water. Filter if necessary through a chloride-free filter, and add 1 ml. of silver nitrate reagent solution. Any turbidity should not exceed that produced by 0.01 mg. of chloride ion (Cl) in an equal volume of solution containing the quantities of reagents used in the test.

Nitrate.

Sample Solution A. Suspend 0.2 gram in 3 ml. of water. Dilute to 50 ml. with brucine sulfate reagent solution.

Control Solution B. Suspend 0.2 gram in 2 ml. of water and 1.0 ml. of the standard nitrate solution containing 0.01 mg. of nitrate ion (NO_3) per ml. Dilute to 50 ml. with brucine sulfate reagent solution.

Blank Solution C. Use 50 ml. of brucine sulfate reagent solution.

Heat Sample Solution A, Control Solution B, and Blank Solution C in a preheated (boiling) water bath until the magnesium oxide is dissolved in A and B, then heat for 10 more minutes. Cool rapidly in an ice bath to room temperature. Set a spectrophotometer at 410 mμ and, using 1-cm. cells, adjust the instrument to read 0 absorbance with Blank Solution C in the light path, then determine the absorbance of Sample Solution A. Adjust the instrument to read 0 absorbance with Sample Solution A in the light path and determine the absorbance of Control Solution B. The absorbance of Sample Solution A should not exceed that of Control Solution B.

Sulfate and sulfite. The sample is digested at $130° \pm 10°C$. with a reducing mixture of red phosphorus, hydriodic acid, and iodine. The resulting hydrogen sulfide is swept by a stream of nitrogen into a reaction mixture of N,N-dimethyl-p-phenylenediamine and ferric sulfate, and the methylene blue produced is determined spectrophotometrically.

Apparatus. Nitrogen flow from a gas cylinder is regulated with a needle valve and a flowmeter. The gas is passed through a gas scrubbing tower containing 5 grams of mercuric chloride in 100 ml. of 2 per cent potassium permanganate to remove any traces of sulfur gases. Water should be added to the tower as needed to maintain the volume at approximately 100 ml. Tubing should be of a non-rubber material. The gas should be preheated to the temperature of the bath described below by passing the gas through a metal tubing, having an outside diameter of approximately ¼ inch, submerged in the bath before it enters the reaction vessel.

An oil bath in a suitable container heated to the prescribed temperature (130° ± 10°C.), with stirring, and a means of regulating the temperature is required. Silicone fluid in a 3-liter stainless steel beaker fitted with a Teflon cover has been found satisfactory. Heat is applied with an electric heating mantle and controlled with a variable transformer. The oil is stirred with an electric or an air stirrer. The cover provides openings for a dial-type metal thermometer, gas tubing inlet and outlet, stirrer shaft, and the reaction vessel.

The reaction vessel is a borosilicate glass test tube fitted with a 24/40 standard taper outer joint with a total capacity of about 30 ml. A head about 5 inches high with a 24/40 standard taper inner joint fits the reaction vessel. An outlet tube emerges at the top of the head and turns at a right angle. An inlet tube, having an outside diameter of 8 mm., enters the side of the head and extends to the bottom of the reaction vessel. The preheated gas bubbles through the sample-reagent mixture while being heated inside the bath. All fittings and tubing leading from the reaction vessel should be glass (glass ball joints are best).

The effluent gas from the reaction vessel should pass through a pair of scrubbing tubes, each the same size and construction as the reaction vessel. The gas is to enter each scrubber through a tube down the center, into the solution specified, and pass out the top into the next vessel. The first scrubber should contain sufficient phosphoric acid $(1 + 1)$ just to cover the tip of the bubbler tube. (Drain and recharge when more than 1 inch of liquid accumulates, but do not interrupt during a day's run.) The second scrubber should contain 10 ml. of water. (Recharge after running 5 samples.) The gas is finally bubbled through a delivery tube, having an outside diameter of 4 or 5 mm., into the absorbing solution in a 50-ml. volumetric receiving flask.

Sample Solution A.   Cool 85 to 90 ml. of hydrochloric acid $(3 + 1)$ in a 250-ml. beaker in a cold water bath. Slowly add 10 grams of sample while stirring, stir until the sample is dissolved, and cool to room temperature. Dilute to 100 ml. with hydrochloric acid $(3 + 1)$ (1 ml. = 0.1 gram).

Standard Solution B.   Dissolve 0.148 gram of anhydrous sodium sulfate, Na_2SO_4, in hydrochloric acid $(3 + 1)$ and dilute to 100 ml.

with hydrochloric acid $(3 + 1)$. Dilute 20 ml. to 1 liter with hydrochloric acid $(3 + 1)$ (1 ml. $= 0.02$ mg. SO_4).

Transfer 5 ml. of acetate absorbing solution* to a 50-ml. volumetric receiving flask, add 30 ml. of water, and place the delivery tube in the flask. Add a 2.0-ml. aliquot of Sample Solution A and 5 ml. of reducing mixture,* previously shaken to produce a slurry, to the reaction vessel. Connect the reaction vessel to the scrubber assembly and place the vessel in the oil bath. Connect the delivery tube to the scrubber assembly, raise the receiving flask so that the delivery tube dips well below the surface of the acetate absorbing solution, and connect the gas line. Adjust the nitrogen flow through the apparatus at a rate of 55 ± 10 ml. per minute and run for 25 minutes.

(**Note.** Discard the first result of a day's run. Use the second result obtained by repeating the entire procedure to this point.) Disconnect the delivery tube, but do not remove from the receiving flask.

(**Caution.** Take the reaction assembly apart in the hood since noxious, white fumes are produced by the hot reducing mixture.)

Add first 5 ml. of N,N-dimethyl-p-phenylenediamine solution* through the delivery tube, then 1 to 2 ml. of water, and swirl to mix. Avoid vigorous shaking. Add 1 ml. of ferric sulfate solution* through the delivery tube followed by 1 to 2 ml. of water. Remove the delivery tube without further washing, stopper the flask, and shake vigorously. When the bubbles dissipate, dilute to volume with water, and allow to stand in the dark for at least 10 minutes. Set a spectrophotometer at 665 mμ and, using 1-cm. cells, read the absorbance versus water on the day that the standard is run. For the standard transfer a 2.0-ml. aliquot of Standard Solution B to a reaction vessel and carry out the entire procedure outlined for Sample Solution A. The absorbance of Sample Solution A should not exceed that of Standard Solution B.

*Reagents. 1. Reducing Mixture. Transfer 50 grams of red phosphorus to a 2-liter round-bottomed flask fitted with a 24/40 joint, add 500 ml. of 47 per cent hydriodic acid through a funnel, and place in an ice bath. Add 170 grams of iodine gradually, with agitation, through the funnel. Wash the iodine into the flask with 100 ml. of water and allow to stand overnight. Connect a water-cooled condenser to the flask in a heating mantle in the hood, insert a glass tube through the condenser to dip into the reagent in the flask, and bubble nitrogen through the reagent at a rate of 100 to 150 bubbles per minute. Heat to boiling, reflux for approximately 2 hours, and cool to room temperature. Shake to produce a slurry before taking an aliquot for each analysis. If the reagent has stood for longer than a day without shaking, stir for 30 minutes before use.

2. Acetate Absorbing Solution. Dissolve 50 grams of zinc acetate, $(CH_3COO)_2Zn \cdot 2H_2O$, and 125 grams of sodium acetate, $CH_3COONa \cdot 3H_2O$, in water. Dilute to 1 liter and filter. Any turbidity which forms on standing is caused by absorption of carbon dioxide from the air and does not interfere with the test.

3. N,N-Dimethyl-p-phenylenediamine Solution. Add 200 ml. of sulfuric acid to approximately 700 ml. of water. Cool to room temperature, add 1 gram of N,N-dimethyl-p-phenylenediamine (p-aminodimethylaniline) monohydrochloride, and dilute to 1 liter with water.

4. Ferric Sulfate Solution. Add 25 ml. of sulfuric acid to 125 grams of ferric sulfate, $Fe_2(SO_4)_3 \cdot nH_2O$. Add about 700 ml. of water, digest on a steam bath to dissolve, cool to room temperature, and dilute to 1 liter with water.

Barium. Dissolve 1.5 grams in 15 ml. of nitric acid. For the control dissolve 0.5 gram in 15 ml. of nitric acid and add 0.05 mg. of barium ion (Ba). Evaporate each solution on the steam bath to a sirupy consistency and add 20 ml. of water. If the solutions are not clear, add 10 per cent nitric acid dropwise until clear. Add 1 ml. of 1N acetic acid and 2 ml. of potassium dichromate reagent solution to each, and adjust the pH to 7 (using a pH meter) with ammonium hydroxide (10 per cent NH_3). Add 25 ml. of methanol to each and stir vigorously. Any turbidity in the solution of the sample should not exceed that in the control.

Calcium. Determine the calcium by the flame photometric method described on page 14. Dissolve 1 gram in 50 ml. of dilute hydrochloric acid $(1 + 4)$ and digest in a covered beaker on the steam bath for 20 minutes. Cool and dilute to 100 ml. with water (1 ml. = 0.01 gram).

Sample Solution A. Dilute a 20-ml. aliquot (0.2 gram) of the solution to 100 ml. with water.

Control Solution B. Add 0.10 mg. of calcium ion (Ca) to another 20-ml. aliquot and dilute to 100 ml. with water.

Observe the emission of Control Solution B at the 422.7-mμ calcium line. Observe the emission of Sample Solution A at the 422.7-mμ calcium line and at a wavelength of 430 mμ. The difference (D_1) between the intensities observed for Sample Solution A at 422.7 mμ and 430 mμ

should not exceed the difference (D_2) observed at 422.7 mμ between Sample Solution A and Control Solution B.

Heavy metals. Dissolve 5 grams in 50 ml. of dilute hydrochloric acid (1 + 1), heat if necessary to obtain complete dissolution, and dilute to 100 ml. with water. For the sample evaporate 15 ml. to dryness on the steam bath. For the control add 0.015 mg. of lead ion (Pb) to 5 ml. of the solution and evaporate to dryness on the steam bath. Dissolve each residue in about 20 ml. of water and dilute to 25 ml. Adjust the pH of the control and sample solutions to between 3 and 4 (using a pH meter) with 1N acetic acid or ammonium hydroxide (10 per cent NH$_3$), dilute to 40 ml., and mix. Add 10 ml. of freshly prepared hydrogen sulfide water to each and mix. Any color in the solution of the sample should not exceed that in the control.

Iron. Add 1 gram to 50 ml. of dilute hydrochloric acid (1 + 1) and boil gently for 5 minutes. Cool and dilute to 50 ml. Dilute 5 ml. of the solution to 50 ml., and add 30 to 50 mg. of ammonium persulfate crystals and 3 ml. of ammonium thiocyanate reagent solution. Any red color should not exceed that produced by 0.01 mg. of iron (Fe) in an equal volume of solution containing 2 ml. of hydrochloric acid and the quantities of ammonium persulfate and ammonium thiocyanate used in the test.

Manganese. Dissolve 5 grams in 20 ml. of water plus 25 ml. of nitric acid and 10 ml. of sulfuric acid. Prepare a standard containing 0.025 mg. of manganese ion (Mn) in 20 ml. of water plus 25 ml. of nitric acid and 10 ml. of sulfuric acid. Evaporate each solution until dense fumes of sulfur trioxide appear, cool, and cautiously add 50 ml. of water plus 20 ml. of nitric acid and 5 ml. of phosphoric acid. Dilute to 100 ml., boil gently for 5 minutes, cool slightly, and add 0.25 gram of potassium periodate to each. Again boil gently for 5 minutes, cool, and dilute to 100 ml. Any pink color in the solution of the sample should not exceed that in the standard.

Sample Solution A for the flame photometric determination of Potassium, Sodium, and Strontium. Dissolve 5 grams in 75 ml. of dilute hydrochloric acid (1 + 1) by warming in a covered beaker on the steam bath. When dissolution is complete, cool, and dilute to 100 ml. with water (1 ml. = 0.05 gram).

Control Solution B for the flame photometric determination of Potassium, Sodium, and Strontium. Dissolve 5 grams in 75 ml. of dilute hydrochloric acid (1 + 1) by warming in a covered beaker on the steam bath. When dissolution is complete, cool, add 0.25 mg. of potassium ion (K) and 0.25 mg. of strontium ion (Sr), and dilute to 100 ml. with water.

Potassium. Determine the potassium by the flame photometric method described on page 14. Observe the emission of Control Solution B at the 767-mμ potassium line. Observe the emission of Sample Solution A at the 767-mμ potassium line and at a wavelength of 750 mμ. The difference (D_1) between the intensities observed for Sample Solution A at 767 mμ and 750 mμ should not exceed the difference (D_2) observed at 767 mμ between Sample Solution A and Control Solution B.

Sodium. Determine the sodium by the flame photometric method described on page 14.

Special Sample Solution A. Dilute 1 ml. (0.05 gram) of Sample Solution A to 100 ml. with water.

Special Control Solution B. Add 0.25 mg. of sodium ion (Na) to 1 ml. of Sample Solution A and dilute to 100 ml. with water.

Observe the emission of Control Solution B at the 589-mμ sodium line. Observe the emission of Sample Solution A at the 589-mμ sodium line and at a wavelength of 580 mμ. The difference (D_1) between the intensities observed for Sample Solution A at 589 mμ and 580 mμ should not exceed the difference (D_2) observed at 589 mμ between Sample Solution A and Control Solution B.

Strontium. Determine the strontium by the flame photometric method described on page 14. Observe the emission of Control Solution B at the 460.7-mμ strontium line. Observe the emission of Sample Solution A at the 460.7-mμ strontium line and at a wavelength of 465 mμ. The difference (D_1) between the intensities observed for Sample Solution A at 460.7 mμ and 465 mμ should not exceed the difference (D_2) observed at 460.7 mμ between Sample Solution A and Control Solution B.

Notes

Magnesium Sulfate

$MgSO_4 \cdot 7H_2O$ Formula Wt. 246.47

REQUIREMENTS

Insoluble matter.   Not more than 0.005 per cent.
pH of a 5 per cent solution.   From 5.0 to 8.2 at 25°C.
Chloride (Cl).   Not more than 0.0005 per cent.
Nitrate (NO_3).   Not more than 0.002 per cent.
Ammonium (NH_4).   Not more than 0.002 per cent.
Arsenic (As).   Not more than 0.0002 per cent.
Calcium (Ca).   Not more than 0.02 per cent.
Heavy metals (as Pb).   Not more than 0.0005 per cent.
Iron (Fe).   Not more than 0.0005 per cent.
Manganese (Mn).   Not more than 0.0005 per cent.
Potassium (K).   Not more than 0.005 per cent.
Sodium (Na).   Not more than 0.005 per cent.
Strontium (Sr).   Not more than 0.005 per cent.

TESTS

Insoluble matter.   Dissolve 20 grams in 200 ml. of water, heat to boiling, and digest in a covered beaker on the steam bath for 1 hour. Filter through a tared filtering crucible, wash thoroughly, and dry at 105°C. The weight of the residue should not exceed 0.0010 gram.

pH of a 5 per cent solution.   Dissolve 10 grams in 200 ml. of carbon dioxide- and ammonia-free water. Determine the pH by the method described on page 18. The pH should be from 5.0 to 8.2 at 25°C. The pH of a 5 per cent solution of pure magnesium sulfate would be 6.8 at 25°C.

Chloride.   Dissolve 2 grams in 20 ml. of water, filter if necessary through a chloride-free filter, and add 1 ml. of nitric acid and 1 ml. of silver nitrate reagent solution. Any turbidity should not exceed that produced by 0.01 mg. of chloride ion (Cl) in an equal volume of solution containing the quantities of reagents used in the test.

Nitrate.

Sample Solution A.   Dissolve 1.0 gram in 5 ml. of water by heating in a water bath. Dilute to 50 ml. with brucine sulfate reagent solution.

Control Solution B.   Dissolve 1.0 gram in 3 ml. of water and 2 ml. of the standard nitrate solution containing 0.01 mg. of nitrate ion (NO_3) per ml. by heating in a boiling water bath. Dilute to 50 ml. with brucine sulfate reagent solution.

Blank Solution C. Use 50 ml. of brucine sulfate reagent solution.

Heat the three solutions in a preheated (boiling) water bath for 10 minutes. Cool rapidly in an ice bath to room temperature. Set a spectrophotometer at 410 mμ and, using 1-cm. cells, adjust the instrument to read 0 absorbance with Blank Solution C in the light path, then determine the absorbance of Sample Solution A. Adjust the instrument to read 0 absorbance with Sample Solution A in the light path and determine the absorbance of Control Solution B. The absorbance of Sample Solution A should not exceed that of Control Solution B.

Ammonium. Dissolve 2 grams in 90 ml. of water, add 10 ml. of 10 per cent sodium hydroxide reagent solution, and allow to settle. Draw off 25 ml. of the clear solution, dilute to 50 ml., and add 2 ml. of Nessler reagent. Any color should not exceed that produced by 0.01 mg. of ammonium ion (NH_4) in an equal volume of solution containing 2.5 ml. of 10 per cent sodium hydroxide solution and 2 ml. of Nessler reagent.

Arsenic. Determine the arsenic in 1 gram by the Gutzeit method (page 11). The amount of stain should not exceed that produced by 0.002 mg. of arsenic (As).

Calcium. Determine the calcium by the flame photometric method described on page 14. Dissolve 5 grams in 50 ml. of dilute hydrochloric acid (1 + 5), digest in a covered beaker on the steam bath for 20 minutes, cool, and dilute to 100 ml.

Sample Solution A. Dilute a 10-ml. aliquot (0.5-gram sample) of the solution to 100 ml. with water.

Control Solution B. Add 0.10 mg. of calcium ion (Ca) to another 10-ml. aliquot of the solution and dilute to 100 ml. with water.

Observe the emission of Control Solution B at the 422.7-mμ calcium line. Observe the emission of Sample Solution A at the 422.7-mμ calcium line and at a wavelength of 430 mμ. The difference (D_1) between the intensities observed for Sample Solution A at 422.7 mμ and 430 mμ should not exceed the difference (D_2) observed at 422.7 mμ between Sample Solution A and Control Solution B.

Heavy metals. Dissolve 6 grams in about 20 ml. of water and dilute to 30 ml. For the control add 0.02 mg. of lead ion (Pb) to a 5-ml. aliquot of the solution and dilute to 25 ml. For the sample use the remaining 25-ml. portion. Adjust the pH of the control and sample solutions to between 3 and 4 (using a pH meter) with 1N acetic acid or ammonium hydroxide (10 per cent NH_3), dilute to 40 ml., and mix. Add 10 ml. of freshly prepared hydrogen sulfide water to each and mix. Any color in the solution of the sample should not exceed that in the control.

Iron. Dissolve 2 grams in 30 ml. of water, add 2 ml. of hydrochloric acid, dilute to 50 ml., and add 30 to 50 mg. of ammonium persulfate crystals and 3 ml. of ammonium thiocyanate reagent solution. Any red color should not exceed that produced by 0.01 mg. of iron (Fe) in an equal volume of solution containing the quantities of reagents used in the test.

Manganese. Dissolve 2 grams in 35 ml. of water plus 10 ml. of nitric acid, 5 ml. of sulfuric acid, and 5 ml. of phosphoric acid. Prepare a standard containing 0.01 mg. of manganese ion (Mn) in 35 ml. of water plus 10 ml. of nitric acid, 5 ml. of sulfuric acid, and 5 ml. of phosphoric acid. Heat the solutions to boiling and boil gently for 5 minutes. Cool slightly, add 0.25 gram of potassium periodate to each, and again boil gently for 5 minutes. Any pink color in the solution of the sample should not exceed that in the standard.

Potassium. Determine the potassium by the flame photometric method described on page 14.

Sample Solution A. Dissolve 5 grams in water and dilute to 100 ml.

Control Solution B. Dissolve 5 grams in water, add 0.25 mg. of potassium ion (K), and dilute to 100 ml.

Observe the emission of Control Solution B at the 767-mμ potassium line. Observe the emission of Sample Solution A at the 767-mμ potassium line and at a wavelength of 750 mμ. The difference (D_1) between the intensities observed for Sample Solution A at 767 mμ and 750 mμ should not exceed the difference (D_2) observed at 767 mμ between Sample Solution A and Control Solution B.

Sodium. Determine the sodium by the flame photometric method described on page 14.

Sample Solution A. Dissolve 5 grams in water and dilute to 100 ml.

Control Solution B. Dissolve 5 grams in water, add 0.25 mg. of sodium ion (Na), and dilute to 100 ml.

Observe the emission of Control Solution B at the 589-mμ sodium line. Observe the emission of Sample Solution A at the 589-mμ sodium line and at a wavelength of 580 mμ. The difference (D_1) between the intensities observed for Sample Solution A at 589 mμ and 580 mμ should not exceed the difference (D_2) observed at 589 mμ between Sample Solution A and Control Solution B.

Strontium. Determine the strontium by the flame photometric method described on page 14.

Sample Solution A. Dissolve 5 grams in water and dilute to 100 ml.

Control Solution B. Dissolve 5 grams in water, add 0.25 mg. of strontium ion (Sr), and dilute to 100 ml.

Observe the emission of Control Solution B at the 460.7-mμ strontium line. Observe the emission of Sample Solution A at the 460.7-mμ strontium line and at a wavelength of 465 mμ. The difference (D_1) between the intensities observed for Sample Solution A at 460.7 mμ and 465 mμ should not exceed the difference (D_2) observed at 460.7 mμ between Sample Solution A and Control Solution B.

Notes

Manganese Sulfate Monohydrate

$MnSO_4 \cdot H_2O$ Formula Wt. 169.01

REQUIREMENTS

Insoluble matter.   Not more than 0.010 per cent.
Loss on ignition.   Not less than 10.0 nor more than 12.0 per cent.
Chloride (Cl).   Not more than 0.005 per cent.
Substances not precipitated by ammonium sulfide.   Not more than 0.50 per cent.
Heavy metals (as Pb).   Not more than 0.002 per cent.
Iron (Fe).   Not more than 0.002 per cent.
Nickel (Ni).   Not more than 0.02 per cent.
Zinc (Zn).   Not more than 0.01 per cent.
Substances reducing permanganate.   To pass test.

TESTS

Insoluble matter.   Dissolve 10 grams in 130 ml. of water, heat to boiling, and digest in a covered beaker on the steam bath for 1 hour. Filter through a tared filtering crucible, wash thoroughly, and dry at 105°C. The weight of the residue should not exceed 0.0010 gram.

Loss on ignition.   Weigh accurately about 2 grams. Ignite to constant weight at 400° to 500°C. The loss in weight should be not less than 10.0 nor more than 12.0 per cent of the weight of the sample.

Chloride.   Dissolve 1 gram in 100 ml. of water, and filter if necessary through a chloride-free filter. To 20 ml. of the solution add 1 ml. of nitric acid and 1 ml. of silver nitrate reagent solution. Any turbidity should not exceed that produced by 0.01 mg. of chloride ion (Cl) in an equal volume of solution containing the quantities of reagents used in the test.

Substances not precipitated by ammonium sulfide.   Dissolve 2 grams in about 90 ml. of water. Add 5 ml. of ammonium hydroxide and warm the solution. Pass a stream of hydrogen sulfide through the solution for about 30 minutes. Dilute the mixture to 100 ml., mix well, allow the precipitate to settle, and decant the supernatant liquid through a filter. Evaporate 50 ml. of the filtrate to dryness in a tared dish and ignite gently to volatilize the ammonium salt. Finally, ignite at 800° ± 25°C. for 15 minutes. The weight of the residue should not exceed 0.0050 gram.

Heavy metals.   Dissolve 1 gram in about 20 ml. of water and dilute to

25 ml. For the standard dilute a solution containing 0.02 mg. of lead ion (Pb) to 25 ml. Adjust the pH of the standard and sample solutions to between 3 and 4 (using a pH meter) with $1N$ acetic acid or ammonium hydroxide (10 per cent NH_3), dilute to 40 ml., and mix. Add 10 ml. of freshly prepared hydrogen sulfide water to each and mix. Any color in the solution of the sample should not exceed that in the standard.

Iron. Dissolve 1 gram in water and dilute to 50 ml. To 25 ml. of the solution add 2 ml. of hydrochloric acid, dilute to 50 ml., and add 30 to 50 mg. of ammonium persulfate crystals and 3 ml. of ammonium thiocyanate reagent solution. Any red color should not exceed that produced by 0.01 mg. of iron (Fe) in an equal volume of solution containing the quantities of reagents used in the test.

Nickel. Dissolve 1 gram in 200 ml. of water. To 20 ml. of this solution add 2 grams of sodium acetate and 10 ml. of hydrogen sulfide water, and allow to stand 1 minute. Add 5 ml. of acetic acid. Any color should not be more than is produced by 0.02 mg. of nickel ion (Ni) in an equal volume of solution containing the quantities of reagents used in the test.

Zinc. Dissolve 1 gram in 50 ml. of dilute hydrochloric acid $(2 + 25)$ and add 25 ml. of ammonium thiocyanate reagent solution. Prepare a standard containing 0.1 mg. of zinc ion (Zn) in 50 ml. of dilute hydrochloric acid $(2 + 25)$, and add 25 ml. of ammonium thiocyanate reagent solution. Treat each solution as follows: transfer the solution to a separatory funnel, add 25 ml. of ether, and shake vigorously. Allow the layers to separate and draw off and reserve the ether layer. Repeat the extraction three times more, using 25-ml. portions of ether each time. Combine the ether extracts and add them to 10 ml. of 25 per cent sulfuric acid reagent solution in a flask. Heat on a steam bath until all the ether has evaporated. Add about 50 ml. of water, filter, wash, and dilute the filtrate and washings to 100 ml. To an 8-ml. aliquot add $1N$ sodium acetate until the pH is 5.0 to 5.5 and add 1 ml. of $0.1N$ sodium thiosulfate. Transfer the solution to a separatory funnel, add 3 ml. of dithizone extraction solution in carbon tetrachloride, and shake vigorously for about 1 minute. Draw off the dithizone layer. Repeat the extractions with successive portions of the dithizone solution until the color of the dithizone solution remains unchanged. Combine the respective extracts and dilute to the smallest uniform volume with dithizone standard solution. Transfer 10 ml. of each solution to separatory funnels and wash with 5-ml. portions of dilute sodium sulfide (20 ml. of a freshly prepared 1 per cent sodium sulfide solution in 500 ml. of water), discarding the aqueous layer each time, until the aqueous layer remains colorless. Any color in the sample should not exceed that produced in the standard.

Substances reducing permanganate. Dissolve 7.5 grams in 200 ml. of water containing 3 ml. of sulfuric acid and 3 ml. of phosphoric acid. To this solution add 0.1 ml. of $0.1N$ potassium permanganate in excess of the amount required to produce a pink color in 200 ml. of water containing 3 ml. of sulfuric acid and 3 ml. of phosphoric acid, and allow to stand for 1 minute. The pink color should not be entirely discharged.

Notes

Mannitol

HOCH$_2$(CHOH)$_4$CH$_2$OH   Formula Wt. 182.17

REQUIREMENTS

Specific rotation $[\alpha]_D^{25°C}$. Not less than +23.3° nor more than +24.3°.
Insoluble matter. Not more than 0.010 per cent.
Loss on drying at 105°C. Not more than 0.050 per cent.
Residue after ignition. Not more than 0.010 per cent.
Acidity (as CH$_3$COOH). Not more than 0.005 per cent.
Reducing sugars. To pass test.
Heavy metals (as Pb). Not more than 0.0005 per cent.

TESTS

Specific rotation. Weigh accurately about 10 grams, transfer to a 100-ml. volumetric flask, and add 12.8 grams of sodium borate. Dissolve the mixture in sufficient water to make about 90 ml. of solution, allow to stand with occasional shaking for 1 hour, and dilute to volume at 25°C. Observe the optical rotation in a polarimeter at 25°C. using sodium light, and calculate the specific rotation. It should not be less than +23.3° nor more than +24.3°.

Insoluble matter. Dissolve 20 grams in 100 ml. of water, heat to boiling, and digest on the steam bath in a covered beaker for 1 hour. Filter through a tared filtering crucible, wash thoroughly, and dry at 105°C. The weight of the residue should not exceed 0.0020 gram.

Loss on drying at 105°C. Weigh accurately 5.0 grams in a tared dish or crucible and dry at 105°C. for 2 hours. The loss in weight should not exceed 0.0025 gram.

Residue after ignition. Gently ignite 10 grams in a tared crucible or dish until charred. Cool, moisten the char with 1 ml. of sulfuric acid, and ignite again slowly until all carbon and excess sulfuric acid have been volatilized. Finally, ignite at 800° ± 25°C. for 15 minutes. The weight of the residue should not exceed 0.0010 gram.

Acidity. To 100 ml. of carbon dioxide-free water add 0.10 ml. of phenolphthalein indicator solution and 0.01N sodium hydroxide until a pink color is produced. Dissolve 10 grams of the sample in this solution and titrate with 0.01N sodium hydroxide to the same end point. Not more than 0.83 ml. should be required.

Reducing sugars. Add 1 ml. of a saturated solution of the mannitol (about 0.2 gram per ml.) to 5 ml. of Benedict's solution* in a boiling water bath for 5 minutes. No more than a slight precipitate should form.

* **Benedict's Solution.** Dissolve 173 grams of sodium citrate and 100 grams of anhydrous sodium carbonate in 800 ml. of water. Heat to aid dissolution, filter if necessary, and dilute to 850 ml. Dissolve 17.3 grams of hydrated copper sulfate in 100 ml. of water. Add this solution, with constant stirring, to the alkaline citrate solution, and dilute to 1 liter.

Heavy metals. Dissolve 4 grams in about 25 ml. of water and dilute to 30 ml. For the standard dilute a solution containing 0.02 mg. of lead ion (Pb) to 30 ml. Adjust the pH of the standard and sample solutions to between 3 and 4 (using a pH meter) with $1N$ acetic acid or ammonium hydroxide (10 per cent NH_3), dilute to 40 ml., and mix. Add 10 ml. of freshly prepared hydrogen sulfide water to each and mix. Any color in the solution of the sample should not exceed that in the standard. Compare 10 minutes after adding the hydrogen sulfide to the sample and standard solutions.

Notes

Mercuric Acetate

$(CH_3COO)_2Hg$ Formula Wt. 318.68

REQUIREMENTS

Assay.   Not less than 98.0 per cent $(CH_3COO)_2Hg$.
Insoluble matter.   Not more than 0.010 per cent.
Residue after ignition.   Not more than 0.020 per cent.
Chloride (Cl).   Not more than 0.005 per cent.
Nitrate (NO_3).   Not more than 0.005 per cent.
Sulfate (SO_4).   Not more than 0.005 per cent.
Foreign heavy metals (as Pb).   Not more than 0.002 per cent.
Iron (Fe).   Not more than 0.001 per cent.
Mercurous mercury (as Hg).   Not more than 0.4 per cent.

TESTS

Assay.   Accurately weigh about 0.7 gram and dissolve in 100 ml. of dilute nitric acid $(1 + 19)$. Add 2 ml. of ferric ammonium sulfate indicator solution and titrate with $0.1N$ thiocyanate. One milliliter of $0.1N$ thiocyanate is equivalent to 0.01593 gram of $(CH_3COO)_2Hg$.

Insoluble matter.   Dissolve 10 grams in 100 ml. of dilute acetic acid $(5 + 95)$. Heat to boiling and digest in a covered beaker on the steam bath for one hour. Filter through a tared filtering crucible, wash thoroughly with dilute acetic acid $(1 + 99)$, and dry at 105°C. The weight of the residue should not exceed 0.0010 gram.

Residue after ignition.   Ignite 5 grams in a tared crucible or dish *in a well ventilated hood*. The rate of heating should be such that from 1 to 2 hours is required to volatilize the sample. When nearly all the sample has been volatilized, cool, and moisten the residue with 0.10 ml. of sulfuric acid. Continue the heating until the remainder of the sample and excess sulfuric acid have been volatilized. Finally, ignite at $800° \pm 25°C$. for 15 minutes. The weight of the residue should not exceed 0.0010 gram.

Sample Solution A.   Dissolve 5 grams in 30 ml. of dilute formic acid $(1 + 9)$. Add 3 ml. of ammonium hydroxide and digest under total reflux until all the mercury is reduced to metal and the solution is clear. Cool, filter through a well washed filter paper, and wash with a small quantity of water. Dilute the filtrate and washings to 50 ml. $(1 \text{ ml.} = 0.1 \text{ gram})$.

Chloride.   Dilute 2 ml. of Sample Solution A (0.2-gram sample) to 20 ml. Add 1 ml. of nitric acid and 1 ml. of silver nitrate reagent solution. Any turbidity should not exceed that produced by 0.01 mg. of chloride ion (Cl) in an equal volume of solution containing the quantities of reagents used in the test.

Nitrate.

Sample Solution A. Dissolve 0.1 gram in 3 ml. of water in a centrifuge tube and heat in a boiling water bath. Dilute to 50 ml. with brucine sulfate reagent solution.

Control Solution B. Dissolve 0.1 gram in 2.5 ml. of water and 0.5 ml. of the standard nitrate solution containing 0.01 mg. of nitrate ion (NO_3) per ml. in a centrifuge tube and heat in a boiling water bath. Dilute to 50 ml. with brucine sulfate reagent solution.

Blank Solution C. Use 50 ml. of the brucine sulfate reagent solution.

Heat the three solutions in a preheated (boiling) water bath for 10 minutes. Cool rapidly in an ice bath to room temperature. Centrifuge Sample Solution A and Control Solution B for 5 minutes and decant the liquid portions. Set a spectrophotometer at 410 mμ and, using 1-cm. cells, adjust the instrument to read 0 absorbance with Blank Solution C in the light path, then determine the absorbance of Sample Solution A. Adjust the instrument to read 0 absorbance with Sample Solution A in the light path and determine the absorbance of Control Solution B. The absorbance of Sample Solution A should not exceed that of Control Solution B.

Sulfate. To 10 ml. of Sample Solution A (1-gram sample) add 10 mg. of sodium carbonate and evaporate to dryness. Prepare a standard containing 0.05 mg. of sulfate ion (SO_4), 0.6 ml. of formic acid, and 0.6 ml. of ammonium hydroxide, and evaporate to dryness. Dissolve the residues in 4 ml. of water plus 1 ml. of dilute hydrochloric acid (1 + 19), filter through a small filter, wash with two 2-ml. portions of water, and dilute to 10 ml. Add 1 ml. of barium chloride reagent solution to each. Any turbidity in the solution of the sample should not exceed that in the standard. Compare 10 minutes after adding the barium chloride to the sample and standard solutions.

Foreign heavy metals. Add 10 mg. of sodium carbonate to 10 ml. of Sample Solution A (1-gram sample) and evaporate to dryness. Dissolve the residue in about 20 ml. of water, filter, and dilute to 25 ml. For the standard dilute a solution containing 0.02 mg. of lead ion (Pb) to 25 ml. Adjust the pH of the standard and sample solutions to between 3 and 4 (using a pH meter) with 1N acetic acid or ammonium hydroxide

(10 per cent NH$_3$), dilute to 40 ml., and mix. Add 10 ml. of freshly pre-pared hydrogen sulfide water to each and mix. Any color in the solution of the sample should not exceed that in the standard.

Iron. Add about 10 mg. of sodium carbonate to 10 ml. of Sample Solution A (1-gram sample) and evaporate to dryness. Dissolve the residue in 2 ml. of hydrochloric acid and dilute to 50 ml. Add 30 to 50 mg. of ammonium persulfate crystals and 3 ml. of ammonium thiocyanate reagent solution. Any red color should not exceed that produced by 0.01 mg. of iron (Fe) in an equal volume of solution containing the quantities of reagents used in the test.

Mercurous mercury. Dissolve 5 grams in 100 ml. of a 12.5 per cent solution of potassium iodide. Add 5.0 ml. of 0.1N iodine and 2 ml. of 1N hydrochloric acid. Allow to stand, protected from the light, for 1 hour and agitate every 15 minutes. Titrate the iodine with 0.1N thiosulfate, adding starch indicator near the end point, and correct for a blank. Not more than 1.0 ml. of 0.1N iodine should have been consumed.

Notes

Mercuric Bromide

HgBr$_2$ Formula Wt. 360.40

REQUIREMENTS

Appearance. White or having at most a very faint yellow tinge. If a mercurous salt is present, the product darkens on exposure to light.

Residue after ignition. Not more than 0.020 per cent.

Insoluble in methanol. Not more than 0.05 per cent.

Chloride (Cl). Not more than 0.25 per cent.

TESTS

Residue after ignition. Ignite 5.0 grams in a tared crucible or dish *in a well ventilated hood*. The rate of heating should be such that from 1 to 2 hours is required to volatilize the sample. When nearly all the sample has been volatilized, cool, and moisten the residue with 0.10 ml. of sulfuric acid. Continue the heating until the remainder of the sample and excess sulfuric acid have been volatilized. Finally, ignite at 800° ± 25°C. for 15 minutes. The weight of the residue should not exceed 0.0010 gram.

Insoluble in methanol. Dissolve 2 grams in 30 ml. of methanol. Filter through a tared filtering crucible, wash with methanol until the washings remain unaffected by hydrogen sulfide, and dry at 105°C. The weight of the residue should not exceed 0.0010 gram.

Chloride. To 0.7 gram add 20 ml. of water, 5 ml. of 10 per cent sodium hydroxide reagent solution, and 4 ml. of 30 per cent hydrogen peroxide, and digest on the steam bath until all reaction ceases. Cool, filter through a chloride-free filter, wash with water, and dilute the filtrate and washings to 100 ml. To a 5-ml. aliquot in a small conical flask, add 20 ml. of water and 1.5 ml. of ammonium carbonate solution [20 grams of ammonium carbonate and 20 ml. of dilute ammonium hydroxide (10 per cent NH$_3$) in sufficient water to make 100 ml.]. Add, with agitation, 5 ml. of silver nitrate reagent solution and allow to stand, with frequent agitation, for 10 minutes. Filter through a chloride-free filter, wash with water, and dilute the filtrate and washings to 100 ml. To a 25-ml. aliquot add 0.5 ml. of nitric acid. Any turbidity should not exceed that in a control obtained by treating 0.2 gram of sample and 1.25 mg. of added chloride ion (Cl) in 20 ml. of water exactly like the solution of the sample.

Mercuric Chloride

HgCl₂ Formula Wt. 271.50

REQUIREMENTS

Residue after ignition. Not more than 0.020 per cent.
Solution in ethyl ether. To pass test.
Iron (Fe). Not more than 0.002 per cent.

TESTS

Residue after ignition. Ignite 5.0 grams in a tared crucible or dish *in a well ventilated hood.* The rate of heating should be such that from 1 to 2 hours is required to volatilize the sample. When nearly all the sample has been volatilized, cool, and moisten the residue with 0.10 ml. of sulfuric acid. Continue the heating until the remainder of the sample and excess sulfuric acid have been volatilized. Finally, ignite at 800° ± 25°C. for 15 minutes. The weight of the residue should not exceed 0.0010 gram. Retain the residue for the test for *Iron.*

Solution in ethyl ether. Dissolve 2 grams in 60 ml. of ethyl ether in a stoppered flask. Shake the flask to agitate the sample and ether, but do not expose the contents to atmospheric moisture. Not more than a faint trace of insoluble residue should remain.

Iron. To the *Residue after ignition* add 3 ml. of dilute hydrochloric acid (1 + 1), cover the dish, and digest on the steam bath for 15 to 20 minutes. Remove the cover and evaporate to dryness. Dissolve the residue in 10 ml. of dilute hydrochloric acid (1 + 9) and dilute to 50 ml. To 5 ml. of this solution add 2 ml. of hydrochloric acid and dilute to 50 ml. Add 30 to 50 mg. of ammonium persulfate crystals and 3 ml. of ammonium thiocyanate reagent solution. Any red color should not exceed that produced by 0.01 mg. of iron (Fe) in an equal volume of solution containing the quantities of reagents used in the test.

Notes

Mercuric Iodide, Red

HgI_2 Formula Wt. 454.40

REQUIREMENTS

Assay. Not less than 99.0 per cent HgI_2.
Solubility in potassium iodide solution. To pass test.
Nonvolatile matter. Not more than 0.020 per cent.
Foreign heavy metals (as Pb). Not more than 0.001 per cent.
Mercurous mercury (as Hg). Not more than 0.10 per cent.
Soluble mercury salts (as Hg). Not more than 0.05 per cent.

TESTS

Assay. Dry about 1 gram over sulfuric acid overnight. Weigh accurately about 0.5 gram of the dried sample, place in a glass-stoppered Erlenmeyer flask, and add 30 ml. of hydrochloric acid and 20 ml. of water. Rotate the flask until the mercuric iodide is dissolved, add 5 ml. of chloroform, and titrate the solution with $0.05M$ potassium iodate until the iodine color is discharged from the aqueous layer. Stopper the flask, shake well for 30 seconds, then continue the titration, shaking vigorously after each addition of the potassium iodate until the chloroform is free of iodine color. One milliliter of $0.05M$ potassium iodate corresponds to 0.02272 gram of HgI_2.

Solubility in potassium iodide solution. Dissolve 10 grams of the sample in 100 ml. of 10 per cent potassium iodide reagent solution in a glass-stoppered flask. A complete, or practically complete, solution results. Retain the solution for the test for *Mercurous mercury*.

Nonvolatile matter. Ignite 5.0 grams in a tared crucible or dish *in a well ventilated hood*. The rate of heating should be such that from 1 to 2 hours is required to volatilize the sample. When nearly all the sample has been volatilized, cool, and moisten the residue with 0.10 ml. of sulfuric acid. Continue the heating until the remainder of the sample and excess sulfuric acid have been volatilized. Finally, ignite at 800° ± 25°C. for 15 minutes. The weight of the residue should not exceed 0.0010 gram. Retain the residue for the test for *Foreign heavy metals*.

Foreign heavy metals. To the residue obtained in the preceding test add 3 ml. of dilute hydrochloric acid (1 + 1), cover the dish, and digest on the steam bath for 20 to 30 minutes. Remove the cover, add 10 ml. of 10 per cent ammonium acetate solution to the residue, replace the cover, and digest for 30 minutes on the steam bath. Filter, wash, and dilute to

50 ml. Add 2 ml. of 1N hydrochloric acid to a 20-ml. aliquot of this solution and dilute to 25 ml. For the standard dilute a solution containing 0.02 mg. of lead ion (Pb) to 25 ml. Adjust the pH of the standard and sample solutions to between 3 and 4 (using a pH meter) with 1N acetic acid or ammonium hydroxide (10 per cent NH₃), dilute to 40 ml., and mix. Add 10 ml. of freshly prepared hydrogen sulfide water to each and mix. Any color in the solution of the sample should not exceed that in the standard.

Mercurous mercury. To the solution reserved from the test for *Solubility in potassium iodide solution* add 5.0 ml. of 0.1N iodine and 3 ml. of 1N hydrochloric acid. Allow to stand in a dark place for 1 hour, agitating every 15 minutes. Titrate the excess iodine with 0.1N sodium thiosulfate, adding starch indicator near the end point, and correct for a blank. Not more than 0.50 ml. of the 0.1N iodine should be consumed.

Soluble mercury salts. Shake 1 gram of the sample with 20 ml. of water for 2 minutes and filter. Dilute 10 ml. of the filtrate to 40 ml. with water and add 10 ml. of hydrogen sulfide water. Any color should not exceed that produced by 0.25 mg. of mercury ion (Hg) in an equal volume of solution containing the quantities of reagents used in the test.

Notes

Mercuric Oxide, Red

HgO

Formula Wt. 216.59

REQUIREMENTS

Insoluble in dilute hydrochloric acid.   Not more than 0.030 per cent.
Residue after ignition.   Not more than 0.025 per cent.
Chloride (Cl).   Not more than 0.005 per cent.
Sulfate (SO$_4$).   Not more than 0.015 per cent.
Nitrogen compounds (as N).   Not more than 0.005 per cent.
Iron (Fe).   Not more than 0.005 per cent.

TESTS

Insoluble in dilute hydrochloric acid.   Dissolve 4 grams in 40 ml. of dilute hydrochloric acid (1 + 3), heat to boiling, and digest in a covered beaker on the steam bath for 1 hour. Filter through a tared filtering crucible, wash well with water, and dry at 105°C. The weight of the residue should not exceed 0.0012 gram.

Residue after ignition.   Ignite 4 grams in a tared crucible or dish *in a well ventilated hood.* The rate of heating should be such that from 1 to 2 hours is required to volatilize the sample. When nearly all the sample has been volatilized, cool, and moisten the residue with 0.10 ml. of sulfuric acid. Continue the heating until the remainder of the sample and excess sulfuric acid have been volatilized. Finally, ignite at 800° ± 25°C. for 15 minutes. The weight of the residue should not exceed 0.0010 gram. Retain the residue for the test for *Iron.*

Chloride.   Dissolve 1 gram in 50 ml. of water plus 1 ml. of formic acid. Add, dropwise, 10 per cent sodium hydroxide reagent solution until a small amount of permanent precipitate is formed. Digest under a reflux condenser until all the mercury is reduced to metal and the solution is clear. Cool, filter through a chloride-free filter, and dilute to 100 ml. To 20 ml. of the solution add 1 ml. of nitric acid and 1 ml. of silver nitrate reagent solution. Any turbidity should not exceed that produced by 0.01 mg. of chloride ion (Cl) in an equal volume of solution containing the quantities of reagents used in the test.

Sample Solution A.   Dissolve 5 grams in 50 ml. of water plus 3 ml. of formic acid. Digest under a reflux condenser until all the mercury is reduced to metal and the supernatant liquid is clear. Cool, filter through a well-washed paper, and dilute to 100 ml. (1 ml. = 0.05 gram).

Sulfate. To 8 ml. of Sample Solution A (0.4-gram sample) add about 10 mg. of sodium carbonate and evaporate to dryness. For the standard evaporate to dryness a solution containing 0.06 mg. of sulfate ion (SO_4), about 10 mg. of sodium carbonate, and 0.24 ml. of formic acid. Dissolve each residue in 4 ml. of water plus 1 ml. of dilute hydrochloric acid (1 + 19). Filter if necessary through a small filter, wash with two 2-ml. portions of water, dilute to 10 ml., and add 1 ml. of barium chloride reagent solution to each. Any turbidity in the solution of the sample should not exceed that in the standard. Compare 10 minutes after adding the barium chloride to the sample and standard solutions.

Nitrogen compounds. Dilute 4 ml. of Sample Solution A (0.2 gram sample) to 60 ml. in a flask connected through a spray trap to a condenser, the end of which dips beneath the surface of 10 ml. of 0.1N hydrochloric acid. Add to the flask 15 ml. of freshly boiled 10 per cent sodium hydroxide reagent solution and 1 gram of aluminum wire in small pieces, allow to stand for 1 hour, and slowly distill about 35 ml. To the distillate add 1 ml. of 10 per cent sodium hydroxide reagent solution, dilute to 50 ml., and add 2 ml. of Nessler reagent. Any color should not exceed that produced when 0.12 ml. of formic acid and a quantity of an ammonium salt containing 0.01 mg. of nitrogen (N) are treated exactly like the 4 ml. of Sample Solution A.

Iron. To the residue obtained in the test for *Residue after ignition* add 3 ml. of dilute hydrochloric acid (1 + 1), cover with a watch glass, and digest on the steam bath for 20 minutes. Remove the watch glass and evaporate to dryness. Dissolve in 2 ml. of dilute hydrochloric acid (1 + 1) and 30 or 40 ml. of water, filter if necessary, and dilute to 100 ml. To 5 ml. of the solution add 2 ml. of hydrochloric acid and dilute to 50 ml. Add 30 to 50 mg. of ammonium persulfate crystals and 3 ml. of ammonium thiocyanate reagent solution. Any red color should not exceed that produced by 0.01 mg. of iron (Fe) in an equal volume of solution containing the quantities of reagents used in the test.

Notes

Mercuric Oxide, Yellow

HgO

Formula Wt. 216.59

REQUIREMENTS

Insoluble in dilute hydrochloric acid.   Not more than 0.030 per cent.
Residue after ignition.   Not more than 0.050 per cent.
Chloride (Cl).   Not more than 0.025 per cent.
Sulfate (SO$_4$).   Not more than 0.010 per cent.
Nitrogen compounds (as N).   Not more than 0.005 per cent.
Iron (Fe).   Not more than 0.003 per cent.

TESTS

Insoluble in dilute hydrochloric acid.   Dissolve 3 grams in 30 ml. of dilute hydrochloric acid (1 + 3), heat to boiling, and digest in a covered beaker on the steam bath for 1 hour. Filter through a tared filtering crucible, wash thoroughly, and dry at 105°C. The weight of the residue should not exceed 0.0009 gram.

Residue after ignition.   Ignite 3.0 grams in a tared crucible or dish *in a well ventilated hood.* The rate of heating should be such that from 1 to 2 hours is required to volatilize the sample. When nearly all the sample has been volatilized, cool, and moisten the residue with 0.10 ml. of sulfuric acid. Continue the heating until the remainder of the sample and excess sulfuric acid have been volatilized. Finally, ignite at 800° ± 25°C. for 15 minutes. The weight of the residue should not exceed 0.0015 gram. Retain the residue for the test for *Iron.*

Chloride.   Dissolve 1 gram in 50 ml. of water plus 1 ml. of formic acid. Add, dropwise, 10 per cent sodium hydroxide reagent solution until a small amount of permanent precipitate is formed. Digest under a reflux condenser until all the mercury is reduced to metal and the solution is clear. Cool, filter through a chloride-free filter, and dilute to 100 ml. Dilute 4 ml. of this solution to 20 ml. and add 1 ml. of nitric acid and 1 ml. of silver nitrate reagent solution. Any turbidity should not exceed that produced by 0.01 mg. of chloride ion (Cl) in an equal volume of solution containing the quantities of reagents used in the test.

Sample Solution A.   Dissolve 5 grams in 50 ml. of water plus 3 ml. of formic acid. Digest under a reflux condenser until all the mercury is reduced to metal, and the supernatant liquid is clear. Cool, filter through a well-washed paper, and dilute to 100 ml. (1 ml. = 0.05 gram).

Sulfate. To 10 ml. of Sample Solution A (0.5-gram sample) add about 10 mg. of sodium carbonate and evaporate to dryness. For the standard evaporate to dryness a solution containing 0.05 mg. of sulfate ion (SO$_4$), about 10 mg. of sodium carbonate, and 0.30 ml. of formic acid. Dissolve each residue in 4 ml. of water plus 1 ml. of dilute hydrochloric acid (1 + 19). Filter if necessary through a small filter, wash with two 2-ml. portions of water, dilute to 10 ml., and add 1 ml. of barium chloride reagent solution to each. Any turbidity in the solution of the sample should not exceed that in the standard. Compare 10 minutes after adding the barium chloride to the sample and standard solutions.

Nitrogen compounds. Dilute 4 ml. of Sample Solution A (0.2 gram sample) to 60 ml. in a flask connected through a spray trap to a condenser, the end of which dips beneath the surface of 10 ml. of 0.1N hydrochloric acid. Add to the flask 15 ml. of freshly boiled 10 per cent sodium hydroxide reagent solution and 1 gram of aluminum wire in small pieces, allow to stand for 1 hour, and slowly distill about 35 ml. To the distillate add 1 ml. of 10 per cent sodium hydroxide reagent solution, dilute to 50 ml., and add 2 ml. of Nessler reagent. Any color should not exceed that produced when 0.12 ml. of formic acid and a quantity of an ammonium salt containing 0.01 mg. of nitrogen (N) are treated exactly like the 4 ml. of Sample Solution A.

Iron. To the residue obtained in the test for *Residue after ignition* add 1 ml. of hydrochloric acid, 0.15 ml. of nitric acid, and about 10 mg. of sodium carbonate, cover, and digest on the steam bath for 15 to 20 minutes. Uncover and evaporate to dryness. Dissolve the residue in 9 ml. of hydrochloric acid and dilute to 90 ml. To 10 ml. of the solution add 1 ml. of hydrochloric acid and dilute to 50 ml. Add 30 to 50 mg. of ammonium persulfate crystals and 3 ml. of ammonium thiocyanate reagent solution. Any red color should not exceed that produced by 0.01 mg. of iron (Fe) in an equal volume of solution containing the quantities of reagents used in the test.

Notes

Mercurous Chloride

HgCl   Formula Wt. 236.04

REQUIREMENTS

Residue after ignition.   Not more than 0.020 per cent.
Mercuric chloride ($HgCl_2$).   Not more than 0.01 per cent.
Sulfate (SO_4).   Not more than 0.01 per cent.

TESTS

Residue after ignition.   Ignite 5 grams in a tared crucible or dish *in a well ventilated hood*. The rate of heating should be such that from 1 to 2 hours is required to volatilize the sample. When nearly all the sample has been volatilized, cool, and moisten the residue with 0.10 ml. of sulfuric acid. Continue the heating until the remainder of the sample and excess sulfuric acid have been volatilized. Finally, ignite at 800° ± 25°C. for 15 minutes. The weight of the residue should not exceed 0.0010 gram.

Mercuric chloride.   Shake 1 gram with 10 ml. of alcohol for 5 minutes, and filter. To 5 ml. of the filtrate add 0.10 ml. of hydrochloric acid and 5 ml. of hydrogen sulfide water. Any darkening should not be more than is produced by 0.05 mg. of mercuric chloride ($HgCl_2$) in a mixture of 5 ml. of alcohol, 0.10 ml. of hydrochloric acid, and 5 ml. of hydrogen sulfide water.

Sulfate.   Digest 1 gram for 10 minutes with 20 ml. of dilute hydrochloric acid (1 + 1). Filter, add 10 mg. of sodium carbonate to one half of the filtrate, and evaporate to dryness on the steam bath. Treat the residue with 1 ml. of dilute hydrochloric acid (1 + 19), dilute to 10 ml., and add 1 ml. of barium chloride reagent solution. Any turbidity should not exceed that produced by 0.05 mg. of sulfate ion (SO_4) in an equal volume of solution containing the quantities of reagents used in the test. Compare 10 minutes after adding the barium chloride to the standard and sample solutions.

Notes

Mercury

Hg   Atomic Wt. 200.59

REQUIREMENTS

Appearance.   To pass test.
Foreign metals.   Not more than 0.0005 per cent.

TESTS

Appearance.   The mercury should have a bright mirrorlike surface, free from film or scum. It should pour freely from a thoroughly clean, dry glass container without leaving any mercury adhering to the glass.

Foreign metals.   Transfer 200 grams to a tared boat of 25- to 30-ml. capacity. Place the boat in the approximate center of a glass combustion tube, about 350 mm. long and 35 mm. in diameter, and mount in a horizontal position. The tube is fitted at one end with a removable closure and the exit end is bent downward at 90° to the horizontal and is drawn out so as to fit into a one-hole rubber stopper held in the mouth of a suction flask. The suction flask is cooled in an ice bath. After the boat and sample are placed in the tube, close the entrance end and reduce the pressure to less than 15 mm. of mercury. Heat gently until all the mercury has distilled from a quiet-surface (without ebullition). Remove the boat, heat it in a muffle furnace at 600°C. for 15 minutes, and cool. The weight of the residue should not exceed 0.0010 gram.

Notes

Methanol

Methyl Alcohol

CH₃OH

Formula Wt. 32.04

REQUIREMENTS

Appearance. Clear.
Color (APHA). Not more than 10.
Water (H₂O). Not more than 0.20 per cent.
Boiling range. 1 ml. to 95 ml., not more than 1.0°C.; 95 ml. to dryness, not more than 1.0°C.
Residue after evaporation. Not more than 0.001 per cent.
Solubility in water. To pass test.
Acetone, aldehydes. To pass test (limit about 0.001 per cent acetone).
Acidity (as HCOOH). Not more than 0.002 per cent.
Alkalinity (as NH₃). Not more than 0.0003 per cent.
Substances darkened by sulfuric acid. To pass test.
Substances reducing permanganate. To pass test.

TESTS

Color (APHA). For the color standard dilute a 2-ml. aliquot of platinum-cobalt stock solution (APHA No. 500) to 100 ml. with water. Compare this solution (APHA No. 10) with 100 ml. of the methanol in 100-ml. Nessler tubes, viewed vertically over a white background.

Water. Place 25 ml. in a dry titration flask and titrate with Karl Fischer reagent to a visually or electrometrically determined end point. Calculate the water content of the sample from the titer and volume of Karl Fischer reagent consumed by the sample.

Boiling range. Distill 100 ml. by the method described on page 12. The difference between the temperatures when 1 ml. and 95 ml. have distilled should not exceed 1.0°C., and the difference in temperatures when 95 ml. have distilled and when the dry point is reached should not exceed 1.0°C. The boiling point of pure methanol at 760-mm. mercury pressure is 64.6°C.

Residue after evaporation. Evaporate 125 ml. (100 grams) in a tared dish on the steam bath and dry the residue at 105°C. for 30 minutes. The weight of the residue should not exceed 0.0010 gram.

Solubility in water. Dilute 15 ml. with 45 ml. of water, mix, and allow to stand for 1 hour. The solution should be as clear as an equal volume of water.

Acetone, aldehydes. Dilute 3.8 ml. (3 grams) to 5 ml. with water, adjust and maintain the temperature at 20°C., and add 5 ml. of Nessler reagent. Any turbidity should not exceed that produced by 0.03 mg. of acetone in an equal volume of solution containing the quantities of reagents used in the test.

Acidity. To 25 ml. of water and 10 ml. of alcohol in a glass-stoppered flask, add 0.50 ml. of phenolphthalein indicator solution and 0.02N sodium hydroxide until a slight pink color persists after shaking for 30 seconds. Add 19 ml. (15 grams) of sample, mix well, and titrate with 0.02N sodium hydroxide until the pink color is restored. Not more than 0.25 ml. should be required.

> **Note.** Special care should be taken during the addition of the sample and titration to avoid contamination from carbon dioxide.

Alkalinity. Dilute 28.6 ml. (22.6 grams) with 25 ml. of water and add 0.05 ml. of methyl red indicator solution. Not more than 0.20 ml. of 0.02N acid should be required to produce a pink color.

Substances darkened by sulfuric acid. Cool 10 ml. of sulfuric acid, contained in a small Erlenmeyer flask, to 10°C. and add dropwise with constant agitation 10 ml. of the sample, keeping the temperature of the mixture below 20°C. The mixture should be colorless or have no more color than the acid or methanol before mixing.

Substances reducing permanganate. Cool 20 ml. to 15°C., add 0.1 ml. of 0.1N potassium permanganate, and allow to stand at 15°C. for 5 minutes. The pink color should not be entirely discharged.

Notes

Methanol

Methyl Alcohol

(Suitable for use in ultraviolet spectrophotometry)

CH_3OH Formula Wt. 32.04

REQUIREMENTS

Absorbance.   To pass test.
Appearance.   Clear.
Water (H_2O).   Not more than 0.20 per cent.
Boiling range.   1 ml. to 95 ml., not more than 1.0°C.; 95 ml. to dryness, not more than 1.0°C.
Residue after evaporation.   Not more than 0.001 per cent.
Solubility in water.   To pass test.
Acetone, aldehydes.   To pass test (limit about 0.001 per cent acetone).
Acidity (as $HCOOH$).   Not more than 0.002 per cent.
Alkalinity (as NH_3).   Not more than 0.0003 per cent.
Substances darkened by sulfuric acid.   To pass test.
Substances reducing permanganate.   To pass test.

TESTS

Absorbance. Determine the absorbance of the sample in a 1.00-cm. cell, throughout the range of 210 mμ to 400 mμ, against water in a similar matched cell set at zero absorbance as the reference liquid. The absorbance should not exceed 0.80 at 210 mμ, 0.40 at 220 mμ, 0.20 at 230 mμ, 0.10 at 240 mμ, 0.04 at 260 mμ, and 0.01 at 280 mμ to 400 mμ. The spectral absorbance curve recorded through the wavelengths indicated should be smooth throughout the prescribed range and should not show any extraneous impurity peaks within this range.

Other tests are the same as for **Methanol,** page 370, except *Color* (*APHA*), which is superseded by the *Absorbance* test.

Notes

Methyl Orange

Sodium p-Dimethylaminoazobenzenesulfonate
p-[[p-(Dimethylamino)phenyl]azo]benzenesulfonic
Acid Sodium Salt

REQUIREMENTS

Insoluble matter. To pass test.
Visual transition interval. From pH 3.2 (pink or red) to pH 4.4 (yellow).

TESTS

Insoluble matter. Dissolve 0.1 gram in 100 ml. of water. Not more than a faint trace of turbidity or insoluble matter should remain. Reserve the solution for the test for *Visual transition interval.*

Visual transition interval. Dissolve 1 gram of potassium chloride in 100 ml. of water. Adjust the pH of the solution to 3.00 (using a pH meter as described on page 18) with 0.01N acid. Add 0.05 to 0.10 ml. of the 0.1 per cent solution reserved from the test for *Insoluble matter.* The solution should have a definite pink color. Titrate the solution with 0.01N sodium hydroxide to a pH of 3.2 (using the pH meter). A small amount of yellow color should appear, producing a pinkish orange color. Continue the titration to pH 3.8; the solution should be flesh colored. Continue the titration to pH 4.4; the solution should have a definite yellow color. Not more than 12.5 ml. of 0.01N sodium hydroxide should be consumed in the entire titration.

Notes

4-Methyl-2-pentanone

Methyl Isobutyl Ketone

$(CH_3)_2CHCH_2COCH_3$ Formula Wt. 100.16

REQUIREMENTS

Appearance. Clear.
Color (APHA). Not more than 15.
Density (grams per ml.) at 25°C. Not less than 0.794 nor more than 0.798.
Boiling range. From 114° to 117°C.
Residue after evaporation. Not more than 0.005 per cent.
Acidity (as CH_3COOH). Not more than 0.01 per cent.
Water. Not more than 0.1 per cent.

TESTS.

Color (APHA). For the color standard dilute a 3-ml. aliquot of platinum-cobalt stock solution (APHA No. 500) to 100 ml. with water. Compare this solution (APHA No. 15) with 100 ml. of the 4-methyl-2-pentanone in 100-ml. Nessler tubes, viewed vertically over a white background.

Boiling range. Distill 100 ml. by the method described on page 12. The temperatures when 1 ml. and 95 ml. have distilled should be from 114° to 117°C. at 760-mm. mercury pressure. The boiling point of pure 4-methyl-2-pentanone at 760-mm. mercury pressure is 116.2°C.

Residue after evaporation. Evaporate 125 ml. (100 grams) to dryness in a tared dish on the steam bath and dry the residue at 125°C. for 30 minutes. The weight of the residue should not exceed 0.0050 gram.

Acidity. To 25.0 ml. of alcohol in a glass-stoppered flask add 0.50 ml. of phenolphthalein indicator solution. Add 0.02N sodium hydroxide solution until a slight pink color persists after shaking for 30 seconds. Add 25 ml. of the sample, mix, and titrate with 0.02N sodium hydroxide until the pink color is restored. Not more than 1.67 ml. of the sodium hydroxide solution should be required.

Note. Great care should be taken in the test during the addition of the sample and the titration to avoid contamination from carbon dioxide.

Water. Place 25 ml. of pyridine in a dry titration flask and add Karl

Fischer reagent to a visually or electrometrically determined end point. Add 25 ml. (20 grams) of the sample, taking care to protect the sample and contents of the flask from moisture. Stir vigorously and titrate with Karl Fischer reagent to the same end point. Calculate the water content of the sample from the titer and volume of Karl Fischer reagent consumed by the sample.

Notes

Methyl Red

o-[[p-(Dimethylamino)phenyl]azo]benzoic Acid
C. I. Acid Red 2

Note. Three forms of this indicator are available: (1) the compound named above (**I**), (2) the sodium salt of the compound (**II**), and (3) the hydrochloride of the compound (**III**). **I** must meet the requirements for *Melting point (range), Insoluble matter in benzene, Insoluble matter in alcohol,* and *Visual transition interval.* This form is recommended for nonaqueous titrations, particularly when an aprotic solvent is used. **II** must meet the requirements for *Insoluble matter in alcohol, Insoluble matter in water,* and *Visual transition interval.* This form is the choice for aqueous titrations. It is suitable, also, for nonaqueous titrations when the medium is an amphiprotic solvent. **III** must meet the requirements for *Insoluble matter in alcohol* and *Visual transition interval.* This form can be used as an indicator in aqueous and amphiprotic solvent titrations.

REQUIREMENTS

Melting point (range). Not below 179°C. nor above 182°C.[I]
Insoluble matter in benzene. To pass test.[I]
Insoluble matter in alcohol. To pass test.[I, II, III]
Insoluble matter in water. To pass test.[II]
Visual transition interval. From pH 4.2 (pink) to 6.2 (yellow).[I, II, III]

TESTS

Insoluble matter. Dissolve 0.1 gram of **I** in 100 ml. of benzene. Dissolve 0.1 gram of **II** in 100 ml. of water. For all three forms (**I, II,** and **III**), dissolve 0.1 gram in 100 ml. of alcohol. Not more than a faint trace of turbidity or insoluble matter should remain. Reserve the alcohol solutions for the test for *Visual transition interval.*

Visual transition interval. Dissolve 1 gram of potassium chloride in 100 ml. of water. Adjust the pH of the solution to 4.20 (using a pH meter as described on page 18) with 0.01N acid. Add 0.05 to 0.10 ml. of the 0.1 per cent solution reserved from the test for *Insoluble matter.* The color of the solution should be pink. Titrate the solution with 0.01N sodium hydroxide to a pH of 5.5 (using the pH meter). The solution should be orange in color. Continue the titration to a pH of 6.2. The solution should be yellow in color. Not more than 1.0 ml. of the 0.01N sodium hydroxide should be consumed in the entire titration.

Methyl Sulfoxide

Dimethyl Sulfoxide

$(CH_3)_2SO$ Formula Wt. 78.13

REQUIREMENTS

Appearance.   Clear, colorless liquid.
Density (grams per ml.) at 25°C.   Not less than 1.095.
Freezing point.   Not below 18.0°C.
Residue after evaporation.   Not more than 0.01 per cent.
Water (H_2O).   Not more than 0.20 per cent.

TESTS

Freezing point.   Place 15 ml. in a test tube (20×150 mm.) in which is centered an accurate thermometer. The sample tube is centered by corks in an outer tube about 38×200 mm. Cool the whole apparatus, without stirring, in a bath of shaved or crushed ice with water enough to wet the outer tube. When the temperature is about 15°C., stir to start the freezing, and read the thermometer every 30 seconds. The temperature which remains constant for 1 or 2 minutes is the freezing point.

Residue after evaporation.   Evaporate 91 ml. (100 grams) to dryness in a tared dish on the hot plate. The weight of the residue should not exceed 0.010 gram.

Water.   Place 25 ml. of methanol in a dry titration flask and add Karl Fischer reagent to a visually or electrometrically determined end point. Add 10 ml. (11.0 grams) of the sample, taking care to protect the sample and contents of the flask from moisture. Stir vigorously and titrate with Karl Fischer reagent to the same end point. Calculate the water content of the sample from the titer and volume of Karl Fischer reagent consumed by the sample.

Notes

Molybdenum Trioxide

Molybdic Acid Anhydride

MoO_3 Formula Wt. 143.94

REQUIREMENTS

Assay.   Not less than 99.5 per cent MoO_3.

Insoluble in dilute ammonium hydroxide.   Not more than 0.010 per cent.

Chloride (Cl).   Not more than 0.002 per cent.

Nitrate (NO_3).   To pass test (limit about 0.003 per cent).

Arsenate, phosphate, and silicate (as SiO_2).   Not more than 0.0005 per cent.

Sulfate (SO_4).   Not more than 0.020 per cent.

Ammonium (NH_4).   Not more than 0.002 per cent.

Heavy metals (as Pb).   Not more than 0.005 per cent.

TESTS

Assay.   Weigh accurately about 1 gram and dissolve in 10 ml. of water plus 1 ml. of ammonium hydroxide. Transfer to a 250-ml. volumetric flask, dilute to volume, and mix thoroughly. To a 50.0-ml. aliquot in a 600-ml. beaker add 250 ml. of water, 20 grams of ammonium chloride, 15 ml. of hydrochloric acid, and 0.15 ml. of methyl orange indicator solution. Heat nearly to boiling and add 18 ml. of a 10 per cent lead acetate reagent solution. To the hot and constantly stirred solution add slowly a saturated solution of ammonium acetate until the solution is alkaline, and then an excess of 15 ml. of the acetate solution. Digest on the hot plate in the covered beaker at a temperature just below boiling until the precipitate has settled (from one-half to one hour). Filter through a Gooch crucible that has been ignited and weighed, wash seven or eight times with a solution containing 10 ml. of nitric acid and 100 ml. of a saturated solution of ammonium acetate in a liter, and wash three times with hot water. Ignite to constant weight in a muffle furnace at 560° to 625°C. Cool and weigh as $PbMoO_4$. One gram of lead molybdate corresponds to 0.3921 gram of MoO_3.

Insoluble in dilute ammonium hydroxide.   Dissolve 10 grams in 120 ml. of dilute ammonium hydroxide ($1 + 6$), heat to boiling, and digest in a covered beaker on the steam bath for 2 hours. Filter through a tared filtering crucible, wash thoroughly, and dry at 105°C. The weight of the residue should not exceed 0.0010 gram.

Chloride. Dissolve 1 gram in 4 ml. of ammonium hydroxide, heat on the steam bath until completely dissolved, and evaporate to dryness. Dissolve the residue in 20 ml. of water, filter if necessary through a chloride-free filter, add 4 ml. of nitric acid, and dilute to 30 ml. To 15 ml. add 1 ml. of silver nitrate reagent solution. Any turbidity should not exceed that produced by 0.01 mg. of chloride ion (Cl) in an equal volume of solution containing the quantities of reagents used in the test. The comparison is best made by superimposing a tube containing the remaining 15 ml. of sample solution and 1 ml. of water over the tube containing the standard turbidity and placing a tube containing 16 ml. of water below the tube containing the sample and added reagents. Both turbidities are thus viewed through the same depth and color of solution. The comparison tubes may be machine-made vials, long style, of about 20-ml. capacity.

Nitrate. Triturate 1 gram with 9 ml. of water and 1 ml. of sodium chloride solution containing 5 mg. of sodium chloride. Add 0.20 ml. of indigo carmine reagent solution and 10 ml. of sulfuric acid. The blue color should not be completely discharged in 5 minutes.

Arsenate, phosphate, and silicate. Dissolve 2.5 grams in 60 ml. of water and enough silica-free ammonium hydroxide to effect dissolution (about 4 ml.) in a platinum dish. For the control dissolve 0.5 gram in 60 ml. of water and enough silica-free ammonium hydroxide to effect dissolution and add 0.01 mg. of silica (SiO_2). Heat on the steam bath until the solutions are neutral as determined with an external indicator (at least 30 minutes). Cool and adjust the pH to 3 to 4 with an external indicator. Transfer to beakers and dilute to 80 ml. Add enough bromine water to impart a distinct yellow color to the solutions. Adjust the pH of each solution to 1.8 with dilute hydrochloric acid (1 + 9) (using a pH meter). Heat just to boiling and allow to cool to room temperature. (If a precipitate forms, it will dissolve when the solution is acidified in the next operation.) Add 10 ml. of hydrochloric acid and dilute to 100 ml. Transfer the solutions to separatory funnels and add 30 ml. of 4-methyl-2-pentanone and 1 ml. of butyl alcohol. Shake vigorously and allow to separate. Draw off and discard the aqueous phase. Wash the ketone phase 3 times with 10-ml. portions of dilute hydrochloric acid (1 + 99), discarding the aqueous phase each time. To the washed ketone phase add 10 ml. of dilute hydrochloric acid (1 + 99) to which has just been added 0.2 ml. of a freshly prepared 2 per cent solution of stannous chloride in hydrochloric acid. Any blue color in the solution of the sample should not exceed that in the control.

Sulfate. Boil 1 gram with 15 ml. of dilute nitric acid $(1 + 2)$ for 5 minutes. Cool thoroughly, dilute to 50 ml., mix well, and filter. Evaporate 10 ml. of the filtrate to dryness on the steam bath. Dissolve the residue in 4 ml. of water plus 1 ml. of dilute hydrochloric acid $(1 + 19)$, filter if necessary through a small filter, wash with two 2-ml. portions of water, and dilute to 10 ml. Add 1 ml. of barium chloride reagent solution. Any turbidity should not exceed that produced by 0.04 mg. of sulfate ion (SO_4) in an equal volume of solution containing the quantities of reagents used in the test. Compare 10 minutes after adding the barium chloride to the sample and standard solutions.

Ammonium. Dissolve 1 gram in 15 ml. of freshly boiled 10 per cent sodium hydroxide reagent solution and dilute to 100 ml. To 50 ml. add 2 ml. of Nessler reagent. Any color should not exceed that produced by 0.01 mg. of ammonium ion (NH_4) in an equal volume of solution containing 1.5 ml. of 10 per cent sodium hydroxide reagent solution and 2 ml. of Nessler reagent.

Heavy metals. Dissolve 1 gram in 15 ml. of 10 per cent sodium hydroxide solution, add 2 ml. of ammonium hydroxide, and dilute to 40 ml. For the control add 0.025 mg. of lead ion (Pb) to a 10-ml. aliquot of the solution and dilute to 40 ml. For the sample dilute the remaining solution to 40 ml. Add 10 ml. of freshly prepared hydrogen sulfide water to each and mix. Any color in the solution of the sample should not exceed that in the control.

Notes

Molybdic Acid, 85 Per Cent

Note. This reagent consists largely of an ammonium molybdate.

REQUIREMENTS

Assay.   Not less than 85 per cent MoO_3.
Insoluble in dilute ammonium hydroxide.   Not more than 0.010 per cent.
Chloride (Cl).   Not more than 0.002 per cent.
Arsenate, phosphate, and silicate (as SiO_2).   Not more than 0.0005 per cent.
Sulfate (SO_4).   Not more than 0.20 per cent.
Heavy metals (as Pb).   Not more than 0.003 per cent.

TESTS

Assay. Weigh accurately about 1 gram and dissolve in 10 ml. of water plus 1 ml. of ammonium hydroxide. Transfer to a 250-ml. volumetric flask, dilute to volume, and mix thoroughly. To a 50.0-ml. aliquot in a 600-ml. beaker add 250 ml. of water, 20 grams of ammonium chloride, 15 ml. of hydrochloric acid, and 0.15 ml. of methyl orange indicator solution. Heat nearly to boiling and add 18 ml. of a 10 per cent lead acetate reagent solution. To the hot and constantly stirred solution add slowly a saturated solution of ammonium acetate until the solution is alkaline and then an excess of 15 ml. of the acetate solution. Digest on the hot plate at a temperature just below boiling until the precipitate has settled (from one-half to one hour). Filter through a Gooch crucible that has been ignited and weighed, wash seven or eight times with a solution containing 10 ml. of nitric acid and 100 ml. of a saturated solution of ammonium acetate in a liter, and wash three times with hot water. Ignite to constant weight in a muffle furnace at 560° to 625°C. Cool and weigh as $PbMoO_4$. One gram of lead molybdate corresponds to 0.3921 gram of MoO_3.

Insoluble in dilute ammonium hydroxide. Dissolve 10 grams in 100 ml. of dilute ammonium hydroxide (1 + 9), heat to boiling, and digest in a covered beaker on the steam bath for 2 hours. Filter through a tared filtering crucible, wash thoroughly, and dry at 105°C. The weight of the insoluble residue should not exceed 0.0010 gram.

Chloride. Dissolve 1 gram in 4 ml. of ammonium hydroxide, heat on the steam bath until completely dissolved, and evaporate to dryness. Dissolve the residue in 20 ml. of water, add 4 ml. of nitric acid, and dilute to 30 ml. To 15 ml. add 1 ml. of silver nitrate reagent solution. Any turbidity should not exceed that produced by 0.01 mg. of chloride ion (Cl) in an equal volume of solution containing the quantities of reagents used in the test. The comparison is best made by superimposing a tube containing the remaining 15 ml. of sample solution and 1 ml. of water over the tube containing the standard turbidity and placing a tube containing 16 ml. of water below the tube containing the sample and added reagents. Both turbidities are thus viewed through the same depth and color of solution. The comparison tubes may be machine-made vials, long style, of about 20-ml. capacity.

Arsenate, phosphate, and silicate. Dissolve 2.5 grams in 60 ml. of water and enough silica-free ammonium hydroxide to effect dissolution (about 4 ml.) in a platinum dish. For the control dissolve 0.5 gram in 60 ml. of water and enough silica-free ammonium hydroxide to effect dissolution and add 0.01 mg. of silica (SiO_2). Heat on the steam bath until the solutions are neutral as determined with an external indicator (at least 30 minutes). Cool and adjust the pH to 3 or 4 with an external indicator. Transfer to beakers and dilute to 80 ml. Add enough bromine water to impart a distinct yellow color to the solutions. Adjust the pH of each solution to 1.8 with dilute hydrochloric acid $(1 + 9)$ (using a pH meter). Heat just to boiling and allow to cool to room temperature. (If a precipitate forms, it will dissolve when the solution is acidified in the next operation.) Add 10 ml. of hydrochloric acid and dilute to 100 ml. Transfer the solutions to separatory funnels and add 30 ml. of 4-methyl-2-pentanone and 1 ml. of butyl alcohol. Shake vigorously and allow to separate. Draw off and discard the aqueous phase. Wash the ketone phase 3 times with 10-ml. portions of dilute hydrochloric acid $(1 + 99)$, discarding the aqueous phase each time. To the washed ketone phase add 10 ml. of dilute hydrochloric acid $(1 + 99)$ to which has just been added 0.2 ml. of a freshly prepared 2 per cent solution of stannous chloride in hydrochloric acid. Any blue color in the solution of the sample should not exceed that in the control.

Sulfate. Boil 1 gram with 15 ml. of dilute nitric acid $(1 + 2)$ for 5 minutes. Cool thoroughly, dilute to 100 ml., and filter. Evaporate 2 ml. of the filtrate to dryness on the steam bath, dissolve the residue in 4 ml. of water plus 1 ml. of dilute hydrochloric acid $(1 + 19)$ and filter if necessary through a small filter. Wash with two 2-ml. portions of water, dilute to 10 ml., and add 1 ml. of barium chloride reagent solution. Any turbidity should not exceed that produced by 0.04 mg. of sulfate ion (SO_4) in an equal volume of solution containing the quantities of reagents used in the test. Compare 10 minutes after adding the barium chloride to the sample and standard solutions.

Heavy metals. Dissolve 1.3 grams in 15 ml. of 10 per cent sodium hydroxide, add 2 ml. of ammonium hydroxide, and dilute to 40 ml. For the control add 0.02 mg. of lead ion (Pb) to a 10-ml. aliquot of the solution and dilute to 40 ml. For the sample dilute the remaining portion to 40 ml. Add 10 ml. of freshly prepared hydrogen sulfide water to each and mix. Any color in the solution of the sample should not exceed that in the control.

Notes

Nickel Sulfate

NiSO$_4$·6H$_2$O   Formula Wt. 262.86

REQUIREMENTS

Insoluble matter.   Not more than 0.005 per cent.
Chloride (Cl).   Not more than 0.001 per cent.
Nitrogen compounds (as N).   Not more than 0.002 per cent.
Substances not precipitated by ammonium sulfide.   Not more than 0.10 per cent.
Cobalt and manganese (as Co).   Not more than 0.003 per cent.
Copper (Cu).   Not more than 0.005 per cent.
Iron (Fe).   Not more than 0.001 per cent.

TESTS

Insoluble matter.   Dissolve 20 grams in 150 ml. of water, heat to boiling, and digest in a covered beaker on the steam bath for 1 hour. Filter through a tared filtering crucible, wash thoroughly, and dry at 105°C. The weight of the residue should not exceed 0.0010 gram.

Chloride.   Dissolve 1 gram in 15 ml. of water, filter if necessary through a small chloride-free filter, and add 1 ml. of nitric acid and 1 ml. of silver nitrate reagent solution. Any turbidity should not exceed that produced by 0.01 mg. of chloride ion (Cl) in an equal volume of solution containing the quantities of reagents used in the test. The comparison is best made by superimposing a tube containing a solution of 1 gram of sample in 17 ml. of water over the tube containing the standard turbidity and placing a similar tube containing 17 ml. of water below the tube containing the sample and added reagents. Both turbidities are thus viewed through the same depth and color of solution. The comparison tubes may be machine-made vials, long style, of about 20-ml. capacity.

Nitrogen compounds.   To 1 gram in a flask connected through a spray trap to a condenser, the end of which dips beneath the surface of 10 ml. of 0.1N hydrochloric acid, add 30 ml. of freshly boiled 10 per cent sodium hydroxide reagent solution and 0.5 gram of aluminum wire in small pieces. Allow to stand for 1 hour, and add 70 ml. of water, and slowly distill about 35 ml. To the distillate add 1 ml. of 10 per cent sodium hydroxide reagent solution, dilute to 50 ml., and add 2 ml. of Nessler reagent. Any color should not exceed that produced when a quantity of ammonium salt containing 0.02 mg. of nitrogen (N) is treated exactly like the sample.

Substances not precipitated by ammonium sulfide. Dissolve 2 grams in 20 ml. of water. Add 1 gram of ammonium chloride and 5 ml. of ammonium hydroxide and dilute to 90 ml. Pass hydrogen sulfide through the solution until all the nickel is precipitated. Dilute to 100 ml., mix well, and filter. Evaporate 50 ml. of the filtrate to dryness in a tared dish or crucible and ignite gently to volatilize the ammonium salts. Finally, ignite at $800° \pm 25°C$. for 15 minutes. The weight of the residue should not exceed 0.0010 gram.

Cobalt and manganese. Dissolve 2 grams in 10 ml. of water. Remove the oxygen by passing carbon dioxide through the solution for 10 to 15 minutes, and add 20 ml. of a solution prepared by dissolving 6 grams of ammonium chloride in 100 ml. of dilute ammonium hydroxide $(2 + 3)$. Stop the flow of carbon dioxide and titrate with $0.001N$ ferricyanide to a potential difference of zero, using a calomel-platinum electrode system. Not more than 1.00 ml. should be required.

Copper. Dissolve 2 grams in 500 ml. of water, mix well, and transfer 50 ml. to a separatory funnel. Prepare a standard containing 0.01 mg. of copper ion (Cu) in 50 ml. of water in a separatory funnel. Adjust the pH of each solution to 4.0 (using a pH meter) with $0.1N$ hydrochloric acid or sodium hydroxide. To each funnel add 10 ml. of dithizone standard solution in carbon tetrachloride, shake for 3 minutes, allow the phases to separate, and draw off the carbon tetrachloride layers. Repeat the extractions with 5 ml. of dithizone solution. Any pinkish color in the carbon tetrachloride from the solution of the sample should not exceed that in the standard. (**Note.** All apparatus must be thoroughly cleaned *and the copper standard solution must be prepared immediately before use.*)

Iron. Dissolve 1 gram in 50 ml. of dilute hydrochloric acid $(1 + 25)$. For the standard add 0.01 mg. of iron (Fe) to 50 ml. of dilute hydrochloric acid $(1 + 25)$. Transfer the solutions to separatory funnels and add to each 30 to 50 mg. of ammonium persulfate crystals, 3 ml. of ammonium thiocyanate reagent solution, and 20 ml. of isopentyl alcohol. Shake vigorously and allow to separate. Any red color in the isopentyl alcohol layer from the solution of the sample should not exceed that in the isopentyl alcohol from the standard.

Notes

Nitric Acid

HNO$_3$ Formula Wt. 63.01

REQUIREMENTS

Appearance. Colorless and free from suspended matter or sediment.
Assay. Not less than 69.0 nor more than 71.0 per cent HNO$_3$.
Residue after ignition. Not more than 0.0005 per cent.
Chloride (Cl). Not more than 0.00005 per cent.
Sulfate (SO$_4$). Not more than 0.0001 per cent.
Arsenic (As). Not more than 0.000001 per cent.
Heavy metals (as Pb). Not more than 0.00002 per cent.
Iron (Fe). Not more than 0.00002 per cent.

TESTS

Appearance. Mix the acid in the original container and transfer 10 ml. to a test tube (20 mm. × 150 mm.) and compare with distilled water in a similar tube. The liquids should be equally clear and free from suspended matter, and on looking across the columns by transmitted light there should be no apparent difference in color between the two liquids.

Assay. Tare a small glass-stoppered flask containing about 15 ml. of water. Quickly add about 2 ml. of the sample, stopper, cool, and weigh accurately. Dilute with about 40 ml. of water, add methyl orange indicator solution, and titrate with 1N sodium hydroxide. One milliliter of 1N sodium hydroxide corresponds to 0.06301 gram of HNO$_3$.

Residue after ignition. To 140 ml. (200 grams) in a tared dish add 0.05 ml. of sulfuric acid, evaporate as far as possible on the steam bath, and heat gently to volatilize the excess sulfuric acid. Finally, ignite at 800° ± 25°C. for 15 minutes. The weight of the residue should not exceed 0.0010 gram.

Chloride. Dilute 14 ml. (20 grams) with 10 ml. of water and add 1 ml. of silver nitrate reagent solution. Prepare a standard containing 0.01 mg. of chloride ion (Cl) in 20 ml. of water and add 1 ml. of silver nitrate reagent solution. Evaporate the solutions to dryness on the steam bath. Dissolve the residues in 0.5 ml. of ammonium hydroxide, dilute to 20 ml. with water, and add 1.5 ml. of nitric acid. Any turbidity in the solution of the sample should not exceed that in the standard.

Sulfate. Add about 10 mg. of sodium carbonate to 28 ml. (40 grams) of the acid. Evaporate to dryness, dissolve in 4 ml. of water plus 1 ml. of dilute hydrochloric acid (1 + 19), and filter if necessary through a small filter. Wash with two 2-ml. portions of water, dilute to 10 ml., and add 1 ml. of barium chloride reagent solution. Any turbidity should not exceed that produced by 0.04 mg. of sulfate ion (SO_4) in an equal volume of solution containing the quantities of reagents used in the test. Compare 10 minutes after adding the barium chloride to the sample and standard solutions.

Arsenic. To 210 ml. (300 grams) in a 250-ml. beaker add 5 ml. of sulfuric acid and evaporate to dense fumes of sulfur trioxide. Cool, dilute with water, and again evaporate to dense fumes of sulfur trioxide. Repeat the dilution and evaporation if necessary to remove all the nitrate, cool, and determine arsenic by the Gutzeit method (page 11). The amount of stain should not exceed that produced by 0.003 mg. of arsenic (As).

Heavy metals. To 70 ml. (100 grams) in a beaker add about 10 mg. of sodium carbonate, evaporate to dryness on the steam bath, dissolve the residue in about 20 ml. of water, and dilute to 25 ml. For the standard dilute a solution containing 0.02 mg. of lead ion (Pb) to 25 ml. Adjust the pH of the standard and sample solutions to between 3 and 4 (using a pH meter) with $1N$ acetic acid or ammonium hydroxide (10 per cent NH_3), dilute to 40 ml., and mix. Add 10 ml. of freshly prepared hydrogen sulfide water to each and mix. Any color in the solution of the sample should not exceed that in the standard.

Iron. Evaporate 35 ml. (50 grams) to dryness, dissolve the residue in 2 ml. of hydrochloric acid, dilute to 50 ml., and add 30 to 50 mg. of ammonium persulfate crystals and 3 ml. of ammonium thiocyanate reagent solution. Any red color should not exceed that produced by 0.01 mg. of iron (Fe) in an equal volume of solution containing the quantities of reagents used in the test.

Notes

Nitric Acid, 90 Per Cent

HNO_3 Formula Wt. 63.01

REQUIREMENTS

Assay.   Not less than 90 per cent HNO_3.
Dilution test.   To pass test.
Residue after ignition.   Not more than 0.002 per cent.
Dissolved oxides.   To pass test (limit about 0.10 per cent as N_2O_3).
Chloride (Cl).   Not more than 0.00007 per cent.
Sulfate (SO_4).   Not more than 0.0005 per cent.
Arsenic (As).   Not more than 0.00003 per cent.
Heavy metals (as Pb).   Not more than 0.0005 per cent.
Iron (Fe).   Not more than 0.0002 per cent.

TESTS

Assay.   Tare a small glass-stoppered flask containing about 15 ml. of water. Quickly add about 2 ml. of the sample, stopper, cool, and weigh accurately. Dilute with about 40 ml. of water, add methyl orange indicator solution, and titrate with $1N$ sodium hydroxide. One milliliter of $1N$ sodium hydroxide corresponds to 0.06301 gram of HNO_3.

Dilution test.   Dilute 1 volume of acid with 3 volumes of water; mix and allow to stand for 1 hour. No turbidity or precipitate should be observed.

Residue after ignition.   To 33 ml. (50 grams) in a tared dish add 0.10 ml. of sulfuric acid, evaporate as far as possible on the steam bath, and heat gently to volatilize the excess sulfuric acid. Finally, ignite at $800° \pm 25°C.$ for 15 minutes. The weight of the residue should not exceed 0.0010 gram.

Dissolved oxides.   Dilute 6.6 ml. (10 grams) to 150 ml. with cold water in a casserole. Add 20 ml. of dilute sulfuric acid $(1 + 4)$ and titrate with $0.1N$ potassium permanganate, rapidly at first, then slowly till the pink color lasts 3 minutes. Not more than 5.0 ml. of the permanganate solution should be required. One milliliter of $0.1N$ permanganate solution corresponds to 0.0019 gram of N_2O_3.

Chloride.   Dilute 10 ml. (15 grams) with 10 ml. of water and add 1 ml. of silver nitrate reagent solution. Prepare a standard of 0.01 mg. of chloride ion (Cl) in 20 ml. of water and add 1 ml. of silver nitrate reagent solution. Evaporate the solutions to dryness on the steam bath. Dissolve the residues in 0.5 ml. of ammonium hydroxide, dilute to 20 ml. with water, and add 1.5 ml. of nitric acid. Any turbidity in the solution of the sample should not exceed that in the standard.

Sulfate.   To 6.6 ml. (10 grams) add about 10 mg. of sodium carbonate, evaporate to dryness, and dissolve the residue in 4 ml. of water plus 1 ml. of dilute hydrochloric acid (1 + 19). Filter if necessary through a small filter, wash with two 2-ml. portions of water, dilute to 10 ml., and add 1 ml. of barium chloride reagent solution. Any turbidity should not exceed that produced by 0.05 mg. of sulfate ion (SO_4) in an equal volume of solution containing the quantities of reagents used in the test. Compare 10 minutes after adding the barium chloride to the sample and standard solutions.

Arsenic.   To 6.6 ml. (10 grams) in a 150-ml. beaker add 2 ml. of sulfuric acid and evaporate to dense fumes of sulfur trioxide. Cool, dilute with water, and again evaporate to dense fumes of sulfur trioxide. Repeat the dilution and evaporation if necessary to remove all the nitrate, cool, and determine arsenic by the Gutzeit method (page 11). The amount of stain should not exceed that produced by 0.003 mg. of arsenic (As).

Heavy metals.   To 2.7 ml. (4 grams) add about 10 mg. of sodium carbonate, evaporate to dryness on the steam bath, dissolve the residue in about 20 ml. of water, and dilute to 25 ml. For the standard dilute a solution containing 0.02 mg. of lead ion (Pb) to 25 ml. Adjust the pH of the standard and sample solutions to between 3 and 4 (using a pH meter) with $1N$ acetic acid or ammonium hydroxide (10 per cent NH_3), dilute to 40 ml., and mix. Add 10 ml. of freshly prepared hydrogen sulfide water to each and mix. Any color in the solution of the sample should not exceed that in the standard.

Iron.   Evaporate 3.3 ml. (5 grams) to dryness, dissolve the residue in 2 ml. of hydrochloric acid, dilute to 50 ml., and add 30 to 50 mg. of ammonium persulfate crystals and 3 ml. of ammonium thiocyanate reagent solution. Any red color should not exceed that produced by 0.01 mg. of iron (Fe) in an equal volume of solution containing the quantities of reagents used in the test.

Notes

Nitrobenzene

$C_6H_5NO_2$ Formula Wt. 123.11

REQUIREMENTS

> Density (grams per ml.) at 25°C. Not less than 1.196 nor more than 1.199.
> Boiling range.   1 ml. to 95 ml., not more than 2.0°C.
> Freezing point.   Not below 5.0°C.
> Residue after evaporation.   Not more than 0.005 per cent.
> Acidity (as HNO_3).   Not more than 0.003 per cent.
> Chloride (Cl).   Not more than 0.0005 per cent.

TESTS

Boiling range. Distill 100 ml. by the method described on page 12. The difference between the temperatures when 1 ml. and 95 ml. have distilled should not exceed 2.0°C. The boiling point of pure nitrobenzene at 760-mm. mercury pressure is 210.9°C.

Freezing point. Place 15 ml. in a test tube (20 × 150 mm.) in which is centered an accurate thermometer. The sample tube is centered by corks in an outer tube about 38 × 200 mm. Cool the whole apparatus, without stirring, in a bath of shaved or crushed ice with water enough to wet the outer tube. When the temperature is about 2°C., stir to start the freezing, and read the thermometer every 30 seconds. The temperature which remains constant for 1 or 2 minutes is the freezing point.

Residue after evaporation. Evaporate 16.7 ml. (20 grams) to dryness in a tared dish on the steam bath and dry the residue at 105°C. for 30 minutes. The residue should not exceed 0.0010 gram.

Acidity. Shake 21 ml. (25 grams) with 60 ml. of water for 1 minute and allow the layers to separate. Draw off and discard the nitrobenzene. Titrate 48 ml. of the water extract with 0.02N sodium hydroxide, using bromophenol blue indicator solution. Not more than 0.5 ml. of 0.02N sodium hydroxide should be required.

Chloride. Dilute the remaining 12 ml. of water from the test for *Acidity* to 25 ml. with water, filter if necessary through a chloride-free filter, and dilute 10 ml. of the filtrate to 20 ml. Add 1 ml. of nitric acid and 1 ml. of silver nitrate reagent solution. Any turbidity should not exceed that produced by 0.01 mg. of chloride ion (Cl) in an equal volume of solution containing the quantities of reagents used in the test.

Oxalic Acid

$(COOH)_2 \cdot 2H_2O$ Formula Wt. 126.07

REQUIREMENTS

Insoluble matter. Not more than 0.005 per cent.
Residue after ignition. Not more than 0.010 per cent.
Chloride (Cl). Not more than 0.002 per cent.
Sulfate (SO₄). Not more than 0.002 per cent.
Calcium (Ca). Not more than 0.001 per cent.
Nitrogen compounds (as N). Not more than 0.001 per cent.
Heavy metals (as Pb). Not more than 0.0005 per cent.
Iron (Fe). Not more than 0.0002 per cent.
Substances darkened by hot sulfuric acid. To pass test.

TESTS

Insoluble matter. Dissolve 20 grams in 250 ml. of water, heat to boiling, and digest in a covered beaker on the steam bath for 1 hour. Filter through a tared filtering crucible, wash thoroughly, and dry at 105°C. The weight of the residue should not exceed 0.0010 gram.

Residue after ignition. Dry 10 grams in a tared crucible or dish for 1 hour at 105° to 110°C., then slowly ignite. The rate of heating should be such that from 1 to 2 hours is required to volatilize the sample. When nearly all the sample has been volatilized, cool, and moisten the residue with 0.10 ml. of sulfuric acid. Continue the heating until the remainder of the sample and excess sulfuric acid have been volatilized. Finally, ignite at 800° ± 25°C. for 15 minutes. The weight of the residue should not exceed 0.0010 gram. Retain the residue for the test for *Iron*.

Chloride. Dissolve 5 grams in water, filter if necessary through a chloride-free filter, and dilute to 100 ml. Dilute 10 ml. of the solution to 20 ml., and add 1 ml. of nitric acid and 1 ml. of silver nitrate reagent solution. Any turbidity should not exceed that produced by 0.01 mg. of chloride ion (Cl) in an equal volume of solution containing the quantities of reagents used in the test.

Sulfate. Digest 2 grams of sample plus about 10 mg. of sodium carbonate with 3 ml. of 30 per cent hydrogen peroxide and 0.5 ml. of nitric acid in a covered beaker on the steam bath until reaction ceases. Remove the cover and evaporate to dryness. Dissolve the residue in 6 ml. of dilute hydrochloric acid (1 + 1) and again evaporate to dryness. Dissolve the residue in 4 ml. of water plus 1 ml. of dilute hydrochloric acid (1 + 19), filter if necessary through a small filter, wash the precipitate with two 2-ml. portions of water, and dilute to 10 ml. Add 1 ml. of barium chloride reagent solution. Any turbidity should not exceed that produced when a solution containing 0.04 mg. of sulfate ion (SO_4) is treated exactly like the 2 grams of sample. Compare 10 minutes after adding the barium chloride to the sample and standard solutions.

Calcium. Determine the calcium by the flame photometric method described on page 14.

Sample Solution A. Suspend 10 grams in 50 ml. of dilute nitric acid (1 + 24) and add 25 ml. of 30 per cent hydrogen peroxide. Cover and digest on the steam bath until reaction ceases. Add 5 ml. more of the hydrogen peroxide and when reaction ceases, uncover and evaporate to dryness. Dissolve the residue in 100 ml. of dilute nitric acid (1 + 99).

Control Solution B. Add 0.10 mg. of calcium ion (Ca) to 10 grams of the sample and treat exactly like the sample.

Observe the emission of Control Solution B at the 422.7-mμ calcium line. Observe the emission of Sample Solution A at the 422.7-mμ calcium line and at a wavelength of 418 mμ. The difference (D_1) between the intensities observed for Sample Solution A at 418 mμ and 422.7 mμ should not exceed the difference (D_2) observed at 422.7 mμ between Sample Solution A and Control Solution B.

Nitrogen compounds. Dissolve 1 gram in 60 ml. of water in a flask connected through a spray trap to a condenser, the end of which dips beneath the surface of 10 ml. of 0.1N hydrochloric acid. Add to the flask 10 ml. of freshly boiled 10 per cent sodium hydroxide reagent solution and 0.5 gram of aluminum wire in small pieces, allow to stand for 1 hour, and slowly distill about 35 ml. To the distillate add 1 ml. of 10 per cent sodium hydroxide reagent solution, dilute to 50 ml., and add 2 ml. of Nessler reagent. Any color should not exceed that produced when a quantity of an ammonium salt containing 0.01 mg. of nitrogen (N) is treated exactly like the sample.

Heavy metals. Place 4 grams in a covered beaker. Prepare a standard containing 0.02 mg. of lead ion (Pb) in a covered beaker. To each add about 10 mg. of sodium carbonate, 5 ml. of 30 per cent hydrogen peroxide, and 0.5 ml. of nitric acid. Digest on the steam bath until reaction ceases, remove the covers, and evaporate to dryness. Digest each residue with 0.5 ml. of hydrochloric acid and 0.1 ml. of nitric acid in a covered beaker for 15 minutes, remove the covers, and again evaporate to dryness. Dissolve each in about 20 ml. of water and dilute to 25 ml. Adjust the pH of the standard and sample solutions to between 3 and 4 (using a pH meter) with $1N$ acetic acid or ammonium hydroxide (10 per cent NH_3), dilute to 40 ml., and mix. Add 10 ml. of freshly prepared hydrogen sulfide water to each and mix. Any color in the solution of the sample should not exceed that in the standard.

Iron. To the *Residue after ignition* add 3 ml. of dilute hydrochloric acid $(1 + 1)$, cover with a watch glass, digest on the steam bath for 15 minutes, remove the cover, and evaporate to dryness. Dissolve the residue in 5 ml. of hydrochloric acid and dilute to 50 ml. Dilute 25 ml. of the solution to 50 ml. and add 30 to 50 mg. of ammonium persulfate crystals and 3 ml. of ammonium thiocyanate reagent solution. Any red color should not exceed that produced by 0.01 mg. of iron (Fe) in an equal volume of solution containing the quantities of reagents used in the test.

Substances darkened by hot sulfuric acid. Dissolve 2 grams in 20 ml. of sulfuric acid and heat at 150°C. for 30 minutes. Any color should not exceed that produced in a color standard of the following composition: 0.2 ml. of cobaltous chloride solution (5.95 grams of $CoCl_2 \cdot 6H_2O$ and 2.5 ml. of hydrochloric acid in 100 ml.), 0.3 ml. of ferric chloride solution (4.50 grams of $FeCl_3 \cdot 6H_2O$ and 2.5 ml. of hydrochloric acid in 100 ml.), and 0.3 ml. of cupric sulfate solution (6.24 grams of $CuSO_4 \cdot 5H_2O$ and 2.5 ml. of hydrochloric acid in 100 ml.), in 20 ml. of solution.

Notes

Perchloric Acid, 70 Per Cent

HClO$_4$ Formula Wt. 100.46

REQUIREMENTS

Assay.   Not less than 70.0 nor more than 72.0 per cent HClO$_4$.
Color (APHA).   Not more than 10.
Residue after ignition.   Not more than 0.003 per cent.
Silicate and phosphate (as SiO$_2$).   Not more than 0.0005 per cent.
Chloride (Cl).   Not more than 0.001 per cent.
Nitrogen compounds (as N).   Not more than 0.001 per cent.
Sulfate (SO$_4$).   Not more than 0.001 per cent.
Heavy metals (as Pb).   Not more than 0.0001 per cent.
Iron (Fe).   Not more than 0.0001 per cent.

TESTS

Assay.   Accurately weigh about 3 ml., dilute to 60 ml., add phenolphthalein indicator solution, and titrate with 1N sodium hydroxide. One milliliter of 1N sodium hydroxide corresponds to 0.1005 gram of HClO$_4$.

Color (APHA).   For the color standard dilute a 2-ml. aliquot of platinum-cobalt stock solution (APHA No. 500) to 100 ml. with water. Compare this solution (APHA No. 10) with 100 ml. of the perchloric acid in 100-ml. Nessler tubes, viewed vertically over a white background.

Residue after ignition.   To 42 ml. (67 grams) in a tared dish add 1 ml. of nitric acid, evaporate to dryness, and ignite at 800° ± 25°C. for 15 minutes. The weight of the residue should not exceed 0.0020 gram.

Silicate and phosphate.   Dilute 1.2 ml. (2 grams) with 50 ml. of water in a platinum dish, add 1 gram of sodium carbonate, and digest on the steam bath for 15 to 30 minutes. Cool, add 5 ml. of a 10 per cent solution of ammonium molybdate, acidify with hydrochloric acid to about pH 4 (indicator paper), and transfer to a beaker. Adjust the pH to 1.8 (using a pH meter) with dilute hydrochloric acid (1 + 9). Dilute to 90 ml., heat just to boiling, and cool to room temperature. Add 10 ml. of hydrochloric acid and dilute to 100 ml. Transfer to a separatory funnel, add 50 ml. of 4-methyl-2-pentanone, shake vigorously, and allow to separate. Draw off and discard the aqueous phase. Wash the ketone layer three times with 20-ml. portions of dilute hydrochloric acid (1 + 99), drawing off and discarding the aqueous layer each time. Add 10 ml. of dilute hydrochloric acid (1 + 99) to which has just been added 0.2 ml. of a freshly prepared 2.0 per cent solution of stannous chloride in hydrochloric acid. Shake vigorously and allow to separate. Any blue color should not exceed that produced by 0.01 mg. of silica (SiO_2) and 1 gram of sodium carbonate treated exactly like the sample.

Chloride. Dilute 0.6 ml. (1 gram) with 25 ml. of water, filter if necessary through a chloride-free filter, and add 1 ml. of nitric acid and 1 ml. of silver nitrate reagent solution. Any turbidity should not exceed that produced by 0.01 mg. of chloride ion (Cl) in an equal volume of solution containing the quantities of reagents used in the test.

Nitrogen compounds. Dilute 3 ml. (5 grams) with 40 ml. of ammonia-free water in a flask connected through a spray trap to a condenser, the end of which dips beneath the surface of 10 ml. of 0.1N hydrochloric acid. Add to the flask 10 ml. of freshly boiled 10 per cent sodium hydroxide reagent solution and 0.5 gram of aluminum wire in small pieces. Allow to stand for 1 hour, slowly distill about 35 ml., and dilute the distillate to 100 ml. To 25 ml. of the diluted distillate add 2 ml. of 10 per cent sodium hydroxide reagent solution, dilute to 50 ml., and add 2 ml. of Nessler reagent. Any color should not exceed that produced when a quantity of an ammonium salt containing 0.05 mg. of nitrogen (N) is treated exactly like the sample.

Sulfate. Dilute 20 ml. (32 grams) to 160 ml. and neutralize with ammonium hydroxide, using litmus paper as indicator. Add 1 ml. of hydrochloric acid, heat to boiling, add 5 ml. of barium chloride reagent solution, digest in a covered beaker on the steam bath for 2 hours, and allow to stand overnight. If a precipitate is formed, filter, wash thoroughly, and ignite. The weight of the precipitate should not be more than 0.0008 gram greater than the weight obtained from a complete blank test, including the evaporated residue from a volume of ammonium hydroxide equal to that used to neutralize the sample.

Sample Solution A. To 25 ml. (40 grams) add 1 ml. of nitric acid and about 20 mg. of sodium carbonate. Evaporate to dryness on a hot plate in a properly ventilated hood, dissolve the residue in 2 ml. of 1N acetic acid, and dilute to 40 ml. (1 ml. = 1 gram).

Heavy metals. For the sample dilute a 20-ml. aliquot of Sample Solution A (20-gram sample) to 25 ml. For the standard dilute a solution containing 0.02 mg. of lead ion (Pb) to 25 ml. Adjust the pH of the standard and sample solutions to between 3 and 4 (using a pH meter) with 1N acetic acid or ammonium hydroxide (10 per cent NH_3), dilute to 40 ml., and mix. Add 10 ml. of freshly prepared hydrogen sulfide water to each and mix. Any color in the solution of the sample should not exceed that in the standard.

Iron. To 10 ml. of Sample Solution A (10-gram sample) add 2 ml. of hydrochloric acid and dilute to 50 ml. Add 30 to 50 mg. of ammonium persulfate crystals and 3 ml. of ammonium thiocyanate reagent solution. Any red color should not exceed that produced by 0.01 mg. of iron (Fe) in an equal volume of solution containing the quantities of reagents used in the test.

Notes

Perchloric Acid, 60 Per Cent

HClO$_4$ Formula Wt. 100.46

REQUIREMENTS

Assay. Not less than 60.0 nor more than 62.0 per cent HClO$_4$.
Color (APHA). Not more than 10.
Residue after ignition. Not more than 0.003 per cent.
Silicate and phosphate (as SiO$_2$). Not more than 0.0005 per cent.
Chloride (Cl). Not more than 0.001 per cent.
Nitrogen compounds (as N). Not more than 0.001 per cent.
Sulfate (SO$_4$). Not more than 0.001 per cent.
Heavy metals (as Pb). Not more than 0.0001 per cent.
Iron (Fe). Not more than 0.0001 per cent.

TESTS

All tests the same as for **Perchloric Acid, 70 per cent.**

Note. The density of the 60 per cent acid is less than that of the 70 per cent reagent, and proper allowance should be made for this when measured volumes are taken for the different tests.

Notes

Petroleum Ether

Ligroine

Note. Extremely flammable. Keep away from heat, sparks, and open flame. Store in a cool place. Keep container closed.

REQUIREMENTS

    Color (APHA). Not more than 10.
    Odor. To pass test.
    Boiling range. From 30° to 60°C.
    Residue after evaporation. Not more than 0.0010 per cent.
    Acidity. To pass test.
    Heavy oils and fats (spot test). To pass test.

TESTS

Color (APHA). For the color standard dilute a 2-ml. aliquot of platinum-cobalt stock solution (APHA No. 500) to 100 ml. with water. Compare this solution (APHA No. 10) with 100 ml. of the petroleum ether in 100-ml. Nessler tubes, viewed vertically over a white background.

Odor. The odor should not be disagreeable or sulfurated.

Boiling range. Distill 100 ml. by the method described on page 12. None should distill below 30°C. and the dry point should not be above 60°C.

Residue after evaporation. Evaporate 150 ml. (100 grams) to dryness in a tared dish at 70° to 80°C. and dry the residue at 105°C. for 30 minutes. The weight of the residue should not exceed 0.0010 gram.

Acidity. Thoroughly shake 10 ml. with 5 ml. of water for 2 minutes and allow to separate. The aqueous layer should not turn blue litmus paper red in 15 seconds.

Heavy oils and fats (spot test). Pour 10 ml. gradually onto the center of a clean filter paper. After 30 minutes there should be no greasy stain visible on the paper and it should have no disagreeable odor.

Notes

1,10-Phenanthroline

CH:CHCH:NC:CCH:CHC:CN:CHCH:CH · H$_2$O   Formula Wt. 198.23

REQUIREMENTS

Melting point. Not below 98°C.
Suitability as redox indicator. To pass test.
Suitability for determining iron. To pass test.

TESTS

Sample Solution A. Dissolve 0.10 gram in water and dilute to 100 ml.

Suitability as redox indicator. To 2.5 ml. of Sample Solution A add 0.1 ml. of 0.1N ferrous ammonium sulfate solution and dilute to 50 ml. with 12N sulfuric acid. A distinct red color should be produced. Add 0.1 ml. of 0.1N potassium dichromate solution. The red color should be discharged.

Suitability for determining iron. To 20 ml. of water add 0.001 mg. of iron (Fe) and 1 ml. of hydroxylamine hydrochloride reagent solution. For the control add 1 ml. of hydroxylamine hydrochloride reagent solution to 20 ml. of water. To each solution add 2.5 ml. of Sample Solution A and allow to stand for 1 hour. The color in the solution containing the added iron should be definitely pink compared with the control. The control containing no added iron should not show any turbidity or color.

Notes

Phenol

C_6H_5OH Formula Wt. 94.11

Note. Phenol that conforms to this specification may contain a stabilizer. If a stabilizer is present, its presence should be stated on the label.

REQUIREMENTS

> **Water.** To pass test (limit about 0.5 per cent).
> **Insoluble matter.** To pass test.
> **Residue after evaporation.** Not more than 0.05 per cent.

TESTS

Water. Transfer 10 grams to a dry test tube with an inner diameter of 18 to 20 mm. and provided with a thermometer. (If the reagent has solidified in its container, the whole should be melted and mixed to ensure taking a representative sample.) Heat to 45° to 50°C. and place the test tube in a water bath maintained at 33° to 35°C. Stir the sample with the thermometer and, if necessary, rub the wall of the test tube with the thermometer to initiate crystallization. When freezing begins, remove the test tube from the bath and stir to promote equilibrium between the solid and liquid phases. The freezing or congealing point (the temperature remaining constant for 1 minute) should not be lower than 39.0°C.

Insoluble matter. Dissolve 5 grams in 100 ml. of water. The solution should be free of turbidity and insoluble residue.

Residue after evaporation. Evaporate 10 grams to dryness in a tared dish on the steam bath and dry the residue at 105°C. for 30 minutes. The weight of the residue should not exceed 0.0050 gram.

Notes

Phenolphthalein

3,3-bis(p-Hydroxyphenyl)phthalide

REQUIREMENTS

Insoluble matter. To pass test.
Visual transition interval. From pH 8.0 (colorless) to pH 10 (red).

TESTS

Insoluble matter. Dissolve 1 gram in 100 ml. of ethyl alcohol. Not more than a faint trace of turbidity or insoluble matter should remain. Reserve the solution for the test for *Visual transition interval.*

Visual transition interval. Dissolve 1 gram of potassium chloride in 100 ml. of water. Adjust the pH of the solution to 8.00 (using a pH meter as described on page 18) with 0.01N acid or base. Add 0.05 to 0.10 ml. of the 1 per cent solution reserved from the test for *Insoluble matter.* The solution should be colorless. Titrate the solution with 0.01N sodium hydroxide until the pH is 8.2 (using the pH meter). The solution should have a pale pink color. Continue the titration until the pH is 8.6 (using the pH meter). The solution should have a definite pink color. Not more than 0.20 ml. of 0.01N sodium hydroxide should be consumed. Each additional 0.20 ml. of 0.01N sodium hydroxide should increase the amount of red color, until at pH 10 the solution should be very red.

Notes

Phenol Red

Phenolsulfonphthalein

α,α-bis(p-Hydroxyphenol)-α-hydroxy-o-toluene γ-Sultone

Note. This specification applies both to the free acid form and to the salt form of this indicator.

REQUIREMENTS

Insoluble matter. To pass test.
Visual transition interval. From pH 6.8 (yellow) to pH 8.2 (red).

TESTS

Insoluble matter. If the indicator is the acid form, dissolve 0.1 gram in 100 ml. of alcohol. If the indicator is a salt form, dissolve 0.1 gram in 100 ml. of water. Not more than a faint trace of turbidity or insoluble matter should remain. Reserve the solution for the test for *Visual transition interval.*

Visual transition interval. Dissolve 1 gram of potassium chloride in 100 ml. of water. Adjust the pH of the solution to 6.80 (using a pH meter as described on page 18) with 0.01N acid or alkali. Add 0.10 to 0.30 ml. of the 0.1 per cent solution reserved from the test for *Insoluble matter.* The color of the solution should be yellow, with not more than a faint trace of green color. Titrate the solution with 0.01N sodium hydroxide to a pH of 7.0 (using the pH meter). The color of the solution should be orange (flesh). Continue the titration to pH 8.2. The color of the solution should be red. Not more than 0.20 ml. of 0.01N sodium hydroxide should be consumed in the entire titration.

Notes

Phosphomolybdic Acid

REQUIREMENTS

Insoluble matter.   Not more than 0.01 per cent.
Chloride (Cl).   Not more than 0.020 per cent.
Sulfate (SO_4).   Not more than 0.025 per cent.
Ammonium (NH_4).   Not more than 0.01 per cent.
Calcium (Ca).   Not more than 0.02 per cent.
Heavy metals (as Pb).   Not more than 0.005 per cent.
Iron (Fe).   Not more than 0.005 per cent.

TESTS

Insoluble matter.   Dissolve 10 grams in 200 ml. of water, heat to boiling, and digest in a covered beaker on the steam bath for 1 hour. Filter through a tared filtering crucible, wash thoroughly, and dry at 105°C. The weight of the residue should not exceed 0.0010 gram.

Chloride.   Dissolve 1 gram in 50 ml. of water, add 1 ml. of nitric acid, filter through a chloride-free filter, and divide into two equal portions. For the control add 0.5 ml. of silver nitrate reagent solution to one-half of the solution, let stand for 10 minutes, filter, and add 0.1 mg. of chloride ion (Cl). For the sample add 0.5 ml. of silver nitrate reagent solution to the remaining half. Any turbidity in the solution of the sample should not exceed that in the control.

Sulfate.   Dissolve 2 grams in 100 ml. of water. To 25 ml. of this solution add 1 ml. of dilute hydrochloric acid (1 + 19) and 2 ml. of barium chloride reagent solution. Any turbidity should not exceed that produced by 0.12 mg. of sulfate ion (SO_4) in an equal volume of solution containing the quantities of reagents used in the test. Compare 10 minutes after adding the barium chloride to the sample and standard solutions.

Ammonium.   Dissolve 1 gram in 50 ml. of water in a distilling flask connected through a spray trap to a condenser, the end of which dips beneath the surface of 10 ml. of 0.1N hydrochloric acid. Add to the solution in the flask 10 ml. of freshly boiled 10 per cent sodium hydroxide reagent solution, slowly distill about 45 ml., and dilute the distillate to 100 ml. To 20 ml. of this solution add 1 ml. of 10 per cent sodium hydroxide reagent solution, dilute to 50 ml., and add 2 ml. of Nessler reagent. Any color should not exceed that produced when a solution containing 0.1 mg. of ammonium ion (NH_4) is treated exactly like the sample.

Calcium.   Dissolve 1 gram in 10 ml. of water and make slightly alkaline with ammonium hydroxide. Boil for 1 minute, filter, and add 2 ml. of ammonium oxalate reagent solution. Any turbidity should not exceed that produced by 0.2 mg. of calcium ion (Ca) in an equal volume of solution containing the quantities of reagents used in the test.

Heavy metals.   Dissolve 3 grams in 30 ml. of water, filter, neutralize the filtrate to litmus with sodium hydroxide reagent solution, and add 5 ml. of $1N$ sodium hydroxide in excess. Heat the solution to boiling to destroy any blue color. For the standard boil a solution containing 5 ml. of $1N$ sodium hydroxide and 0.15 mg. of lead ion (Pb) in 30 ml. of water. Cool the solutions to about 10°C. and to each add 4.5 ml. of $1N$ hydrochloric acid and 10 ml. of 10 per cent (W/V) sodium sulfide reagent solution. Any color in the solution of the sample should not exceed that in the standard.

Iron.   Dissolve 5 grams in 30 ml. of water, make alkaline with ammonium hydroxide, and add 0.25 to 0.30 ml. of bromine water. Boil for a few minutes, filter, wash the precipitate several times, and discard the filtrate and washings. Pass 25 ml. of dilute hydrochloric acid $(1 + 1)$ through the filter to dissolve any precipitate, wash thoroughly, and dilute to 50 ml. Dilute 20 ml. of this solution to 45 ml. and add 2 ml. of ammonium thiocyanate reagent solution. Any red color should not exceed that produced by 0.1 mg. of ferric ion (Fe^{+3}) in an equal volume of solution containing 10 ml. of dilute hydrochloric acid $(1 + 1)$ and 2 ml. of ammonium thiocyanate reagent solution.

Notes

Phosphoric Acid

H_3PO_4 Formula Wt. 98.00

REQUIREMENTS

Assay.   Not less than 85 per cent H_3PO_4.
Color (APHA).   Not more than 10.
**Insoluble matter, calcium, magnesium, and ammonium hydroxide pre-
cipitate.**   Not more than 0.005 per cent.
Chloride (Cl).   Not more than 0.0003 per cent.
Nitrate (NO$_3$).   Not more than 0.0005 per cent.
Sulfate (SO$_4$).   Not more than 0.003 per cent.
Volatile acids (as CH_3COOH).   Not more than 0.0010 per cent.
Arsenic (As).   Not more than 0.0001 per cent.
Heavy metals (as Pb).   Not more than 0.001 per cent.
Iron (Fe).   Not more than 0.003 per cent.
Manganese (Mn).   Not more than 0.00005 per cent.
Potassium (K).   Not more than 0.005 per cent.
Sodium (Na).   Not more than 0.025 per cent.
Reducing substances.   To pass test.

TESTS

Assay.   Weigh accurately about 1 ml., dilute with 120 ml. of water, add
0.5 ml. of thymolphthalein indicator solution, and titrate with $1N$ sodium
hydroxide to the first appearance of a blue color. One milliliter of $1N$
sodium hydroxide corresponds to 0.04900 gram of H_3PO_4.

Color (APHA).   For the color standard dilute a 2-ml. aliquot of platinum-
cobalt stock solution (APHA No. 500) to 100 ml. with water. Compare
this solution (APHA No. 10) with 100 ml. of the phosphoric acid in
100-ml. Nessler tubes, viewed vertically over a white background.

**Insoluble matter, calcium, magnesium, and ammonium hydroxide pre-
cipitate.**   Dilute 12 ml. (20 grams) to 100 ml. with water. Add ammonium hydroxide until just alkaline to litmus, hydrochloric acid until acid
to litmus, and 0.5 ml. of acid in excess. Add 5 ml. of ammonium oxalate
reagent solution and 10 ml. of ammonium hydroxide, and allow to stand
overnight. If a precipitate is formed, filter, wash with water containing
2.5 per cent of ammonium hydroxide and 0.1 per cent of ammonium
oxalate, and ignite. The weight of the residue should not exceed 0.0010
gram.

Chloride.   Dilute 2.0 ml. (3.4 grams) to 25 ml. and add 0.5 ml. of nitric
acid and 1 ml. of silver nitrate reagent solution. Any turbidity should

not exceed that produced by 0.01 mg. of chloride ion (Cl) in an equal volume of solution containing the quantities of reagents used in the test.

Nitrate.

Sample Solution A. Add 2.4 ml. (4 grams) to 2.0 ml. of water, dilute to 50 ml. with brucine sulfate reagent solution, and mix.

Control Solution B. Add 2.4 ml. (4 grams) to 2.0 ml. of the standard nitrate solution containing 0.01 mg. of nitrate ion (NO_3) per ml., dilute to 50 ml. with brucine sulfate reagent solution, and mix.

Blank Solution C. Use 50 ml. of brucine sulfate reagent solution.

Heat the three solutions in a preheated (boiling) water bath for 10 minutes. Cool rapidly in an ice bath to room temperature. Set a spectrophotometer at 410 mμ and, using 1-cm. cells, adjust the instrument to read 0 absorbance with Blank Solution C in the light path, then determine the absorbance of Sample Solution A. Adjust the instrument to read 0 absorbance with Sample Solution A in the light path and determine the absorbance of Control Solution B. The absorbance of Sample Solution A should not exceed that of Control Solution B.

Sulfate. Dilute 12 ml. (20 grams) with 190 ml. of water, add ammonium hydroxide until just alkaline to methyl orange, and then add hydrochloric acid until just acid. Boil, add 10 ml. of barium chloride reagent solution, digest in a covered beaker on the steam bath for 2 hours, and allow to stand overnight. If a precipitate is formed, filter, wash thoroughly, and ignite. The weight of the precipitate should not be more than 0.0015 gram greater than the weight of the precipitate obtained in a complete blank test.

Volatile acids. Dilute 37.5 ml. (64 grams) with 75 ml. of freshly boiled and cooled water in a distilling flask provided with a spray trap and distill off 50 ml. To the distillate add 0.15 ml. of phenolphthalein indicator solution and titrate with 0.1N sodium hydroxide. Not more than 0.1 ml. of the 0.1N sodium hydroxide should be required to produce a pink color.

Arsenic. Determine the arsenic in 1.7 ml. (3.0 grams) by the Gutzeit method (page 11). The amount of stain should not exceed that produced by 0.003 mg. of arsenic (As).

Heavy metals. Dilute 2.4 ml. (4.0 grams) to 32 ml. with water. For the control add 0.02 mg. of lead ion (Pb) to an 8-ml. aliquot of this solution and dilute to 25 ml. For the sample dilute the remaining 24-ml.

portion to 25 ml. Adjust the pH of the control and sample solutions to between 3 and 4 (using a pH meter) with $1N$ acetic acid or ammonium hydroxide (10 per cent NH_3), dilute to 40 ml., and mix. Add 10 ml. of freshly prepared hydrogen sulfide water to each and mix. Any color in the solution of the sample should not exceed that in the standard.

Iron. Dilute 6 ml. (10 grams) to 100 ml. To 5 ml. of the solution add 8 ml. of $0.5N$ sodium acetate, 6 ml. of 10 per cent hydroxylamine hydrochloride reagent solution, and 4 ml. of 1,10-phenanthroline reagent solution and dilute to 25 ml. Any red color should not exceed that produced by 0.015 mg. of iron (Fe) in an equal volume of solution containing the quantities of reagents used in the test. Compare 1 hour after the reagents are added to the sample and standard solutions.

Manganese. Add 15 ml. (25 grams) to 100 ml. of dilute sulfuric acid $(1 + 9)$. For the control add 3 ml. (5 grams) of sample and 0.01 mg. of manganese ion (Mn) to 100 ml. of dilute sulfuric acid $(1 + 9)$. To each solution add 20 ml. of nitric acid, heat to boiling, and boil gently for 5 minutes. Cool slightly, add 0.25 gram of potassium periodate, and again boil for 5 minutes. Any red color in the solution of the sample should not exceed that in the control.

Potassium. Determine the potassium by the flame photometric method described on page 14.

Sample Solution A. Dilute 2 ml. of sample (3.4 grams) to 100 ml. with water.

Control Solution B. To another 2 ml. of the sample add 0.17 mg. of potassium ion (K) and dilute to 100 ml. with water.

Observe the emission of Control Solution B at the 767-mμ potassium line. Observe the emission of Sample Solution A at the 767-mμ potassium line and at a wavelength of 750 mμ. The difference (D_1) between the intensities observed for Sample Solution A at 767 mμ and 750 mμ should not exceed the difference (D_2) observed at 767 mμ between Sample Solution A and Control Solution B.

Sodium. Determine the sodium by the flame photometric method described on page 14.

Sample Solution A. Dilute 1 ml. of sample (1.7 grams) to 250 ml. with water.

Control Solution B. To another 1 ml. of the sample add 0.42 mg. of sodium ion (Na) and dilute to 250 ml. with water.

Observe the emission of Control Solution B at the 589-mμ sodium line. Observe the emission of Sample Solution A at the 589-mμ sodium line and at a wavelength of 580 mμ. The difference (D_1) between the intensities observed for Sample Solution A at 580 mμ and 589 mμ should not exceed the difference (D_2) observed at 589 mμ between Sample Solution A and Control Solution B.

Reducing substances. Add 5.0 ml. of 0.1N bromine solution to each of two 500-ml. "iodine determination" flasks. To each flask add 120 ml. of cold dilute sulfuric acid $(1 + 59)$ and to one of the flasks add rapidly 10 ml. (17 grams) of the sample. Stopper the flasks, shake gently, seal with water, and allow to stand at room temperature for 10 minutes. Cool in an ice bath, add 10 ml. of potassium iodide reagent solution, and re-seal with water. Shake gently to dissolve all fumes and place in the ice bath for about 5 minutes. Wash the stoppers and inside walls of the flasks and titrate each with 0.01N sodium thiosulfate solution, adding starch indicator solution near the end of the titration. The difference between the two titrations should not exceed 1.0 ml. of 0.01N sodium thiosulfate.

Notes

Phosphoric Acid, Meta-

Vitreous Sodium Acid Metaphosphate

Note. This reagent contains as a stabilizer a somewhat greater proportion of sodium metaphosphate than that corresponding to the empirical formula $NaH(PO_3)_2$.

REQUIREMENTS

Assay.   Not less than 34.0 nor more than 36.0 per cent HPO_3.
Stabilizer.   Not less than 58.0 nor more than 62.0 per cent $NaPO_3$.
Chloride (Cl).   Not more than 0.001 per cent.
Nitrate (NO_3).   Not more than 0.001 per cent.
Sulfate (SO_4).   Not more than 0.005 per cent.
Arsenic (As).   Not more than 0.0001 per cent.
Heavy metals (as Pb).   Not more than 0.005 per cent.
Iron (Fe).   Not more than 0.005 per cent.
Substances reducing permanganate (as H_3PO_3).   Not more than 0.020 per cent.

TESTS

Assay.   Weigh accurately about 5 grams, dissolve in 400 ml. of water, and titrate with $1N$ sodium hydroxide solution to a pH of 4.4 (using a pH meter). One milliliter of $1N$ sodium hydroxide corresponds to 0.07998 gram of metaphosphoric acid (HPO_3).

Stabilizer.   Weigh accurately about 20 grams, dissolve in water, and dilute to a volume of 1 liter. To a 50.0-ml. aliquot of this solution in a 200-ml. volumetric flask add 50 ml. of water and 50 ml. of a 10 per cent solution of lead acetate, dilute to 200 ml., mix thoroughly, and decant through a filter. Treat 100 ml. of the clear filtrate with hydrogen sulfide sufficiently to precipitate the excess of lead, filter, and wash with about 20 ml. of water. To the filtrate add 2 ml. of sulfuric acid, evaporate to dryness in a tared dish, and ignite to constant weight at $800° \pm 25°C$. Calculate the weight of $NaPO_3$ by multiplying the weight of sodium sulfate by the factor 1.4356.

Sample Solution A for the determination of Chloride, Arsenic, Heavy metals, Iron, and Substances reducing permanganate.   Dissolve 20 grams in 150 ml. of water, cool, and dilute to 200 ml. (1 ml. = 0.1 gram).

Chloride. Dilute 10 ml. of Sample Solution A (1-gram sample) to 25 ml., filter if necessary through a chloride-free filter, and add 0.5 ml. of nitric acid and 1 ml. of silver nitrate reagent solution. Any turbidity should not exceed that produced by 0.01 mg. of chloride ion (Cl) in an equal volume of solution containing the quantities of reagents used in the test.

Nitrate.

Sample Solution A. Dissolve 1.0 gram in 4.0 ml. of water, dilute to 50 ml. with brucine sulfate reagent solution, and mix.

Control Solution B. Dissolve 1.0 gram in 3.0 ml. of water and 1.0 ml. of the standard nitrate solution containing 0.01 mg. of nitrate ion (NO_3) per ml. Dilute to 50 ml. with brucine sulfate reagent solution and mix.

Blank Solution C. Use 50 ml. of brucine sulfate reagent solution.

Heat the three solutions in a preheated (boiling) water bath for 10 minutes. Cool rapidly in an ice bath to room temperature. Set a spectrophotometer at 410 mμ and, using 1-cm. cells, adjust the instrument to read 0 absorbance with Blank Solution C in the light path, then determine the absorbance of Sample Solution A. Adjust the instrument to read 0 absorbance with Sample Solution A in the light path and determine the absorbance of Control Solution B. The absorbance of Sample Solution A should not exceed that of Control Solution B.

Sulfate. Dissolve 8 grams in 180 ml. of water, heat the solution to boiling, cool, filter, and heat again to boiling. Add 10 ml. of barium chloride reagent solution, digest in a covered beaker on the steam bath for 2 hours, and allow to stand overnight. If a precipitate is formed, filter, wash thoroughly, and ignite. The weight of the precipitate should not be more than 0.0010 gram greater than the weight obtained in a complete blank test, including filtration of a solution of 2 ml. of hydrochloric acid in 200 ml. of water.

Arsenic. Determine the arsenic in 20 ml. of Sample Solution A (2-gram sample) by the Gutzeit method (page 11). The amount of stain should not exceed that produced by 0.002 mg. of arsenic (As).

Heavy metals. To 50 ml. of Sample Solution A (5-gram sample) add 0.10 ml. of phenolphthalein indicator solution and neutralize with ammonium hydroxide. Adjust the pH of this solution to between 3 and 4 (using a pH meter) with 1N sulfuric acid and dilute to 250 ml. For the sample use a 40-ml. aliquot of the solution. For the control add 0.02 mg. of lead ion (Pb) to a 20-ml. aliquot of the solution and dilute to 40 ml. Add 10 ml. of freshly prepared hydrogen sulfide water to each and mix. Any color in the solution of the sample should not exceed that in the control.

Iron. To 2 ml. of Sample Solution A (0.2-gram sample) add 5 ml. of water and 3 ml. of hydrochloric acid. Boil gently for 10 minutes, cool, and adjust the pH to between 4 and 6 with ammonium hydroxide. Add 3.5 ml. of 0.5N sodium acetate, 6 ml. of hydroxylamine hydrochloride reagent solution, and 4 ml. of 1,10-phenanthroline reagent solution. Any red color should not exceed that produced by 0.01 mg. of iron (Fe) in an equal volume of solution containing the quantities of reagents used in the test. Compare 1 hour after adding the reagents to the sample and standard solutions.

Substances reducing permanganate. To 50 ml. of Sample Solution A (5-gram sample) add 10 ml. of 10 per cent sulfuric acid reagent solution, heat the solution to boiling, and titrate with 0.1N potassium permanganate solution to a pink color that remains for 5 minutes. Not more than 0.25 ml. of permanganate should be required.

Notes

Phosphorus Pentoxide

P_2O_5 Formula Wt. 141.94

REQUIREMENTS

Assay.   Not less than 98.0 per cent P_2O_5.
Insoluble matter.   Not more than 0.02 per cent.
Phosphorus trioxide (P_2O_3).   Not more than 0.02 per cent.
Ammonium (NH_4).   Not more than 0.01 per cent.
Arsenic (As).   Not more than 0.005 per cent.
Heavy metals (as Pb).   Not more than 0.01 per cent.

TESTS

Note.   When making a solution, the phosphorus pentoxide must be added carefully and in small portions to water that has been cooled. Quiet dissolution may be achieved by allowing the sample to remain overnight in the uncovered weighing bottle placed in a covered beaker containing the necessary water. The pentoxide will absorb enough water from the air to dissolve without sputtering.

Assay.   Weigh accurately about 1 gram, carefully dissolve in 100 ml. of water, and evaporate to about 25 ml. Cool, dilute to 120 ml., add 0.5 ml. of 0.1 per cent thymolphthalein solution, and titrate with 1N sodium hydroxide. One milliliter of 1N sodium hydroxide corresponds to 0.03549 gram of P_2O_5.

Insoluble matter.   Carefully dissolve 5 grams in 40 ml. of water, warming if necessary. Filter through a tared filtering crucible and set aside the filtrate for Sample Solution A. Wash the residue thoroughly and dry at 105°C. The weight of the insoluble residue should not exceed 0.0010 gram.

Sample Solution A.   Dilute to 100 ml. the filtrate, without washings, obtained in the preceding test (1 ml. = 0.05 gram).

Phosphorus trioxide.   To 60 ml. of Sample Solution A (3-gram sample) add 0.20 ml. of 0.1N potassium permanganate solution. Heat to boiling and allow to digest on the steam bath for 10 minutes. The pink color should not be entirely discharged.

Ammonium.   Dilute 2 ml. of Sample Solution A (0.1-gram sample) to 40 ml., and add 10 ml. of freshly boiled 10 per cent sodium hydroxide reagent solution and 2 ml. of Nessler reagent. Any color should not exceed that produced by 0.01 mg. of ammonium ion (NH_4) in an equal volume of solution containing the quantities of reagents used in the test.

Arsenic. Determine the arsenic in 1.0 ml. of Sample Solution A (0.05-gram sample) by the Gutzeit method (page 11). The amount of stain should not exceed that produced by 0.0025 mg. of arsenic (As).

Heavy metals. Dilute 8 ml. of Sample Solution A (0.4-gram sample) to about 30 ml., boil for 5 minutes, cool, and dilute to 32 ml. For the control add 0.02 mg. of lead ion (Pb) to an 8-ml. aliquot of this solution and dilute to 25 ml. For the sample dilute the remaining 24-ml. portion to 25 ml. Adjust the pH of the control and sample solutions to between 3 and 4 (using a pH meter) with $1N$ acetic acid or ammonium hydroxide (10 per cent NH_3), dilute to 40 ml., and mix. Add 10 ml. of freshly prepared hydrogen sulfide water to each and mix. Any color in the solution of the sample should not exceed that in the control.

Notes

Picric Acid

2,4,6-Trinitrophenol

$(NO_2)_3C_6H_2OH$ Formula Wt. 229.11

REQUIREMENTS

> Water (H_2O).   Not less than 10 nor more than 15 per cent.
> Melting point (dried).   Not below 121°C. nor above 123°C.
> Insoluble and resinous matter.   Not more than 0.010 per cent.
> Insoluble in benzene.   Not more than 0.10 per cent.
> Sulfate (SO_4).   Not more than 0.01 per cent.

TESTS

Water.   Dissolve about 1 gram, accurately weighed, in 200 ml. of water. Titrate with 0.1N sodium hydroxide, using phenolphthalein indicator solution. One milliliter of 0.1N sodium hydroxide corresponds to 0.02291 gram of $(NO_2)_3C_6H_2OH$. Subtract the per cent of picric acid from 100 per cent to determine the water content.

Insoluble and resinous matter.   Dissolve 10 grams in 500 ml. of water, add 1 ml. of sulfuric acid, and digest on the steam bath for 1 hour. Filter through a tared filtering crucible, wash thoroughly, and dry at 105°C. No resinous material should be apparent in the crucible. The weight of the residue should not exceed 0.0010 gram.

Insoluble in benzene.   Dry 5 grams at 70°C. and dissolve 4 grams of the dried sample in 100 ml. of warm benzene. Filter off any insoluble material using a tared filtering crucible, wash thoroughly with warm benzene, and dry at 105°C. The weight of the residue should not exceed 0.0040 gram.

Sulfate.   Add 5 grams to 25 ml. of nitric acid and evaporate to dryness on the steam bath. Add 150 ml. of water and 1 ml. of hydrochloric acid, heat to boiling, cool, and filter. Heat the filtrate to boiling, add 5 ml. of barium chloride reagent solution, digest in a covered beaker on the steam bath for 2 hours, and allow to stand overnight. If a precipitate is formed, filter, wash thoroughly, and ignite. The weight of the precipitate should not exceed 0.0013 gram.

Notes

Potassium Acetate

CH$_3$COOK   Formula Wt. 98.15

REQUIREMENTS

Insoluble matter.   Not more than 0.005 per cent.
pH of 5 per cent solution.   From 6.5 to 9.0 at 25°C.
Chloride (Cl).   Not more than 0.003 per cent.
Phosphate (PO$_4$).   Not more than 0.001 per cent.
Sulfate (SO$_4$).   Not more than 0.002 per cent.
Calcium, magnesium, and R$_2$O$_3$ precipitate.   Not more than 0.010 per cent.
Heavy metals (as Pb).   Not more than 0.0005 per cent.
Iron (Fe).   Not more than 0.0005 per cent.
Sodium (Na).   Not more than 0.01 per cent.

TESTS

Insoluble matter.   Dissolve 20 grams in 200 ml. of water, add 0.10 ml. of methyl red indicator solution and enough hydrochloric acid to produce a red color, heat to boiling, and digest on the steam bath in a covered beaker for 1 hour. Filter through a tared filtering crucible, reserve the filtrate for the test for *Calcium, magnesium, and R$_2$O$_3$ precipitate*, wash thoroughly, and dry at 105°C. The weight of the residue should not exceed 0.0010 gram.

pH of a 5 per cent solution.   Dissolve 10 grams in 200 ml. of carbon dioxide- and ammonia-free water. Protect from the carbon dioxide and ammonia in the air. Determine the pH by the method described on page 18. The pH should be from 6.5 to 9.0 at 25°C. The pH of a 5 per cent solution of pure potassium acetate would be 9.0 at 25°C.

Chloride.   Dissolve 0.5 gram in 20 ml. of water, filter if necessary through a chloride-free filter, and add 1 ml. of nitric acid and 1 ml. of silver nitrate reagent solution. Any turbidity should not exceed that produced by 0.015 mg. of chloride ion (Cl) in an equal volume of solution containing the quantities of reagents used in the test.

Phosphate.   Dissolve 1 gram in 10 ml. of nitric acid and evaporate to near dryness on the steam bath. Gently heat with a burner until the salt is dry. Add 10 ml. of nitric acid and repeat the evaporation and drying. Dissolve in 80 ml. of water, add 0.5 gram of ammonium molybdate, and adjust the pH to 1.8 (using a pH meter) with dilute hydrochloric acid (1 + 9). Heat to boiling, cool, and add 10 ml. of hydrochloric acid. Transfer to a separatory funnel, add 35 ml. of ether, shake vigorously, and allow the layers to separate. Draw off and discard the aqueous layer. Wash the ether layer twice with 10 ml. of dilute hydrochloric acid (1 + 9), drawing off and discarding the aqueous layer each time. Add 0.2 ml. of a freshly prepared 2 per cent solution of stannous chloride in hydrochloric acid. If the solution is cloudy, shake it with a small amount of dilute hydrochloric acid (1 + 9) to clear it. Any blue color should not exceed that produced by 0.01 mg. of phosphate ion (PO_4) treated in the same manner as the sample after addition of 80 ml. of water.

Sulfate. Dissolve 20 grams in 150 ml. of water, add 1 ml. of hydrochloric acid, and filter. Heat to boiling, add 5 ml. of barium chloride reagent solution, digest in a covered beaker on the steam bath for 2 hours, and allow to stand overnight. If a precipitate is formed, filter, wash thoroughly, and ignite. The weight of the precipitate should not be more than 0.0010 gram greater than the weight obtained in a complete blank test.

Calcium, magnesium, and R_2O_3 precipitate. To the filtrate, without washings, reserved from the test for *Insoluble matter*, add 10 ml. of ammonium oxalate reagent solution, 4 ml. of ammonium phosphate reagent solution, and 30 ml. of ammonium hydroxide solution, and allow to stand overnight. Filter, wash thoroughly with water containing 2.5 per cent ammonia and about 0.1 per cent ammonium oxalate, and ignite. The weight of the precipitate should not exceed 0.0020 gram.

Heavy metals. Dissolve 6 grams in about 10 ml. of water, add 15 ml. of 10 per cent hydrochloric acid, and dilute to 30 ml. For the control add 0.02 mg. of lead ion (Pb) to a 5-ml. aliquot of the solution and dilute to 25 ml. For the sample use the remaining 25-ml. portion. Adjust the pH of the control and sample solutions to between 3 and 4 (using a pH meter) with $1N$ acetic acid or ammonium hydroxide (10 per cent NH_3), dilute to 40 ml., and mix. Add 10 ml. of freshly prepared hydrogen sulfide water to each and mix. Any color in the solution of the sample should not exceed that in the control.

Iron. Dissolve 2 grams in about 40 ml. of water, add 2 ml. of hydrochloric acid, dilute to 50 ml., and add 30 to 50 mg. of ammonium persulfate crystals and 3 ml. of ammonium thiocyanate reagent solution. Any red color should not exceed that produced by 0.01 mg. of iron (Fe) in an equal volume of solution containing the quantities of reagents used in the test.

Sodium. Determine the sodium by the flame photometric method described on page 14.

Sample Solution A. Dissolve 1 gram in water and dilute to 100 ml.

Control Solution B. Dissolve 1 gram in water, add 0.10 mg. of sodium ion (Na), and dilute to 100 ml.

Observe the emission of Control Solution B at the 589-mμ sodium line. Observe the emission of Sample Solution A at the 589-mμ sodium line and at a wavelength of 580 mμ. The difference (D_1) between the intensities observed for Sample Solution A at 589 mμ and 580 mμ should not exceed the difference (D_2) observed at 589 mμ between Sample Solution A and Control Solution B.

Notes

Potassium Bicarbonate

KHCO$_3$ Formula Wt. 100.12

REQUIREMENTS

Assay.   Not less than 99.7 nor more than 100.3 per cent KHCO$_3$.
Insoluble matter.   Not more than 0.01 per cent.
Chloride (Cl).   Not more than 0.001 per cent.
Phosphate (PO$_4$).   Not more than 0.0005 per cent.
Sulfur compounds (as SO$_4$).   Not more than 0.003 per cent.
Ammonium (NH$_4$).   Not more than 0.0005 per cent.
Calcium, magnesium, and R$_2$O$_3$ precipitate.   Not more than 0.005 per cent.
Heavy metals (as Pb).   Not more than 0.0005 per cent.
Iron (Fe).   Not more than 0.0005 per cent.
Sodium (Na).   Not more than 0.03 per cent.

TESTS

Assay.   Weigh accurately about 3 grams, previously dried over sulfuric acid for 24 hours, dissolve it in 50 ml. of water, add methyl orange indicator solution, and titrate with 1N acid. The potassium bicarbonate calculated from the total alkalinity, as determined by the titration, should not be less than 99.7 nor more than 100.3 per cent of the weight taken. One milliliter of 1N acid corresponds to 0.1001 gram of KHCO$_3$.

Insoluble matter.   Dissolve 10 grams in 100 ml. of hot water, heat to boiling, and boil gently for 2 to 3 minutes. Digest in a covered beaker on the steam bath for 1 hour. Filter through a tared filtering crucible, other than glass, wash thoroughly, and dry at 105°C. The weight of the residue should not exceed 0.0010 gram.

Chloride.   Dissolve 1 gram in 20 ml. of water, filter if necessary through a chloride-free filter, neutralize with nitric acid, and add an excess of 1 ml. of nitric acid and 1 ml. of silver nitrate reagent solution. Any turbidity should not exceed that produced by 0.01 mg. of chloride ion (Cl) in an equal volume of solution containing the quantities of reagents used in the test.

Phosphate.   Dissolve 4 grams in 20 ml. of water, add 5 ml. of hydrochloric acid, and evaporate to dryness on the steam bath. Dissolve the residue in 25 ml. of approximately 0.5N sulfuric acid, add 1 ml. of ammonium molybdate reagent solution and 1 ml. of p-methylaminophenol sulfate reagent solution, and allow to stand for 2 hours at room temperature. Any blue color should not exceed that produced by 0.02 mg. of phosphate ion (PO$_4$) in an equal volume of solution containing the quantities of reagents used in the test, including the residue from the evaporation of 5 ml. of hydrochloric acid.

Sulfur compounds.   Dissolve 15 grams in 150 ml. of water, add 0.5 ml. of saturated bromine water, and heat to boiling. Cool, neutralize with hydrochloric acid, add an excess of 2 ml. of hydrochloric acid, and filter. Heat the filtrate to boiling, add 10 ml. of barium chloride reagent solution, digest in a covered beaker on the steam bath for 2 hours, and allow to stand overnight. If a precipitate is formed, filter, wash thoroughly, and ignite. The weight of the precipitate should not be more than 0.0010 gram greater than the weight obtained in a complete blank test.

Ammonium.   Dissolve 2 grams in 40 ml. of water, and add 10 ml. of 10 per cent sodium hydroxide reagent solution and 2 ml. of Nessler reagent solution. Any color should not exceed that produced by 0.01 mg. of ammonium ion (NH_4) in an equal volume of solution containing the quantities of reagents used in the test.

Calcium, magnesium, and R_2O_3 precipitate.   Dissolve 20 grams in 200 ml. of hot water, neutralize with hydrochloric acid, and add 0.5 ml. of the acid in excess. Filter, if necessary, add to the filtrate 5 ml. of ammonium oxalate reagent solution, 2 ml. of ammonium phosphate reagent solution, and 20 ml. of ammonium hydroxide, and allow to stand overnight. Filter, wash thoroughly with water containing 2.5 per cent ammonium hydroxide and about 0.1 per cent ammonium oxalate, ignite in a tared crucible, cool, and weigh. The weight of the residue should not exceed 0.0010 gram.

Heavy metals.   To 5 grams in a 150-ml. beaker add 10 ml. of water, mix, and add cautiously 10 ml. of hydrochloric acid. For the control dissolve 1 gram of the sample and 0.02 mg. of lead ion (Pb) in 10 ml. of water, and cautiously add 10 ml. of hydrochloric acid. Evaporate both solutions to dryness on the steam bath, dissolve each residue in about 20 ml. of water, and dilute to 25 ml. Adjust the pH of the control and sample solutions to between 3 and 4 (using a pH meter) with $1N$ acetic acid or ammonium hydroxide (10 per cent NH_3), dilute to 40 ml., and mix. Add 10 ml. of freshly prepared hydrogen sulfide water to each and mix. Any color in the solution of the sample should not exceed that in the control.

Iron.   Dissolve 2 grams in 20 ml. of water, cautiously add 5 ml. of hydrochloric acid, and dilute to 50 ml. Add 30 to 50 mg. of ammonium persulfate crystals and 3 ml. of ammonium thiocyanate reagent solution. Any red color should not exceed that produced by 0.01 mg. of iron (Fe) in an equal volume of solution containing 3 ml. of hydrochloric acid and the quantities of ammonium persulfate and thiocyanate used in the test.

Sodium. Determine the sodium by the flame photometric method described on page 14.

Sample Solution A. Dissolve 1 gram in 10 ml. of dilute hydrochloric acid $(1 + 1)$ and evaporate to dryness. Add 1 ml. of hydrochloric acid, dissolve in water, and dilute to 100 ml.

Control Solution B. Dissolve 1 gram plus 0.3 mg. of sodium ion (Na) in 10 ml. of dilute hydrochloric acid and evaporate to dryness. Add 1 ml. of dilute hydrochloric acid, dissolve in water, and dilute to 100 ml.

Observe the emission of Control Solution B at the 589-mμ sodium line. Observe the emission of Sample Solution A at the 589-mμ sodium line and at a wavelength of 580 mμ. The difference (D_1) between the intensities observed for Sample Solution A at 580 mμ and 589 mμ should not exceed the difference (D_2) observed at 589 mμ between Sample Solution A and Control Solution B.

Notes

Potassium Bromate

KBrO₃

KBrO$_3$ Formula Wt. 167.00

REQUIREMENTS

Assay. Not less than 99.8 per cent KBrO$_3$.

Insoluble matter. Not more than 0.005 per cent.

pH of a 5 per cent solution. From 5.0 to 9.0 at 25°C.

Bromide (Br). To pass test (limit about 0.05 per cent).

Nitrogen compounds (as N). Not more than 0.001 per cent.

Sulfate (SO$_4$). Not more than 0.005 per cent.

Heavy metals (as Pb). Not more than 0.0005 per cent.

Iron (Fe). Not more than 0.002 per cent.

Sodium (Na). Not more than 0.010 per cent.

TESTS

Assay. Dry a powdered sample to constant weight at 150°C. Weigh accurately about 1 gram, dissolve in water, and dilute to 250 ml. in a volumetric flask. To a 25-ml. aliquot of the solution add 3 grams of potassium iodide and 3 ml. of hydrochloric acid. Allow to stand for 5 minutes and titrate the liberated iodine with 0.1N sodium thiosulfate, adding starch indicator solution near the end point. Correct for a blank test. One milliliter of 0.1N sodium thiosulfate corresponds to 0.002783 gram of KBrO$_3$.

Insoluble matter. Dissolve 20 grams in 150 ml. of hot water, heat to boiling, and digest in a covered beaker on the steam bath for 1 hour. Filter through a tared filtering crucible, wash thoroughly, and dry at 105°C. The weight of the residue should not exceed 0.0010 gram.

pH of a 5 per cent solution. Dissolve 10 grams in carbon dioxide- and ammonia-free water. Determine the pH of the solution by the method described on page 18. The pH should be from 5.0 to 9.0 at 25°C. The pH of a 5 per cent solution of pure potassium bromate would be 7.0 at 25°C.

Bromide. Dissolve 4 grams in 80 ml. of water and divide the solution into two equal portions. Add 0.15 ml. of 1N sulfuric acid to one portion. At the end of 2 minutes this portion should show no more yellow color than the portion to which no acid was added.

Nitrogen compounds. Dissolve 1 gram in 40 ml. of water in a flask connected through a spray trap to a condenser, the end of which dips beneath the surface of 10 ml. of 0.1N hydrochloric acid. Add to the flask

10 ml. of freshly boiled 10 per cent sodium hydroxide reagent solution and about 0.5 gram of aluminum wire in small pieces, allow to stand for 1 hour, and slowly distill about 35 ml. To the distillate add 1 ml. of 10 per cent sodium hydroxide reagent solution, dilute to 50 ml., and add 2 ml. of Nessler reagent. Any color should not exceed that produced when a quantity of an ammonium salt containing 0.01 mg. of nitrogen (N) is treated exactly like the sample.

Sulfate. Dissolve 10 grams in 60 ml. of dilute hydrochloric acid $(1 + 1)$ and evaporate to dryness. Add 20 ml. of dilute hydrochloric acid $(1 + 1)$ and again evaporate to dryness. Dissolve the residue in 100 ml. of water, add 1 ml. of hydrochloric acid, filter, and heat to boiling. Add 5 ml. of barium chloride reagent solution, digest in a covered beaker on the steam bath for 2 hours, and allow to stand overnight. If a precipitate is formed, filter, wash thoroughly, and ignite. The weight of the precipitate should not be more than 0.0012 gram greater than the weight obtained in a complete blank test.

Heavy metals. Dissolve 5 grams in 20 ml. of dilute hydrochloric acid $(1 + 1)$. For the control dissolve 1 gram of the sample in 20 ml. of dilute hydrochloric acid $(1 + 1)$ and add 0.02 mg. of lead ion (Pb). Evaporate both solutions to dryness on the steam bath. Add 10 ml. more of dilute hydrochloric acid $(1 + 1)$ and again evaporate to dryness. Dissolve each in about 20 ml. of water and dilute to 25 ml. Adjust the pH of the control and sample solutions to between 3 and 4 (using a pH meter) with $1N$ acetic acid or ammonium hydroxide (10 per cent NH_3), dilute to 40 ml., and mix. Add 10 ml. of freshly prepared hydrogen sulfide water to each and mix. Any color in the solution of the sample should not exceed that in the control.

Iron. Dissolve 1 gram in 20 ml. of dilute hydrochloric acid $(1 + 1)$. For the control add 0.02 mg. of iron (Fe) to 20 ml. of dilute hydrochloric acid $(1 + 1)$. Evaporate both solutions to dryness on the steam bath. Add 10 ml. more of hydrochloric acid and again evaporate to dryness. Dissolve in water, add 4 ml. of hydrochloric acid, and dilute to 100 ml. To 50 ml. of each solution add 30 to 50 mg. of ammonium persulfate crystals and 3 ml. of ammonium thiocyanate reagent solution. Any red color in the solution of the sample should not exceed that in the control.

Sodium. Determine the sodium by the flame photometric method described on page 14. Dissolve 2 grams in 25 ml. of dilute hydrochloric acid $(1 + 3)$ and digest in a covered beaker on the steam bath until the reaction ceases. Uncover, evaporate to dryness, add 10 ml. of dilute hydrochloric acid $(1 + 3)$, and dilute to 100 ml. with dilute hydrochloric acid $(1 + 99)$.

Sample Solution A. Dilute a 50-ml. aliquot of this solution to 100 ml.

Control Solution B. Add 0.1 mg. of sodium ion (Na) to the remaining 50-ml. portion and dilute to 100 ml.

Observe the emission of Control Solution B at the 589-mμ sodium line. Observe the emission of Sample Solution A at the 589-mμ sodium line and at a wavelength of 580 mμ. The difference (D_1) between the intensities observed for Sample Solution A at 580 mμ and 589 mμ should not exceed the difference (D_2) observed at 589 mμ between Sample Solution A and Control Solution B.

Notes

Potassium Bromide

KBr   Formula Wt. 119.01

REQUIREMENTS

Insoluble matter.   Not more than 0.005 per cent.
pH of a 5 per cent solution.   From 5.0 to 8.8 at 25°C.
Bromate (BrO_3).   To pass test (limit about 0.001 per cent).
Chloride (Cl).   Not more than 0.20 per cent.
Nitrogen compounds (as N).   Not more than 0.001 per cent.
Sulfate (SO_4).   Not more than 0.005 per cent.
Barium (Ba).   Not more than 0.002 per cent.
Calcium, magnesium, and R_2O_3 precipitate.   Not more than 0.005 per cent.
Heavy metals (as Pb).   Not more than 0.0005 per cent.
Iron (Fe).   Not more than 0.0005 per cent.
Sodium (Na).   Not more than 0.020 per cent.

TESTS

Insoluble matter.   Dissolve 20 grams in 150 ml. of water, heat to boiling, and digest in a covered beaker on the steam bath for 1 hour. Filter through a tared filtering crucible, wash thoroughly, and dry at 105°C. The weight of the residue should not exceed 0.0010 gram. Save the filtrate separate from the washings for the test for *Calcium, magnesium, and R_2O_3 precipitate*.

pH of a 5 per cent solution.   Dissolve 10 grams in 200 ml. of carbon dioxide- and ammonia-free water. Determine the pH by the method described on page 18. The pH should be from 5.0 to 8.8 at 25°C. The pH of a 5 per cent solution of pure potassium bromide would be 7.0 at 25°C.

Bromate.   Dissolve 1 gram in 10 ml. of freshly boiled and cooled water, and add 0.10 ml. of 10 per cent potassium iodide reagent solution, 1 ml. of starch indicator solution, and 0.25 ml. of 1N sulfuric acid. No blue or violet color should be produced after standing 10 minutes at 25°C.

Chloride.   Dissolve 0.5 gram in 15 ml. of dilute nitric acid (1 + 2) in a small flask. Add 3 ml. of 30 per cent hydrogen peroxide and digest on the steam bath until the solution is colorless. Wash down the sides of the flask with a little water, digest for an additional 15 minutes, cool, and dilute to 200 ml. Dilute a 2-ml. aliquot to 20 ml. and add 1 ml. of nitric acid and 1 ml. of silver nitrate reagent solution. Any turbidity should not exceed that produced by 0.01 mg. of chloride ion (Cl) in an equal volume of solution containing the quantities of reagents used in the test.

Nitrogen compounds. Dissolve 1 gram in 60 ml. of water in a flask connected through a spray trap to a condenser, the end of which dips beneath the surface of 10 ml. of $0.1N$ hydrochloric acid. Add to the flask 20 ml. of freshly boiled 10 per cent sodium hydroxide reagent solution and about 0.5 gram of aluminum wire in small pieces, allow to stand for 1 hour, and slowly distill about 35 ml. To the distillate add 1 ml. of 10 per cent sodium hydroxide reagent solution, dilute to 50 ml., and add 2 ml. of Nessler reagent. Any color should not exceed that produced when a quantity of ammonium salt containing 0.01 mg. of nitrogen (N) is treated exactly like the sample.

Sulfate. Dissolve 10 grams in 100 ml. of water, filter if necessary, and add 1 ml. of hydrochloric acid. Bring to a boil, add 5 ml. of barium chloride reagent solution, digest in a covered beaker on the steam bath for 2 hours, and allow to stand overnight. If a precipitate is formed, filter, wash thoroughly, and ignite. The weight of the precipitate should not be more than 0.0012 gram greater than the weight obtained in a complete blank test.

Barium. For the sample dissolve 6 grams in 15 ml. of water. For the control dissolve 1 gram in 15 ml. of water and add 0.10 mg. of barium ion (Ba). To each solution add 5 ml. of acetic acid, 5 ml. of 30 per cent hydrogen peroxide, and 1 ml. of hydrochloric acid. Digest in a covered beaker on the steam bath until reaction ceases, uncover, and evaporate to dryness. Dissolve the residues in 15 ml. of water, filter if necessary, and dilute to 23 ml. Add 2 ml. of 10 per cent potassium dichromate reagent solution and add ammonium hydroxide until the orange color is just dissipated and the yellow color persists. Add 25 ml. of methanol, stir vigorously, and allow to stand for 10 minutes. The turbidity in the solution of the sample should not exceed that in the control.

Calcium, magnesium, and R_2O_3 precipitate. To the filtrate from the test for *Insoluble matter* add 5 ml. of ammonium oxalate reagent solution, 2 ml. of ammonium phosphate reagent solution, and 10 ml. of ammonium hydroxide. Allow to stand overnight, filter, wash with water containing 2.5 per cent ammonia and about 0.1 per cent ammonium oxalate, and ignite. The weight of the residue should not exceed 0.0010 gram.

Heavy metals. Dissolve 6 grams in about 20 ml. of water and dilute to 30 ml. For the control add 0.02 mg. of lead ion (Pb) to a 5-ml. aliquot of the solution and dilute to 25 ml. For the sample use the remaining 25-ml. portion. Adjust the pH of the control and sample solutions to between 3 and 4 (using a pH meter) with $1N$ acetic acid or ammonium hydroxide (10 per cent NH_3), dilute to 40 ml. and mix. Add 10 ml. of

freshly prepared hydrogen sulfide water to each and mix. Any color in the solution of the sample should not exceed that in the control.

Iron.   Dissolve 2 grams in 40 ml. of water plus 2 ml. of hydrochloric acid, and dilute to 50 ml. Add 30 to 50 mg. of ammonium persulfate crystals and 3 ml. of ammonium thiocyanate reagent solution. Any red color should not exceed that produced by 0.01 mg. of iron (Fe) in an equal volume of solution containing the quantities of reagents used in the test.

Sodium.   Determine the sodium by the flame photometric method described on page 14.

Sample Solution A.   Dissolve 1 gram in water and dilute to 100 ml.

Control Solution B.   Dissolve 1 gram in water, add 0.20 mg. of sodium ion (Na), and dilute to 100 ml.

Observe the emission of Control Solution B at the 589-mμ sodium line. Observe the emission of Sample Solution A at the 589-mμ sodium line and at a wavelength of 580 mμ. The difference (D_1) between the intensities observed for Sample Solution A at 589 mμ and 580 mμ should not exceed the difference (D_2) observed at 589 mμ between Sample Solution A and Control Solution B.

Notes

Potassium Carbonate, Anhydrous

K₂CO₃   Formula Wt. 138.21

REQUIREMENTS

Insoluble matter.   Not more than 0.010 per cent.
Loss on heating at 285°C.   Not more than 1.0 per cent.
Chloride and chlorate (as Cl).   To pass test (limit about 0.003 per cent).
Nitrogen compounds (as N).   Not more than 0.001 per cent.
Phosphate (PO₄).   Not more than 0.001 per cent.
Silica (SiO₂).   Not more than 0.005 per cent.
Sulfur compounds (as SO₄).   Not more than 0.004 per cent.
Ammonium hydroxide precipitate.   Not more than 0.010 per cent.
Calcium and magnesium precipitate.   Not more than 0.010 per cent.
Arsenic (As).   Not more than 0.0001 per cent.
Heavy metals (as Pb).   Not more than 0.0005 per cent.
Iron (Fe).   Not more than 0.0005 per cent.
Sodium (Na).   Not more than 0.020 per cent.

TESTS

Insoluble matter.   Dissolve 10 grams in 100 ml. of water, heat to boiling, and digest in a covered beaker on the steam bath for 1 hour. Filter through a tared porous porcelain or a platinum filtering crucible, wash thoroughly, and dry at 105°C. The weight of the residue should not exceed 0.0010 gram.

Loss on heating at 285°C.   Weigh accurately about 2 grams and heat to constant weight at 270° to 300°C. The loss in weight should not exceed 1.0 per cent of the weight of the sample.

Chloride and chlorate.   Ignite 1 gram at 800° ± 25°C. Dissolve the residue in about 40 ml. of water plus 6 ml. of nitric acid. Filter through a chloride-free filter, wash, and dilute the filtrate to 60 ml. To a 20-ml. aliquot add 1 ml. of silver nitrate reagent solution. Any turbidity should not exceed that produced by 0.01 mg. of chloride ion (Cl) in an equal volume of solution containing the quantities of reagents used in the test.

Nitrogen compounds.   Dissolve 1 gram in 60 ml. of water in a flask connected through a spray trap to a condenser, the end of which dips beneath the surface of 10 ml. of 0.1N hydrochloric acid. Add to the flask 10 ml. of freshly boiled 10 per cent sodium hydroxide reagent solution and 0.5 gram of aluminum wire in small pieces, allow to stand for 1 hour, and slowly distill about 35 ml. To the distillate add 1 ml. of 10 per cent sodium hydroxide reagent solution, dilute to 50 ml., and add 2 ml. of

Nessler reagent. Any color should not exceed that produced when a quantity of an ammonium salt containing 0.01 mg. of nitrogen (N) is treated exactly like the sample.

Phosphate. Dissolve 1 gram in 50 ml. of water in a platinum dish and digest on the steam bath for 30 minutes. Cool, neutralize with dilute sulfuric acid (1 + 19) to a pH of about 4, and dilute to about 75 ml. Prepare a standard containing 0.01 mg. of phosphate ion (PO_4) and 0.05 mg. of silica (SiO_2) in about 85 ml. Add 0.5 gram of ammonium molybdate to each solution, and when it is dissolved, adjust the pH to 1.8 (using a pH meter) with dilute hydrochloric acid (1 + 9). Heat the solutions to boiling, cool to room temperature, add 10 ml. of hydrochloric acid, and dilute to 100 ml. Transfer the solutions to separatory funnels, add 35 ml. of ether to each, shake vigorously, and allow to separate. Draw off the aqueous phase and reserve it for the determination of *Silica*. Wash the ether phase by shaking with 10 ml. of dilute hydrochloric acid (1 + 9), allow to separate, and draw off and discard the aqueous phase. Add 0.2 ml. of a freshly prepared 2 per cent solution of stannous chloride in hydrochloric acid to the ether and shake. Any blue color in the solution of the sample should not exceed that in the standard. If the ether extracts are turbid, wash them with 10 ml. of dilute hydrochloric acid (1 + 9).

Silica. Add 10 ml. of hydrochloric acid to the solutions reserved from the determination of *Phosphate* and transfer to separatory funnels. Add 40 ml. of butanol, shake vigorously, and allow to separate. Draw off and discard the aqueous phase. Wash the butanol three times with 20-ml. portions of dilute hydrochloric acid (1 + 99), discarding the washings each time. Dilute each butanol solution to 50 ml., take a 10-ml. aliquot from each, and dilute each to 50 ml. with butanol. Add 0.5 ml. of a freshly prepared 2 per cent solution of stannous chloride in hydrochloric acid. The blue color in the extract from the sample should not exceed that in the control. If the butanol extracts are turbid, wash them with 10 ml. of dilute hydrochloric acid (1 + 99).

Sulfur compounds. Dissolve 10 grams in 100 ml. of water, add 0.25 ml. of saturated bromine water, and boil. Cool, neutralize with hydrochloric acid, add an excess of 1 ml., and filter. Boil the filtrate, add 5 ml. of barium chloride reagent solution, digest in a covered beaker on the steam bath for 2 hours, and allow to stand overnight. If a precipitate is formed, filter, wash thoroughly, and ignite. The weight of the precipitate should not be more than 0.0010 gram greater than the weight obtained in a complete blank test.

Ammonium hydroxide precipitate. Dissolve 10 grams in 100 ml. of water. Cautiously add 12 ml. of sulfuric acid to 12 ml. of water, cool, add the mixture to the solution of the sample, and evaporate to dense fumes. Cool, dissolve the residue in 130 ml. of hot water, and add ammonium hydroxide until the solution is just alkaline to methyl red. Heat to boiling and filter, reserving the filtrate and washings for the test for *Calcium and magnesium*. Continue to wash the precipitate, but reject the washings, and finally ignite. The weight of the residue should not exceed 0.0010 gram. The residue includes some, but not all, of the silica in the sample.

Calcium and magnesium precipitate. To the filtrate from the test for *Ammonium hydroxide precipitate* add 0.5 ml. of hydrochloric acid, 5 ml. of ammonium oxalate reagent solution, 2 ml. of ammonium phosphate reagent solution, and 10 ml. of ammonium hydroxide. Allow to stand overnight. If any precipitate is formed, filter, wash with water containing 2.5 per cent of ammonia and about 0.1 per cent of ammonium oxalate, and ignite. The weight of the residue should not exceed 0.0010 gram.

Arsenic. Dissolve 3 grams in 20 to 30 ml. of water, acidify with sulfuric or hydrochloric acid, and determine arsenic by the Gutzeit method (page 11). The stain should not exceed that produced by 0.003 mg. of arsenic (As).

Heavy metals. To 5 grams in a 150-ml. beaker add 10 ml. of water, mix, and cautiously add 10 ml. of hydrochloric acid. For the control dissolve 1 gram of the sample in 10 ml. of water, add 0.02 mg. of lead ion (Pb) and cautiously add 10 ml. of hydrochloric acid. Evaporate both solutions to dryness on the steam bath, dissolve each residue in about 20 ml. of water, and dilute to 25 ml. Adjust the pH of the control and sample solutions to between 3 and 4 (using a pH meter) with $1N$ acetic acid or ammonium hydroxide (10 per cent NH_3), dilute to 40 ml., and mix. Add 10 ml. of freshly prepared hydrogen sulfide water to each and mix. Any color in the solution of the sample should not exceed that in the control.

Iron. Dissolve 2 grams in 30 ml. of water plus 4 ml. of hydrochloric acid and dilute to 50 ml. Add 30 to 50 mg. of ammonium persulfate crystals and 3 ml. of ammonium thiocyanate reagent solution. Any red color should not exceed that produced by 0.01 mg. of iron (Fe) in an equal volume of solution containing the quantities of reagents used in the test.

Sodium. Determine the sodium by the flame photometric method described on page 14.

Sample Solution A. Dissolve 1 gram in water and dilute to 100 ml.

Control Solution B. Dissolve 1 gram in water, add 0.20 mg. of sodium ion (Na), and dilute to 100 ml.

Observe the emission of Control Solution B at the 589-mμ sodium line. Observe the emission of Sample Solution A at the 589-mμ sodium line and at a wavelength of 580 mμ. The difference (D_1) between the intensities observed for Sample Solution A at 589 mμ and 580 mμ should not exceed the difference (D_2) observed at 589 mμ between Sample Solution A and Control Solution B.

Notes

Potassium Carbonate, Crystals

$K_2CO_3 \cdot 1\frac{1}{2} H_2O$ Formula Wt. 165.24

REQUIREMENTS

Insoluble matter.   Not more than 0.010 per cent.
Loss on heating at 285°C.   Not less than 14.0 nor more than 16.5 per cent.
Chloride and chlorate (as Cl).   To pass test (limit about 0.003 per cent).
Nitrogen compounds (as N).   Not more than 0.001 per cent.
Phosphate (PO_4).   Not more than 0.001 per cent.
Silica (SiO_2).   Not more than 0.005 per cent.
Sulfur compounds (as SO_4).   Not more than 0.004 per cent.
Ammonium hydroxide precipitate.   Not more than 0.010 per cent.
Calcium and magnesium precipitate.   Not more than 0.010 per cent.
Arsenic (As).   Not more than 0.00005 per cent.
Heavy metals (as Pb).   Not more than 0.0005 per cent.
Iron (Fe).   Not more than 0.0005 per cent.
Sodium (Na).   Not more than 0.020 per cent.

TESTS

Insoluble matter.   Dissolve 10 grams in 100 ml. of water, heat to boiling, and digest in a covered beaker on the steam bath for 1 hour. Filter through a tared porous porcelain or a platinum filtering crucible, wash thoroughly, and dry at 105°C. The weight of the residue should not exceed 0.0010 gram.

Loss on heating at 285°C.   Weigh accurately about 2 grams and heat to constant weight at 270° to 300°C. The loss in weight should not be less than 14.0 nor more than 16.5 per cent of the weight of the sample.

Chloride and chlorate.   Ignite 1 gram at 800° ± 25°C. Dissolve the residue in about 40 ml. of water plus 6 ml. of nitric acid. Filter through a chloride-free filter, wash, and dilute the filtrate to 60 ml. To a 20-ml. aliquot add 1 ml. of silver nitrate reagent solution. Any turbidity should not exceed that produced by 0.01 mg. of chloride ion (Cl) in an equal volume of solution containing the quantities of reagents used in the test.

Nitrogen compounds.   Dissolve 1 gram in 60 ml. of water in a flask connected through a spray trap to a condenser, the end of which dips beneath the surface of 10 ml. of 0.1N hydrochloric acid. Add to the flask 10 ml. of freshly boiled 10 per cent sodium hydroxide reagent solution and 0.5 gram of aluminum wire in small pieces, allow to stand for 1 hour, and slowly distill about 35 ml. To the distillate add 1 ml. of 10 per cent sodium hydroxide reagent solution, dilute to 50 ml., and add 2 ml. of Nessler reagent. Any color should not exceed that produced when a quantity of an ammonium salt containing 0.01 mg. of nitrogen (N) is treated exactly like the sample.

Phosphate. Dissolve 1 gram in 50 ml. of water in a platinum dish and digest on the steam bath for 30 minutes. Cool, neutralize with dilute sulfuric acid (1 + 19) to a pH of about 4, and dilute to about 75 ml. Prepare a standard containing 0.01 mg. of phosphate ion (PO_4) and 0.05 mg. of silica (SiO_2) in about 85 ml. Add 0.5 gram of ammonium molybdate to each solution, and when it is dissolved, adjust the pH to 1.8 (using a pH meter) with dilute hydrochloric acid (1 + 9). Heat the solutions to boiling, cool to room temperature, add 10 ml. of hydrochloric acid, and dilute to 100 ml. Transfer the solutions to separatory funnels, add 35 ml. of ether to each, shake vigorously, and allow to separate. Draw off the aqueous phase and save it for the determination of *Silica*. Wash the ether phase by shaking with 10 ml. of dilute hydrochloric acid (1 + 9), allow to separate, and draw off and discard the aqueous phase. Add 0.2 ml. of a freshly prepared 2 per cent solution of stannous chloride in hydrochloric acid to the ether and shake. Any blue color in the solution of the sample should not exceed that in the standard. If the ether extracts are turbid, wash them with 10 ml. of dilute hydrochloric acid (1 + 9).

Silica. Add 10 ml. of hydrochloric acid to the solutions reserved from the determination of *Phosphate* and transfer to separatory funnels. Add 40 ml. of butyl alcohol, shake vigorously, and allow to separate. Draw off and discard the aqueous phase. Wash the butyl alcohol three times with 20-ml. portions of dilute hydrochloric acid (1 + 99), discarding the washings each time. Dilute the butyl alcohol solutions to 50 ml., take a 10-ml. aliquot of each, and dilute each to 50 ml. with butyl alcohol. Add 0.2 ml. of a freshly prepared 2 per cent solution of stannous chloride in hydrochloric acid. The blue color in the extract from the sample should not exceed that in the control. If the butyl alcohol extracts are turbid, wash them with 10 ml. of dilute hydrochloric acid (1 + 99).

Sulfur compounds. Dissolve 10 grams in 100 ml. of water, add 0.25 ml. of saturated bromine water, and boil. Cool, neutralize with hydrochloric acid, add an excess of 1 ml., and filter. Boil the filtrate, add 5 ml. of barium chloride reagent solution, digest in a covered beaker on the steam bath for 2 hours, and allow to stand overnight. If a precipitate is formed, filter, wash thoroughly, and ignite. The weight of the precipitate should not be more than 0.0010 gram greater than the weight obtained in a complete blank test.

Ammonium hydroxide precipitate. Dissolve 10 grams in 100 ml. of water. Cautiously add 12 ml. of sulfuric acid to 12 ml. of water, cool, add the mixture to the solution of the sample, and evaporate to strong fuming. Cool, dissolve the residue in 130 ml. of hot water, and add ammonium hydroxide until the solution is just alkaline to methyl red. Heat to boiling and filter, reserving the filtrate without the washings for the test for *Calcium and magnesium precipitate.* Wash with hot water, rejecting the washings, and ignite. The weight of the residue should not exceed 0.0010 gram. The residue includes some, but not all, of the silica in the sample.

Calcium and magnesium precipitate. To the filtrate from the test for *Ammonium hydroxide precipitate* add 0.5 ml. of hydrochloric acid, 5 ml. of ammonium oxalate reagent solution, 2 ml. of ammonium phosphate reagent solution, and 10 ml. of ammonium hydroxide. Allow to stand overnight. If any precipitate is formed, filter, wash with water containing 2.5 per cent of ammonia and about 0.1 per cent of ammonium oxalate, and ignite. The weight of the residue should not exceed 0.0010 gram.

Arsenic. Dissolve 6 grams in 20 to 30 ml. of water, acidify with sulfuric or hydrochloric acid, and determine arsenic by the Gutzeit method (page 11). Any stain should not exceed that produced by 0.003 mg. of arsenic (As).

Heavy metals. To 5 grams in a 150-ml. beaker add 10 ml. of water, mix, and add cautiously 10 ml. of hydrochloric acid. For the control dissolve 1 gram of the sample in 10 ml. of water, add 0.02 mg. of lead ion (Pb), and cautiously add 10 ml. of hydrochloric acid. Evaporate both solutions to dryness on the steam bath, dissolve each residue in about 20 ml. of water, and dilute to 25 ml. Adjust the pH of the control and sample solutions to between 3 and 4 (using a pH meter) with $1N$ acetic acid or ammonium hydroxide (10 per cent NH_3), dilute to 40 ml., and mix. Add 10 ml. of freshly prepared hydrogen sulfide water to each and mix. Any color in the solution of the sample should not exceed that in the control.

Iron. Dissolve 2 grams in 30 ml. of water plus 4 ml. of hydrochloric acid and dilute to 50 ml. Add 30 to 50 mg. of ammonium persulfate crystals and 3 ml. of ammonium thiocyanate reagent solution. Any red color should not exceed that produced by 0.01 mg. of iron (Fe) in an equal volume of solution containing the quantities of reagents used in the test.

Sodium. Determine the sodium by the flame photometric method described on page 14.

Sample Solution A. Dissolve 1 gram in water and dilute to 100 ml.

Control Solution B. Dissolve 1 gram in water, add 0.20 mg. of sodium ion (Na), and dilute to 100 ml.

Observe the emission of Control Solution B at the 589-mμ sodium line. Observe the emission of Sample Solution A at the 589-mμ sodium line and at a wavelength of 580 mμ. The difference (D_1) between the intensities observed for Sample Solution A at 589 mμ and 580 mμ should not exceed the difference (D_2) observed at 589 mμ between Sample Solution A and Control Solution B.

Notes

Potassium Chlorate

$KClO_3$ Formula Wt. 122.55

REQUIREMENTS

Insoluble matter. Not more than 0.005 per cent.
Bromate (BrO_3). Not more than 0.015 per cent.
Chloride (Cl). Not more than 0.001 per cent.
Nitrogen compounds (as N). Not more than 0.001 per cent.
Sulfate (SO_4). To pass test (limit about 0.002 per cent).
Arsenic (As). Not more than 0.00005 per cent.
Calcium, magnesium, and R_2O_3 precipitate. Not more than 0.005 per cent.
Heavy metals (as Pb). Not more than 0.0005 per cent.
Iron (Fe). Not more than 0.0003 per cent.
Sodium (Na). Not more than 0.010 per cent.

TESTS

Insoluble matter. Dissolve 20 grams in 250 ml. of water, heat to boiling, and digest in a covered beaker on the steam bath for 1 hour. Filter through a tared filtering crucible, wash thoroughly with hot water, and dry at 105°C. The weight of the residue should not exceed 0.0010 gram.

Bromate. Dissolve 4 grams in 200 ml. of freshly boiled and cooled water in a glass-stoppered flask, and at the same time prepare a blank of the same volume of water. To the solution of the sample and to the blank solution add 10 ml. of 1N hydrochloric acid, mix well, and add 10 ml. of freshly prepared 10 per cent potassium iodide reagent solution and 5 ml. of starch indicator solution. Stopper the flasks, set aside for 1 hour in a dark place, and titrate the liberated iodine with 0.1N sodium thiosulfate. The volume of thiosulfate solution required for the sample should not be more than 0.3 ml. greater than the volume required for the blank.

Chloride. Dissolve 2 grams in 40 ml. of warm water, and filter if necessary through a chloride-free filter. Add 0.25 ml. of nitric acid, free from lower oxides of nitrogen, and 1 ml. of silver nitrate reagent solution. Any turbidity should not exceed that produced by 0.02 mg. of chloride ion (Cl) in an equal volume of solution containing the quantities of reagents used in the test.

Nitrogen compounds. Dissolve 1 gram in 60 ml. of water in a flask connected through a spray trap to a condenser, the end of which dips beneath the surface of 10 ml. of 0.1N hydrochloric acid. Add to the flask 10 ml. of freshly boiled 10 per cent sodium hydroxide reagent solution and 0.5 gram of aluminum wire in small pieces, allow to stand for 1 hour, and slowly distill about 35 ml. To the distillate add 1 ml. of 10 per cent sodium hydroxide reagent solution, dilute to 50 ml., and add 2 ml. of Nessler reagent. Any color should not exceed that produced when a quantity of an ammonium salt containing 0.01 mg. of nitrogen (N) is treated exactly like the sample.

Sulfate. Dissolve 5 grams in 150 ml. of water, filter if necessary, and add 1 ml. of 10 per cent hydrochloric acid reagent solution and 5 ml. of barium chloride reagent solution. No precipitate should be produced on standing overnight.

Arsenic. Dissolve 4 grams in 30 ml. of dilute hydrochloric acid $(1+1)$ and evaporate to dryness on the steam bath. Test the residue by the Gutzeit method (page 11). The amount of stain should not exceed that produced by 0.002 mg. of arsenic (As).

Calcium, magnesium, and R_2O_3 precipitate. Dissolve 10 grams in 75 ml. of dilute hydrochloric acid $(1+2)$ and boil gently until no more chlorine is evolved. Dilute to about 80 ml., filter if necessary, heat to boiling, and add 5 ml. of ammonium oxalate reagent solution, 2 ml. of ammonium phosphate reagent solution, and 15 ml. of ammonium hydroxide. Allow to stand overnight, filter, wash with water containing 2.5 per cent of ammonia and about 0.1 per cent of ammonium oxalate, and ignite. The weight of the residue should not exceed 0.0005 gram.

Heavy metals. Dissolve 5 grams in 20 ml. of dilute hydrochloric acid $(1+1)$. For the control dissolve 1 gram of the sample in 20 ml. of dilute hydrochloric acid $(1+1)$ and add 0.02 mg. of lead ion (Pb). Evaporate both solutions to dryness on the steam bath, then add 5 ml. more of dilute hydrochloric acid $(1+1)$ to each, and again evaporate to dryness. Dissolve each residue in about 20 ml. of water and dilute to 25 ml. Adjust the pH of the control and sample solutions to between 3 and 4 (using a pH meter) with $1N$ acetic acid or ammonium hydroxide (10 per cent NH_3), dilute to 40 ml., and mix. Add 10 ml. of freshly prepared hydrogen sulfide water to each and mix. Any color in the solution of the sample should not exceed that in the control.

Iron. Dissolve 5 grams in 20 ml. of dilute hydrochloric acid $(1+1)$ and evaporate to dryness on the steam bath. Add 5 ml. of dilute hydrochloric acid $(1+1)$ and again evaporate to dryness. Dissolve in 50 ml. of dilute hydrochloric acid $(1+25)$ and add 30 to 50 mg. of ammonium persulfate crystals and 3 ml. of ammonium thiocyanate reagent solution. Any red color should not exceed that produced by 0.015 mg. of iron (Fe) in an equal volume of solution containing the quantities of reagents used in the test, including the residue from evaporation of 15 ml. of hydrochloric acid.

Sodium. Determine the sodium by the flame photometric method described on page 14. Dissolve 2 grams in 25 ml. of dilute hydrochloric acid $(1 + 3)$ and digest in a covered beaker on the steam bath until the reaction ceases. Uncover the beaker and evaporate to dryness. Add 10 ml. of dilute hydrochloric acid $(1 + 3)$ and again evaporate to dryness. Dissolve in dilute hydrochloric acid $(1 + 99)$ and dilute to 100 ml. with dilute hydrochloric acid $(1 + 99)$.

Sample Solution A. Dilute 50 ml. (1 gram) of this solution to 100 ml.

Control Solution B. Add 0.10 mg. of sodium ion (Na) to the remaining 50-ml. portion and dilute to 100 ml.

Observe the emission of Control Solution B at the 589-mμ sodium line. Observe the emission of Sample Solution A at the 589-mμ sodium line and at a wavelength of 580 mμ. The difference (D_1) between the intensities observed for Sample Solution A at 580 mμ and 589 mμ should not exceed the difference (D_2) observed at 589 mμ between Sample Solution A and Control Solution B.

Notes

Potassium Chloride

KCl

Formula Wt. 74.56

REQUIREMENTS

Insoluble matter.   Not more than 0.005 per cent.
pH of a 5 per cent solution.   From 5.4 to 8.6 at 25°C.
Iodide (I).   Not more than 0.002 per cent.
Bromide (Br).   To pass test (limit about 0.01 per cent).
Chlorate and nitrate (as NO_3).   Not more than 0.003 per cent.
Nitrogen compounds (as N).   Not more than 0.001 per cent.
Phosphate (PO_4).   Not more than 0.0005 per cent.
Sulfate (SO_4).   Not more than 0.001 per cent.
Barium (Ba).   To pass test (limit about 0.001 per cent).
Calcium, magnesium, and R_2O_3 precipitate.   Not more than 0.005 per cent.
Heavy metals (as Pb).   Not more than 0.0005 per cent.
Iron (Fe).   Not more than 0.0003 per cent.
Sodium (Na).   Not more than 0.005 per cent.

TESTS

Insoluble matter.   Dissolve 20 grams in 150 ml. of water, heat to boiling, and digest in a covered beaker on the steam bath for 1 hour. Filter through a tared filtering crucible, wash thoroughly, and dry at 105°C. The weight of the residue should not exceed 0.0010 gram. Save the filtrate separate from the washings for the test for *Calcium, magnesium, and R₂O₃ precipitate.*

pH of a 5 per cent solution.   Dissolve 10 grams in 200 ml. of carbon dioxide- and ammonia-free water. Determine the pH by the method described on page 18. The pH should be from 5.4 to 8.6 at 25°C. The pH of a 5 per cent solution of pure potassium chloride would be 7.0 at 25°C.

Iodide.   Dissolve 11 grams in 50 ml. of water. Prepare a control by dissolving 1 gram of the sample, 0.2 mg. of iodide ion (I), and 1 mg. of bromide ion (Br) in 50 ml. of water. To each solution, in a separatory funnel, add 2 ml. of hydrochloric acid and 5 ml. of ferric chloride reagent solution. Allow to stand for 5 minutes. Add 10 ml. of carbon tetrachloride, shake for 1 minute, allow the phases to separate, and draw off the carbon tetrachloride layer. Reserve the water solution for the test for *Bromide.* Any violet color in the carbon tetrachloride extract from the solution of the sample should not exceed that in the extract from the control.

Bromide. Treat both the solution of the sample and the control obtained in the test for *Iodide* as follows: wash twice by shaking with 10-ml. portions of carbon tetrachloride. Each time allow to separate, then draw off and discard the carbon tetrachloride. To each of the water solutions add 10 ml. of water, 65 ml. of cold dilute sulfuric acid (1 + 1), and 15 ml. of a solution of chromic acid prepared by dissolving 10 grams in 100 ml. of dilute sulfuric acid (1 + 3). Allow to stand for 5 minutes. Add 10 ml. of carbon tetrachloride, shake for 1 minute, allow to settle, and draw off. (Half a 7-cm. piece of filter paper rolled and placed in the stem of the separatory funnel will absorb any of the aqueous solution that may pass the stopcock, and thus assure a clear extract.) Any yellow-brown color in the carbon tetrachloride extract from the solution of the sample should not exceed that in the extract from the control.

Chlorate and nitrate.

Sample Solution A. Dissolve 0.5 gram in 3 ml. of water by heating in a boiling water bath. Dilute to 50 ml. with brucine sulfate reagent solution.

Control Solution B. Dissolve 0.5 gram in 1.5 ml. of water and 1.5 ml. of the standard nitrate solution containing 0.01 mg. of nitrate ion (NO_3) per ml. by heating in a boiling water bath. Dilute to 50 ml. with brucine sulfate reagent solution.

Blank Solution B. Use 50 ml. of brucine sulfate reagent solution.

Heat the three solutions in a preheated (boiling) water bath for 10 minutes. Cool rapidly in an ice bath to room temperature. Set a spectrophotometer at 410 mμ and, using 1-cm. cells, adjust the instrument to read 0 absorbance with Blank Solution C in the light path, then determine the absorbance of Sample Solution A. Adjust the instrument to read 0 absorbance with Sample Solution A in the light path and determine the absorbance of Control Solution B. The absorbance of Sample Solution A should not exceed that of Control Solution B.

Nitrogen compounds. Dissolve 1 gram in 60 ml. of water in a flask connected through a spray trap to a condenser, the end of which dips beneath the surface of 10 ml. of 0.1N hydrochloric acid. Add to the flask 10 ml. of 10 per cent sodium hydroxide reagent solution and 0.5 gram of aluminum wire in small pieces, allow to stand for 1 hour, and slowly distill about 35 ml. To the distillate add 1 ml. of 10 per cent sodium hydroxide reagent solution, dilute to 50 ml., and add 2 ml. of Nessler reagent. Any color should not exceed that produced when a quantity of an ammonium salt containing 0.01 mg. of nitrogen (N) is treated exactly like the sample.

Phosphate. Dissolve 4 grams in 25 ml. of approximately $0.5N$ sulfuric acid, add 1 ml. of ammonium molybdate reagent solution and 1 ml. of *p*-methylaminophenol sulfate reagent solution, and allow to stand at room temperature for 2 hours. Any blue color should not exceed that produced by 0.02 mg. of phosphate ion (PO_4) in an equal volume of solution containing the quantities of reagents used in the test.

Sulfate. Dissolve 25 grams in 200 ml. of water, add 2 ml. of hydrochloric acid, heat to boiling, add 10 ml. of barium chloride reagent solution, digest in a covered beaker on the steam bath for 2 hours, and allow to stand overnight. If a precipitate is formed, filter, wash thoroughly, and ignite. The weight of the precipitate should not be more than 0.0006 gram greater than the weight obtained in a complete blank test.

Barium. Dissolve 4 grams in 20 ml. of water, filter if necessary, and divide into two portions. To one portion add 2 ml. of 10 per cent sulfuric acid reagent solution and to the other 2 ml. of water. The solutions should be equally clear at the end of 2 hours.

Calcium, magnesium, and R$_2$O$_3$ precipitate. To the filtrate from the test for *Insoluble matter* add 5 ml. of ammonium oxalate reagent solution, 2 ml. of ammonium phosphate reagent solution, and 10 ml. of ammonium hydroxide. Allow to stand overnight. Filter, wash with water containing 2.5 per cent ammonia and about 0.1 per cent ammonium oxalate, and ignite. The weight of the residue should not exceed 0.0010 gram.

Heavy metals. Dissolve 6 grams in about 20 ml. of water and dilute to 30 ml. For the control add 0.02 mg. of lead ion (Pb) to a 5-ml. aliquot of the solution and dilute to 25 ml. For the sample use the remaining 25-ml. portion. Adjust the pH of the control and sample solutions to between 3 and 4 (using a pH meter) with $1N$ acetic acid or ammonium hydroxide (10 per cent NH$_3$), dilute to 40 ml., and mix. Add 10 ml. of freshly prepared hydrogen sulfide water to each and mix. Any color in the solution of the sample should not exceed that in the control.

Iron. Dissolve 5 grams in 30 ml. of water plus 2 ml. of hydrochloric acid and dilute to 50 ml. Add 30 to 50 mg. of ammonium persulfate crystals and 3 ml. of ammonium thiocyanate reagent solution. Any red color should not exceed that produced by 0.015 mg. of iron (Fe) in an equal volume of solution containing the quantities of reagents used in the test.

Sodium. Determine the sodium by the flame photometric method described on page 14.

Sample Solution A. Dissolve 1 gram in water and dilute to 100 ml.

Control Solution B. Dissolve 1 gram in water, add 0.05 mg. of sodium ion (Na), and dilute to 100 ml.

Observe the emission of Control Solution B at the 589-mμ sodium line. Observe the emission of Sample Solution A at the 589-mμ sodium line and at a wavelength of 580 mμ. The difference (D_1) between the intensities observed for Sample Solution A at 580 mμ and 589 mμ should not exceed the difference (D_2) observed at 589 mμ between Sample Solution A and Control Solution B.

Notes

Potassium Chromate

K_2CrO_4 Formula Wt. 194.20

REQUIREMENTS

Insoluble matter.   Not more than 0.005 per cent.
Chloride (Cl).   Not more than 0.005 per cent.
pH of a 5 per cent solution.   From 8.6 to 9.8 at 25°C.
Sulfate (SO_4).   Not more than 0.030 per cent.
Calcium (Ca).   Not more than 0.005 per cent.
Sodium (Na).   Not more than 0.02 per cent.

TESTS

Insoluble matter.   Dissolve 20 grams in 150 ml. of water, heat to boiling, and digest in a covered beaker on the steam bath for 1 hour. Filter through a tared filtering crucible, wash the insoluble residue thoroughly, and dry at 105°C. The weight of the residue should not exceed 0.0010 gram.

Chloride.   Dissolve 0.2 gram in 10 ml. of water, filter if necessary through a small chloride-free filter, and add 1 ml. of ammonium hydroxide, 1 ml. of silver nitrate reagent solution, and 2 ml. of nitric acid. Any turbidity should not exceed that produced by 0.01 mg. of chloride ion (Cl) in an equal volume of solution containing the quantities of reagents used in the test. The comparison is best made by superimposing a tube containing 0.2 gram of sample in 11 ml. of water plus 1 ml. of ammonium hydroxide and 2 ml. of nitric acid over the tube containing the standard turbidity and placing a tube containing 11 ml. of water plus 1 ml. of ammonium hydroxide and 2 ml. of nitric acid below the tube containing the sample and added reagents. Both turbidities are thus viewed through the same depth and color of solution. The comparison tubes may be machine-made vials, long style, of about 20-ml. capacity.

pH of a 5 per cent solution.   Dissolve 10 grams in 200 ml. of carbon dioxide- and ammonia-free water. Determine the pH by the method described on page 18. The pH should be from 8.6 to 9.8 at 25°C. The pH of a 5 per cent solution of pure potassium chromate would be 9.3 at 25°C.

Sulfate.   Dissolve 10 grams in 250 ml. of water plus 4.5 ml. of hydrochloric acid. Heat to boiling and add 25 ml. of a solution containing 1 gram of barium chloride and 2 ml. of hydrochloric acid in 100 ml. Digest in a covered beaker on the steam bath for 2 hours and allow to stand overnight. If a precipitate is formed, filter, wash thoroughly, and ignite.

Fuse the residue with 1 gram of sodium carbonate. Extract the fused mass with water and filter to remove the insoluble residue. Add 5 ml. of hydrochloric acid to the filtrate, dilute to about 200 ml., heat to boiling, and add 10 ml. of alcohol. Digest on the steam bath until the reduction of chromate is complete, as indicated by the change to a clear green or colorless solution. Neutralize the solution with ammonium hydroxide and add 2 ml. of hydrochloric acid. Heat to boiling, add 10 ml. of barium chloride reagent solution, digest in a covered beaker on the steam bath for 2 hours, and allow to stand overnight. Filter, wash thoroughly, and ignite. The weight of the precipitate should not exceed 0.0073 gram.

Calcium. Dissolve 5 grams in 50 ml. of water, add 0.2 ml. of ammonium hydroxide and 5 ml. of ammonium oxalate reagent solution, and allow to stand overnight. If a precipitate is formed, it should not be more than is formed in a slightly ammoniacal solution of an equal volume containing 0.25 mg. of calcium ion (Ca) and 5 ml. of ammonium oxalate reagent solution.

Sodium. Determine the sodium by the flame photometric method described on page 14.

Sample Solution A. Dissolve 1 gram in water and dilute to 100 ml.

Control Solution B. Dissolve 1 gram in water, add 0.20 mg. of sodium ion (Na), and dilute to 100 ml.

Observe the emission of Control Solution B at the 589-mμ sodium line. Observe the emission of Sample Solution A at the 589-mμ sodium line and at a wavelength of 580 mμ. The difference (D_1) between the intensities observed for Sample Solution A at 580 mμ and 589 mμ should not exceed the difference (D_2) observed at 589 mμ between Sample Solution A and Control Solution B.

Notes

Potassium Cyanide

KCN

Formula Wt. 65.12

REQUIREMENTS

Assay. Not less than 96 per cent KCN.
Chloride (Cl). Not more than 0.50 per cent.
Phosphate (PO_4). Not more than 0.005 per cent.
Sulfate (SO_4). Not more than 0.04 per cent.
Sulfide (S). Not more than 0.003 per cent.
Thiocyanate (SCN). To pass test (limit about 0.020 per cent).
Iron, total (as Fe). Not more than 0.030 per cent.
Lead (Pb). Not more than 0.0002 per cent.
Sodium (Na). Not more than 0.50 per cent.

TESTS

Caution. Because of the extremely poisonous nature of potassium cyanide and of the hydrogen cyanide gas (HCN) evolved on treatment of the salt or solution of the salt with an acid, all tests must be made in a fume hood with a strong draft. Special care must be taken to avoid inhaling any of the fumes or allowing the salt or solution of the salt to come in contact with open cuts of the skin. If safety pipets are not available for measuring aliquots, use a graduated cylinder. *Under no conditions should suction by mouth be used to fill an ordinary pipet.*

Assay. Weigh accurately about 0.5 gram and dissolve in 30 ml. of water. Add 0.2 ml. of 10 per cent potassium iodide reagent solution and 1 ml. of ammonium hydroxide and titrate with 0.1N silver nitrate to a slight yellowish permanent turbidity. One milliliter of 0.1N silver nitrate corresponds to 0.01302 gram of KCN.

Sample Solution A. Dissolve 10 grams in water and dilute to 200 ml. Filter, if necessary, under a hood into a dry flask (1 ml. = 0.05 gram).

Chloride. Dilute 1 ml. of Sample Solution A to 50 ml. To 2 ml. (0.002-gram sample) of this solution add 2 ml. of 30 per cent hydrogen peroxide and allow to stand in a covered beaker until reaction ceases, then digest in the covered beaker on the steam bath for 20 to 30 minutes. Cool, dilute to 25 ml., and add 1 ml. of nitric acid and 1 ml. of silver nitrate reagent solution. Any turbidity should not exceed that produced by 0.01 mg. of chloride ion (Cl) in an equal volume of solution containing the quantities of reagents used in the test.

Phosphate. Dissolve 1 gram in 5 ml. of water, add 2 ml. of hydrochloric acid, and evaporate to dryness in a well ventilated hood. Add 5 ml. of dilute hydrochloric acid $(1 + 1)$ and evaporate to dryness again. Dissolve in 50 ml. of approximately $0.5N$ sulfuric acid. To 20 ml. of the solution add 5 ml. of approximately $0.5N$ sulfuric acid, 1 ml. of ammonium molybdate reagent solution, and 1 ml. of p-methylaminophenol sulfate reagent solution and allow to stand for 2 hours at room temperature. Any blue color should not exceed that produced by 0.02 mg. of phosphate ion (PO_4) in an equal volume of solution containing the quantities of reagents used in the test.

Sulfate. To 40 ml. of Sample Solution A (measured in a graduated cylinder) (2-gram sample) add 5 ml. of hydrochloric acid and evaporate to dryness (in hood). Warm the residue with 40 ml. of water plus 1 ml. of hydrochloric acid, filter if necessary, and dilute to 100 ml. Heat to boiling, add 5 ml. of barium chloride reagent solution, digest in a covered beaker on the steam bath for 2 hours, and allow to stand overnight. If a precipitate is formed, filter, wash thoroughly, and ignite. The weight should not be more than 0.0020 gram greater than the weight obtained in a complete blank test.

Sulfide. To 20 ml. of Sample Solution A (measured in a graduated cylinder) (1-gram sample) add 0.15 ml. of alkaline lead solution (made by adding 10 per cent sodium hydroxide reagent solution to a 10 per cent lead acetate reagent solution until the precipitate is redissolved). The color should not be darker than is produced by 0.03 mg. of sulfide ion (S) in an equal volume of solution when treated with 0.15 ml. of the alkaline lead solution.

Thiocyanate. To 20 ml. of Sample Solution A (measured in a graduated cylinder) (1-gram sample) add 4 ml. of hydrochloric acid and 0.20 ml. of ferric chloride reagent solution. At the end of 5 minutes the solution should show no reddish tint when compared with 20 ml. of water to which have been added the quantities of hydrochloric acid and ferric chloride used in the test.

Iron, total. Transfer 10 ml. of Sample Solution A (0.5-gram sample) to a platinum evaporating dish, add 3 ml. of hydrochloric acid, and evaporate to dryness in a well ventilated hood. Heat for one-half hour at about 650°C. Cool, add 2 ml. of hydrochloric acid and 10 ml. of water, and digest on the steam bath until dissolution is complete. Dilute to 30 ml. Dilute 2 ml. of this solution to 45 ml. and add 2 ml. of hydrochloric acid, 30 to 50 mg. of ammonium persulfate crystals, and 3 ml. of ammonium thiocyanate reagent solution. Any red color should not exceed that produced by 0.01 mg. of iron (Fe) in an equal volume of solution containing the quantities of reagents used in the test.

Lead. Dissolve 1.2 grams in 10 ml. of water in a separatory funnel. Add 5 ml. of ammonium citrate reagent solution, 2 ml. of hydroxylamine hydrochloride reagent solution for the dithizone test, and 0.10 ml. of phenol red indicator solution, and make the solution alkaline if necessary by the addition of ammonium hydroxide. Add 5 ml. of standard dithizone solution in chloroform, shake gently but well for 1 minute, and allow the layers to separate. The intensity of the red color of the chloroform layer should be no greater than that of a control made with 0.002 mg. of lead ion (Pb) and 0.2 gram of the sample treated exactly like the solution of 1.2 grams of sample in 10 ml. of water.

Sodium. Determine the sodium by the flame photometric method described on page 14.

Sample Solution A-1. Dilute a 4-ml. aliquot (0.2 gram sample) of Sample Solution A to 10 ml.

Control Solution B. Add 1.0 mg. of sodium ion (Na) to a 4-ml. aliquot of Sample Solution A and dilute to 10 ml.

Add 5 ml. of 30 per cent hydrogen peroxide to each solution. Digest in a covered beaker on the steam bath in a well ventilated hood until the reaction ceases. Wash down the cover glass and sides of the beaker and evaporate to dryness. Dissolve each residue in 100 ml. of dilute hydrochloric acid (1 + 99). Observe the emission of Control Solution B at the 589-mμ sodium line. Observe the emission of Sample Solution A-1 at the 589-mμ sodium line and at a wavelength of 580 mμ. The difference (D_1) between the intensities observed for Sample Solution A-1 at 589 mμ and 580 mμ should not exceed the difference (D_2) observed at 589 mμ between Sample Solution A-1 and Control Solution B.

Notes

Potassium Dichromate

$K_2Cr_2O_7$ Formula Wt. 294.19

REQUIREMENTS

Insoluble matter and ammonium hydroxide precipitate. Not more than 0.005 per cent.
Loss on drying. Not more than 0.05 per cent.
Chloride (Cl). Not more than 0.001 per cent.
Sulfate (SO_4). Not more than 0.005 per cent.
Calcium (Ca). Not more than 0.003 per cent.
Sodium (Na). Not more than 0.02 per cent.

TESTS

Insoluble matter and ammonium hydroxide precipitate. Dissolve 20 grams in 200 ml. of water, add 2 ml. of ammonium hydroxide, heat to boiling, and digest in a covered beaker on the steam bath for 1 hour. Filter, wash thoroughly, and ignite. The weight of the residue should not exceed 0.0010 gram. Retain the filtrate for the determination of *Calcium.*

Loss on drying. Weigh accurately about 2 grams and dry to constant weight at 105°C. The loss in weight should not exceed 0.05 per cent of the weight of the sample.

Chloride. Dissolve 1 gram in 10 ml. of water, filter if necessary through a small chloride-free filter, and add 1 ml. of ammonium hydroxide and 1 ml. of silver nitrate reagent solution. Prepare a standard containing 0.01 mg. of chloride ion (Cl) in 10 ml. of water and add 1 ml. of ammonium hydroxide and 1 ml. of silver nitrate reagent solution. Add 2 ml. of nitric acid to each. Any turbidity in the solution of the sample should not exceed that in the standard. The color in the sample can be compensated for by superimposing a tube containing 1 gram of the sample in 11 ml. of water plus 1 ml. of ammonium hydroxide and 2 ml. of nitric acid over the tube containing the standard, and placing a tube containing 11 ml. of water plus 1 ml. of ammonium hydroxide and 2 ml. of nitric acid below the tube containing the sample. Both turbidities are thus viewed through the same depth and color of solutions. The comparison tubes may be machine-made vials, long style, of about 20-ml. capacity.

Sulfate. Dissolve 10 grams in 250 ml. of water, filter if necessary, and heat to boiling. Add 25 ml. of a solution containing 1 gram of barium chloride and 2 ml. of hydrochloric acid per 100 ml. of solution. Digest in a covered beaker on the steam bath for 2 hours and allow to stand overnight. If a precipitate is formed, filter, wash thoroughly, and ignite. Fuse the residue with 1 gram of sodium carbonate. Extract the fused mass with water and filter off the insoluble residue. Add 5 ml. of hydrochloric acid to the filtrate, dilute to about 200 ml., heat to boiling, and add 10 ml. of alcohol. Digest in a covered beaker on the steam bath until reduction of chromate is complete, as indicated by the change to a clear green or colorless solution. Neutralize the solution with ammonium hydroxide and add 2 ml. of hydrochloric acid. Heat to boiling and add 10 ml. of barium chloride reagent solution. Digest in a covered beaker on the steam bath for 2 hours and allow to stand overnight. Filter, wash thoroughly, and ignite. The weight of the precipitate should not be more than 0.0012 gram greater than the weight obtained in a complete blank test. If the original precipitate of barium sulfate weighs less than 0.0012 gram, the fusion with sodium carbonate is not necessary.

Calcium.   To one half of the filtrate from the *Insoluble matter and ammonium hydroxide precipitate* add 10 ml. of ammonium oxalate reagent solution and 5 ml. of ammonium hydroxide, and allow to stand overnight. If a precipitate is formed, filter, wash with a solution containing about 0.1 per cent of ammonium oxalate, and ignite. Add 0.10 ml. of sulfuric acid to the cooled residue and ignite again. The weight of the residue should not exceed 0.0010 gram.

Sodium.   Determine the sodium by the flame photometric method described on page 14.

Sample Solution A.   Dissolve 1 gram in water, add 1 ml. of ammonium hydroxide, and dilute to 100 ml.

Control Solution B.   Dissolve 1 gram plus 0.2 mg. of sodium ion (Na) in water, add 1 ml. of ammonium hydroxide, and dilute to 100 ml.

Observe the emission of Control Solution B at the 589-mμ sodium line. Observe the emission of Sample Solution A at the 589-mμ sodium line and at a wavelength of 580 mμ. The difference (D_1) between the intensities observed for Sample Solution A at 580 mμ and 589 mμ should not exceed the difference (D_2) observed at 589 mμ between Sample Solution A and Control Solution B.

Notes

Potassium Ferricyanide

K₃Fe(CN)₆

Formula Wt. 329.26

REQUIREMENTS

Insoluble matter. Not more than 0.005 per cent.
Chloride (Cl). Not more than 0.010 per cent.
Sulfate (SO₄). To pass test (limit about 0.01 per cent).
Ferro compounds. Not more than 0.05 per cent as ferrocyanide radical [Fe(CN)₆].

TESTS

Insoluble matter. Dissolve 20 grams in 200 ml. of water at room temperature, filter promptly through a tared filtering crucible, wash thoroughly, and dry at 105°C. The weight of the residue should not exceed 0.0010 gram.

Chloride. Dissolve 2 grams in 175 ml. of water in a cylinder, add 2.5 grams of cupric sulfate crystals dissolved in 25 ml. of water, mix thoroughly, and allow the precipitate to settle. Filter the supernatant liquid, if necessary, through a chloride-free filter. To 10 ml. of the clear solution add 1 ml. of nitric acid, 10 ml. of water, and 1 ml. of silver nitrate reagent solution. Any turbidity should not exceed that produced by 0.01 mg. of chloride ion (Cl) in an equal volume of solution containing the quantities of nitric acid and silver nitrate used in the test and enough cupric sulfate to match the color in the test solution.

Sulfate. Dissolve 5 grams in 100 ml. of water without heating, filter promptly, and to the filtrate add 0.2 ml. of glacial acetic acid and 5 ml. of barium chloride reagent solution. No turbidity should be observed in 10 minutes.

Ferro compounds. Mix 400 ml. of water with 10 ml. of 25 per cent sulfuric acid reagent solution and add 0.1N potassium permanganate until the pink color persists for 1 minute. Dissolve 4 grams of the sample in the solution, add 0.10 ml. of the 0.1N permanganate solution, and stir. The solution should retain a pink tint in comparison with a blank prepared with the same quantities of ferricyanide, water, and acid.

Notes

Potassium Ferrocyanide

$K_4Fe(CN)_6 \cdot 3H_2O$ Formula Wt. 422.41

REQUIREMENTS

Insoluble matter.   Not more than 0.005 per cent.
Chloride (Cl).   Not more than 0.010 per cent.
Sulfate (SO_4).   To pass test (limit about 0.01 per cent).

TESTS

Insoluble matter.   Dissolve 20 grams in 200 ml. of water, heat to boiling, and digest in a covered beaker on the steam bath for 1 hour. Filter through a tared filtering crucible, wash thoroughly, and dry at 105°C. The weight of the residue should not exceed 0.0010 gram.

Chloride.   Dissolve 2 grams in 175 ml. of water, filter if necessary through a chloride-free filter, add 2.5 grams of cupric sulfate crystals dissolved in 25 ml. of water, mix thoroughly, and allow the precipitate to settle in a cylinder. To 10 ml. of the clear supernatant liquid add 1 ml. of nitric acid, 10 ml. of water, and 1 ml. of silver nitrate reagent solution. Any turbidity should not exceed that produced by 0.01 mg. of chloride (Cl) ion in an equal volume of solution containing the quantities of nitric acid and silver nitrate used in the test and enough cupric sulfate to match the color in the test solution.

Sulfate.   Dissolve 5 grams in 100 ml. of water without heating, filter, and to the filtrate add 0.2 ml. of glacial acetic acid and 5 ml. of barium chloride reagent solution. No turbidity should be observed in 10 minutes.

Notes

Potassium Hydrogen Phthalate, Acidimetric Standard

Potassium Acid Phthalate

Phthalic Acid Monopotassium Salt

HOCOC$_6$H$_4$COOK   Formula Wt. 204.23

Note. This reagent is satisfactory for use as a pH standard. For use as an acidimetric standard this material should be lightly crushed and dried for 2 hours at 120°C. to remove any absorbed moisture.

REQUIREMENTS

Assay. Not less than 99.95 nor more than 100.05 per cent HOCOC$_6$H$_4$COOK.

Insoluble matter. Not more than 0.005 per cent.

pH of a 0.05M solution. 4.00 at 25°C.

Chlorine compounds (as Cl). To pass test (limit about 0.003 per cent).

Sulfur compounds (as S). To pass test (limit about 0.002 per cent).

Heavy metals (as Pb). Not more than 0.0005 per cent.

Iron (Fe). Not more than 0.0005 per cent.

Sodium (Na). Not more than 0.005 per cent.

TESTS

Assay. This is a comparative procedure in which the potassium hydrogen phthalate to be assayed is compared with an N.B.S. standard sample of potassium hydrogen phthalate. Accurately weighed portions of anhydrous sodium carbonate, dissolved in water, are allowed to react with accurately weighed portions of the two potassium hydrogen phthalate samples of such size as to provide a small excess of the latter. The carbon dioxide is removed by boiling and the excess potassium hydrogen phthalate is determined by titration with carbonate-free sodium hydroxide using phenolphthalein indicator.

Caution. Due to the small tolerance in *Assay* limits for this acidimetric standard, extreme care must be observed in the weighing, transferring, and titrating operations in the following procedure. Strict adherence to the specified sample weights and final titration volumes is absolutely necessary. It is recommended that the titrations be run at least in duplicate on both the sample and the N.B.S. standard. Duplicate values of M, the number of milliequivalents of total alkali required per gram of potassium hydrogen phthalate, obtained on the sample and on the N.B.S.

standard, should agree within 2 parts in 5000 to be acceptable for averaging.

Procedure. Place duplicate 1.300 ± 0.001-gram portions of a uniform sample of anhydrous sodium carbonate in clean, dry weighing bottles. Dry at 285°C. for 3 hours, stopper the bottles, and cool in a desiccator for at least 2 hours. Open the weighing bottles momentarily to equalize the pressure, weigh each bottle and its contents to the nearest 0.1 mg., and transfer the entire contents of each bottle to a clean, dry 50-ml. beaker. Store the beaker in a desiccator until ready for use, weigh each bottle again, and determine by difference, to the nearest 0.1 mg., the weight of each portion of sodium carbonate.

Transfer the portions of sodium carbonate to 500-ml. titration flasks*
by pouring them through powder funnels. Rinse the beakers, funnels, and sides of the flasks thoroughly with several small portions of water. In the same manner add to these flasks 5.100 ± 0.003-gram portions of the potassium hydrogen phthalate to be assayed and of the N.B.S. standard potassium hydrogen phthalate, both of which have been previously crushed (not ground) in an agate or mullite mortar to approximately 100-mesh fineness, dried at 120°C. for 2 hours, and cooled in a desiccator for at least 2 hours.

Dilute the contents of each titration flask to about 90 ml. with water, swirl to dissolve the samples, stopper, and bubble carbon dioxide-free air through the solutions at a moderately fast rate during all subsequent operations. Boil the solutions gently for 20 minutes to complete the removal of carbon dioxide, taking care to prevent loss of solutions by spraying. Cool the solutions to room temperature in an ice bath, add 0.30 ml. of an alcohol solution of phenolphthalein (1 in 2000) to each, and dilute to 75 to 80 ml. with *carbon dioxide-free* water. Titrate each solution with 0.02N carbonate-free sodium hydroxide until the color matches that of a similar volume of buffer solution** (pH = 8.75) containing 0.30 ml. of the same phenolphthalein solution.

Calculations. Calculate the number of milliequivalents of total alkali (sodium carbonate plus sodium hydroxide) required to neutralize 1 gram of the sample of potassium hydrogen phthalate and of the N.B.S. standard by the following formulas:

$$M_u = \frac{\dfrac{B}{0.052994} + (C \times D)}{W_u}$$

$$M_s = \frac{\dfrac{B}{0.052994} + (C \times D)}{W_s \times F}$$

where:

M_u = number of milliequivalents of total alkali required per gram of potassium hydrogen phthalate being assayed

M_s = number of milliequivalents of total alkali required per gram of N.B.S. standard potassium hydrogen phthalate

B = weight, in grams, of sodium carbonate

C = volume, in ml., of NaOH standard solution

D = exact normality of NaOH standard solution

W_u = weight, in grams, of potassium hydrogen phthalate being assayed

W_s = weight, in grams, of N.B.S. standard potassium hydrogen phthalate

F = assay value of N.B.S. standard in per cent divided by 100

Calculate the *Assay* value of the sample of potassium hydrogen phthalate as follows:

$$A = \frac{M_u \times 100}{M_s}$$

where:

A = per cent of potassium hydrogen phthalate in the sample being assayed and M_u and M_s are defined as above.

*Note 1. **Titration Flask.** This is a 500-ml. conical flask fitted with a small glass tube sealed through the side. The tube inside the flask terminates in a constricted tip positioned as close to the bottom as possible. The tube outside the flask is bent at a right angle to permit the attachment of the carbon dioxide-free air supply.

Note 2. **Buffer Solution (pH = 8.75). Weigh 3.1 grams of boric acid (H_3BO_3) and 3.8 grams of potassium chloride, dissolve in water, add 17.0 ml. of $1N$ sodium hydroxide, and dilute to 1 liter.

Insoluble matter. Dissolve 20 grams in 200 ml. of water, heat to boiling, and digest in a covered beaker on the steam bath for 1 hour. Filter through a tared filtering crucible, wash thoroughly, and dry at 105°C. The weight of the residue should not exceed 0.0010 gram.

ACS SPECIFICATIONS 453

pH of a 0.05M solution. Dissolve 1.021 grams in 100 grams of carbon dioxide- and ammonia-free water (1.018 grams per 100 grams of solution). Determine the pH by the method described on page 18. The pH should be 4.00 at 25°C.

Chlorine compounds. Mix 1 gram with 0.5 gram of sodium carbonate, moisten the mixture, and ignite until thoroughly charred, avoiding an unduly high temperature. Treat the residue with 30 ml. of water, cautiously add 3 ml. of nitric acid, and filter through a chloride-free filter. Wash the residue with a few milliliters of hot water, dilute the filtrate to 50 ml., and to 25 ml. of the filtrate add 1 ml. of silver nitrate reagent solution. Any turbidity should not exceed that produced by 0.015 mg. of chloride ion (Cl) in an equal volume of solution containing the quantities of reagents used in the test.

Sulfur compounds. Mix 2 grams with 1 gram of sodium carbonate, add in small portions 15 ml. of water, evaporate, and thoroughly ignite, protected from sulfur in the flame. Treat the residue with 20 ml. of water and 2 ml. of 30 per cent hydrogen peroxide and heat on the steam bath for 15 minutes. Add 5 ml. of hydrochloric acid and evaporate to dryness on the steam bath. Dissolve the residue in 10 ml. of water, filter, wash with several portions of water, and dilute the filtrate to 25 ml. Add to this solution 0.5 ml. of 1N hydrochloric acid and 2 ml. of barium chloride reagent solution. Any turbidity should not exceed that in a standard prepared as follows: treat 1 gram of sodium carbonate with 2 ml. of 30 per cent hydrogen peroxide and 5 ml. of hydrochloric acid and evaporate to dryness on the steam bath. Dissolve the residue and 0.12 mg. of sulfate ion (SO_4) in sufficient water to make 25 ml. and add 0.5 ml. of 1N hydrochloric acid and 2 ml. of barium chloride reagent solution.

Heavy metals. Dissolve 6.6 grams in warm water and dilute to 50 ml. For the control add 0.02 mg. of lead ion (Pb) to a 10-ml. aliquot of the solution and dilute to 40 ml. For the sample use the remaining 40-ml. portion. If necessary, adjust the pH of the control and sample solutions to between 3 and 4 (using a pH meter) with 1N acetic acid or ammonium hydroxide (10 per cent NH_3) added dropwise, dilute to 41 ml., and mix. Add 10 ml. of freshly prepared hydrogen sulfide water to each and mix. Any color in the solution of the sample should not exceed that in the control.

Iron. Dissolve 2 grams in 35 ml. of water, add 2 ml. of hydrochloric acid, filter, and dilute to 50 ml. Add 30 to 50 mg. of ammonium persulfate crystals and 3 ml. of ammonium thiocyanate reagent solution. Any red color should not exceed that produced by 0.01 mg. of iron (Fe) in an equal volume of solution containing the quantities of reagents used in the test.

Sodium. Determine the sodium by the flame photometric method described on page 14.

Sample Solution A. Dissolve 1 gram in water and dilute to 100 ml.

Control Solution B. Dissolve 1 gram in water, add 0.05 mg. of sodium ion (Na), and dilute to 100 ml.

Observe the emission of Control Solution B at the 589-mμ sodium line. Observe the emission of Sample Solution A at the 589-mμ sodium line and at a wavelength of 580 mμ. The difference (D_1) between the intensities observed for Sample Solution A at 580 mμ and 589 mμ should not exceed the difference (D_2) observed at 589 mμ between Sample Solution A and Control Solution B.

Notes

Potassium Hydroxide

KOH   Formula Wt. 56.11

Note. Reagent potassium hydroxide normally contains 10 to 15 per cent water.

REQUIREMENTS

Potassium hydroxide (**KOH**).   Not less than 85.0 per cent.
Potassium carbonate (**K_2CO_3**).   Not more than 2.0 per cent.
Chloride (**Cl**).   Not more than 0.010 per cent.
Nitrogen compounds (as **N**).   Not more than 0.001 per cent.
Phosphate (**PO_4**).   Not more than 0.0005 per cent.
Sulfate (**SO_4**).   Not more than 0.003 per cent.
Ammonium hydroxide precipitate.   Not more than 0.020 per cent.
Heavy metals (as **Ag**).   Not more than 0.001 per cent.
Iron (**Fe**).   Not more than 0.001 per cent.
Nickel (**Ni**).   Not more than 0.001 per cent.
Sodium (**Na**).   Not more than 0.05 per cent.

TESTS

Note. Special care must be taken in sampling to obtain a representative sample and to avoid absorption of water and carbon dioxide by the sample taken.

Potassium hydroxide and carbonate. Weigh rapidly 35 to 40 grams, to within 0.1 gram, dissolve, cool, and dilute to 1 liter, using carbon dioxide-free water throughout. Dilute 50.0 ml. of the well mixed solution to 200 ml. with carbon dioxide-free water, add 5 ml. of barium chloride reagent solution, shake, and allow to stand for a few minutes. Titrate with 1N hydrochloric acid to the phenolphthalein end point. One milliliter of 1N hydrochloric acid corresponds to 0.05611 gram of KOH. Continue the titration with 1N hydrochloric acid to the methyl orange end point to determine the carbonate. One milliliter of 1N hydrochloric acid corresponds to 0.06911 gram of K_2CO_3.

Sample Solution A for the determination of Chloride, Nitrogen Compounds, Phosphate, Sulfate, Heavy metals, Iron, and Nickel. Dissolve 50.0 grams in carbon dioxide- and ammonia-free water, cool, and dilute to 500 ml. (1 ml. = 0.1 gram).

Chloride. Dilute 10 ml. of Sample Solution A (1-gram sample) to 50 ml., and filter if necessary through a chloride-free filter. To 5 ml. of the diluted solution add 15 ml. of water, 1 ml. of nitric acid, and 1 ml. of silver nitrate reagent solution. Any turbidity should not exceed that produced by 0.01 mg. of chloride ion (Cl) in an equal volume of solution containing the quantities of reagents used in the test.

Nitrogen compounds. Dilute 20 ml. of Sample Solution A (2-gram sample) with 50 ml. of ammonia-free water in a flask connected through a spray trap to a condenser, the end of which dips beneath the surface of 10 ml. of 0.1N hydrochloric acid. For the control, take 50 ml. of ammonia-free water in a similar flask, and add 10 ml. of Sample Solution A and a solution of an ammonium salt containing 0.01 mg. of combined nitrogen (N). To each flask add 0.5 gram of aluminum wire in small pieces, allow to stand for 1 hour, and slowly distill about 35 ml. To each distillate add 2 ml. of freshly boiled 10 per cent sodium hydroxide reagent solution, dilute to 50 ml., and add 2 ml. of Nessler reagent. Any color in the solution of the sample should not exceed that in the control.

Phosphate. To 40 ml. of Sample Solution A (4-gram sample) add 10 ml. of hydrochloric acid and evaporate to dryness on the steam bath. Dissolve the residue in 25 ml. of approximately 0.5N sulfuric acid, add 1 ml. of ammonium molybdate reagent solution and 1 ml. of p-methylaminophenol sulfate reagent solution, and allow to stand for 2 hours at room temperature. Any blue color should not exceed that produced by 0.02 mg. of phosphate ion (PO_4) in an equal volume of solution containing the quantities of reagents used in the test, including the residue from evaporation of 5 ml. of hydrochloric acid.

Sulfate. To 167 ml. of Sample Solution A (16.7-gram sample) add about 75 ml. of water, neutralize with hydrochloric acid, and add an excess of 2 ml. of the acid. Heat to boiling, add 10 ml. of barium chloride reagent solution, digest in a covered beaker on the steam bath for 2 hours, and allow to stand overnight. If a precipitate is formed, filter, wash thoroughly, and ignite. The weight of the precipitate should not be more than 0.0012 gram greater than the weight obtained in a complete blank test.

Ammonium hydroxide precipitate. Weigh about 10 grams and dissolve in about 100 ml. of water. Cautiously add 12 ml. of sulfuric acid to 12 ml. of water, cool, add the mixture to the solution of the sample, and evaporate to dense fumes. Cool, dissolve the residue in 130 ml. of hot water, and add ammonium hydroxide until the solution is just alkaline to methyl red. Heat to boiling, filter, wash with hot water, and ignite. The weight of the residue should not be greater than 0.020 per cent of the weight of the sample. The residue includes some, but not all, of the silica in the sample.

Heavy metals. To 60 ml. of Sample Solution A (6-gram sample) cautiously add 15 ml. of nitric acid. For the control add 0.05 mg. of silver ion (Ag) to 10 ml. of Sample Solution A and cautiously add 15 ml. of nitric acid. Evaporate both solutions to dryness over a low flame or on an electric hot plate. Dissolve each residue in about 20 ml. of water, filter if necessary through a chloride-free filter, and dilute to 25 ml. Adjust the pH of the control and sample solutions to between 3 and 4 (using a pH meter) with 1N acetic acid or ammonium hydroxide (10 per cent NH_3), dilute to 40 ml., and mix. Add 10 ml. of freshly prepared hydrogen sulfide water to each and mix. Any yellowish brown color in the solution of the sample should not exceed that in the control.

Iron. Neutralize 10 ml. of Sample Solution A (1-gram sample) with hydrochloric acid, using phenolphthalein indicator, add 2 ml. in excess, and dilute to 50 ml. For the control add 0.01 mg. of iron (Fe) and 2 ml. of hydrochloric acid to the residue obtained from evaporation of the quantity of hydrochloric acid used to neutralize the potassium hydroxide and dilute to 50 ml. To each add 30 to 50 mg. of ammonium persulfate crystals and 3 ml. of ammonium thiocyanate reagent solution. Any red color in the solution of the sample should not exceed that in the control.

Nickel. Dilute 20 ml. of Sample Solution A (2-gram sample) to 50 ml. with water and neutralize with hydrochloric acid. Dilute to 85 ml. and adjust the pH to 8 with ammonium hydroxide. Add 5 ml. of bromine water, 5 ml. of 1 per cent dimethylglyoxime solution in alcohol, and 5 ml. of 10 per cent sodium hydroxide reagent solution. Any red color should not exceed that produced by 0.02 mg. of nickel ion (Ni) in an equal volume of solution containing the quantities of reagents used in the test.

Sodium. Determine the sodium by the flame photometric method described on page 14.

Sample Solution A. Dissolve 1 gram in water and dilute to 100 ml.

Control Solution B. Dissolve 1 gram in water, add 0.5 mg. of sodium ion (Na), and dilute to 100 ml.

Observe the emission of Control Solution B at the 589-mμ sodium line. Observe the emission of Sample Solution A at the 589-mμ sodium line and at a wavelength of 580 mμ. The difference (D_1) between the intensities observed for Sample Solution A at 580 mμ and 589 mμ should not exceed the difference (D_2) observed at 589 mμ between Sample Solution A and Control Solution B.

Potassium Iodate

KIO$_3$ Formula Wt. 214.00

REQUIREMENTS

Insoluble matter. Not more than 0.005 per cent.
pH of a 5 per cent solution. From 5.0 to 8.0 at 25°C.
Chloride and bromide (as Cl). Not more than 0.01 per cent.
Iodide (I). Not more than 0.001 per cent.
Nitrogen compounds (as N). Not more than 0.005 per cent.
Sulfate (SO$_4$). Not more than 0.005 per cent.
Heavy metals (as Pb). Not more than 0.0005 per cent.
Iron (Fe). Not more than 0.001 per cent.
Sodium (Na). Not more than 0.005 per cent.

TESTS

Insoluble matter. Dissolve 20 grams in 250 ml. of water, heat to boiling, and digest in a covered beaker on the steam bath for 1 hour. Filter through a tared filtering crucible, wash thoroughly, and dry at 105°C. The weight of the residue should not exceed 0.0010 gram.

pH of a 5 per cent solution. Dissolve 10 grams in 200 ml. of carbon dioxide- and ammonia-free water. Determine the pH of the solution by the method described on page 18. The pH should be from 5.0 to 8.0 at 25°C. The pH of a 5 per cent solution of pure potassium iodate would be 7.0 at 25°C.

Chloride and bromide. Dissolve 1 gram in 100 ml. of water in a flask, filter if necessary through a chloride-free filter, and add 6 ml. of hydrogen peroxide and 1 ml. of phosphoric acid. Heat to boiling and boil gently until all the iodine is expelled and the solution is colorless. Cool, wash down the sides of the flask, and add 0.5 ml. of hydrogen peroxide. If an iodine color develops, boil until the solution is colorless and for 10 minutes longer. If no color develops, boil for 10 minutes. Dilute to 100 ml., take a 10-ml. aliquot, and dilute to 23 ml. Prepare a standard containing 0.01 mg. of chloride ion (Cl) and 0.6 ml. of hydrogen peroxide in 23 ml. of water. Add 1 ml. of nitric acid and 1 ml. of silver nitrate reagent solution to each. Any turbidity in the solution of the sample should not exceed that in the standard.

Iodide. Dissolve 11 grams in 160 ml. of water; add 1 gram of citric acid and 5 ml. of chloroform. Prepare a control solution containing 1 gram of the sample, 1 gram of citric acid, and 0.1 mg. of iodide ion (I) in 160 ml. of water; add 5 ml. of chloroform. Shake vigorously and allow the chloroform to separate. Any pink color in the chloroform layer from the sample should not exceed that in the chloroform layer from the control.

Nitrogen compounds. Dissolve 1 gram in 60 ml. of water in a flask connected through a spray trap to a condenser, the end of which dips beneath the surface of 10 ml. of 0.1N hydrochloric acid. Add to the flask 10 ml. of freshly boiled 10 per cent sodium hydroxide reagent solution and 0.5 gram of aluminum wire in small pieces. Allow to stand for 1 hour, slowly distill about 35 ml., and dilute the distillate to 50 ml. To 10 ml. of the diluted distillate add 2 ml. of 10 per cent sodium hydroxide reagent solution, dilute to 50 ml., and add 2 ml. of Nessler reagent. Any color should not exceed that produced when a quantity of an ammonium salt containing 0.05 mg. of nitrogen (N) is treated exactly like the sample.

Sulfate. Treat 10 grams with 30 ml. of hydrochloric acid and evaporate to dryness. Repeat twice, using 10 ml. of hydrochloric acid each time. Dissolve the residue in 100 ml. of water plus 1 ml. of hydrochloric acid. Filter, heat to boiling, add 5 ml. of barium chloride reagent solution, digest in a covered beaker on the steam bath for 2 hours, and allow to stand overnight. Filter, wash thoroughly, and ignite. The weight of the precipitate should not be more than 0.0012 gram greater than the weight obtained in a complete blank test.

Heavy metals. Dissolve 7 grams in 50 ml. of water, heat to boiling, add 1.5 ml. of dilute formic acid $(1 + 9)$, and continue heating until the initial reaction ceases. Add dropwise 50 ml. of dilute formic acid $(1 + 9)$ and continue boiling until the solution appears to be free of iodine. Wash down the sides of the container and boil again if the iodine color reappears. Repeat the washing down and boiling until the solution remains colorless. Evaporate to dryness on the steam bath. Dissolve the residue in about 20 ml. of water and dilute to 35 ml. (Reserve 5 ml. of this solution for the test for *Iron.*) For the control add 0.02 mg. of lead ion (Pb) to a 5-ml. aliquot of the solution and dilute to 25 ml. For the sample use the remaining 25-ml. portion. Adjust the pH of the control and sample solutions to between 3 and 4 (using a pH meter) with 1N acetic acid or ammonium hydroxide (10 per cent NH_3), dilute to 40 ml., and mix. Add 10 ml. of freshly prepared hydrogen sulfide water to each and mix. Any color in the solution of the sample should not exceed that in the control.

Iron. To the 5 ml. of the solution reserved from the test for *Heavy metals* add 6 ml. of hydroxylamine hydrochloride reagent solution and 4 ml. of 1,10-phenanthroline reagent solution, and dilute to 25 ml. Any red color should not exceed that produced by 0.01 mg. of iron (Fe) in an equal volume of solution containing the quantities of reagents used in the test. The comparison should be made 1 hour after the reagents are added to the sample and standard solutions.

Sodium. Determine the sodium by the flame photometric method described on page 14.

Sample Solution A. Dissolve 1 gram in 10 ml. of dilute hydrochloric acid (1 + 3) and evaporate to dryness. Redissolve in 10 ml. of dilute hydrochloric acid (1 + 3) and evaporate to dryness again. Dissolve in 100 ml. of dilute hydrochloric acid (1 + 99).

Control Solution B. Dissolve 1 gram in 10 ml. of dilute hydrochloric acid (1 + 3), add 0.05 mg. of sodium ion (Na), and evaporate to dryness. Redissolve in 10 ml. of dilute hydrochloric acid (1 + 3) and evaporate to dryness again. Dissolve in 100 ml. of dilute hydrochloric acid (1 + 99).

Observe the emission of Control Solution B at the 589-mμ sodium line. Observe the emission of Sample Solution A at the 589-mμ sodium line and at a wavelength of 580 mμ. The difference (D_1) between the intensities observed for Sample Solution A at 580 mμ and 589 mμ should not exceed the difference (D_2) observed at 589 mμ between Sample Solution A and Control Solution B.

Notes

Potassium Iodide

KI   Formula Wt. 166.00

REQUIREMENTS

Insoluble matter.   Not more than 0.005 per cent.
Loss on drying at 150°C.   Not more than 0.20 per cent.
pH of a 5 per cent solution.   From 6.0 to 9.2 at 25°C.
Chloride and bromide (as Cl).   Not more than 0.01 per cent.
Iodate (IO_3).   To pass test (limit about 0.0003 per cent).
Nitrogen compounds (as N).   Not more than 0.001 per cent.
Phosphate (PO_4).   Not more than 0.001 per cent.
Sulfate (SO_4).   Not more than 0.005 per cent.
Barium (Ba).   Not more than 0.002 per cent.
Calcium, magnesium, and R_2O_3 precipitate.   Not more than 0.005 per cent.
Heavy metals (as Pb).   Not more than 0.0005 per cent.
Iron (Fe).   Not more than 0.0003 per cent.
Sodium (Na).   Not more than 0.005 per cent.

TESTS

Insoluble matter.   Dissolve 20 grams in 150 ml. of water, heat to boiling, and digest in a covered beaker on the steam bath for 1 hour. Filter through a tared filtering crucible, wash thoroughly, and dry at 105°C. The weight of the residue should not exceed 0.0010 gram. Retain the filtrate, without the washings, for the test for *Calcium, magnesium, and R_2O_3 precipitate*.

Loss on drying.   Weigh accurately about 2 grams of a sample in which the large crystals have been crushed, but which has not been ground for very long in a mortar. Dry in a weighed dish for 6 hours at 150°C. The loss in weight should not be more than 0.20 per cent of the weight of the sample.

pH of a 5 per cent solution.   Dissolve 10 grams in 200 ml. of carbon dioxide- and ammonia-free water. Determine the pH by the method described on page 18. The pH should be from 6.0 to 9.2 at 25°C. The pH of a 5 per cent solution of pure potassium iodide would be 7.0 at 25°C.

Chloride and bromide.   Dissolve 1 gram in 100 ml. of water in a distilling flask. Add 1 ml. of hydrogen peroxide and 1 ml. of phosphoric acid, heat to boiling, and boil gently until all the iodine is expelled and the solution is colorless. Cool, wash down the sides of the flask, and add

0.5 ml. of hydrogen peroxide. If an iodine color develops, boil until the solution is colorless and for 10 minutes longer. If no color develops, boil for 10 minutes, filter if necessary through a chloride-free filter, and dilute to 100 ml. Dilute a 10-ml. aliquot to 23 ml. and add 1 ml. of nitric acid and 1 ml. of silver nitrate reagent solution. Any turbidity should not exceed that produced by 0.01 mg. of chloride ion (Cl) in an equal volume of solution containing the quantities of nitric acid and silver nitrate used in the test.

Iodate.　Dissolve 1 gram in 20 ml. of freshly boiled water, and add 1 ml. of starch indicator solution and 0.25 ml. of 1N sulfuric acid. No blue or violet color should be produced in 1 minute. Special care must be taken to ensure that the water used in the test is free of oxygen.

Nitrogen compounds.　Dissolve 1 gram in 60 ml. of water in a flask connected through a spray trap to a condenser, the end of which dips beneath the surface of 10 ml. of 0.1N hydrochloric acid. Add to the flask 10 ml. of freshly boiled 10 per cent sodium hydroxide reagent solution and 0.5 gram of aluminum wire in small pieces, allow to stand for 1 hour, and slowly distill about 35 ml. To the distillate add 1 ml. of 10 per cent sodium hydroxide reagent solution, dilute to 50 ml., and add 2 ml. of Nessler reagent. Any color should not exceed that produced when a quantity of an ammonium salt containing 0.01 mg. of nitrogen (N) is treated exactly like the sample.

Phosphate.　Dissolve 2 grams in water and add 10 ml. of nitric acid and 5 ml. of hydrochloric acid. Evaporate to dryness on the steam bath. Dissolve the residue in 25 ml. of approximately 0.5N sulfuric acid, add 1 ml. of ammonium molybdate reagent solution and 1 ml. of p-methylaminophenol sulfate reagent solution, and allow to stand at room temperature for 2 hours. Any blue color should not exceed that produced by 0.02 mg. of phosphate ion (PO_4) in an equal volume of solution containing the quantities of reagents used in the test, including the residue from the evaporation of the quantities of acids used in the test.

Sulfate.　Dissolve 10 grams in 100 ml. of water, filter if necessary, and add 1 ml. of hydrochloric acid. Heat to boiling, add 5 ml. of barium chloride reagent solution, digest in a covered beaker on the steam bath for 2 hours, and allow to stand overnight. If a precipitate is formed, filter, wash thoroughly, and ignite. The weight of the precipitate should not be more than 0.0012 gram greater than the weight obtained in a complete blank test.

Barium. Dissolve 3 grams of the sample in 10 ml. of dilute hydrochloric acid $(1 + 1)$ and add 5 ml. of nitric acid. For the control dissolve 0.5 gram of sample and 0.05 mg. of barium ion (Ba) in 10 ml. of dilute hydrochloric acid $(1 + 1)$ and add 5 ml. of nitric acid. Evaporate both solutions to dryness. Dissolve the residues in 10 ml. of dilute hydrochloric acid $(1 + 1)$, add 5 ml. of nitric acid, and again evaporate to dryness. Dissolve each residue in water and dilute to 23 ml. To each solution add 2 ml. of potassium dichromate reagent solution and 10 per cent ammonium hydroxide reagent solution until the orange color is just dissipated and the yellow color persists. To each solution add with constant stirring 25 ml. of methanol. Any turbidity in the solution of the sample should not exceed that in the control.

Calcium, magnesium, and R$_2$O$_3$ precipitate. To the filtrate from the test for *Insoluble matter* add 5 ml. of ammonium oxalate reagent solution, 2 ml. of ammonium phosphate reagent solution, and 20 ml. of ammonium hydroxide. Allow to stand overnight, filter, wash with water containing 2.5 per cent ammonia and about 0.1 per cent ammonium oxalate, and ignite. The weight of the residue should not exceed 0.0010 gram.

Heavy metals. Dissolve 6 grams in water and dilute to 30 ml. For the control add 0.02 mg. of lead ion (Pb) to a 5-ml. aliquot of the solution and dilute to 25 ml. Adjust the pH of the control and sample solutions to between 3 and 4 (using a pH meter) with $1N$ acetic acid or ammonium hydroxide (10 per cent NH$_3$), dilute to 40 ml., and mix. Add 10 ml. of freshly prepared hydrogen sulfide water to each and mix. Any color in the solution of the sample should not exceed that in the control.

Iron. Dissolve 5 grams in 50 ml. of water, and add 0.1 ml. of ammonium hydroxide, 6 ml. of hydroxylamine hydrochloride reagent solution, and 4 ml. of 1,10-phenanthroline reagent solution. Any red color should not exceed that produced by 0.015 mg. of iron (Fe) in an equal volume of solution containing the quantities of reagents used in the test. Compare 1 hour after adding the reagents to the sample and standard solutions.

Sodium. Determine the sodium by the flame photometric method described on page 14.

Sample Solution A. Dissolve 1 gram in water and dilute to 100 ml.

Control Solution B. Dissolve 1 gram in water, add 0.05 mg. of sodium ion (Na), and dilute to 100 ml.

Observe the emission of Control Solution B at the 589-mμ sodium line. Observe the emission of Sample Solution A at the 589-mμ sodium line and at a wavelength of 580 mμ. The difference (D_1) between the intensities observed for Sample Solution A at 589 mμ and 580 mμ should not exceed the difference (D_2) observed at 589 mμ between Sample Solution A and Control Solution B.

Notes

Potassium Nitrate

KNO$_3$ Formula Wt. 101.11

REQUIREMENTS

Insoluble matter.   Not more than 0.005 per cent.
pH of a 5 per cent solution.   From 4.5 to 8.5 at 25°C.
Chlorine, total (as Cl).   Not more than 0.002 per cent.
Iodate and nitrite.   To pass test (limit about 0.0005 per cent IO$_3$; about 0.001 per cent NO$_2$).
Phosphate (PO$_4$).   Not more than 0.0005 per cent.
Sulfate (SO$_4$).   Not more than 0.003 per cent.
Calcium, magnesium, and R$_2$O$_3$ precipitate.   Not more than 0.010 per cent.
Heavy metals (as Pb).   Not more than 0.0005 per cent.
Iron (Fe).   Not more than 0.0003 per cent.
Sodium (Na).   Not more than 0.005 per cent.

TESTS

Insoluble matter.   Dissolve 20 grams in 150 ml. of water, heat to boiling, and digest in a covered beaker on the steam bath for 1 hour. Filter through a tared filtering crucible, wash thoroughly, and dry at 105°C. The weight of the residue should not exceed 0.0010 gram.

pH of a 5 per cent solution.   Dissolve 10 grams in 200 ml. of carbon dioxide- and ammonia-free water. Determine the pH by the method described on page 18. The pH should be from 4.5 to 8.5 at 25°C. The pH of a 5 per cent solution of pure potassium nitrate would be 7.0 at 25°C.

Chlorine, total.   Ignite 1 gram, at first gently, and then for a few minutes at about 500°C. Cool, dissolve in about 20 ml. of water, filter if necessary through a chloride-free filter, and dilute to 40 ml. To a 20-ml. aliquot of the solution add 1 ml. of nitric acid and 1 ml. of silver nitrate reagent solution. Any turbidity should not exceed that produced by 0.01 mg. of chloride ion (Cl) in an equal volume of solution containing the quantities of reagents used in the test.

Iodate and nitrite.   Dissolve 1 gram in 10 ml. of water and add 0.10 ml. of 10 per cent potassium iodide reagent solution, 1 ml. of chloroform, and 1 ml. of acetic acid. Shake gently for a few minutes. A pink or violet color should not be observed in the chloroform layer.

Phosphate.   Dissolve 4 grams in 25 ml. of approximately 0.5N sulfuric acid, add 1 ml. of ammonium molybdate reagent solution and 1 ml. of

p-methylaminophenol sulfate reagent solution, and allow to stand at room temperature for 2 hours. Any blue color should not exceed that produced by 0.02 mg. of phosphate (PO_4) in an equal volume of solution containing the quantities of reagents used in the test.

Sulfate.   Dissolve 12 grams in 50 ml. of dilute hydrochloric acid ($1 + 1$) and evaporate to dryness. Treat the residue with 30 ml. of dilute hydrochloric acid ($1 + 1$), again evaporate to dryness, and heat for 1 hour at 120°C. Dissolve the residue in 75 ml. of water plus 1 ml. of hydrochloric acid and filter. Heat the filtrate to boiling, add 5 ml. of barium chloride reagent solution, digest in a covered beaker on the steam bath for 2 hours, and allow to stand overnight. If any precipitate is formed, filter, wash thoroughly, and ignite. The weight of the precipitate should not be more than 0.0010 gram greater than the weight obtained in a complete blank test.

Calcium, magnesium, and R$_2$O$_3$ precipitate.   Dissolve 10 grams in 75 ml. of water, filter, and add 5 ml. of ammonium oxalate reagent solution, 2 ml. of ammonium phosphate reagent solution, and 15 ml. of ammonium hydroxide. Stir well and allow to stand overnight. If any precipitate forms, filter, wash with water containing 2.5 per cent ammonia and about 0.1 per cent ammonium oxalate, and ignite. The weight of the residue should not exceed 0.0010 gram.

Heavy metals.   Dissolve 6 grams in about 20 ml. of water and dilute to 30 ml. For the control add 0.02 mg. of lead ion (Pb) to a 5-ml aliquot of the solution and dilute to 25 ml. For the sample use the remaining 25-ml. portion. Adjust the pH of the control and sample solutions to between 3 and 4 (using a pH meter) with 1N acetic acid or ammonium hydroxide (10 per cent NH$_3$), dilute to 40 ml., and mix. Add 10 ml. of freshly prepared hydrogen sulfide water to each and mix. Any color in the solution of the sample should not exceed that in the control.

Iron.   Dissolve 5 grams in 40 ml. of water, add 2 ml. of hydrochloric acid, and dilute to 50 ml. Add 30 to 50 mg. of ammonium persulfate crystals and 3 ml. of ammonium thiocyanate reagent solution. Any red color should not exceed that produced by 0.015 mg. of iron (Fe) in an equal volume of solution containing the quantities of reagents used in the test.

Sodium.   Determine the sodium by the flame photometric method described on page 14.

Sample Solution A.   Dissolve 1 gram in water and dilute to 100 ml.

Control Solution B.   Dissolve 1 gram in water, add 0.05 mg. of sodium ion (Na), and dilute to 100 ml.

Observe the emission of Control Solution B at the 589-mμ sodium line. Observe the emission of Sample Solution A at the 589-mμ sodium line and at a wavelength of 580 mμ. The difference (D_1) between the intensities observed for Sample Solution A at 580 mμ and 589 mμ should not exceed the difference (D_2) observed at 589 mμ between Sample Solution A and Control Solution B.

Notes

Potassium Nitrite

KNO_2 Formula Wt. 85.11

REQUIREMENTS

Assay. Not less than 94 per cent KNO_2.
Insoluble matter. Not more than 0.010 per cent.
Chloride (Cl). Not more than 0.03 per cent.
Sulfate (SO_4). Not more than 0.01 per cent.
Calcium, magnesium, and R_2O_3 precipitate. Not more than 0.005 per cent.
Heavy metals (as Pb). Not more than 0.001 per cent.
Iron (Fe). Not more than 0.001 per cent.
Sodium (Na). Not more than 0.01 per cent.

TESTS

Assay. Weigh accurately 6 to 7 grams, dissolve in water, and dilute to 1 liter in a volumetric flask. Add 5 ml. of sulfuric acid to 300 ml. of water and, while the solution is still warm, add 0.1N potassium permanganate until a faint pink color that persists for 2 minutes is produced. Then add 40.0 ml. of 0.1N potassium permanganate and mix gently. Add, slowly and with constant agitation, 25.0 ml. of the sample solution, holding the tip of the pipet well below the surface of the liquid. Add 15.0 ml. of 0.1N ferrous ammonium sulfate, allow the solution to stand for 5 minutes, and titrate the excess ferrous ammonium sulfate with 0.1N potassium permanganate. Each milliliter of 0.1N potassium permanganate consumed by the potassium nitrite corresponds to 0.004256 gram of KNO_2.

Insoluble matter. Dissolve 20 grams in 200 ml. of water, heat to boiling, and digest in a covered beaker on the steam bath for 1 hour. Filter through a tared filtering crucible, reserve the filtrate without the washings for the test for *Calcium, magnesium, and R_2O_3* precipitate, wash thoroughly, and dry at 105°C. The weight of the residue should not exceed 0.0020 gram.

Chloride. Dissolve 3.3 grams in 20 ml. of water, filter if necessary through a chloride-free filter, and dilute to 100 ml. Dilute 1 ml. of this solution with 15 ml. of water and slowly add 1 ml. of acetic acid. Heat to boiling, boil gently for 5 minutes, cool, and dilute to 20 ml. Add 1 ml. of nitric acid and 1 ml. of silver nitrate reagent solution. Any turbidity should not exceed that produced by 0.01 mg. of chloride ion (Cl) in an equal volume of solution containing the quantities of reagents used in the test.

ACS SPECIFICATIONS   **469**

Sample Solution A for the determination of Sulfate, Heavy metals, and Iron. Dissolve 10 grams in water and dilute to 100 ml. (1 ml. = 0.1 gram).

Sulfate. To 4 ml. of Sample Solution A (0.4-gram sample) add slowly 1 ml. of hydrochloric acid and evaporate to dryness on the steam bath. Dissolve the residue in 4 ml. of water plus 1 ml. of dilute hydrochloric acid (1 + 19), filter if necessary through a small filter, and dilute to 10 ml. Add 1 ml. of barium chloride reagent solution. Any turbidity should not exceed that produced by 0.04 mg. of sulfate ion (SO_4) in an equal volume of solution containing the quantities of reagents used in the test. Compare 10 minutes after adding the barium chloride to the sample and standard solutions.

Calcium, magnesium, and R_2O_3 precipitate. To the filtrate without the washings retained from the test for *Insoluble matter,* add 10 ml. of ammonium oxalate reagent solution, 5 ml. of ammonium phosphate reagent solution, and 5 ml. of ammonium hydroxide, and allow to stand overnight. If any precipitate is formed, filter, wash with water containing 2.5 per cent ammonia and about 0.1 per cent ammonium oxalate, and ignite. The weight of the residue should not exceed 0.0010 gram.

Heavy metals. To 30 ml. of Sample Solution A (3-gram sample) add 5 ml. of hydrochloric acid. For the control add 0.02 mg. of lead ion (Pb) and 5 ml. of hydrochloric acid to 10 ml. of Sample Solution A. Evaporate both to dryness on the steam bath. Add 5 ml. of hydrochloric acid to each residue and again evaporate to dryness. Dissolve in about 20 ml. of water, filter if necessary, and dilute to 25 ml. Adjust the pH of the control and sample solutions to between 3 and 4 (using a pH meter) with 1N acetic acid or ammonium hydroxide (10 per cent NH_3), dilute to 40 ml., and mix. Add 10 ml. of freshly prepared hydrogen sulfide water to each and mix. Any color in the solution of the sample should not exceed that in the control.

Iron. To 10 ml. of Sample Solution A (1-gram sample) add 5 ml. of hydrochloric acid and evaporate to dryness on the steam bath. Dissolve in 15 to 20 ml. of water, add 2 ml. of hydrochloric acid, filter if necessary, and dilute to 50 ml. Add 30 to 50 mg. of ammonium persulfate crystals and 3 ml. of ammonium thiocyanate reagent solution. Any red color should not exceed that produced by 0.01 mg. of iron (Fe) in an equal volume of solution containing the quantities of reagents used in the test.

Sodium. Determine the sodium by the flame photometric method described on page 14.

Sample Solution A. Dissolve 1 gram in water and dilute to 100 ml.

Control Solution B. Dissolve 1 gram in water, add 0.10 mg. of sodium ion (Na), and dilute to 100 ml.

Observe the emission of Control Solution B at the 589-mμ sodium line. Observe the emission of Sample Solution A at the 589-mμ sodium line and at a wavelength of 580 mμ. The difference (D_1) between the intensities observed for Sample Solution A at 580 mμ and 589 mμ should not exceed the difference (D_2) observed at 589 mμ between Sample Solution A and Control Solution B.

Notes

Potassium Oxalate

$(COOK)_2 \cdot H_2O$ Formula Wt. 184.24

REQUIREMENTS

Insoluble matter.   Not more than 0.010 per cent.
Neutrality.   To pass test.
Chloride (Cl).   Not more than 0.002 per cent.
Sulfate (SO_4).   Not more than 0.010 per cent.
Ammonium (NH_4).   Not more than 0.002 per cent.
Heavy metals (as Pb).   Not more than 0.002 per cent.
Iron (Fe).   Not more than 0.001 per cent.
Sodium (Na).   Not more than 0.02 per cent.
Substances darkened by hot sulfuric acid.   To pass test.

TESTS

Insoluble matter.   Dissolve 10 grams in 100 ml. of water, heat to boiling, and digest in a covered beaker on the steam bath for 1 hour. Filter through a tared filtering crucible, wash thoroughly, and dry at 105°C. The weight of the residue should not exceed 0.0010 gram.

Neutrality.   Dissolve 2 grams in 200 ml. of water, and add 10.0 ml. of 0.01N oxalic acid and 0.20 ml. of a 1 per cent solution of phenolphthalein. Boil the solution in a flask for 10 minutes, passing through it a stream of carbon dioxide-free air. Cool the solution rapidly to room temperature while keeping the flow of carbon dioxide-free air passing through it and titrate with 0.01N sodium hydroxide. Not less than 9.2 nor more than 10.5 ml. of 0.01N sodium hydroxide should be required to match the pink color produced in a buffer solution containing 0.20 ml. of a 1 per cent solution of phenolphthalein. The buffer solution contains in 1 liter 3.1 grams of boric acid (H_3BO_3), 3.8 grams of potassium chloride, and 5.90 ml. of 1N sodium hydroxide.

Chloride.   Ignite 1 gram in a platinum crucible, dissolve the residue in 20 ml. of water, neutralize the solution with nitric acid, filter if necessary through a chloride-free filter, and dilute to 40 ml. To 20 ml. of the solution add 1 ml. of nitric acid and 1 ml. of silver nitrate reagent solution. Any turbidity should not exceed that produced by 0.01 mg. of chloride ion (Cl) in an equal volume of solution containing the quantities of reagents used in the test.

Sulfate.   Mix 0.5 gram with 1 ml. of water, add 1 ml. of nitric acid and 1 ml. of 30 per cent hydrogen peroxide, and digest in a covered beaker on the steam bath until the reaction ceases. Remove the cover and evaporate to dryness. Dissolve the residue in 6 ml. of dilute hydrochloric acid $(1 + 1)$ and again evaporate to dryness. Dissolve the residue in 4 ml. of water plus 1 ml. of dilute hydrochloric acid $(1 + 19)$. Filter if necessary through a small filter, wash with two 2-ml. portions of water, and dilute to 10 ml. Add 1 ml. of barium chloride reagent solution. Any turbidity should not exceed that produced when a solution containing 0.05 mg. of sulfate ion (SO_4) is treated exactly like the sample. Compare ten minutes after adding the barium chloride to the sample and standard solutions.

Ammonium.   Dissolve 1 gram in 50 ml. of ammonia-free water and add 2 ml. of Nessler reagent. Any color should not exceed that produced by 0.02 mg. of ammonium ion (NH_4) in an equal volume of solution containing 2 ml. of Nessler reagent.

Heavy metals.   Mix 2 grams with 2 ml. of water, add 2 ml. of nitric acid and 2 ml. of 30 per cent hydrogen peroxide, and digest in a covered beaker on a steam bath until reaction ceases. Remove the cover and evaporate to dryness. Dissolve the residue in 4 ml. of dilute nitric acid $(1 + 1)$ and again evaporate to dryness. Dissolve the residue in about 20 ml. of water and dilute to 32 ml. For the control evaporate one half the quantities of nitric acid and hydrogen peroxide used in the preparation of the sample solution. Dissolve the residue in about 10 ml. of water, add an 8-ml. aliquot of the sample solution plus 0.02 mg. of lead ion (Pb), and dilute to 25 ml. For the sample dilute the remaining 24-ml portion to 25 ml. Adjust the pH of the control and sample solutions to between 3 and 4 (using a pH meter) with $1N$ acetic acid or ammonium hydroxide (10 per cent NH_3), dilute to 40 ml., and mix. Add 10 ml. of freshly prepared hydrogen sulfide water to each and mix. Any color in the solution of the sample should not exceed that in the control.

Iron.   Mix 2 grams with 2 ml. of water, add 2 ml. of nitric acid and 2 ml. of 30 per cent hydrogen peroxide, and digest in a covered beaker on the steam bath until reaction ceases. Remove the cover and evaporate to dryness. Add 5 ml. of hydrochloric acid and again evaporate to dryness. Dissolve the residue in water plus 4 ml. hydrochloric acid and dilute to 100 ml. To 50 ml. of the solution add 30 to 50 mg. of ammonium persulfate crystals and 3 ml. of ammonium thiocyanate reagent solution. Any red color should not exceed that produced by 0.01 mg. of iron (Fe) in an equal volume of solution containing the quantities of reagents used in the test, including the residue from evaporation of 1 ml. each of nitric acid and 30 per cent hydrogen peroxide and 2.5 ml. of hydrochloric acid.

Sodium.   Determine the sodium by the flame photometric method described on page 14.

Sample Solution A.   Treat 1 gram with 1 ml. of nitric acid and 2 ml. of hydrogen peroxide in a covered beaker on the steam bath until reaction ceases. Add 1 ml. of hydrogen peroxide and continue with digestion until reaction ceases. Remove cover and evaporate to dryness. Dissolve the residue in water and dilute to 100 ml.

Control Solution B.   Treat 1 gram plus 0.20 mg. of sodium ion (Na) exactly like Sample Solution A.

Observe the emission of Control Solution B at the 589-mμ sodium line. Observe the emission of Sample Solution A at the 589-mμ sodium line and at a wavelength of 580 mμ. The difference (D_1) between the intensities observed for Sample Solution A at 580 mμ and 589 mμ should not exceed the difference (D_2) observed at 589 mμ between Sample Solution A and Control Solution B.

Substances darkened by hot sulfuric acid.   Heat 1 gram in a recently ignited test tube with 10 ml. of sulfuric acid until the appearance of dense fumes. The acid when cooled should have no more color than a mixture of the following composition: 0.2 ml. of cobaltous chloride solution (5.95 grams of $CoCl_2 \cdot 6H_2O$ and 2.5 ml. of hydrochloric acid in 100 ml.), 0.3 ml. of ferric chloride solution (4.50 grams of $FeCl_3 \cdot 6H_2O$ and 2.5 ml. of hydrochloric acid in 100 ml.), 0.3 ml. of cupric sulfate solution (6.24 grams of $CuSO_4 \cdot 5H_2O$ and 2.5 ml. of hydrochloric acid in 100 ml.), and 9.2 ml. of water.

Notes

Potassium Periodate

Potassium Metaperiodate

(Suitable for determination of manganese)

KIO$_4$ Formula Wt. 230.00

REQUIREMENTS

Assay. Not less than 99.8 nor more than 100.3 per cent KIO$_4$.
Other halogens (as Cl). Not more than 0.01 per cent.
Manganese (Mn). Not more than 0.0001 per cent.

TESTS

Assay. Weigh accurately about 1 gram, previously dried over sulfuric acid for 6 hours, dissolve in water, and dilute to 500 ml. in a volumetric flask. To a 50-ml. aliquot in a glass-stoppered flask add 10 grams of potassium iodide and 10 ml. of a cooled solution of dilute sulfuric acid $(1 + 5)$. Allow to stand for 5 minutes, add 100 ml. of cold water, and titrate the liberated iodine with 0.1N sodium thiosulfate, adding starch indicator solution near the end point. Carry out a complete blank test and make any necessary correction. One milliliter of 0.1N thiosulfate corresponds to 0.002875 gram of KIO$_4$.

Other halogens. Dissolve 0.5 gram in a mixture of 10 ml. of water and 16 ml. of sulfurous acid and boil for 3 minutes. Cool, add 5 ml. of ammonium hydroxide and 20 ml. of 2.5 per cent silver nitrate solution, and filter. Dilute the filtrate to 100 ml. and to 20 ml. of this solution add 1.5 ml. of nitric acid. Any turbidity should not exceed that produced by 0.01 mg. of chloride ion (Cl) in an equal volume of solution containing 0.5 ml. of ammonium hydroxide, 1.5 ml. of nitric acid, and 1 ml. of silver nitrate reagent solution.

Manganese. Add 5.5 grams to 85 ml. of 10 per cent sulfuric acid reagent solution. For the control add 0.5 gram of the sample and 0.005 mg. of manganese ion (Mn) to 85 ml. of 10 per cent sulfuric acid reagent solution. Add 10 ml. of nitric acid and 5 ml. of phosphoric acid to each, boil gently for 10 minutes, and cool. Any pink color in the solution of the sample should not exceed that in the control.

Notes

Potassium Permanganate

KMnO$_4$ Formula Wt. 158.04

REQUIREMENTS

Insoluble matter. Not more than 0.20 per cent.
Chloride and chlorate (as Cl). Not more than 0.005 per cent.
Nitrogen compounds (as N). Not more than 0.005 per cent.
Sulfate (SO$_4$). Not more than 0.02 per cent.

TESTS

Insoluble matter. Dissolve 2 grams in 150 ml. of warm water at steam bath temperature. Filter at once through a tared filtering crucible, wash thoroughly, and dry at 105°C. The weight of the residue should not exceed 0.0040 gram.

Chloride and chlorate. Dissolve 1 gram in 75 ml. of water and add 5 ml. of nitric acid and 3 ml. of 30 per cent hydrogen peroxide. After reduction is complete, filter if necessary through a chloride-free filter, and dilute to 100 ml. To 20 ml. of this solution add 1 ml. of silver nitrate reagent solution. Any turbidity should not exceed that produced by 0.01 mg. of chloride ion (Cl) in an equal volume of solution containing the quantities of reagents used in the test.

Nitrogen compounds. Dissolve 1 gram in 100 ml. of water in a flask connected through a spray trap to a condenser, the end of which dips beneath the surface of 10 ml. of 0.1N hydrochloric acid. Add to the flask 40 ml. of freshly boiled 10 per cent sodium hydroxide reagent solution and 0.5 gram of aluminum wire in small pieces. Allow to stand for 1 hour, slowly distill about 60 ml., and dilute the distillate to 100 ml. To 25 ml. of the diluted distillate add 1 ml. of 10 per cent sodium hydroxide reagent solution, dilute to 50 ml., and add 2 ml. of Nessler reagent. Any color should not exceed that produced when a quantity of an ammonium salt containing 0.05 mg. of nitrogen (N) is treated exactly like the sample.

Sulfate. Dissolve 5 grams in 75 ml. of water, and add 10 ml. of alcohol and 10 ml. of hydrochloric acid. Heat until colorless, adding more alcohol and a little hydrochloric acid if necessary. Evaporate to dryness. Dissolve the residue in 100 ml. of dilute hydrochloric acid (1 + 99), filter, and heat to boiling. Add 5 ml. of barium chloride reagent solution, digest in a covered beaker on the steam bath for 2 hours, and allow to stand overnight. Filter, wash thoroughly, and ignite. The weight of the precipitate should not be more than 0.0024 gram greater than the weight obtained in a complete blank test.

Notes

Potassium Phosphate, Dibasic
Dipotassium Hydrogen Phosphate

K_2HPO_4 Formula Wt. 174.18

REQUIREMENTS

Insoluble matter.   Not more than 0.010 per cent.
Loss on drying at 105°C.   Not more than 1.0 per cent.
pH of a 5 per cent solution.   From 8.5 to 9.6 at 25°C.
Chloride (Cl).   Not more than 0.003 per cent.
Nitrogen compounds (as N).   Not more than 0.001 per cent.
Sulfate (SO_4).   Not more than 0.005 per cent.
Heavy metals (as Pb).   Not more than 0.0005 per cent.
Iron (Fe).   Not more than 0.001 per cent.

TESTS

Insoluble matter.   Dissolve 10 grams in 100 ml. of water, heat to boiling, and digest in a covered beaker on the steam bath for 1 hour. Filter through a tared filtering crucible (not glass), wash thoroughly with hot water, and dry at 105°C. The weight of the residue should not exceed 0.0010 gram.

Loss on drying at 105°C.   Weigh accurately about 2 grams. Dry to constant weight at 105°C. The loss in weight should not exceed 1.0 per cent.

pH of a 5 per cent solution.   Dissolve 10 grams in 200 ml. of carbon dioxide- and ammonia-free water. Determine the pH by the method described on page 18. The pH should be from 8.5 to 9.6 at 25°C.

Chloride.   Dissolve 1 gram in 20 ml. of water, filter if necessary through a chloride-free filter, add 3 ml. of nitric acid, and dilute to 30 ml. Dilute 10 ml. of this solution to 20 ml. and add 1 ml. of silver nitrate reagent solution. Any turbidity should not exceed that produced by 0.01 mg. of chloride ion (Cl) in an equal volume of solution containing the quantities of reagents used in the test.

Nitrogen compounds.   Dissolve 1 gram in 60 ml. of water in a flask connected through a spray trap to a condenser, the end of which dips beneath the surface of 10 ml. of 0.1N hydrochloric acid. Add to the flask 10 ml. of freshly boiled 10 per cent sodium hydroxide reagent solution and 0.5 gram of aluminum wire in small pieces, allow to stand for 1 hour, and distill 35 ml. To the distillate add 1 ml. of 10 per cent sodium hydroxide reagent solution, dilute to 50 ml., and add 2 ml. of

Nessler reagent. Any color should not exceed that produced when a solution of an ammonium salt containing 0.01 mg. of nitrogen (N) is treated exactly like the sample.

Sulfate. Dissolve 10 grams in 200 ml. of water, add sufficient hydrochloric acid to make the solution acid to methyl orange, heat to boiling, and filter. Heat again to boiling, add 10 ml. of barium chloride reagent solution, digest in a covered beaker on the steam bath for 2 hours, and allow to stand overnight. If a precipitate is formed, filter, wash thoroughly, and ignite. The weight of the precipitate should not be more than 0.0012 gram greater than the weight obtained in a complete blank test.

Heavy metals. Dissolve 6 grams in about 20 ml. of water, add 6 ml. of 4N hydrochloric acid, and dilute to 30 ml. For the control add 0.02 mg. of lead ion (Pb) to a 5-ml. aliquot of the solution and dilute to 25 ml. For the sample use the remaining 25-ml. portion. Adjust the pH of the control and sample solutions to between 3 and 4 (using a pH meter) with 1N acetic acid or ammonium hydroxide (10 per cent NH_3), dilute to 40 ml., and mix. Add 10 ml. of freshly prepared hydrogen sulfide water to each and mix. Any color in the solution of the sample should not exceed that in the control.

Iron. To 1 gram in 10 ml. of water add 6 ml. of hydroxylamine hydrochloride reagent solution and 4 ml. of 1,10-phenanthroline reagent solution, and dilute to 25 ml. Any color should not exceed that produced by 0.01 mg. of iron (Fe) in an equal volume of solution containing the quantities of reagents used in the test. Compare 1 hour after adding the reagents to the sample and standard solutions.

Notes

Potassium Phosphate, Monobasic

Potassium Dihydrogen Phosphate

KH_2PO_4 Formula Wt. 136.09

REQUIREMENTS

Insoluble matter, calcium and ammonium hydroxide precipitate.   Not
   more than 0.010 per cent.
Loss on drying over sulfuric acid.   Not more than 0.20 per cent.
pH of a 5 per cent solution.   From 4.1 to 4.5 at 25°C.
Chloride (Cl).   Not more than 0.001 per cent.
Nitrogen compounds (as N).   Not more than 0.001 per cent.
Sulfate (SO_4).   Not more than 0.003 per cent.
Heavy metals (as Pb).   Not more than 0.001 per cent.
Iron (Fe).   Not more than 0.002 per cent.
Sodium (Na).   Not more than 0.005 per cent.

TESTS

Insoluble matter, calcium and ammonium hydroxide precipitate.   Dissolve 10 grams in 100 ml. of water, add 5 ml. of ammonium oxalate
reagent solution, and add ammonium hydroxide until the solution is distinctly alkaline to litmus. Add an excess of 15 ml. of ammonium hydroxide
and allow to stand overnight. If a precipitate is formed, filter, wash with
water containing 2.5 per cent ammonia and about 0.1 per cent ammonium
oxalate, and ignite at 800° ± 25°C. for 15 minutes. The weight of the
residue should not exceed 0.0010 gram.

Loss on drying over sulfuric acid.   Weigh accurately about 2 grams and
dry for 24 hours over sulfuric acid. The loss in weight should not exceed
0.20 per cent.

pH of a 5 per cent solution.   Dissolve 10 grams in 200 ml. of carbon
dioxide- and ammonia-free water. Determine the pH by the method described on page 18. The pH should be from 4.1 to 4.5 at 25°C. The pH
of a 5 per cent solution of pure potassium phosphate, monobasic, would
be 4.2 at 25°C.

Chloride.   Dissolve 1 gram in 20 ml. of water, filter if necessary through
a chloride-free filter, and add 2 ml. of nitric acid and 1 ml. of silver nitrate
reagent solution. Any turbidity should not exceed that produced by 0.01
mg. of chloride ion (Cl) in an equal volume of solution containing the
quantities of reagents used in the test.

Nitrogen compounds. Dissolve 1 gram in 60 ml. of water in a flask connected through a spray trap to a condenser, the end of which dips beneath the surface of 10 ml. of 0.1N hydrochloric acid. Add to the flask 20 ml. of freshly boiled 10 per cent sodium hydroxide reagent solution and 0.5 gram of aluminum wire in small pieces, allow the solution to stand for 1 hour, and distill about 35 ml. To the distillate add 1 ml. of 10 per cent sodium hydroxide reagent solution, dilute to 50 ml., and add 2 ml. of Nessler reagent. Any color should not exceed that produced when a quantity of an ammonium salt containing 0.01 mg. of nitrogen (N) is treated exactly like the sample.

Sulfate. Dissolve 13.7 grams in 150 ml. of water plus 2 ml. of hydrochloric acid, filter if necessary, and heat to boiling. Add 5 ml. of barium chloride reagent solution, digest in a covered beaker on the steam bath for 2 hours, and allow to stand overnight. If a precipitate is formed, filter, wash thoroughly, and ignite. The weight of the precipitate should not be more than 0.0010 gram greater than the weight obtained in a complete blank test.

Heavy metals. Dissolve 4 grams in about 20 ml. of water and dilute to 32 ml. For the control add 0.02 mg. of lead ion (Pb) to an 8-ml. aliquot of the solution and dilute to 25 ml. For the sample dilute the remaining 24-ml. portion to 25 ml. Adjust the pH of the control and sample solutions to between 3 and 4 (using a pH meter) with 1N acetic acid or ammonium hydroxide (10 per cent NH_3), dilute to 40 ml., and mix. Add 10 ml. of freshly prepared hydrogen sulfide water to each and mix. Any color in the solution of the sample should not exceed that in the control.

Iron. Dissolve 1 gram in water and dilute to 20 ml. To 10 ml. of the solution add 6 ml. of hydroxylamine hydrochloride reagent solution and 4 ml. of 1,10-phenanthroline reagent solution and dilute to 25 ml. Any red color should not exceed that produced by 0.01 mg. of iron (Fe) in an equal volume of solution containing the quantities of reagents used in the test. Compare 1 hour after adding the reagents to the sample and standard solutions.

Sodium. Determine the sodium by the flame photometric method described on page 14.

Sample Solution A. Dissolve 1 gram in water and dilute to 100 ml.

Control Solution B. Dissolve 1 gram in water, add 0.05 mg. of sodium ion (Na), and dilute to 100 ml.

Observe the emission of Control Solution B at the 589-mμ sodium line. Observe the emission of Sample Solution A at the 589-mμ sodium line and at a wavelength of 580 mμ. The difference (D_1) between the intensities observed for Sample Solution A at 580 mμ and 589 mμ should not exceed the difference (D_2) observed at 589 mμ between Sample Solution A and Control Solution B.

Notes

Potassium Pyrosulfate

Note. This product is usually a mixture of potassium pyrosulfate, $K_2S_2O_7$, and potassium bisulfate, $KHSO_4$.

REQUIREMENTS

Acidity (as H_2SO_4). Not less than 35.0 nor more than 37.0 per cent.
Water (H_2O). Not more than 2.5 per cent.
Insoluble matter and ammonium hydroxide precipitate. Not more than 0.010 per cent.
Chloride (Cl). Not more than 0.002 per cent.
Phosphate (PO_4). Not more than 0.001 per cent.
Arsenic (As). Not more than 0.0005 per cent.
Calcium and magnesium precipitate. Not more than 0.005 per cent.
Heavy metals (as Pb). Not more than 0.001 per cent.
Iron (Fe). Not more than 0.002 per cent.
Sodium (Na). Not more than 0.01 per cent.

TESTS

Acidity. Weigh accurately about 4 grams, dissolve in 50 ml. of water, and titrate with $1N$ alkali, using methyl orange as indicator. One milliliter of $1N$ alkali corresponds to 0.04904 gram of H_2SO_4.

Water. Weigh accurately about 5 grams, dissolve in water, and dilute to 250 ml. Evaporate 25.0 ml. of the solution to dryness in a tared platinum container and ignite to remove all sulfuric acid and leave K_2SO_4. Calculate the percentage of K_2SO_4 (B).

Calculate the percentage of SO_3 (A) from the percentage of H_2SO_4 obtained in the test for acidity. One per cent of H_2SO_4 is equivalent to 0.8163 per cent of SO_3.

Calculate the percentage of H_2O (C) as the difference between 100 per cent and the sum of the percentages of SO_3 and K_2SO_4.

$$C = 100 - (A + B)$$

Insoluble matter and ammonium hydroxide precipitate. Dissolve 20 grams in 200 ml. of water, add ammonium hydroxide until the solution is alkaline to methyl red, boil for 1 minute, and digest in a covered beaker on the steam bath for 1 hour. Filter through a tared filtering crucible, saving the filtrate separate from the washings for the test for *Calcium and magnesium precipitate.* Wash thoroughly and dry at 105°C. The weight of the residue should not exceed 0.0020 gram.

Chloride. Dissolve 1 gram in 50 ml. of water, filter if necessary through a chloride-free filter, and to 25 ml. of the solution add 1 ml. of nitric acid and 1 ml. of silver nitrate reagent solution. Any turbidity should not exceed that produced by 0.01 mg. of chloride ion (Cl) in an equal volume of solution containing the quantities of reagents used in the test.

Phosphate. Dissolve 2 grams in 15 ml. of dilute ammonium hydroxide (1 + 2), and evaporate to dryness. Dissolve the residue in 25 ml. of approximately 0.5N hydrochloric acid, add 1 ml. of ammonium molybdate reagent solution and 1 ml. of p-methylaminophenol sulfate reagent solution, and allow to stand for 2 hours at room temperature. Any blue color should not exceed that produced by 0.02 mg. of phosphate ion (PO_4) in an equal volume of solution containing the quantities of reagents used in the test, including the residue from evaporation of 5 ml. of ammonium hydroxide.

Arsenic. Determine the arsenic in 0.4 gram by the Gutzeit method (page 11). The amount of stain should not exceed that produced by 0.002 mg. of arsenic (As).

Calcium and magnesium precipitate. To the filtrate from the test for *Insoluble matter and ammonium hydroxide precipitate* (without the washings) add 5 ml. of ammonium oxalate reagent solution, 3 ml. of ammonium phosphate reagent solution, and 10 ml. of ammonium hydroxide. If any precipitate forms on standing overnight, filter, wash thoroughly with water containing 2.5 per cent ammonia and about 0.1 per cent ammonium oxalate, and ignite. The weight of the residue should not exceed 0.0010 gram.

Heavy metals. Dissolve 4 grams in about 20 ml. of water and dilute to 32 ml. For the control add 0.02 mg. of lead ion (Pb) to an 8-ml. aliquot of the solution and dilute to 25 ml. For the sample dilute the remaining 24-ml. portion to 25 ml. Adjust the pH of the control and sample solutions to between 3 and 4 (using a pH meter) with 1N acetic acid or ammonium hydroxide (10 per cent NH_3), dilute to 40 ml., and mix. Add 10 ml. of freshly prepared hydrogen sulfide water to each and mix. Any color in the solution of the sample should not exceed that in the control.

Iron. Dissolve 5 grams in 80 ml. of dilute hydrochloric acid (1 + 3) and boil gently for 10 minutes. Cool and dilute to 100 ml. Dilute 10 ml. of this solution to 50 ml. and add 30 to 50 mg. of ammonium persulfate crystals and 3 ml. of ammonium thiocyanate reagent solution. Any red color should not exceed that produced by 0.01 mg. of iron (Fe) in an

equal volume of solution containing the quantities of reagents used in the test.

Sodium. Determine the sodium by the flame photometric method described on page 14.

Sample Solution A. Dissolve 1 gram in water and dilute to 100 ml.

Control Solution B. Dissolve 1 gram in water, add 0.10 mg. of sodium ion (Na), and dilute to 100 ml.

Observe the emission of Control Solution B at the 589-mμ sodium line. Observe the emission of Sample Solution A at the 589-mμ sodium line and at a wavelength of 580 mμ. The difference (D_1) between the intensities observed for Sample Solution A at 580 mμ and 589 mμ should not exceed the difference (D_2) observed at 589 mμ between Sample Solution A and Control Solution B.

Notes

Potassium Sodium Tartrate

KOCOCHOHCHOHCOONa·4H$_2$O   Formula Wt. 282.23

REQUIREMENTS

Insoluble matter.   Not more than 0.005 per cent.
pH of a 5 per cent solution.   From 6.0 to 8.5 at 25°C.
Chloride (Cl).   Not more than 0.001 per cent.
Phosphate (PO$_4$).   Not more than 0.002 per cent.
Sulfate (SO$_4$).   Not more than 0.005 per cent.
Ammonium (NH$_4$).   Not more than 0.002 per cent.
Calcium (Ca).   Not more than 0.005 per cent.
Heavy metals (as Pb).   Not more than 0.0005 per cent.
Iron (Fe).   Not more than 0.001 per cent.

TESTS

Insoluble matter.   Dissolve 20 grams in 200 ml. of water, heat to boiling, and digest in a covered beaker on the steam bath for 1 hour. Filter through a tared filtering crucible, wash thoroughly, and dry at 105°C. The weight of the residue should not exceed 0.0010 gram. Retain the filtrate for the test for *Sulfate*.

pH of a 5 per cent solution.   Dissolve 10 grams in 200 ml. of carbon dioxide- and ammonia-free water. Determine the pH by the method described on page 18. The pH should be from 6.0 to 8.5 at 25°C. The pH of a 5 per cent solution of pure potassium sodium tartrate would be 8.4 at 25°C.

Chloride.   Dissolve 1 gram in 20 ml. of water, filter if necessary through a chloride-free filter, and add 2 ml. of nitric acid and 1 ml. of silver nitrate reagent solution. Any turbidity should not exceed that produced by 0.01 mg. of chloride ion (Cl) in an equal volume of solution containing the quantities of reagents used in the test.

Phosphate.   Ignite 1 gram in a platinum dish. Dissolve the residue in 5 ml. of water, add 5 ml. of nitric acid, and evaporate to dryness. Dissolve the residue in 25 ml. of approximately 0.5N sulfuric acid, add 1 ml. of ammonium molybdate reagent solution and 1 ml. of *p*-methylaminophenol sulfate reagent solution, and allow to stand for 2 hours at room temperature. Any blue color should not exceed that produced by 0.02 mg. of phosphate ion (PO$_4$) in an equal volume of solution containing the quantities of reagents used in the test.

Sulfate. To the filtrate obtained in the test for *Insoluble matter,* which should measure about 200 ml., add 10 ml. of hydrochloric acid. Heat to boiling, add 10 ml. of barium chloride reagent solution, digest in a covered beaker on the steam bath for 2 hours, and allow to stand overnight. If a precipitate is formed, filter, wash thoroughly, and ignite. The weight of the precipitate should not be more than 0.0025 gram greater than the weight obtained in a complete blank test.

Ammonium. Dissolve 1 gram in 50 ml. of water. To 25 ml. of the solution add 2 ml. of 10 per cent sodium hydroxide reagent solution, dilute to 50 ml., and add 2 ml. of Nessler reagent. Any color should not exceed that produced by 0.01 mg. of ammonium ion (NH_4) in an equal volume of solution containing the quantities of reagents used in the test.

Calcium. Determine the calcium by the flame photometric method described on page 14. Dissolve 10 grams in 80 ml. of dilute hydrochloric acid $(1 + 7)$ and digest in a covered beaker on the steam bath for 20 minutes. Cool and dilute to 100 ml. with water.

Sample Solution A. Dilute a 20-ml. aliquot (2 gram) of this solution to 100 ml. with water.

Control Solution B. Add 0.10 mg. of calcium ion (Ca) to another 20-ml. aliquot and dilute to 100 ml. with water.

Observe the emission of Control Solution B at the 422.7-mμ calcium line. Observe the emission of Sample Solution A at the 422.7-mμ calcium line and at wavelength of 416.7 mμ. The difference (D_1) between the intensities observed for Sample Solution A at 422.7 mμ and 416.7 mμ should not exceed the difference (D_2) observed at 422.7 mμ between Sample Solution A and Control Solution B.

Heavy metals. Dissolve 8 grams in about 20 ml. of water and dilute to 32 ml. For the control add 0.02 mg. of lead ion (Pb) to an 8-ml. aliquot of the solution and dilute to 25 ml. For the sample dilute the remaining 24-ml. portion to 25 ml. Adjust the pH of the control and sample solutions to between 3 and 4 (using a pH meter) with 1N acetic acid or ammonium hydroxide (10 per cent NH_3), dilute to 40 ml., and mix. Add 10 ml. of freshly prepared hydrogen sulfide water to each and mix. Any color in the solution of the sample should not exceed that in the control.

Iron. Dissolve 1 gram in 40 ml. of water and add 2 ml. of hydrochloric acid, dilute to 50 ml., and add 30 to 50 mg. of ammonium persulfate crystals and 3 ml. of ammonium thiocyanate reagent solution. Any red color should not exceed that produced by 0.01 mg. of iron (Fe) in an equal volume of solution containing the quantities of reagents used in the test.

Notes

Potassium Sulfate

K$_2$SO$_4$ Formula Wt. 174.27

REQUIREMENTS

Insoluble matter. Not more than 0.010 per cent.
pH of a 5 per cent solution. From 5.5 to 8.5 at 25°C.
Chloride (Cl). Not more than 0.001 per cent.
Nitrogen compounds (as N). Not more than 0.0005 per cent.
Arsenic (As). Not more than 0.0002 per cent.
Calcium, magnesium, and R$_2$O$_3$ precipitate. Not more than 0.020 per cent.
Heavy metals (as Pb). Not more than 0.0005 per cent.
Iron (Fe). Not more than 0.0005 per cent.
Sodium (Na). Not more than 0.02 per cent.

TESTS

Insoluble matter. Dissolve 10 grams in 150 ml. of water, heat to boiling, and digest in a covered beaker on the steam bath for 1 hour. Filter through a tared filtering crucible, wash thoroughly, and dry at 105°C. The weight of the residue should not exceed 0.0010 gram.

pH of a 5 per cent solution. Dissolve 10 grams in 200 ml. of carbon dioxide- and ammonia-free water. Determine the pH of the solution by the method described on page 18. The pH should be from 5.5 to 8.5 at 25°C. The pH of a 5 per cent solution of pure potassium sulfate would be 7.3 at 25°C.

Chloride. Dissolve 1 gram in 25 ml. of water, filter if necessary through a chloride-free filter, and add 1 ml. of nitric acid and 1 ml. of silver nitrate reagent solution. Any turbidity should not exceed that produced by 0.01 mg. of chloride ion (Cl) in an equal volume of solution containing the quantities of reagents used in the test.

Nitrogen compounds. Dissolve 2 grams in 60 ml. of warm water in a flask that is connected through a spray trap to a condenser, the end of which dips beneath the surface of 10 ml. of 0.1N hydrochloric acid. Add to the flask 10 ml. of freshly boiled 10 per cent sodium hydroxide reagent solution and 0.5 gram of aluminum wire in small pieces, allow to stand for 1 hour, and slowly distill about 35 ml. To the distillate add 1 ml. of 10 per cent sodium hydroxide reagent solution, dilute to 50 ml., and add 2 ml. of Nessler reagent. Any color should not exceed that produced when a quantity of an ammonium salt containing 0.01 mg. of nitrogen (N) is treated exactly like the sample.

Arsenic. Determine the arsenic in 1 gram by the Gutzeit method (page 11). The amount of stain should not exceed that produced by 0.002 mg. of arsenic (As).

Calcium, magnesium, and R$_2$O$_3$ precipitate. Dissolve 5 grams in 75 ml. of water, filter, and add 5 ml. of ammonium oxalate reagent solution, 2 ml. of ammonium phosphate reagent solution, and 10 ml. of ammonium hydroxide. Allow to stand overnight. If any precipitate is formed, filter, wash with water containing 2.5 per cent ammonia and about 0.1 per cent ammonium oxalate, and ignite. The weight of the residue should not exceed 0.0010 gram.

Heavy metals. Dissolve 6 grams in water and dilute to 54 ml. For the control add 0.02 mg. of lead ion (Pb) to a 9-ml. aliquot of the solution and dilute to 45 ml. For the sample use the remaining 45-ml. portion. Adjust the pH of the control and sample solutions to between 3 and 4 (using a pH meter) with 1N acetic acid or ammonium hydroxide (10 per cent NH$_3$), dilute to 50 ml., and mix. Add 10 ml. of freshly prepared hydrogen sulfide water to each and mix. Any color in the solution of the sample should not exceed that in the control.

Iron. Dissolve 2 grams in 30 ml. of water plus 2 ml. of hydrochloric acid and dilute to 50 ml. Add 30 to 50 mg. of ammonium persulfate crystals and 3 ml. of ammonium thiocyanate reagent solution. Any red color should not exceed that produced by 0.01 mg. of iron (Fe) in an equal volume of solution containing the quantities of reagents used in the test.

Sodium. Determine the sodium by the flame photometric method described on page 14.

Sample Solution A. Dissolve 1 gram in water and dilute to 100 ml.

Control Solution B. Dissolve 1 gram in water, add 0.2 mg. of sodium ion (Na), and dilute to 100 ml.

Observe the emission of Control Solution B at the 589-mμ sodium line. Observe the emission of Sample Solution A at the 589-mμ sodium line and at a wavelength of 580 mμ. The difference (D$_1$) between the intensities observed for Sample Solution A at 580 mμ and 589 mμ should not exceed the difference (D$_2$) observed at 589 mμ between Sample Solution A and Control Solution B.

Potassium Thiocyanate

KSCN   Formula Wt. 97.18

REQUIREMENTS

Appearance. Colorless or white crystals.
Insoluble in water. Not more than 0.005 per cent.
Insoluble in alcohol. Not more than 0.010 per cent.
pH of a 5 per cent solution. From 5.3 to 8.7 at 25°C.
Chloride (Cl). Not more than 0.005 per cent.
Sulfate (SO$_4$). Not more than 0.005 per cent.
Ammonium (NH$_4$). Not more than 0.003 per cent.
Heavy metals (as Pb). Not more than 0.0005 per cent.
Iron (Fe). Not more than 0.0002 per cent.
Sodium (Na). Not more than 0.005 per cent.
Iodine-consuming substances. To pass test (not more than 0.2 ml. of 0.1N iodine solution per gram).

TESTS

Insoluble in water. Dissolve 20 grams in 200 ml. of water, heat to boiling, and digest in a covered beaker on the steam bath for 1 hour. Filter through a tared filtering crucible, wash thoroughly, and dry at 105°C. The weight of the residue should not exceed 0.0010 gram.

Insoluble in alcohol. Dissolve 10 grams in 100 ml. of alcohol in an Erlenmeyer flask provided with a reflux condenser and boil for 1 hour. Cool, filter through a tared filtering crucible, wash with alcohol, and dry at 105°C. The weight of the residue should not exceed 0.0010 gram.

pH of a 5 per cent solution. Dissolve 10 grams in 200 ml. of carbon dioxide- and ammonia-free water. Determine the pH of the solution by the method described on page 18. The pH of the solution should be from 5.3 to 8.7 at 25°C. The pH of a 5 per cent solution of pure potassium thiocyanate would be 7.0 at 25°C.

Chloride. Dissolve 1 gram in 20 ml. of water, filter if necessary through a chloride-free filter, and add 10 ml. of 25 per cent sulfuric acid reagent solution and 7 ml. of 30 per cent hydrogen peroxide. Evaporate to 20 ml. by boiling *in a well ventilated hood*, add 15 to 20 ml. of water, and evaporate again. Repeat until all the cyanide has been volatilized, cool, and dilute to 100 ml. To 20 ml. of this solution add 1 ml. of nitric acid and 1 ml. of silver nitrate reagent solution. Any turbidity should not exceed that produced by 0.01 mg. of chloride ion (Cl) in an equal volume of solution containing the quantities of reagents used in the test.

ACS SPECIFICATIONS   **491**

Sulfate. To 10 grams in 100 ml. of hot water add 1 ml. of hydrochloric acid and 5 ml. of barium chloride reagent solution, digest in a covered beaker on the steam bath for 2 hours, and allow to stand overnight. If any precipitate is formed, filter, wash thoroughly, and ignite. The weight of the precipitate should not be more than 0.0012 gram greater than the weight obtained in a complete blank test.

Ammonium. Dissolve 1 gram in 50 ml. of water in a flask connected through a spray trap to a condenser, the end of which dips beneath the surface of 10 ml. of 0.1N hydrochloric acid. Add to the flask 10 ml. of freshly boiled 10 per cent sodium hydroxide reagent solution. Distill about 45 ml. and dilute the distillate to 100 ml. To 50 ml. of this solution add 1 ml. of 10 per cent sodium hydroxide reagent solution and 2 ml. of Nessler reagent. Any color should not exceed that produced when a quantity of an ammonium salt containing 0.03 mg. of ammonium ion (NH_4) is treated exactly like the sample.

Heavy metals. Dissolve 6 grams in about 20 ml. of water and dilute to 30 ml. For the control add 0.02 mg. of lead ion (Pb) to a 5-ml. aliquot of the solution and dilute to 25 ml. For the sample use the remaining 25-ml. portion. Adjust the pH of the control and sample solutions to between 3 and 4 (using a pH meter) with 1N acetic acid or ammonium hydroxide (10 per cent NH_3), dilute to 40 ml., and mix. Add 10 ml. of freshly prepared hydrogen sulfide water to each and mix. Any color in the solution of the sample should not exceed that in the control.

Iron. Dissolve 10 grams in 60 ml. of water. To 30 ml. of the solution add 0.1 ml. of hydrochloric acid, 6 ml. of hydroxylamine hydrochloride reagent solution, and 4 ml. of 1,10-phenanthroline reagent solution, and add ammonium hydroxide to bring the pH to approximately 5. Any red color should not exceed that produced by 0.01 mg. of iron (Fe) in an equal volume of solution containing the quantities of reagents used in the test. Compare 1 hour after adding the reagents to the sample and standard solutions.

Sodium. Determine the sodium by the flame photometric method described on page 14.

Sample Solution A. Dissolve 1 gram in water and dilute to 100 ml.

Control Solution B. Dissolve 1 gram in water, add 0.05 mg. of sodium ion (Na), and dilute to 100 ml.

Observe the emission of Control Solution B at the 589-mμ sodium line. Observe the emission of Sample Solution A at the 589-mμ sodium line and at a wavelength of 580 mμ. The difference (D$_1$) between the intensities observed for Sample Solution A at 580 mμ and 589 mμ should not exceed the difference (D$_2$) observed at 589 mμ between Sample Solution A and Control Solution B.

Iodine-consuming substances.   Dissolve 5 grams in 50 ml. of water and add 1.7 ml. of 10 per cent sulfuric acid reagent solution. Add 1 gram of potassium iodide and 1 ml. of starch indicator solution and titrate with 0.1N iodine solution. Not more than 1 ml. of the 0.1N iodine solution should be required.

Notes

Pyridine

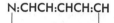

N:CHCH:CHCH:CH

Formula Wt. 79.10

REQUIREMENTS

Boiling range.   Not more than 2.0°C.
Solubility in water.   To pass test.
Residue after evaporation.   Not more than 0.002 per cent.
Water (H_2O).   Not more than 0.10 per cent.
Chloride (Cl).   Not more than 0.001 per cent.
Sulfate (SO_4).   Not more than 0.001 per cent.
Ammonia (NH_3).   Not more than 0.002 per cent.
Copper (Cu).   To pass test (limit about 0.0005 per cent).
Reducing substances.   To pass test.

TESTS

Boiling range.   Distill 100 ml. by the method described on page 12. The difference between the temperatures when 1 ml. and 95 ml. have distilled should not exceed 2.0°C. The boiling point of pure pyridine at 760-mm. mercury pressure is 115.2°C.

Solubility in water.   Dilute 10 ml. with 90 ml. of water. The solution should show no turbidity in 30 minutes.

Residue after evaporation.   Evaporate 51 ml. (50 grams) to dryness on the steam bath and dry the residue at 105°C. for 30 minutes. The weight of the residue should not exceed 0.0010 gram.

Water.   Place 25 ml. of methanol in a dry titration flask and add Karl Fischer reagent to a visually or electrometrically determined end point. Add 10 ml. (9.8 grams) of the sample, taking care to protect the contents of the flask from moisture. Stir vigorously and titrate with Karl Fischer reagent to the same end point. Calculate the water content of the sample from the titer and volume of Karl Fischer reagent consumed by the sample.

Chloride.   Add 1 ml. (1 gram) to 25 ml. of water, filter if necessary through a chloride-free filter, and add 1 ml. of nitric acid and 1 ml. of silver nitrate reagent solution. Any turbidity should not exceed that produced by 0.01 mg. of chloride ion (Cl) in an equal volume of solution containing the quantities of reagents used in the test.

Sulfate.   To 5 ml. (5 grams) of sample add about 10 mg. of sodium carbonate and evaporate to dryness on the steam bath. Dissolve the residue in 4 ml. of water plus 1 ml. of dilute hydrochloric acid $(1 + 19)$, filter if necessary through a small filter, wash with two 2-ml. portions of water, and dilute to 10 ml. To the filtrate add 1 ml. of barium chloride reagent solution. Any turbidity should not exceed that produced by 0.05 mg. of sulfate ion (SO_4) in an equal volume of solution containing the quantities of reagents used in the test. Compare 10 minutes after adding the barium chloride to the sample and standard solutions.

Ammonia. Add 2 ml. (2 grams) to 10 ml. of carbon dioxide–free water. Add 0.10 ml. of phenolphthalein indicator solution. If a pink color develops it should be discharged by not more than 0.12 ml. of 0.02N hydrochloric acid.

Copper. Add 5 ml. (5 grams) to 15 ml. of water; add 2 ml. of glacial acetic acid, 2 ml. of ammonium thiocyanate reagent solution, and 5 ml. of chloroform. Shake vigorously in a 60-ml. separatory funnel and allow to separate. The chloroform layer should not be colored green and, at most, only faintly yellow.

Reducing substances. To 5 ml. (5 grams) add 0.5 ml. of 0.1N potassium permanganate solution. The pink color should not be entirely discharged in 30 minutes.

Notes

8-Quinolinol

8-Hydroxyquinoline
Oxine

HOC$_6$H$_3$N:CHCH:CH

Formula Wt. 145.16

REQUIREMENTS

Melting point.   Not below 72.5°C. nor above 74.0°C.
Insoluble in alcohol.   Not more than 0.050 per cent.
Residue after ignition.   Not more than 0.050 per cent.
Sulfate (SO$_4$).   To pass test (limit about 0.02 per cent).
Suitability for magnesium determination.   To pass test.

TESTS

Insoluble in alcohol.   Dissolve 3 grams in 40 ml. of alcohol, filter through a tared filtering crucible, wash with 95 per cent alcohol, and dry at 105°C. The weight of the insoluble residue should not exceed 0.0015 gram.

Residue after ignition.   Gently ignite 2 grams in a tared crucible or dish until charred. Cool, moisten the char with 1 ml. of sulfuric acid, and ignite again slowly until the remaining carbon and excess sulfuric acid have been volatilized. Finally, ignite at 800° ± 25°C. for 15 minutes. The weight of the residue should not exceed 0.0010 gram.

Sulfate.   Dissolve 1 gram in 1 ml. of hydrochloric acid and dilute with 20 ml. of water. Heat to boiling and add 1 ml. of barium chloride reagent solution. No turbidity should be observed after standing 30 minutes.

Suitability for magnesium determination.   Dissolve 2.5 grams in 5 ml. of glacial acetic acid, warming if necessary, and dilute to 100 ml. Add 3.5 ml. of this solution to 50 ml. of a solution containing 6.0 mg. of magnesium ion (Mg). Heat to 80°C. and add with stirring 2 ml. of ammonium hydroxide and allow to stand for 10 minutes. Filter, and to the filtrate, which should be alkaline and yellow in color, add a solution containing 3.0 mg. of magnesium ion (Mg) and heat to 80°C. The characteristic yellow magnesium quinolate precipitate should form.

Notes

Silver Nitrate

AgNO$_3$

Formula Wt. 169.87

REQUIREMENTS

Insoluble matter. To pass test.
Chloride (Cl). Not more than 0.0005 per cent.
Free acid. To pass test.
Substances not precipitated by hydrochloric acid. Not more than 0.010 per cent.
Sulfate (SO$_4$). Not more than 0.002 per cent.
Copper (Cu). Not more than 0.0002 per cent.
Iron (Fe). Not more than 0.0002 per cent.
Lead (Pb). Not more than 0.001 per cent.

TESTS

Insoluble matter. Dissolve 20 grams in 20 ml. of water. No insoluble material should be observed. Reserve the solution for the test for *Substances not precipitated by hydrochloric acid.*

Chloride. Dissolve 2 grams in 40 ml. of water, add ammonium hydroxide dropwise until the precipitate first formed is redissolved, and dilute to 50 ml. Transfer the solution to a 100-ml. platinum dish which is made the cathode. Insert a rotating anode and electrolyze for 1 hour, starting with a current of 1 ampere. Decant the solution and evaporate to approximately 25 ml. Neutralize the solution to the phenolphthalein end point with nitric acid, and add 1 ml. of nitric acid in excess and 1 ml. of silver nitrate reagent solution. Any turbidity should not exceed that produced by 0.01 mg. of chloride ion (Cl) in an equal volume of solution containing 1 ml. of nitric acid and 1 ml. of silver nitrate reagent solution.

Free acid. Dissolve 5 grams in 50 ml. of water, add 0.25 ml. of bromocresol green indicator solution (0.04 per cent), and mix well. The solution should be colored blue, not green or yellow.

Substances not precipitated by hydrochloric acid. Dilute the solution obtained in the test for *Insoluble matter* to about 600 ml. Heat to boiling and add hydrochloric acid to precipitate the silver completely (about 11 ml.). Allow to stand overnight and filter. Evaporate the filtrate to dryness, and add 0.15 ml. of hydrochloric acid and 10 ml. of water. Heat, filter, and wash with about 10 ml. of water. Evaporate the resulting filtrate to dryness in a tared dish or crucible and dry at 105°C. The weight of the residue should not be more than 0.0020 gram greater than the weight obtained in a complete blank test. Reserve the residues for the preparation of Sample Solution A and Blank Solution B.

Sample Solution A and Blank Solution B. To each of the residues remaining from the test for *Substances not precipitated by hydrochloric acid* add 3 ml. of dilute hydrochloric acid $(1 + 1)$, cover with a watch glass, and digest on the steam bath for 15 to 20 minutes. Cool and dilute to 100 ml. One is Sample Solution A $(1 \text{ ml.} = 0.2 \text{ gram})$; the other is Blank Solution B.

Sulfate. To 10 ml. of Sample Solution A (2-gram sample) add 1 ml. of dilute hydrochloric acid $(1 + 19)$ and 1 ml. of barium chloride reagent solution. Any turbidity should not exceed that produced by 0.04 mg. of sulfate ion (SO_4) in 10 ml. of Blank Solution B containing the quantities of reagents used in the test. Compare 10 minutes after adding the barium chloride to the sample and standard solutions.

Copper. Add a slight excess of ammonium hydroxide to 25 ml. of Sample Solution A (5-gram sample). For the standard add 0.01 mg. of copper ion (Cu) to 25 ml. of Blank Solution B and make slightly alkaline with ammonium hydroxide. Add 10 ml. of 0.1 per cent solution of sodium diethyldithiocarbamate to each. Any yellow color in the solution of the sample should not exceed that in the standard. Estimate the copper content to aid in the test for *Lead*.

Iron. Dilute 25 ml. of Sample Solution A (5-gram sample) to 50 ml. For the standard add 0.01 mg. of iron (Fe) to 25 ml. of Blank Solution B and dilute to 50 ml. To each add 2 ml. of hydrochloric acid, 30 to 50 mg. of ammonium persulfate crystals, and 3 ml. of ammonium thiocyanate reagent solution. Any red color in the solution of the sample should not exceed that in the standard.

Lead. Dilute a 25-ml. aliquot of Sample Solution A (5-gram sample) to 35 ml. For the standard add 0.05 mg. of lead ion (Pb) and the amount of copper estimated to be present in the test for *Copper* to a 25-ml. aliquot of Blank Solution B, and dilute to 35 ml. Adjust the pH of the standard and sample solutions to between 3 and 4 (using a pH meter) with 1N acetic acid or ammonium hydroxide (10 per cent NH_3), dilute to 40 ml, and mix. Add 10 ml. of freshly prepared hydrogen sulfide water to each and mix. Any color in the solution of the sample should not exceed that in the standard.

Silver Sulfate

Ag_2SO_4 Formula Wt. 311.80

REQUIREMENTS

Insoluble matter and silver chloride. Not more than 0.020 per cent.
Nitrate (NO_3). Not more than 0.001 per cent.
Substances not precipitated by hydrochloric acid. Not more than 0.030 per cent.
Iron (Fe). Not more than 0.001 per cent.

TESTS

Insoluble matter and silver chloride. Add 5 grams of the powdered salt to 500 ml. of boiling water and boil gently until the silver sulfate is dissolved. If any insoluble matter remains, filter while hot through a tared filtering crucible (retain the filtrate for the test for *Substances not precipitated by hydrochloric acid*), wash thoroughly with hot water (discard the washings), and dry at 105°C. The weight of the residue should not exceed 0.0010 gram.

Nitrate. To 0.5 gram of the powdered salt add 2 ml. of phenoldisulfonic acid reagent solution and heat on the steam bath for 15 minutes. Cool, dilute with 20 ml. of water, and make alkaline with ammonium hydroxide. Any yellow color should not exceed that produced when a solution containing 0.005 mg. of nitrate ion (NO_3) is evaporated to dryness and the residue is treated in the same manner as the sample.

Substances not precipitated by hydrochloric acid. Heat to boiling the filtrate obtained in the test for *Insoluble matter and silver chloride*, add 5 ml. of hydrochloric acid, and allow to stand overnight. Dilute to 500 ml. and filter. Evaporate 250 ml. of the filtrate to dryness, and add 0.15 ml. of hydrochloric acid and 10 ml. of water. Heat and filter. Add 0.10 ml. of sulfuric acid to the resulting filtrate, evaporate to dryness in a tared dish, and ignite at 800° ± 25°C. for 15 minutes. The weight of the residue should not be more than 0.0008 gram greater than the weight obtained in a complete blank test. Retain the residue for the test for *Iron*.

Iron. To the residue obtained in the preceding test add 3 ml. of dilute hydrochloric acid (1 + 1), cover with a watch glass, and digest on the steam bath for 15 to 20 minutes. Remove the watch glass and evaporate to dryness. Dissolve the residue in 35 ml. of dilute hydrochloric acid

$(1 + 6)$, filter if necessary, and dilute to 50 ml. Dilute 20 ml. of the solution to 50 ml. and add 30 to 50 mg. of ammonium persulfate crystals and 3 ml. of ammonium thiocyanate reagent solution. Any red color should not exceed that produced by 0.01 mg. of iron (Fe) in an equal volume of solution containing the quantities of reagents used in the test.

Notes

Soda Lime

Note. Soda lime is a mixture of variable proportions of sodium hydroxide with calcium oxide or hydroxide. This reagent may or may not include an indicator.

REQUIREMENTS

Loss on drying at 200°C. Not more than 7 per cent.
Carbon dioxide absorption capacity. Not less than 25 per cent.
Fines. Not more than 1 per cent.

TESTS

Loss on drying. Weigh accurately about 10 grams and dry at 200°C. for 18 hours. The loss in weight should not exceed 7 per cent.

Carbon dioxide absorption capacity. To a tared Schwartz-type U-tube containing about 5 grams of anhydrous calcium chloride confined in one arm by a small plug of glass wool add 7 to 10 grams of the sample and reweigh. Connect the outlet of the U-tube to a glass tube dipping into water. Connect the inlet end through a three-way stopcock to a source of air-free carbon dioxide,* dried over anhydrous calcium chloride. Connect the third arm of the stopcock to a piece of glass tubing of 5-mm. inside diameter which dips into water to a depth of 5 or 6 cm. Pass the carbon dioxide through this arm until the flow of gas is regulated at 75 to 100 bubbles a minute. Then allow the gas to pass into the U-tube which is set in a beaker of water during the period of the test. When bubbles begin to appear from the exit tube,* close and disconnect the U-tube, wipe it dry, and weigh. The gain in weight should not be less than 25 per cent of the weight of the sample.

* If the carbon dioxide is from a cylinder, the first bubble or two at the exit tube makes a satisfactory end point. If the gas used contains air, the exit tube should discharge into a solution of barium hydroxide that is protected from the atmospheric carbon dioxide, and the appearance of a turbidity is the end point.

Fines. Place 100 grams on a clean U. S. No. 100 standard sieve nested in a receiving pan. Cover the sieve and shake on a mechanical shaker for 5 minutes. The weight of the fine material in the receiving pan should not exceed 1.0 gram.

Sodium

Na

REQUIREMENTS

Chloride (Cl).　Not more than 0.002 per cent.
Nitrogen (N).　To pass test (limit about 0.003 per cent).
Phosphate (PO$_4$).　Not more than 0.0005 per cent.
Sulfate (SO$_4$).　To pass test (limit about 0.002 per cent).
Heavy metals (as Pb).　Not more than 0.0005 per cent.
Iron (Fe).　Not more than 0.001 per cent.

TESTS

Sample Solution A. If the metal contains any adhering oil or other foreign material, shave off a thin layer and use only bright clean metal for the sample. Weigh 20 grams and cut it into small pieces. Cool about 100 ml. of water in a beaker in an ice bath. Add the small pieces of sodium one at a time to the ice-cold water. Keep the solution cool and do not add another piece until the preceding one has completely reacted and dissolved. If desired, a magnetic stirrer may be used to aid dissolution. After all the sample has been dissolved, cool, and dilute to 500 ml. (1 ml. = 0.04 gram).

Chloride. Neutralize 25 ml. of Sample Solution A (1-gram sample) with nitric acid, filter if necessary through a chloride-free filter, and add 1 ml. of nitric acid in excess and 1 ml. of silver nitrate reagent solution. Any turbidity should not exceed that produced by 0.02 mg. of chloride ion (Cl) in an equal volume of solution containing the quantities of reagents used in the test.

Nitrogen. Dilute 12.5 ml. of Sample Solution A (0.5-gram sample) to 50 ml. and add 2 ml. of Nessler reagent. The color should not exceed that produced by the addition of 2 ml. of Nessler reagent to an equal volume of solution containing a quantity of an ammonium salt corresponding to 0.015 mg. of nitrogen (N).

Phosphate. To 100 ml. of Sample Solution A (4-gram sample) add 15 ml. of hydrochloric acid and evaporate to about 30 ml. Add 30 ml. of hydrochloric acid, filter through a filtering crucible, and wash the precipitated sodium chloride twice with 5-ml. portions of hydrochloric acid. Evaporate the filtrate and washings to dryness on the steam bath. Dissolve the residue in 25 ml. of approximately 0.5N sulfuric acid, add

1 ml. of ammonium molybdate reagent solution and 1 ml. of p-methyl-aminophenol sulfate reagent solution, and allow to stand for 2 hours at room temperature. Any blue color should not exceed that produced by 0.02 mg. of phosphate ion (PO_4) in an equal volume of solution containing the quantities of reagents used in the test, including the residue from evaporation of 55 ml. of hydrochloric acid.

Sulfate. Neutralize 125 ml. of Sample Solution A with hydrochloric acid and evaporate to about 90 ml. Add 1 ml. of hydrochloric acid and 5 ml. of barium chloride reagent solution and allow to stand overnight. No turbidity or precipitate should be formed.

Heavy metals. For the sample carefully add 25 ml. of hydrochloric acid to a 125-ml. aliquot of Sample Solution A. For the control add 25 ml. of hydrochloric acid plus 0.02 mg. of lead ion (Pb) to a 25-ml. aliquot of Sample Solution A. Evaporate the solutions to dryness, dissolve each residue in about 20 ml. of water, and dilute to 25 ml. Adjust the pH of the control and sample solutions to between 3 and 4 (using a pH meter) with $1N$ acetic acid or ammonium hydroxide (10 per cent NH_3), filter, dilute to 40 ml., and mix. Add 10 ml. of freshly prepared hydrogen sulfide water to each and mix. Any color in the solution of the sample should not exceed that in the control.

Iron. Neutralize 25 ml. of Sample Solution A with hydrochloric acid, add an excess of 2 ml. of hydrochloric acid, and dilute to 50 ml. Add 30 to 50 mg. of ammonium persulfate crystals and 3 ml. of ammonium thiocyanate reagent solution. Any red color should not exceed that produced by 0.01 mg. of iron (Fe) in an equal volume of solution containing the quantities of reagents used in the test.

Notes

Sodium Acetate

$CH_3COONa \cdot 3H_2O$ Formula Wt. 136.08

REQUIREMENTS

Insoluble matter.   Not more than 0.005 per cent.
pH of a 5 per cent solution.   From 7.5 to 9.2 at 25°C.
Chloride (Cl).   Not more than 0.001 per cent.
Phosphate (PO_4).   Not more than 0.0005 per cent.
Sulfate (SO_4).   Not more than 0.002 per cent.
Calcium, magnesium, and R_2O_3 precipitate.   Not more than 0.010 per cent.
Heavy metals (as Pb).   Not more than 0.0005 per cent.
Iron (Fe).   Not more than 0.0005 per cent.
Substances reducing permanganate.   To pass test.
Potassium (K).   Not more than 0.005 per cent.

TESTS

Insoluble matter.   Dissolve 20 grams in 150 ml. of water, heat to boiling, and digest in a covered beaker on the steam bath for 1 hour. Filter through a tared filtering crucible, wash thoroughly, and dry at 105°C. The weight of the residue should not exceed 0.0010 gram.

pH of a 5 per cent solution.   Dissolve 5 grams in water having a pH of 6.5 to 7.4 and dilute to 100 ml. Determine the pH by the method described on page 18. The pH should be from 7.5 to 9.2 at 25°C. The pH of a 5 per cent solution of pure sodium acetate would be 8.9 at 25°C.

Chloride.   Dissolve 1 gram in 20 ml. of water, filter if necessary through a chloride-free filter, and add 1 ml. of nitric acid and 1 ml. of silver nitrate reagent solution. Any turbidity should not exceed that produced by 0.01 mg. of chloride ion (Cl) in an equal volume of solution containing the quantities of reagents used in the test.

Phosphate.   Dissolve 2 grams in 10 ml. of nitric acid and evaporate to dryness on the steam bath. Add 10 ml. of nitric acid and repeat the evaporation. Dissolve in 80 ml. of water, add 0.5 gram of ammonium molybdate, and adjust the pH to 1.8 (using a pH meter) with dilute hydrochloric acid (1 + 9). Heat to boiling, cool, and add 10 ml. of hydrochloric acid. Transfer to a separatory funnel, add 35 ml. of ether, shake vigorously, and allow the layers to separate. Draw off and discard the aqueous layer. Wash the ether layer twice with 10 ml. of dilute hydrochloric acid (1 + 9), drawing off and discarding the aqueous layer each

time. Add 0.2 ml. of a 2 per cent solution of stannous chloride in hydrochloric acid. If the solution is cloudy, shake with a small amount of
dilute hydrochloric acid $(1 + 9)$ to clear. Any blue color should not exceed that produced by 0.01 mg. of phosphate ion (PO_4) treated in the
same manner as the sample after the addition of 80 ml. of water.

Sulfate. Dissolve 20 grams in 150 ml. of water, add 1 ml. of hydrochloric
acid, and filter. Heat to boiling, add 5 ml. of barium chloride reagent
solution, digest in a covered beaker on the steam bath for 2 hours, and
allow to stand overnight. If a precipitate is formed, filter, wash thoroughly, and ignite. The weight of the precipitate should not be more than
0.0010 gram greater than the weight obtained in a complete blank test.

Calcium, magnesium, and R₂O₃ precipitate. Dissolve 10 grams in 100
ml. of water, filter, and add 5 ml. of ammonium oxalate reagent solution,
2 ml. of ammonium phosphate reagent solution, and 15 ml. of ammonium
hydroxide. Allow to stand overnight. Filter, wash with water containing
2.5 per cent ammonia and about 0.1 per cent ammonium oxalate, and
ignite. The weight of the residue should not exceed 0.0010 gram.

Heavy metals. Dissolve 6 grams in about 10 ml. of water, add 15 ml. of
dilute hydrochloric acid (10 per cent HCl), and dilute to 30 ml. For the
control add 0.02 mg. of lead ion (Pb) to a 5-ml aliquot of the solution.
For the sample use the remaining 25-ml. portion. Adjust the pH of the
control and sample solutions to between 3 and 4 (using a pH meter)
with $1N$ acetic acid or ammonium hydroxide (10 per cent NH_3), dilute
to 40 ml. and mix. Add 10 ml. of freshly prepared hydrogen sulfide water
to each and mix. Any color in the solution of the sample should not exceed that in the control.

Iron. Dissolve 2 grams in 50 ml. of dilute hydrochloric acid $(1 + 24)$,
and add 30 to 50 mg. of ammonium persulfate crystals and 3 ml. of
ammonium thiocyanate reagent solution. Any red color should not exceed
that produced by 0.01 mg. of iron (Fe) in an equal volume of solution
containing the quantities of reagents used in the test.

Substances reducing permanganate. Dissolve 5 grams in 50 ml. of water,
and add 5 ml. of 10 per cent sulfuric acid reagent solution and 0.10 ml.
of $0.1N$ potassium permanganate. The pink color should persist for at
least 1 hour.

Potassium. Determine the potassium by the flame photometric method
described on page 14. Dissolve 10 grams in water and dilute to 100 ml.

   Sample Solution A. Dilute a 10-ml. aliquot of the solution to 100 ml.

Control Solution B. To another 10-ml. aliquot of the solution add 0.05 mg. of potassium ion (K) and dilute to 100 ml.

Observe the emission of Control Solution B at the 767-mμ potassium line. Observe the emission of Sample Solution A at the 767-mμ potassium line and at a wavelength of 750 mμ. The difference (D_1) between the intensities observed for Sample Solution A at 767 mμ and 750 mμ should not exceed the difference (D_2) observed at 767 mμ between Sample Solution A and Control Solution B.

Notes

Sodium Bicarbonate

NaHCO$_3$ Formula Wt. 84.01

REQUIREMENTS

Insoluble matter. Not more than 0.015 per cent.

Assay. Not less than 99.7 per cent nor more than 100.3 per cent NaHCO$_3$.

Chloride (Cl). Not more than 0.003 per cent.

Phosphate (PO$_4$). Not more than 0.001 per cent.

Sulfur compounds (as SO$_4$). Not more than 0.003 per cent.

Ammonium (NH$_4$). Not more than 0.0005 per cent.

Calcium, magnesium, and R$_2$O$_3$ precipitate. Not more than 0.020 per cent.

Heavy metals (as Pb). Not more than 0.0005 per cent.

Iron (Fe). Not more than 0.001 per cent.

Potassium (K). Not more than 0.005 per cent.

TESTS

Insoluble matter. Dissolve 10 grams in 100 ml. of hot water, boil for 2 or 3 minutes, and digest in a covered beaker on the steam bath for 1 hour. Filter through a tared porous porcelain or platinum filtering crucible, wash thoroughly, and dry at 105°C. The weight of the residue should not exceed 0.0015 gram.

Assay. Weigh accurately about 3 grams, previously dried over sulfuric acid for 24 hours, dissolve it in 50 ml. of water, add methyl orange indicator solution, and titrate with 1N hydrochloric acid. The sodium bicarbonate calculated from the total alkalinity, as determined by the titration, should not be less than 99.7 nor more than 100.3 per cent of the weight taken. One milliliter of 1N acid corresponds to 0.08401 gram of NaHCO$_3$.

Chloride. Dissolve 1 gram in 50 ml. of water and filter if necessary through a chloride-free filter. Neutralize 25 ml. of the solution with nitric acid, add an excess of 1 ml. of the acid, and add 1 ml. of silver nitrate reagent solution. Any turbidity should not exceed that produced by 0.015 mg. of chloride ion (Cl) in an equal volume of solution containing the quantities of reagents used in the test.

Phosphate. Dissolve 2 grams in 15 ml. of dilute hydrochloric acid (1 + 2) and evaporate to dryness on the steam bath. Dissolve the residue in 25 ml. of approximately 0.5N sulfuric acid, add 1 ml. of ammonium molybdate reagent solution and 1 ml. of p-methylaminophenol sulfate reagent solution, and allow to stand for 2 hours at room temperature. Any blue color should not exceed that produced by 0.02 mg. of phosphate ion (PO_4) in an equal volume of solution containing the quantities of reagents used in the test, including the residue from the evaporation of 5 ml. of hydrochloric acid.

Sulfur compounds. Dissolve 10 grams in 100 ml. of hot water, add 0.25 ml. of saturated bromine water, and boil. Cool, neutralize with hydrochloric acid, add an excess of 1 ml. of the acid, and filter. Heat the filtrate to boiling, add 5 ml. of barium chloride reagent solution, digest in a covered beaker on the steam bath for 2 hours, and allow to stand overnight. If a precipitate is formed, filter, wash thoroughly, and ignite. The weight of the precipitate should not be more than 0.0008 gram greater than the weight obtained in a complete blank test.

Ammonium. Dissolve 2 grams in 40 ml. of ammonia-free water, and add 10 ml. of 10 per cent sodium hydroxide reagent solution and 2 ml. of Nessler reagent. Any color should not exceed that produced by 0.01 mg. of ammonium ion (NH_4) in an equal volume of solution containing the quantities of reagents used in the test.

Calcium, magnesium, and R_2O_3 precipitate. Dissolve 10 grams in 100 ml. of water and add 12 ml. of hydrochloric acid. Boil to remove carbon dioxide and filter if necessary. Add 5 ml. of ammonium oxalate reagent solution, 2 ml. of ammonium phosphate reagent solution, and 10 ml. of ammonium hydroxide. Stir well and allow to stand overnight. If any precipitate is formed, filter, wash with water containing 2.5 per cent of ammonia and about 0.1 per cent of ammonium oxalate, and ignite. The weight of the residue should not exceed 0.0020 gram.

Heavy metals. To 5 grams in a 150-ml. beaker add 10 ml. of water, mix, and cautiously add 10 ml. of hydrochloric acid. For the control dissolve 1 gram of the sample in 10 ml. of water, add 0.02 mg. of lead ion (Pb), and cautiously add 10 ml. of hydrochloric acid. Evaporate both solutions to dryness on the steam bath, dissolve each residue in about 20 ml. of water, and dilute to 25 ml. Adjust the pH of the control and sample solutions to between 3 and 4 (using a pH meter) with $1N$ acetic acid or ammonium hydroxide (10 per cent NH_3), dilute to 40 ml., and mix. Add 10 ml. of freshly prepared hydrogen sulfide water to each and mix. Any color in the solution of the sample should not exceed that in the control.

Iron. Dissolve 1 gram in 30 ml. of dilute hydrochloric acid $(1 + 9)$ and dilute to 50 ml. Add 30 to 50 mg. of ammonium persulfate crystals and 3 ml. of ammonium thiocyanate reagent solution. Any red color should not exceed that produced by 0.01 mg. of iron (Fe) in an equal volume of solution containing the quantities of reagents used in the test.

Potassium.   Determine the potassium by the flame photometric method described on page 14. Dissolve 10 grams in water and dilute to 100 ml.

Sample Solution A.   Dilute a 10-ml. aliquot of the solution to 100 ml.

Control Solution B.   To another 10-ml. aliquot of the solution add 0.05 mg. of potassium ion (K) and dilute to 100 ml.

Observe the emission of Control Solution B at the 767-mμ potassium line. Observe the emission of Sample Solution A at the 767-mμ potassium line and at a wavelength of 750 mμ. The difference (D_1) between the intensities observed for Sample Solution A at 750 mμ and 767 mμ should not exceed the difference (D_2) observed at 767 mμ between Sample Solution A and Control Solution B.

Notes

Sodium Bismuthate

$NaBiO_3$

Formula Wt. 279.97

REQUIREMENTS

Assay.   Not less than 80 per cent $NaBiO_3$.
Chloride (Cl).   Not more than 0.002 per cent.
Manganese (Mn).   Not more than 0.0005 per cent.
Oxidizing efficiency.   Not less than 99.9 per cent.

TESTS

Assay.   Weigh accurately about 0.7 gram, place in a flask, add 25.0 ml. of ferrous sulfate solution,* and stopper the flask. Transfer 25.0 ml. of the ferrous sulfate solution to another flask and stopper the flask. Allow each flask to stand for 30 minutes, shaking frequently, and titrate the ferrous sulfate in each with 0.1N potassium permanganate. The difference in the volume of permanganate consumed in the two titrations is equivalent to the sodium bismuthate. One milliliter of 0.1N potassium permanganate corresponds to 0.01400 gram of $NaBiO_3$.

Ferrous Sulfate Solution.   Dissolve 7 grams of clear crystals of ferrous sulfate, $FeSO_4 \cdot 7H_2O$, in 90 ml. of freshly boiled and cooled water, and add sulfuric acid to make 100 ml. The solution must be freshly prepared.

Chloride.   Add 1 gram to 25 ml. of water, heat to boiling, and keep at the boiling temperature for 10 minutes. Dilute to 50 ml. and filter through a chloride-free filter. To 25 ml. of the filtrate add 0.15 ml. of 30 per cent hydrogen peroxide to clear the solution, and then add 1 ml. of nitric acid and 1 ml. of silver nitrate reagent solution. Any turbidity should not exceed that produced by 0.01 mg. of chloride ion (Cl) in an equal volume of solution containing the quantities of reagents used in the test.

Manganese.   Dissolve 2 grams in 35 ml. of dilute nitric acid $(5 + 2)$, heat to boiling, and boil gently for 5 minutes. Prepare a standard containing 0.01 mg. of manganese ion (Mn) in 35 ml. of dilute nitric acid $(5 + 2)$. To each add 5 ml. of sulfuric acid, 5 ml. of phosphoric acid, and 0.5 ml. of sulfurous acid. Boil gently to expel oxides of nitrogen, cool the solutions to 15°C., and add 0.5 gram of sodium bismuthate to each. Allow to stand for 5 minutes with occasional stirring, dilute each with 25 ml. of water, and filter through a filter other than paper. Any pink color in the solution of the sample should not exceed that in the standard.

Oxidizing efficiency. To 0.200 gram of oxidimetric standard manganese metal * in a 1-liter Erlenmeyer flask, add 15 ml. of dilute nitric acid (1 + 3), and heat cautiously until the manganese is dissolved. Add 8 ml. of 70 per cent perchloric acid and boil gently until the acid fumes strongly and manganese dioxide begins to separate. Cool, add 5 ml. of water and 25 ml. of dilute nitric acid (1 + 3), and boil for several minutes to expel free chlorine. Add sufficient sulfurous acid or sodium nitrite solution to just dissolve the manganese dioxide. Boil the solution to expel completely oxides of nitrogen. Cool to room temperature, add 225 ml. of colorless, dilute nitric acid (2 + 5) and sufficient water to bring the total volume to 250 ml., and cool to 10° to 15°C.

Add 7 grams of sodium bismuthate (weighed to the nearest 10 mg.) to the flask, agitate briskly for 1 minute, dilute with 250 ml. of cold water (10° to 15°C.), and filter immediately through an asbestos pad. (Pretreat the asbestos in hot nitric acid and then wash it free of acid with hot water.) The filter can be washed free of manganese more readily if not allowed to run dry during the filtering and washing. Wash the filter with cold, freshly boiled dilute nitric acid (3 + 97) until the washings are entirely colorless, and immediately treat the filtrate and washings as directed in the next paragraph.

Add 8.5 grams of ferrous ammonium sulfate (weighed to the nearest mg.) to the filtered solution of permanganic acid. Stir briskly. As soon as reduction is complete and all the salt is dissolved, add 0.01M 1,10-phenanthroline indicator solution, and titrate the excess of ferrous ions with 0.1N potassium permanganate to a clear green color that persists for at least 30 seconds. (Standardize the 0.1N potassium permanganate against oxidimetric standard oxalic acid supplied by the National Bureau of Standards.)

Determine the manganese equivalent of the ferrous ammonium sulfate by titrating 1.75 grams of the salt with the 0.1N potassium permanganate in 500 ml. of cold, dilute nitric acid that has been pretreated with 2 grams of sodium bismuthate under the conditions described above.

Calculate the oxidizing efficiency of the sodium bismuthate as follows:

$$\text{Oxidizing efficiency} = \frac{(A - B) \times 0.0110}{C} \times 100$$

where:

A = milliliters of exactly 0.1N potassium permanganate equivalent to the ferrous sulfate added

B = milliliters of exactly 0.1N potassium permanganate required to titrate the excess ferrous ions

C = grams of manganese used, taking into account the assay of the metal

*Manganese Metal for Use as Oxidimetric Standard. Assay a selected lot of commercial high-purity electrolytic manganese (see note below), previously screened through a number 10 and retained on a number 20 screen, by determining the concentration of impurities. Metals at levels below 0.03 per cent can be evaluated with sufficient accuracy by the spectrographic semi-quantitative method; those at higher concentrations are determined by suitable quantitative methods; carbon and sulfur by classical combustion methods. Oxygen, hydrogen, and nitrogen are determined by vacuum fusion analysis employing a 25-gram iron bath containing 2 to 3 grams of tin. The sample is placed in a tin capsule and dropped into the bath which is held at 1500° to 1550°C. Up to three samples can be analyzed before discarding the bath. The assay of the manganese metal for use as an oxidimetric standard should not be less than 99.8 per cent Mn. (Due to the tendency of the metal to react with oxygen, it must be stored in a tightly sealed container after the assay has been performed.)

Note. "Elmang," available from Union Carbide Corporation, Metals Division, has been found satisfactory for this purpose.

Notes

Sodium Bisulfate, Fused

Note. This product is usually a mixture of sodium pyrosulfate, $Na_2S_2O_7$, and sodium bisulfate, $NaHSO_4$.

REQUIREMENTS

Acidity as (H_2SO_4). Not less than 39.0 nor more than 42.0 per cent.
Insoluble matter and ammonium hydroxide precipitate. Not more than 0.010 per cent.
Chloride (Cl). Not more than 0.001 per cent.
Phosphate (PO_4). Not more than 0.001 per cent.
Arsenic (As). Not more than 0.0001 per cent.
Calcium and magnesium precipitate. Not more than 0.005 per cent.
Heavy metals (as Pb). Not more than 0.0005 per cent.
Iron (Fe). Not more than 0.002 per cent.

TESTS

Acidity. Weigh accurately about 4 grams, dissolve in 50 ml. of water, and titrate with $1N$ alkali using methyl orange as indicator. One milliliter of $1N$ alkali corresponds to 0.04904 gram of H_2SO_4.

Insoluble matter and ammonium hydroxide precipitate. Dissolve 20 grams in 200 ml. of water, add ammonium hydroxide until the solution is alkaline to methyl red, boil for 1 minute, and digest in a covered beaker on the steam bath for 1 hour. Filter through a tared filtering crucible, saving the filtrate separate from the washings for the test for *Calcium and magnesium precipitate*. Wash thoroughly and dry at 105°C. The weight of the residue should not exceed 0.0020 gram.

Chloride. Dissolve 1 gram in 20 ml. of water, filter if necessary through a chloride-free filter, and add 1 ml. of nitric acid and 1 ml. of silver nitrate reagent solution. Any turbidity should not exceed that produced by 0.01 mg. of chloride ion (Cl) in an equal volume of solution containing the quantities of reagents used in the test.

Phosphate. Dissolve 2 grams in 15 ml. of dilute ammonium hydroxide $(1 + 2)$ and evaporate to dryness. Dissolve the residue in 25 ml. of approximately $0.5N$ hydrochloric acid, add 1 ml. of ammonium molybdate reagent solution and 1 ml. of p-methylaminophenol sulfate reagent solution, and allow to stand for 2 hours at room temperature. Any blue color should not exceed that produced by 0.02 mg. of phosphate ion (PO_4) in an equal volume of solution containing the quantities of reagents used in the test, including the residue from evaporation of 5 ml. of ammonium hydroxide.

Arsenic. Dissolve 2 grams in 20 ml. of water. Determine the arsenic by the Gutzeit method (page 11). The amount of stain should not exceed that produced by 0.002 mg. of arsenic (As).

Calcium and magnesium precipitate. To the filtrate from the test for *Insoluble matter and ammonium hydroxide precipitate* (without the washings) add 5 ml. of ammonium oxalate reagent solution, 3 ml. of ammonium phosphate reagent solution, and 10 ml. of ammonium hydroxide. If any precipitate forms on standing overnight, filter, wash thoroughly with water containing 2.5 per cent ammonia and about 0.1 per cent ammonium oxalate, and ignite. The weight of the residue should not exceed 0.0010 gram.

Heavy metals. Dissolve 6 grams in about 25 ml. of water and dilute to 30 ml. For the control add 0.02 mg. of lead ion (Pb) to a 5-ml. aliquot of the solution and dilute to 25 ml. For the sample use the remaining 25-ml. portion. Adjust the pH of the control and sample solutions to between 3 and 4 (using a pH meter) with $1N$ acetic acid or ammonium hydroxide (10 per cent NH_3), dilute to 40 ml., and mix. Add 10 ml. of freshly prepared hydrogen sulfide water to each and mix. Any color in the solution of the sample should not exceed that in the control.

Iron. Dissolve 5 grams in 80 ml. of dilute hydrochloric acid $(1 + 3)$ and boil gently for 10 minutes. Cool and dilute to 100 ml. Dilute 10 ml. of this solution to 50 ml. and add 30 to 50 mg. of ammonium persulfate crystals and 3 ml. of ammonium thiocyanate reagent solution. Any red color should not exceed that produced by 0.01 mg. of iron (Fe) in an equal volume of solution containing the quantities of reagents used in the test.

Notes

Sodium Bisulfite

Note. This product is usually a mixture of sodium bisulfite, $NaHSO_3$, and sodium metabisulfite, $Na_2S_2O_5$.

REQUIREMENTS

Assay (SO_2). Not less than 58.5 per cent SO_2.
Insoluble matter. Not more than 0.005 per cent.
Chloride (Cl). Not more than 0.02 per cent.
Arsenic (As). Not more than 0.0001 per cent.
Heavy metals (as Pb). Not more than 0.001 per cent.
Iron (Fe). Not more than 0.002 per cent.

TESTS

Assay. Weigh accurately about 0.47 gram, add to a mixture of 100.0 ml. of $0.1N$ iodine and 5 ml. of 10 per cent hydrochloric acid solution, and swirl gently until the sample dissolves. Titrate the excess iodine with $0.1N$ sodium thiosulfate, adding starch indicator solution near the end point. One milliliter of $0.1N$ iodine corresponds to 0.003203 gram of SO_2.

Insoluble matter. Dissolve 20 grams in 200 ml. of water, heat to boiling, and digest in a covered beaker on the steam bath for 1 hour. Filter through a tared filtering crucible, wash thoroughly, and dry at 105°C. The weight of the residue should not exceed 0.0010 gram.

Chloride. Dissolve 0.5 gram in 100 ml. of water and transfer 10 ml. of the well-mixed solution to a platinum dish. Add 10 per cent sodium hydroxide solution until the solution is slightly alkaline to litmus, making note of the volume of sodium hydroxide added. Prepare a standard containing 0.01 mg. of chloride ion (Cl) in 10 ml. of water, and add the same volume of 10 per cent sodium hydroxide solution as was added to the sample solution. To each solution add, dropwise, 2 ml. of 30 per cent hydrogen peroxide and allow to stand at room temperature for 10 minutes. Evaporate the solutions to dryness on the steam bath, dissolve the residues in 10 ml. of water, and add 1 ml. of nitric acid and 1 ml. of silver nitrate reagent solution to each. Any turbidity in the solution of the sample should not exceed that in the standard.

Arsenic. Dissolve 2 grams in 10 ml. of water, add 3 ml. of sulfuric acid, and heat until dense fumes of sulfur trioxide are evolved. Cool, cautiously add 5 ml. of water and 3 ml. of sulfuric acid, and heat again to fumes of sulfur trioxide. Determine the arsenic in this solution by the Gutzeit method (page 11). The amount of stain should not exceed that produced by 0.002 mg. of arsenic (As).

Heavy metals. Dissolve 3 grams in a solution of 15 ml. of water and 8 ml. of hydrochloric acid. For the control dissolve 1 gram of sample and 0.02 mg. of lead ion (Pb) in 15 ml. of water and add 8 ml. of hydrochloric acid. Evaporate each solution to dryness, dissolve the residues in 5 ml. of hydrochloric acid, and evaporate again to dryness. Dissolve each in about 20 ml. of water and dilute to 25 ml. Adjust the pH of the control and sample solutions to between 3 and 4 (using a pH meter) with 1N acetic acid or ammonium hydroxide (10 per cent NH_3), dilute to 40 ml., and mix. Add 10 ml. of freshly prepared hydrogen sulfide water to each and mix. Any color in the solution of the sample should not exceed that in the control.

Iron. Dissolve 1 gram in 10 ml. of water, add 2 ml. of hydrochloric acid, and evaporate to dryness on the steam bath. Dissolve the residue in a mixture of 5 ml. of water and 2 ml. of hydrochloric acid, and again evaporate to dryness. Dissolve the residue in 4 ml. of hydrochloric acid and dilute to 100 ml. with water. To 50 ml. add 30 to 50 mg. of ammonium persulfate crystals and 3 ml. of ammonium thiocyanate reagent solution. Any red color should not exceed that produced by 0.01 mg. of iron (Fe) in an equal volume of solution containing the quantities of reagents used in the test.

Notes

Sodium Borate

Borax, Sodium Tetraborate

$Na_2B_4O_7 \cdot 10H_2O$ Formula Wt. 381.37

REQUIREMENTS

Insoluble matter.   Not more than 0.005 per cent.
pH of a 0.01M solution.   From 9.15 to 9.20 at 25°C.
Chloride (Cl).   Not more than 0.001 per cent.
Phosphate (PO$_4$).   Not more than 0.001 per cent.
Sulfate (SO$_4$).   Not more than 0.005 per cent.
Calcium (Ca).   Not more than 0.005 per cent.
Heavy metals (as Pb).   Not more than 0.001 per cent.
Iron (Fe).   Not more than 0.0005 per cent.

TESTS

Insoluble matter.   Dissolve 20 grams in 300 ml. of water, heat to boiling, and digest in a covered beaker on the steam bath for 1 hour. Filter through a tared porous porcelain or a platinum filtering crucible, wash thoroughly, and dry at 105°C. The weight of the residue should not exceed 0.0010 gram.

pH of a 0.01M solution.   Dissolve 0.3814 gram in water and dilute to 100 ml., using water having a pH of 6.5 to 7.4. Determine the pH by the method described on page 18. The pH should be from 9.15 to 9.20 at 25°C.

Chloride.   Dissolve 1 gram in 20 ml. of water, filter if necessary through a chloride-free filter, and add 1 ml. of nitric acid and 1 ml. of silver nitrate reagent solution. Any turbidity should not exceed that produced by 0.01 mg. of chloride ion (Cl) in an equal volume of solution containing the quantities of reagents used in the test.

Phosphate.   Dissolve 2 grams in 10 ml. of warm water, add 2 ml. of hydrochloric acid, and evaporate to dryness on the steam bath. Dissolve in 25 ml. of approximately 0.5N sulfuric acid and filter out any precipitated boric acid if necessary. To the clear filtrate add 1 ml. of ammonium molybdate reagent solution and 1 ml. of p-methylaminophenol sulfate reagent solution and allow to stand for 2 hours at room temperature. Any blue color should not exceed that produced by 0.02 mg. of phosphate ion (PO$_4$) in an equal volume of solution containing the quantities of reagents used in the test, including the residue from evaporation of 2 ml. of hydrochloric acid.

Sulfate. Dissolve 8 grams in 120 ml. of warm water plus 6 ml. of hydrochloric acid. Filter and wash with 30 ml. of water. Heat to boiling, add 5 ml. of barium chloride reagent solution, digest in a covered beaker on the steam bath for 2 hours, and allow to stand overnight. Heat to dissolve any boric acid that may be crystallized. If a precipitate is formed, filter, wash thoroughly, and ignite. The weight of the precipitate should not be more than 0.0010 gram greater than the weight obtained in a complete blank test.

Calcium. Determine the calcium by the flame photometric method described on page 14.

> **Sample Solution A.** Dissolve 2 grams in water and dilute to 100 ml.

> **Control Solution B.** Dissolve 2 grams in water, add 0.1 mg. of calcium ion (Ca), and dilute to 100 ml.

Observe the emission of Control Solution B at the 422.7-mμ calcium line. Observe the emission of Sample Solution A at the 422.7-mμ calcium line and at a wavelength of 416.7 mμ. The difference (D_1) between the intensities observed for Sample Solution A at 422.7 mμ and 416.7 mμ should not exceed the difference (D_2) observed at 422.7 mμ between Sample Solution A and Control Solution B.

Heavy metals. Dissolve 4 grams in 40 ml. of hot water, add 5 ml. of glacial acetic acid, and dilute to 48 ml. For the control add 0.02 mg. of lead ion (Pb) to a 12-ml. aliquot of the solution and dilute to 36 ml. For the sample use the remaining 36-ml. portion. Adjust the pH of the control and sample solutions to between 3 and 4 (using a pH meter) with 1N acetic acid or ammonium hydroxide (10 per cent NH_3), dilute to 40 ml., and mix. Heat the solutions to about 80°C., add 10 ml. of freshly prepared hydrogen sulfide water to each, and mix. Any color in the solution of the sample should not exceed that in the control.

Iron. Dissolve 2 grams in 40 ml. of water plus 3 ml. of hydrochloric acid, heating if necessary, and dilute to 50 ml. Add 30 to 50 mg. of ammonium persulfate crystals and 3 ml. of ammonium thiocyanate reagent solution. Any red color should not exceed that produced by 0.01 mg. of iron (Fe) in an equal volume of solution containing the quantities of reagents used in the test.

Notes

Sodium Carbonate, Anhydrous

Na$_2$CO$_3$ Formula Wt. 105.99

REQUIREMENTS

Insoluble matter.   Not more than 0.010 per cent.
Loss on heating at 285°C.   Not more than 1.0 per cent.
Chloride (Cl).   Not more than 0.002 per cent.
Nitrogen compounds (as N).   Not more than 0.001 per cent.
Phosphate (PO$_4$).   Not more than 0.001 per cent.
Silica (SiO$_2$).   Not more than 0.005 per cent.
Sulfur compounds (as SO$_4$).   Not more than 0.003 per cent.
Ammonium hydroxide precipitate.   Not more than 0.010 per cent.
Arsenic (As).   Not more than 0.0001 per cent.
Calcium and magnesium precipitate.   Not more than 0.010 per cent.
Heavy metals (as Pb).   Not more than 0.0005 per cent.
Iron (Fe).   Not more than 0.0005 per cent.
Potassium (K).   Not more than 0.005 per cent.

TESTS

Insoluble matter.   Dissolve 10 grams in 100 ml. of water, heat to boiling, and digest in a covered beaker on the steam bath for 1 hour. Filter through a tared porous porcelain or a platinum filtering crucible, wash thoroughly, and dry at 105°C. The weight of the residue should not exceed 0.0010 gram.

Loss on heating at 285°C.   Accurately weigh 1 gram in a tared dish or crucible. Heat to constant weight at 270° to 300°C. The loss in weight should not exceed 0.0100 gram.

Chloride.   Dissolve 1.5 grams in about 40 ml. of water, filter if necessary through a chloride-free filter, add 4 ml. of nitric acid, and dilute to 60 ml. To 20 ml. of this solution add 1 ml. of silver nitrate reagent solution. Any turbidity should not exceed that produced by 0.01 mg. of chloride ion (Cl) in an equal volume of solution containing the quantities of reagents used in the test.

Nitrogen compounds.   Dissolve 1 gram in 60 ml. of water in a flask connected through a spray trap to a condenser, the end of which dips beneath the surface of 10 ml. of 0.1N hydrochloric acid. Add to the flask 20 ml. of freshly boiled 10 per cent sodium hydroxide reagent solution and 0.5 gram of aluminum wire in small pieces, allow to stand for 1 hour, and distill about 35 ml. To the distillate add 1 ml. of 10 per cent sodium hydroxide reagent solution, dilute to 50 ml., and add 2 ml. of Nessler reagent. Any color should not exceed that produced when a quantity of an ammonium salt containing 0.01 mg. of nitrogen (N) is treated exactly like the sample.

Phosphate.   Dissolve 1 gram in 50 ml. of water in a platinum dish and digest on the steam bath for 30 minutes. Cool, neutralize with dilute sulfuric acid $(1 + 19)$ to a pH of about 4, and dilute to about 75 ml. Prepare a standard containing 0.01 mg. of phosphate ion (PO_4) and 0.05 mg. of silica (SiO_2) in about 75 ml. Add 0.5 gram of ammonium molybdate to each solution, and when it is dissolved, adjust the pH to 1.8 (using a pH meter) with dilute hydrochloric acid $(1 + 9)$. Heat the solutions to boiling, cool to room temperature, add 10 ml. of hydrochloric acid, and dilute to 100 ml. Transfer the solutions to separatory funnels, add 35 ml. of ether to each, shake vigorously, and allow to separate. Draw off the aqueous phase and reserve it for determination of *Silica.* Wash the ether phase by shaking with 10 ml. of dilute hydrochloric acid $(1 + 9)$, allow to separate, and draw off and discard the aqueous phase. Add 0.2 ml. of a freshly prepared 2 per cent solution of stannous chloride in hydrochloric acid to the ether and shake. The blue color in the solution of the sample should not exceed that in the standard. If the ether extracts are turbid, wash with 10 ml. of dilute hydrochloric acid $(1 + 9)$.

Silica.   Add 10 ml. of hydrochloric acid to the solutions reserved from the determination of *Phosphate* and transfer to separatory funnels. Add 40 ml. of butyl alcohol, shake vigorously, and allow to separate. Draw off and discard the aqueous phase. Wash the butyl alcohol three times with 20-ml. portions of dilute hydrochloric acid $(1 + 99)$, discarding the washings each time. Dilute each butyl alcohol solution to 50 ml., take a 10-ml. aliquot from each, and dilute each to 50 ml. with butyl alcohol. Add 0.5 ml. of a freshly prepared 2 per cent solution of stannous chloride in hydrochloric acid. The blue color in the extract from the sample should not exceed that in the standard. If the butyl alcohol extracts are turbid, wash with 10 ml. of dilute hydrochloric acid $(1 + 99)$.

Sulfur compounds.   Dissolve 15 grams in 100 ml. of water, add 0.25 ml. of bromine water, and boil. Cool, neutralize with hydrochloric acid, add an excess of 1 ml. of hydrochloric acid, and filter. Boil the filtrate, add 5 ml. of barium chloride reagent solution, digest in a covered beaker on the steam bath for 2 hours, and allow to stand overnight. If a precipitate is formed, filter, wash thoroughly, and ignite. The weight of the precipitate should not be more than 0.0011 gram greater than the weight obtained in a complete blank test.

Ammonium hydroxide precipitate. Dissolve 10 grams in 100 ml. of water and filter if necessary. Cautiously add 30 ml. of cooled dilute sulfuric acid $(1 + 1)$ and evaporate until dense fumes of sulfur trioxide appear. Cool, dissolve the residue in 130 ml. of hot water, and add ammonium hydroxide until the solution is just alkaline to methyl red. Heat to boiling, boil gently for 5 minutes, and filter, reserving the filtrate for the test for *Calcium and magnesium precipitate*. Wash the precipitate with hot water, rejecting the washings, and ignite. The weight of the residue should not exceed 0.0010 gram. The residue includes some, but not all, of the silica in the sample.

Arsenic. Dissolve 3 grams in a small volume of water, neutralize with sulfuric or hydrochloric acid, and determine the arsenic by the Gutzeit method (page 11). The stain produced should correspond to not more than 0.003 mg. of arsenic (As).

Calcium and magnesium precipitate. Neutralize the filtrate from the test for *Ammonium hydroxide precipitate* with hydrochloric acid and add an excess of 0.5 ml. of the acid. Add 5 ml. of ammonium oxalate reagent solution, 2 ml. of ammonium phosphate reagent solution, and 10 ml. of ammonium hydroxide. Stir well and allow to stand overnight. Filter, wash the precipitate with water containing 2.5 per cent ammonia and about 0.1 per cent ammonium oxalate, and ignite. The weight of the residue should not exceed 0.0010 gram.

Heavy metals. To 5 grams in a 150-ml. beaker add 10 ml. of water, mix, and cautiously add 10 ml. of hydrochloric acid. For the control dissolve 1 gram of the sample in 10 ml. of water, add 0.02 mg. of lead ion (Pb), and cautiously add 10 ml. of hydrochloric acid. Evaporate both solutions to dryness on the steam bath, dissolve each residue in about 20 ml. of water, and dilute to 25 ml. Adjust the pH of the control and sample solutions to between 3 and 4 (using a pH meter) with $1N$ acetic acid or ammonium hydroxide (10 per cent NH_3), dilute to 40 ml., and mix. Add 10 ml. of freshly prepared hydrogen sulfide water to each and mix. Any color in the solution of the sample should not exceed that in the control.

Iron. Dissolve 2 grams in 50 ml. of dilute hydrochloric acid $(1 + 9)$. Add 30 to 50 mg. of ammonium persulfate crystals and 3 ml. of ammonium thiocyanate reagent solution. Any red color should not exceed that produced by 0.01 mg. of iron (Fe) in an equal volume of solution containing 2 ml. of hydrochloric acid and the quantities of ammonium persulfate and ammonium thiocyanate used in the test.

Potassium. Determine the potassium by the flame photometric method described on page 14. Dissolve 10 grams in water and dilute to 100 ml.

Sample Solution A. Dilute a 10-ml. aliquot of the solution to 100 ml.

Control Solution B. To another 10-ml. aliquot of the solution add 0.05 mg. of potassium ion (K) and dilute to 100 ml.

Observe the emission of Control Solution B at the 767-mμ potassium line. Observe the emission of Sample Solution A at the 767-mμ potassium line and at a wave-length of 750 mμ. The difference (D_1) between the intensities observed for Sample Solution A at 750 mμ and 767 mμ should not exceed the difference (D_2) observed at 767 mμ between Sample Solution A and Control Solution B.

Notes

Sodium Carbonate, Alkalimetric Standard

Na_2CO_3 Formula Wt. 105.99

Note. For use as an alkalimetric standard this material should be heated at 285°C. for 2 hours.

REQUIREMENTS

Assay. Not less than 99.95 nor more than 100.05 per cent Na_2CO_3.
Insoluble matter. Not more than 0.010 per cent.
Loss on heating at 285°C. Not more than 1.0 per cent.
Chloride (Cl). Not more than 0.002 per cent.
Nitrogen compounds (as N). Not more than 0.001 per cent.
Phosphate (PO_4). Not more than 0.001 per cent.
Silica (SiO_2). Not more than 0.005 per cent.
Sulfur compounds (as SO_4). Not more than 0.003 per cent.
Ammonium hydroxide precipitate. Not more than 0.010 per cent.
Arsenic (As). Not more than 0.0001 per cent.
Calcium and magnesium precipitate. Not more than 0.010 per cent.
Heavy metals (as Pb). Not more than 0.0005 per cent.
Iron (Fe). Not more than 0.0005 per cent.
Potassium (K). Not more than 0.005 per cent.

TESTS

Assay. Transfer a quantity of N.B.S. certified potassium hydrogen phthalate to an agate or mullite mortar and grind to approximately 100-mesh fineness. Place 5.100 ± 0.003 grams of the 100-mesh material in a weighing bottle, dry at 120°C. for 2 hours, and cool in a desiccator for at least 2 hours. Weigh the bottle and contents accurately, transfer the contents to the titration flask,* and weigh the empty bottle to obtain the exact weight of the potassium hydrogen phthalate.

Place 1.300 grams of the alkalimetric standard sodium carbonate in a clean, dry weighing bottle. Heat at 285°C. for 2 hours, cool in a desiccator for at least 2 hours, and weigh the bottle and contents accurately. Transfer the contents to a clean, dry 50-ml. beaker and weigh the empty bottle to obtain the exact weight of the sodium carbonate.

Transfer the sodium carbonate to the titration flask* by pouring it through a powder funnel. Rinse the beaker and funnel thoroughly with carbon dioxide-free water, using several small portions of the water to rinse the funnel and sides of the flask. Dilute the solution to 90 ml., swirl to dissolve the sample, stopper the flask, and bubble carbon dioxide-free air through the solution during all subsequent operations. Boil the solution for 15 minutes, cool to room temperature in an ice bath, add 0.30 ml. of a solution of phenolphthalein in 95 per cent alcohol (1 in 2000), and dilute with carbon dioxide-free water to 75 to 80 ml. Titrate with 0.02N sodium hydroxide until the color matches that of 100 ml. of buffer solution (pH = 8.75)** containing 0.30 ml. of the same phenolphthalein solution. Calculate the per cent Na_2CO_3 from the following formula:

$$A = \frac{25.9486\ F}{B}$$

in which,

A = per cent Na_2CO_3 in the sample
B = weight, in grams, of the Na_2CO_3 sample
F = calculation factor

The calculation factor, F, is obtained as follows:

F = (C × D) − 0.20423 EG

in which,

C = weight, in grams, of the potassium hydrogen phthalate
D = assay value of the potassium hydrogen phthalate
E = exact normality of the sodium hydroxide solution, as determined against N.B.S. certified potassium hydrogen phthalate using the method in the N.B.S. assay certificate
G = volume, in milliliters, of sodium hydroxide consumed

*Note 1. Titration Flask. This is a 500-ml. conical flask fitted with a tube sealed into the side. The tube inside the flask is constricted and as close to the bottom as possible. The tube outside the flask is bent at a right angle to permit attachment of the carbon dioxide-free air supply.

**Note 2. Buffer Solution (pH = 8.75). Weigh 3.1 grams of boric acid (H_3BO_3) and 3.8 grams of potassium chloride, dissolve in water, add 17.0 ml. of 1N sodium hydroxide, and dilute to 1 liter.

Insoluble matter and other tests except *Assay* are the same as for **Sodium Carbonate, Anhydrous,** page 519.

Notes

Sodium Carbonate, Monohydrate

$Na_2CO_3 \cdot H_2O$ Formula Wt. 124.00

REQUIREMENTS

Insoluble matter.   Not more than 0.010 per cent.
Loss on drying at 150°C.   Not less than 13.0 nor more than 15.0 per cent.
Chloride (Cl).   Not more than 0.003 per cent.
Nitrogen compounds (as N).   Not more than 0.001 per cent.
Phosphate (PO_4).   Not more than 0.0005 per cent.
Silica (SiO_2).   Not more than 0.005 per cent.
Sulfur compounds (as SO_4).   Not more than 0.004 per cent.
Ammonium hydroxide precipitate.   Not more than 0.010 per cent.
Arsenic (As).   Not more than 0.0001 per cent.
Calcium and magnesium precipitate.   Not more than 0.010 per cent.
Heavy metals (as Pb).   Not more than 0.0005 per cent.
Iron (Fe).   Not more than 0.0005 per cent.
Potassium (K).   Not more than 0.005 per cent.

TESTS

Insoluble matter.   Dissolve 10 grams in 100 ml. of water, heat to boiling, and digest in a covered beaker on the steam bath for 1 hour. Filter through a tared porous porcelain or a platinum filtering crucible, wash thoroughly, and dry at 105°C. The weight of the residue should not exceed 0.0010 gram.

Loss on drying.   Weigh accurately about 1 gram and dry at 150°C. to constant weight. The loss in weight should not be less than 13.0 nor more than 15.0 per cent.

Chloride.   Dissolve 1 gram in 20 ml. of warm water, filter if necessary through a chloride-free filter, add 3 ml. of nitric acid, cool, and dilute to 30 ml. Dilute 10 ml. of the solution to 20 ml., and add 1 ml. of silver nitrate reagent solution. Any turbidity should not exceed that produced by 0.01 mg. of chloride ion (Cl) in an equal volume of solution containing the quantities of reagents used in the test.

Nitrogen compounds.   Dissolve 1 gram in 60 ml. of water in a flask connected through a spray trap to a condenser, the end of which dips beneath the surface of 10 ml. of $0.1N$ hydrochloric acid. Add to the flask 10 ml. of freshly boiled 10 per cent sodium hydroxide reagent solution and 0.5 gram of aluminum wire in small pieces, allow to stand for 1 hour, and distill about 35 ml. To the distillate add 1 ml. of 10 per cent sodium hydroxide reagent solution, dilute to 50 ml., and add 2 ml. of Nessler reagent. Any color should not exceed that produced when a quantity of an ammonium salt containing 0.01 mg. of nitrogen (N) is treated exactly like the sample.

Phosphate. Dissolve 2 grams in 50 ml. of water in a platinum dish and digest on the steam bath for 30 minutes. Cool, neutralize with dilute sulfuric acid (1 + 19) to a pH of about 4, and dilute to about 75 ml. Prepare a standard containing 0.01 mg. of phosphate ion (PO_4) and 0.10 mg. of silica (SiO_2) in about 75 ml. Add 0.5 gram of ammonium molybdate to each solution, and when it is dissolved, adjust the pH to 1.8 (using a pH meter) with dilute hydrochloric acid (1 + 9). Heat the solutions to boiling, cool to room temperature, add 10 ml. of hydrochloric acid, and dilute to 100 ml. Transfer the solutions to separatory funnels, add 35 ml. of ether to each, shake vigorously, and allow to separate. Draw off the aqueous phase and reserve it for the determination of *Silica*. Wash the ether phase by shaking with 10 ml. of dilute hydrochloric acid (1 + 9), allow to separate, and draw off and discard the aqueous phase. Add 0.2 ml. of freshly prepared 2 per cent solution of stannous chloride in hydrochloric acid, and shake. The blue color in the solution of the sample should not exceed that in the standard. If the ether extracts are turbid, wash with 10 ml. of dilute hydrochloric acid (1 + 9).

Silica. Add 10 ml. of hydrochloric acid to the solutions reserved from the determination of *Phosphate* and transfer to separatory funnels. Add 40 ml. of butyl alcohol, shake vigorously, and allow to separate. Draw off and discard the aqueous phase. Wash the butyl alcohol three times with 20-ml. portions of dilute hydrochloric acid (1 + 99), discarding the washings each time. Dilute each butyl alcohol solution to 50 ml., take a 10-ml. aliquot from each, and dilute each to 50 ml. with butyl alcohol. Add 0.5 ml. of a freshly prepared 2 per cent solution of stannous chloride in hydrochloric acid. The blue color in the extract from the sample should not exceed that in the standard. If the butyl alcohol extracts are turbid, wash with 10 ml. of dilute hydrochloric acid (1 + 99).

Sulfur compounds. Dissolve 10 grams in 100 ml. of water, add 0.25 ml. of bromine water, and boil. Cool, neutralize with hydrochloric acid, add an excess of 1 ml. of hydrochloric acid, and filter. Boil the filtrate, add 5 ml. of barium chloride reagent solution, digest in a covered beaker on the steam bath for 2 hours, and allow to stand overnight. If a precipitate is formed, filter, wash thoroughly, and ignite. The weight of the precipitate should not be more than 0.0011 gram greater than the weight obtained in a complete blank test.

Ammonium hydroxide precipitate. Dissolve 10 grams in 100 ml. of water and filter if necessary. Cautiously add 30 ml. of cooled dilute sulfuric acid $(1 + 1)$. Evaporate until dense fumes of sulfur trioxide appear. Cool, dissolve the residue in 130 ml. of hot water, and add ammonium hydroxide until the solution is just alkaline to methyl red. Heat to boiling, boil gently for 5 minutes, and filter, reserving the filtrate for the test for *Calcium and magnesium precipitate.* Wash the precipitate with hot water, rejecting the washings, and ignite. The weight of the residue should not exceed 0.0010 gram. The residue includes some, but not all, of the silica in the sample.

Arsenic. Dissolve 3 grams in a small volume of water, neutralize with sulfuric or hydrochloric acid, and determine the arsenic by the Gutzeit method (page 11). The stain produced should correspond to not more than 0.003 mg. of arsenic (As).

Calcium and magnesium precipitate. Neutralize the filtrate from the test for *Ammonium hydroxide precipitate* with hydrochloric acid and add an excess of 0.5 ml. of the acid. Add 5 ml. of ammonium oxalate reagent solution, 2 ml. of ammonium phosphate reagent solution, and 10 ml. of ammonium hydroxide. Stir well and allow to stand overnight. Filter, wash the precipitate with water containing 2.5 per cent ammonia and about 0.1 per cent ammonium oxalate, and ignite. The weight of the residue should not exceed 0.0010 gram.

Heavy metals. To 5 grams in a 150-ml. beaker add 10 ml. of water, mix, and cautiously add 10 ml. of hydrochloric acid. For the control dissolve 1 gram of the sample in 10 ml. of water, add 0.02 mg. of lead ion (Pb), and cautiously add 10 ml. of hydrochloric acid. Evaporate both solutions to dryness on the steam bath, dissolve each residue in about 20 ml. of water, and dilute to 25 ml. Adjust the pH of the control and sample solutions to between 3 and 4 (using a pH meter) with $1N$ acetic acid or ammonium hydroxide (10 per cent NH_3), dilute to 40 ml., and mix. Add 10 ml. of freshly prepared hydrogen sulfide water to each and mix. Any color in the solution of the sample should not exceed that in the control.

Iron. Dissolve 2 grams in 50 ml. of dilute hydrochloric acid $(1 + 9)$. Add 30 to 50 mg. of ammonium persulfate crystals and 3 ml. of ammonium thiocyanate reagent solution. Any red color should not exceed that produced by 0.01 mg. of iron (Fe) in an equal volume of solution containing the quantities of ammonium persulfate and ammonium thiocyanate used in the test.

Potassium. Determine the potassium by the flame photometric method described on page 14. Dissolve 10 grams in water and dilute to 100 ml.

Sample Solution A. Dilute a 10-ml. aliquot of the solution to 100 ml.

Control Solution B. To another 10-ml. aliquot of the solution add 0.05 mg. of potassium ion (K) and dilute to 100 ml.

Observe the emission of Control Solution B at the 767-mμ potassium line. Observe the emission of Sample Solution A at the 767-mμ potassium line and at a wavelength of 750 mμ. The difference (D_1) between the intensities observed for Sample Solution A at 750 mμ and 767 mμ should not exceed the difference (D_2) observed at 767 mμ between Sample Solution A and Control Solution B.

Notes

Sodium Chloride

NaCl   Formula Wt. 58.44

REQUIREMENTS

Insoluble matter. Not more than 0.005 per cent.
pH of a 5 per cent solution. From 5.0 to 9.0 at 25°C.
Iodide (I). Not more than 0.002 per cent.
Bromide (Br). To pass test (limit about 0.01 per cent).
Chlorate and nitrate (as NO_3). Not more than 0.003 per cent.
Nitrogen compounds (as N). Not more than 0.001 per cent.
Phosphate (PO_4). Not more than 0.0005 per cent.
Sulfate (SO_4). Not more than 0.001 per cent.
Barium (Ba). To pass test (limit about 0.001 per cent).
Calcium, magnesium, and R_2O_3 precipitate. Not more than 0.005 per cent.
Heavy metals (as Pb). Not more than 0.0005 per cent.
Iron (Fe). Not more than 0.0002 per cent.
Potassium (K). Not more than 0.005 per cent.

TESTS

Insoluble matter. Dissolve 20 grams in 200 ml. of water, heat to boiling, and digest in a covered beaker on the steam bath for 1 hour. Filter through a tared filtering crucible, wash thoroughly, and dry at 105°C. The weight of the residue should not exceed 0.0010 gram. Save the filtrate separate from the washings for the test for *Calcium, magnesium, and R_2O_3 precipitate.*

pH of a 5 per cent solution. Dissolve 10 grams in 200 ml. of carbon dioxide- and ammonia-free water. Determine the pH by the method described on page 18. The pH should be from 5.0 to 9.0 at 25°C. The pH of a 5 per cent solution of pure sodium chloride would be 7.0 at 25°C.

Iodide. Dissolve 11 grams in 50 ml. of water. Prepare a control by dissolving 1 gram of the sample, 0.2 mg. of iodide ion (I), and 1.0 mg. of bromide ion (Br) in 50 ml. of water. To each solution, in a separatory funnel, add 2 ml. of hydrochloric acid and 5 ml. of ferric chloride reagent solution. Allow to stand for 5 minutes. Add 10 ml. of carbon tetrachloride, shake for 1 minute, allow the carbon tetrachloride to settle, and draw it off. Reserve the water solution for the test for *Bromide.* Any violet color in the carbon tetrachloride extract from the solution of the sample should not exceed that in the extract from the control.

Bromide. Treat both the solution of the sample and the control, obtained in the test for *Iodide,* as follows: wash twice by shaking with 10-ml. portions of carbon tetrachloride. Each time allow to settle, then draw off and discard the carbon tetrachloride. To each of the water solutions add 10 ml. of water, 65 ml. of cool, dilute sulfuric acid $(1 + 1)$, and 15 ml. of a solution of chromic acid prepared by dissolving 10 grams of chromium trioxide (CrO_3) in 100 ml. of dilute sulfuric acid $(1 + 3)$. Allow to stand for 5 minutes. Add 10 ml. of carbon tetrachloride, shake for 1 minute, allow to settle, and draw off. (Half of a 7-cm. piece of filter paper rolled and placed in the stem of the separatory funnel will absorb any of the aqueous solution that may pass the stopcock and thus assure a clear extract.) Any yellow-brown color in the carbon tetrachloride extract from the solution of the sample should not exceed that in the extract from the control.

Chlorate and nitrate.

Sample Solution A. Dissolve 0.5 gram in 3 ml. of water by heating in a boiling water bath. Dilute to 50 ml. with brucine sulfate reagent solution.

Control Solution B. Dissolve 0.5 gram in 1.5 ml. of water and 1.5 ml. of the standard nitrate solution containing 0.01 mg. of nitrate ion (NO_3) per ml. by heating in a boiling water bath. Dilute to 50 ml. with brucine sulfate reagent solution.

Blank Solution C. Use 50 ml. of brucine sulfate reagent solution.

Heat the three solutions in a preheated (boiling) water bath for 10 minutes. Cool rapidly in an ice bath to room temperature. Set a spectrophotometer at 410 mμ and adjust the instrument to read 0 absorbance with Blank Solution C in the light path, then determine the absorbance of Sample Solution A. Adjust the instrument to read 0 absorbance with Sample Solution A in the light path and determine the absorbance of Control Solution B. The absorbance for Sample Solution A should not exceed that of Control Solution B.

Nitrogen compounds. Dissolve 1 gram in 40 ml. of water in a flask connected through a spray trap to a condenser, the end of which dips beneath the surface of 10 ml. of 0.1N hydrochloric acid. Add to the flask 10 ml. of freshly boiled 10 per cent sodium hydroxide reagent solution and 0.5 gram of aluminum wire in small pieces, allow to stand for 1 hour, and distill about 35 ml. To the distillate add 1 ml. of 10 per cent sodium hydroxide reagent solution, dilute to 50 ml., and add 2 ml.

of Nessler reagent. Any color should not exceed that produced when a quantity of an ammonium salt containing 0.01 mg. of nitrogen (N) is treated exactly like the sample.

Phosphate. Dissolve 4 grams in 25 ml. of approximately 0.5N sulfuric acid, add 1 ml. of ammonium molybdate reagent solution and 1 ml. of p-methylaminophenol sulfate reagent solution, and allow to stand for 2 hours at room temperature. Any blue color should not exceed that produced by 0.02 mg. of phosphate ion (PO_4) in an equal volume of solution containing the quantities of reagents used in the test.

Sulfate. Dissolve 25 grams in 200 ml. of water, filter if necessary, and add 2 ml. of hydrochloric acid. Heat to boiling, add 10 ml. of barium chloride reagent solution, digest in a covered beaker on the steam bath for 2 hours, and allow to stand overnight. If a precipitate is formed, filter, wash thoroughly, and ignite. The weight of the precipitate should not be more than 0.0006 gram greater than the weight obtained in a complete blank test.

Barium. Dissolve 4 grams in 20 ml. of water, filter if necessary, and divide into two equal portions. To one portion add 2 ml. of 10 per cent sulfuric acid reagent solution and to the other 2 ml. of water. The solutions should be equally clear at the end of 2 hours.

Calcium, magnesium, and R₂O₃ precipitate. To the filtrate (without washings) from the test for *Insoluble matter* add 5 ml. of ammonium oxalate reagent solution, 2 ml. of ammonium phosphate reagent solution, and 30 ml. of ammonium hydroxide, and allow to stand overnight. If a precipitate is formed, filter, wash with water containing 2.5 per cent of ammonia and about 0.1 per cent of ammonium oxalate, and ignite. The weight of the residue should not exceed 0.0010 gram.

Heavy metals. Dissolve 6 grams in about 20 ml. of water and dilute to 30 ml. For the control add 0.02 mg. of lead ion (Pb) to a 5-ml. aliquot of the solution and dilute to 25 ml. For the sample use the remaining 25-ml. portion. Adjust the pH of the control and sample solutions to between 3 and 4 (using a pH meter) with 1N acetic acid or ammonium hydroxide (10 per cent NH_3), dilute to 40 ml., and mix. Add 10 ml. of freshly prepared hydrogen sulfide water to each and mix. Any color in the solution of the sample should not exceed that in the control.

Iron. Dissolve 5 grams in 40 ml. of water plus 2 ml. of hydrochloric acid, dilute to 50 ml., and add 30 to 50 mg. of ammonium persulfate crystals and 3 ml. of ammonium thiocyanate reagent solution. Any red color should not exceed that produced by 0.01 mg. of iron (Fe) in an

equal volume of solution containing the quantities of reagents used in the test.

Potassium. Determine the potassium by the flame photometric method described on page 14. Dissolve 10 grams in water and dilute to 100 ml.

Sample Solution A. Dilute a 10-ml. aliquot of the solution to 100 ml.

Control Solution B. To another 10-ml. aliquot of the solution add 0.05 mg. of potassium ion (K) and dilute to 100 ml.

Observe the emission of Control Solution B at the 767-mμ potassium line. Observe the emission of Sample Solution A at the 767-mμ potassium line and at a wavelength of 750 mμ. The difference (D_1) between the intensities observed for Sample Solution A at 750 mμ and 767 mμ should not exceed the difference (D_2) observed at 767 mμ between Sample Solution A and Control Solution B.

Notes

Sodium Cobaltinitrite

(For determination of potassium)

REQUIREMENTS

Insoluble matter. Not more than 0.02 per cent.
Suitability for determination of potassium. To pass test.

TESTS

Insoluble matter. Dissolve 5 grams in 25 ml. of dilute acetic acid (1 + 25), and allow to stand in a covered beaker overnight. Filter through a tared filtering crucible, wash thoroughly with cold water, and dry at 105°C. The weight of the residue should not exceed 0.0010 gram.

Suitability for determination of potassium. Dissolve 1.583 grams of potassium chloride in water and dilute to 500 ml. To 10.0 ml. of this solution (20 mg. of K_2O) in a 50-ml. beaker, add 2 ml. of $1N$ nitric acid and 8 ml. of water. Dissolve 5 grams of the sodium cobaltinitrite in distilled water, dilute to 25 ml., and filter. Cool both solutions to approximately 20°C. and add 10 ml. of the cobaltinitrite solution to the potassium chloride solution. Allow to stand for 2 hours and filter through a sintered-glass crucible that has been washed with alcohol, dried at 105°C., and weighed. Wash the precipitate with $0.01N$ nitric acid saturated with potassium sodium cobaltinitrite, finally wash with 5 to 10 ml. of alcohol, and dry at 105°C. The weight of the potassium sodium cobaltinitrite precipitate $[K_2NaCo(NO_2)_6 \cdot H_2O]$ should be between 0.0945 and 0.0985 gram.

Notes

Sodium Cyanide

NaCN   Formula Wt. 49.01

REQUIREMENTS

Assay. Not less than 95 per cent NaCN.
Chloride (Cl). Not more than 0.15 per cent.
Phosphate (PO$_4$). Not more than 0.020 per cent.
Sulfate (SO$_4$). Not more than 0.05 per cent.
Sulfide (S). Not more than 0.005 per cent.
Thiocyanate (SCN). Not more than 0.020 per cent.
Iron, total (as Fe). Not more than 0.005 per cent.
Lead (Pb). Not more than 0.0005 per cent.

TESTS

Caution. Because of the extremely poisonous nature of sodium cyanide and of the hydrogen cyanide gas (HCN) evolved on treatment of the salt or solution of the salt with an acid, all tests must be made in a fume hood with a strong draft. Special care must be taken to avoid inhaling any of the fumes or allowing the salt or solution of the salt to come in contact with open cuts of the skin. If safety pipets are not available for measuring aliquots, use a graduated cylinder. *Under no conditions should suction by mouth be used to fill an ordinary pipet.*

Assay. Weigh accurately about 0.4 gram and dissolve in 30 ml. of water. Add 0.20 ml. of 10 per cent potassium iodide reagent solution and 1 ml. of ammonium hydroxide and titrate with 0.1N silver nitrate until a slight permanent yellowish turbidity is formed. One milliliter of the 0.1N silver nitrate corresponds to 0.009802 gram of NaCN.

Sample Solution A. Dissolve 10 grams in water, filter if necessary through a chloride-free filter, and dilute to 200 ml. (1 ml. = 0.05 gram).

Chloride. Dilute 1 ml. of Sample Solution A (0.05-gram sample) to 50 ml. To 10 ml. of this solution add 5 ml. of 30 per cent hydrogen peroxide and cover the beaker until the reaction ceases. Digest in the covered beaker on the steam bath for about one-half hour, cool, and neutralize with nitric acid. Dilute to 25 ml. and add 1 ml. of nitric acid and 1 ml. of silver nitrate reagent solution. The turbidity should not exceed that produced by 0.015 mg. of chloride ion (Cl) in an equal volume of solution containing the quantities of reagents used in the test.

Phosphate. Dissolve 1 gram in 5 ml. of water, add 2 ml. of hydrochloric acid, and evaporate to dryness in a well ventilated hood. Add 5 ml. of dilute hydrochloric acid ($1 + 1$) and evaporate to dryness again. Dissolve in 50 ml. of approximately $0.5N$ sulfuric acid. To 5 ml. of the solution add 20 ml. of approximately $0.5N$ sulfuric acid, 1 ml. of ammonium molybdate reagent solution, and 1 ml. of p-methylaminophenol sulfate reagent solution, and allow to stand for 2 hours at room temperature. Any blue color should not exceed that produced by 0.02 mg. of phosphate ion (PO_4) in an equal volume of solution containing the quantities of reagents used in the test.

Sulfate. To 16 ml. of Sample Solution A (measured in a graduated cylinder) (0.8-gram sample) add 10 ml. of hydrochloric acid and evaporate to dryness in a well ventilated hood. Warm the residue with 50 ml. of water plus 1 ml. of hydrochloric acid, filter if necessary, and dilute to 100 ml. Heat to boiling, add 5 ml. of barium chloride reagent solution, digest in a covered beaker on the steam bath for 2 hours, and allow to stand overnight. If a precipitate is formed, filter, wash thoroughly, and ignite. The weight of the precipitate should not be more than 0.0010 gram greater than the weight obtained in a complete blank test.

Sulfide. To 10 ml. of Sample Solution A (measured in a graduated cylinder) (0.5-gram sample) add 10 ml. of water and 0.15 ml. of alkaline lead solution (made by adding 10 per cent sodium hydroxide reagent solution to a 10 per cent lead acetate reagent solution until the precipitate first formed is redissolved). The color should not be darker than that produced by 0.025 mg. of sulfide ion (S) in a equal volume of solution when treated with 0.15 ml. of the alkaline lead solution.

Thiocyanate. To 20 ml. of Sample Solution A (measured in a graduated cylinder) (1-gram sample) add 4 ml. of hydrochloric acid and 0.20 ml. of ferric chloride reagent solution. At the end of 5 minutes the solution should show no reddish tint when compared with 20 ml. of water to which have been added the quantities of hydrochloric acid and ferric chloride used in the test.

Iron, total. To 4 ml. of Sample Solution A (0.2-gram sample) in a platinum evaporating dish, add 3 ml. of hydrochloric acid and evaporate to dryness in a well ventilated hood. Heat for 30 minutes at about 650°C. Cool, add 2 ml. of hydrochloric acid and 10 ml. of water, cover with a watch glass, and digest on the steam bath until dissolution is complete. Dilute to 50 ml. and add 30 to 50 mg. of ammonium persulfate crystals and 3 ml. of ammonium thiocyanate reagent solution. Any red color should not exceed that produced by 0.01 mg. of iron (Fe) in an equal volume of solution containing the quantities of reagents used in the test.

Lead. Dissolve 0.5 gram in 10 ml. of water in a separatory funnel. Add 5 ml. of ammonium citrate reagent solution (lead-free), 2 ml. of hydroxylamine hydrochloride reagent solution for the dithizone test, and 0.10 ml. of phenol red indicator solution, and make the solution alkaline if necessary by adding ammonium hydroxide. Add 5 ml. of dithizone standard solution in chloroform, shake gently but well for 1 minute, and allow the layers to separate. The intensity of the red color of the chloroform layer should be no greater than that of a control made with 0.002 mg. of lead ion (Pb) and 0.1 gram of the sample dissolved in 10 ml. of water and treated exactly like the solution of 0.5 gram of sample in 10 ml. of water.

Notes

Sodium Diethyldithiocarbamate

$(CH_3CH_2)_2NCSSNa \cdot 3H_2O$ Formula Wt. 225.31

REQUIREMENTS

Solubility in water.   To pass test.
Sodium (as Na_2SO_4).   Not less than 30.5 per cent nor more than 32.5 per cent.
Sensitivity.   To pass test.

TESTS

Solubility in water.   Dissolve 1 gram in 50 ml. of water. There should be no undissolved residue and the solution should be substantially clear. Retain the solution for the test for *Sensitivity*.

> **Note.**   Because of inherent instability, this reagent may be expected to react with oxygen of the atmosphere to form insoluble oxidation products. After storage for some time the reagent may fail to meet the requirement for solubility in water.

Sodium.   Accurately weigh about 2 grams in a tared dish or crucible. Moisten the sample with concentrated sulfuric acid and ignite cautiously to char the material. Finally, ignite to constant weight at $800° \pm 25°C$. The weight of the residue should be between 30.5 per cent and 32.5 per cent of the weight of the sample.

Sensitivity.   Solution A.   Dilute 5 ml. of the solution retained from the test for *Solubility in water* to 100 ml. For the sample prepare a solution containing 0.002 mg. of copper ion (Cu) in 100 ml. of dilute ammonium hydroxide (1 + 99). For the control use 100 ml. of dilute ammonium hydroxide (1 + 99). Transfer the solutions to separatory funnels and add to each 10 ml. of Solution A and 10 ml. of isopentyl alcohol. Shake for about 1 minute and allow to separate (about 30 minutes). The isopentyl alcohol separated from the solution containing the 0.002 mg. of copper should show a distinct yellow color when compared with the isopentyl alcohol from the control.

Notes

Sodium Fluoride

NaF

Formula Wt. 41.99

REQUIREMENTS

Insoluble matter.   Not more than 0.020 per cent.
Loss on drying at 150°C.   Not more than 0.3 per cent.
Chloride (Cl).   Not more than 0.005 per cent.
Free acid (HF).   Not more than 0.05 per cent.
Free alkali (as Na_2CO_3).   Not more than 0.10 per cent.
Sodium fluosilicate (Na_2SiF_6).   Not more than 0.10 per cent.
Sulfate (SO_4).   Not more than 0.03 per cent.
Sulfite (SO_3).   Not more than 0.005 per cent.
Heavy metals (as Pb).   Not more than 0.003 per cent.
Iron (Fe).   To pass test (limit about 0.003 per cent).

TESTS

Insoluble matter.   Dissolve 5.0 grams in 100 ml. of warm water in a platinum dish, heat to boiling, and digest on the steam bath for 1 hour, adding water, when necessary, to keep the volume about constant. Filter through a tared filtering crucible, wash thoroughly with hot water, and dry at 105°C. The weight of the residue should not exceed 0.0010 gram.

Loss on drying at 150°C.   Weigh accurately about 1 gram in a tared platinum dish or crucible and dry to constant weight at 150°C. The loss in weight should not exceed 0.3 per cent of the weight of the sample.

Chloride.   Dissolve 1 gram plus 1 gram of boric acid in 80 ml. of water, filter if necessary through a chloride-free filter, and dilute to 100 ml. To 20 ml. of the solution add 1 ml. of nitric acid and 1 ml. of silver nitrate reagent solution. Any turbidity should not exceed that produced by 0.01 mg. of chloride ion (Cl) in an equal volume of solution containing the quantities of reagents used in the test.

Free acid. Dissolve 2 grams in 50 ml. of water (free from carbon dioxide) in a platinum dish, add 10 ml. of a saturated solution of potassium nitrate, cool the solution to 0°C., and add 0.15 ml. of phenolphthalein indicator solution. If a pink color is produced, omit the titration for free acid and reserve the solution for the test for *Free alkali.* If no pink color is produced, titrate with 0.1N sodium hydroxide until the pink color persists for 15 seconds while the temperature of the solution is near 0°C. Not more than 0.5 ml. of the 0.1N sodium hydroxide should be required. Reserve the solution for the test for *Sodium fluosilicate.*

Free alkali. If a pink color was produced in the solution prepared in the test for *Free acid,* add 0.1N hydrochloric acid, stirring the liquid only gently, until the pink color is discharged. Not more than 0.20 ml. of the acid should be required. Reserve the solution for the test for *Sodium fluosilicate.*

Sodium fluosilicate. Heat the solution reserved from one of the preceding tests to boiling and titrate while hot with 0.1N sodium hydroxide until a permanent pink color is obtained. Not more than 0.43 ml. of the sodium hydroxide should be required.

Sulfate. To 1 gram in a platinum dish add 10 ml. of hydrochloric acid and evaporate to dryness on the steam bath. Repeat the treatment four times. Dissolve the residue in water, filter if necessary, and dilute to 50 ml. To 10 ml. of this solution add 1 ml. of dilute hydrochloric acid (1 + 19) and 1 ml. of barium chloride reagent solution. Any turbidity should not exceed that produced by 0.06 mg. of sulfate ion (SO_4) in an equal volume of solution containing the quantities of reagents used in the test, including the residue from evaporation of 10 ml. of hydrochloric acid. Compare 10 minutes after adding the barium chloride to the sample and standard solutions.

Sulfite. Dissolve 8 grams in 150 ml. of water, and add 2 ml. of hydrochloric acid and 0.25 ml. of starch indicator solution. Titrate immediately with 0.1N iodine. Not more than 0.10 ml. of the 0.1N iodine should be required to produce a blue color.

Heavy metals. Dissolve 1 gram in about 25 ml. of water and dilute to 30 ml. For the control add 0.02 mg. of lead ion (Pb) to a 5-ml. aliquot of the solution and dilute to 25 ml. For the sample use the remaining 25-ml. portion. Adjust the pH of the control and sample solutions to between 3 and 4 (using a pH meter) with 1N acetic acid or ammonium hydroxide (10 per cent NH_3), dilute to 40 ml., and mix. Add 10 ml. of freshly prepared hydrogen sulfide water to each and mix. Any color in the solution of the sample should not exceed that in the control.

Iron. Treat 1 gram in a platinum crucible or dish with 10 ml. of hydrochloric acid and evaporate to dryness. Repeat the evaporation with another 10 ml. of the acid. Warm the residue with a few drops of hydrochloric acid and dissolve in 30 ml. of warm water. To 10 ml. of the solution add 2 ml. of hydrochloric acid and dilute to 50 ml. Add 30 to 50 mg. of ammonium persulfate crystals and 3 ml. of ammonium thiocyanate reagent solution. Any red color should not exceed that produced by 0.01 mg. of iron (Fe) in an equal volume of solution containing the quantities of reagents used in the test, including the residue from evaporation of 7 ml. of hydrochloric acid.

Notes

Sodium Hydroxide

NaOH   Formula Wt. 40.00

REQUIREMENTS

Sodium hydroxide (NaOH).   Not less than 97.0 per cent.
Sodium carbonate (Na_2CO_3).   Not more than 1.0 per cent.
Chloride (Cl).   Not more than 0.005 per cent.
Nitrogen compounds (as N).   Not more than 0.001 per cent.
Phosphate (PO_4).   Not more than 0.001 per cent.
Sulfate (SO_4).   Not more than 0.003 per cent.
Ammonium hydroxide precipitate.   Not more than 0.020 per cent.
Heavy metals (as Ag).   Not more than 0.002 per cent.
Iron (Fe).   Not more than 0.001 per cent.
Nickel (Ni).   Not more than 0.001 per cent.
Potassium (K).   Not more than 0.02 per cent.

TESTS

General.   Special care must be taken in sampling to obtain a representative sample and to avoid absorption of water and carbon dioxide by the sample taken.

Sodium hydroxide and carbonate.   Accurately weigh 35 to 40 grams, dissolve, and dilute to 1 liter, using carbon dioxide–free water. Dilute 50.0 ml. of this solution to 200 ml. with carbon dioxide–free water. Add 5 ml. of barium chloride reagent solution, stopper, and allow to stand for 5 minutes. Titrate with 1N hydrochloric acid to the phenolphthalein end point to determine the hydroxide. One milliliter of 1N hydrochloric acid corresponds to 0.04000 gram of NaOH. Continue the titration with 1N hydrochloric acid to the methyl orange end point to determine the carbonate. One milliliter of 1N hydrochloric acid corresponds to 0.05300 gram of Na_2CO_3.

Sample Solution A for the determination of Chloride, Nitrogen compounds, Phosphate, Sulfate, Heavy metals, Iron, and Nickel.   Dissolve 50.0 grams in carbon dioxide- and ammonia-free water, cool, and dilute to 500 ml. (1 ml. = 0.1 gram).

Chloride.   Dilute 10 ml. of Sample Solution A (1-gram sample) to 100 ml., and filter if necessary through a chloride-free filter. To 20 ml. of this solution add 1 ml. of nitric acid and 1 ml. of silver nitrate reagent solution. Any turbidity should not exceed that produced by 0.01 mg. of chloride ion (Cl) in an equal volume of solution containing the quantities of reagents used in the test.

Nitrogen compounds. Dilute 20 ml. of Sample Solution A (2-gram sample) with 50 ml. of ammonia-free water in a flask connected through a spray trap to a condenser, the end of which dips beneath the surface of 10 ml. of 0.1N hydrochloric acid. For the control, take 50 ml. of ammonia-free water in a similar flask, and add 10 ml. of Sample Solution A and a solution of an ammonium salt containing 0.01 mg. of nitrogen (N). To each flask add 0.5 gram of aluminum wire in small pieces, allow to stand for 1 hour, and slowly distill about 35 ml. To each distillate add 1 ml. of freshly boiled 10 per cent sodium hydroxide reagent solution, dilute to 50 ml., and add 2 ml. of Nessler reagent. Any color in the solution of the sample should not exceed that in the control.

Phosphate. To 20 ml. of Sample Solution A (2-gram sample) add 5 ml. of hydrochloric acid and evaporate to dryness on the steam bath. Dissolve the residue in 25 ml. of approximately 0.5N sulfuric acid, add 1 ml. of ammonium molybdate reagent solution and 1 ml. of p-methylaminophenol sulfate reagent solution, and allow to stand for 2 hours at room temperature. Any blue color should not exceed that produced by 0.02 mg. of phosphate ion (PO_4) in an equal volume of solution containing the quantities of reagents used in the test, including the residue from the evaporation of 5 ml. of hydrochloric acid.

Sulfate. Dilute 167 ml. of Sample Solution A (16.7-gram sample) with about 90 ml. of water. Neutralize with hydrochloric acid and add an excess of 2 ml. of the acid. Heat to boiling, add 10 ml. of barium chloride reagent solution, digest in a covered beaker on the steam bath for 2 hours, and allow to stand overnight. If a precipitate is formed, filter, wash thoroughly, and ignite. The weight of the precipitate should not be more than 0.0012 gram greater than the weight obtained in a complete blank test.

Ammonium hydroxide precipitate. Weigh about 10 grams and dissolve in about 100 ml. of water. Cautiously add 15 ml. of sulfuric acid to 15 ml. of water, cool, add the mixture to the solution of the sample, and evaporate to strong fuming. Cool, dissolve the residue in 130 ml. of hot water, and add ammonium hydroxide until the solution is just alkaline to methyl red. Heat to boiling, filter, wash with hot water, and ignite. The weight of the residue should not be more than 0.020 per cent of the weight of the sample. The residue includes some, but not all, of the silica in the sample.

Heavy metals. To 30 ml. of Sample Solution A (3-gram sample) cautiously add 10 ml. of nitric acid. For the control add 0.05 mg. of silver ion (Ag) to 5 ml. of Sample Solution A and cautiously add 10 ml. of nitric acid. Evaporate both solutions to dryness over a low flame or on an electric hot plate. Dissolve each residue in about 20 ml. of water, filter if necessary through a chloride-free filter, and dilute to 25 ml. Adjust the pH of the control and sample solutions to between 3 and 4 (using a pH meter) with $1N$ acetic acid or ammonium hydroxide (10 per cent NH_3), dilute to 40 ml., and mix. Add 10 ml. of freshly prepared hydrogen sulfide water to each and mix. Any yellowish brown color in the solution of the sample should not exceed that in the control.

Iron. Neutralize 10 ml. of Sample Solution A (1-gram sample) with hydrochloric acid, using phenolphthalein indicator, add 2 ml. in excess, and dilute to 50 ml. For the standard add 0.01 mg. of iron (Fe) and 2 ml. of hydrochloric acid to the residue obtained from evaporation of the quantity of hydrochloric acid used to neutralize the sodium hydroxide and dilute to 50 ml. To each add 30 to 50 mg. of ammonium persulfate crystals and 3 ml. of ammonium thiocyanate reagent solution. Any red color in the solution of the sample should not exceed that in the standard.

Nickel. Dilute 20 ml. of Sample Solution A (2-gram sample) to 50 ml. with water and neutralize with hydrochloric acid. Dilute to 85 ml. and adjust the pH to 8 with ammonium hydroxide. Add 5 ml. of bromine water, 5 ml. of 1 per cent dimethylglyoxime solution in alcohol, and 5 ml. of 10 per cent sodium hydroxide reagent solution. Any red color should not exceed that produced by 0.02 mg. of nickel ion (Ni) in an equal volume of solution containing the quantities of reagents used in the test.

Potassium. Determine the potassium by the flame photometric method described on page 14. Dissolve 10 grams in water and dilute to 100 ml.

Sample Solution A. Dilute a 10-ml. aliquot of the solution to 100 ml.

Control Solution B. Add 0.20 mg. of potassium ion (K) to another 10-ml. aliquot of the solution and dilute to 100 ml.

Observe the emission of Control Solution B at the 767-mμ potassium line. Observe the emission of Sample Solution A at the 767-mμ potassium line and at a wavelength of 750 mμ. The difference (D_1) between the intensities observed for Sample Solution A at 767 mμ and 750 mμ should not exceed the difference (D_2) observed at 767 mμ between Sample Solution A and Control Solution B.

Sodium Metabisulfite

$Na_2S_2O_5$ Formula Wt. 190.10

REQUIREMENTS

Assay.   Not less than 97.0 per cent.
Insoluble matter.   Not more than 0.005 per cent.
Chloride (Cl).   Not more than 0.05 per cent.
Thiosulfate (S_2O_3).   Not more than 0.05 per cent.
Arsenic (As).   Not more than 0.0001 per cent.
Heavy metals (as Pb).   Not more than 0.001 per cent.
Iron (Fe).   Not more than 0.002 per cent.

TESTS

Assay.   Weigh accurately about 0.45 gram, add it to a mixture of 100.0 ml. of 0.1N iodine and 5 ml. of 10 per cent hydrochloric acid solution (the metabisulfite must be added to the iodine solution), and swirl until the sample is dissolved. Titrate the excess iodine with 0.1N sodium thiosulfate, adding starch indicator near the end point. One milliliter of 0.1N iodine corresponds to 0.004753 gram of $Na_2S_2O_5$.

Insoluble matter.   Dissolve 20 grams in 200 ml. of water, heat to boiling, and digest in a covered beaker on the steam bath for 1 hour. Filter through a tared filtering crucible, wash thoroughly, and dry at 105°C. The weight of the residue should not exceed 0.0010 gram.

Chloride.   Dissolve 1 gram in 10 ml. of water, filter if necessary through a small chloride-free filter, and add 6 ml. of 30 per cent hydrogen peroxide. Add 1N sodium hydroxide until the solution is slightly alkaline to phenolphthalein and dilute to 100 ml. Dilute 2 ml. of this solution to 20 ml., and add 1 ml. of nitric acid and 1 ml. of silver nitrate reagent solution. Any turbidity should not exceed that produced by 0.01 mg. of chloride ion (Cl) in an equal volume of solution containing the quantities of reagents used in the test.

Thiosulfate.   Dissolve 2.2 grams in 10 ml. of 10 per cent hydrochloric acid solution in a 50-ml. beaker. Boil gently for 5 minutes, cool, and transfer to a small test tube. Any turbidity should not be greater than that produced by a standard of 0.10 ml. of 0.1N sodium thiosulfate solution carried through the entire procedure.

Arsenic.   Dissolve 5 grams in 10 ml. of water, add 3 ml. of sulfuric acid, and heat to dense fumes of sulfur trioxide. Cool, add 5 ml. of water and 3 ml. of sulfuric acid, and heat again to dense fumes. Determine the arsenic in this solution by the Gutzeit method (page 11). The amount of stain should not exceed that produced by 0.005 mg. of arsenic (As).

Heavy metals. Dissolve 3 grams in 25 ml. of dilute hydrochloric acid (2 + 3). For the control dissolve 1 gram in 25 ml. of dilute hydrochloric acid (2 + 3) and add 0.02 mg. of lead ion (Pb). Evaporate both solutions to dryness on the steam bath, add 5 ml. of hydrochloric acid to each, and again evaporate to dryness. Dissolve each residue in about 20 ml. of water and dilute to 25 ml. Adjust the pH of the control and sample solutions to between 3 and 4 (using a pH meter) with 1N acetic acid or ammonium hydroxide (10 per cent NH₃), dilute to 40 ml., and mix. Add 10 ml. of freshly prepared hydrogen sulfide to each and mix. Any color in the solution of the sample should not exceed that in the control.

Iron. Dissolve 1 gram in 14 ml. of dilute hydrochloric acid (2 + 5) and evaporate to dryness on the steam bath. Dissolve the residue in 7 ml. of dilute hydrochloric acid (2 + 5) and evaporate again to dryness. Dissolve the residue in 2 ml. of hydrochloric acid, dilute to 50 ml., and add 30 to 50 mg. of ammonium persulfate crystals and 3 ml. of ammonium thiocyanate reagent solution. Any red color should not exceed that produced by 0.02 mg. of iron (Fe) in an equal volume of solution containing the quantities of reagents used in the test.

Notes

Sodium Nitrate

$NaNO_3$ Formula Wt. 84.99

REQUIREMENTS

Insoluble matter. Not more than 0.005 per cent.
pH of a 5 per cent solution. From 5.5 to 8.3 at 25°C.
Chlorine, total. Not more than 0.001 per cent.
Iodate and nitrite. To pass test (limit about 0.0005 per cent IO_3; about 0.001 per cent NO_2).
Phosphate (PO_4). Not more than 0.0005 per cent.
Sulfate (SO_4). Not more than 0.003 per cent.
Calcium, magnesium, and R_2O_3 precipitate. Not more than 0.005 per cent.
Heavy metals (as Pb). Not more than 0.0005 per cent.
Iron (Fe). Not more than 0.0003 per cent.

TESTS

Insoluble matter. Dissolve 20 grams in 100 ml. of water, heat to boiling, and digest in a covered beaker on the steam bath for 1 hour. Filter through a tared filtering crucible, retain the filtrate without the washings for the test for *Calcium, magnesium, and R_2O_3 precipitate,* wash thoroughly, and dry at 105°C. The weight of the residue should not exceed 0.0010 gram.

pH of a 5 per cent solution. Dissolve 10 grams in 200 ml. of carbon dioxide- and ammonia-free water. Determine the pH by the method described on page 18. The pH should be from 5.5 to 8.3 at 25°C. The pH of a 5 per cent solution of pure sodium nitrate would be 7.0 at 25°C.

Chlorine, total. Ignite 1 gram, at first gently, and then for a few minutes at about 500°C. Cool, dissolve in 20 ml. of water, filter if necessary through a chloride-free filter, and add 1 ml. of nitric acid and 1 ml. of silver nitrate reagent solution. Any turbidity should not exceed that produced by 0.01 mg. of chloride ion (Cl) in an equal volume of solution containing the quantities of reagents used in the test.

Iodate and nitrite. Dissolve 1 gram in 10 ml. of water, and add 0.10 ml. of 10 per cent potassium iodide reagent solution, 1 ml. of chloroform, and 1 ml. of acetic acid. Shake gently for 5 minutes. The chloroform should not acquire a pink or violet color.

Phosphate. Dissolve 4 grams in 25 ml. of approximately $0.5N$ sulfuric acid, add 1 ml. of ammonium molybdate reagent solution and 1 ml. of

p-methylaminophenol sulfate reagent solution, and allow to stand at room temperature for 2 hours. Any blue color should not exceed that produced by 0.02 mg. of phosphate ion (PO_4) in an equal volume of solution containing the quantities of reagents used in the test.

Sulfate.   Dissolve 12 grams in 50 ml. of dilute hydrochloric acid ($1 + 1$), and evaporate to dryness. Dissolve the residue in 30 ml. of dilute hydrochloric acid ($1 + 1$), and again evaporate to dryness. Dissolve the residue in 75 ml. of water, add 1 ml. of hydrochloric acid, filter if not perfectly clear, heat to boiling, add 5 ml. of barium chloride reagent solution, digest in a covered beaker on the steam bath for 2 hours, and allow to stand overnight. If any precipitate is formed, filter, wash thoroughly, and ignite. The weight of the precipitate should not be more than 0.0010 gram greater than the weight obtained in a complete blank test.

Calcium, magnesium, and R$_2$O$_3$ precipitate.   To the filtrate, without washings, from the test for *Insoluble matter* add 5 ml. of ammonium oxalate reagent solution, 3 ml. of ammonium phosphate reagent solution, and 15 ml. of ammonium hydroxide. Allow to stand overnight. If any precipitate is formed, filter, wash with a solution containing 2.5 per cent ammonia and about 0.1 per cent ammonium oxalate, and ignite. The weight of the residue should not exceed 0.0010 gram.

Heavy metals.   Dissolve 6 grams in about 20 ml. of water and dilute to 30 ml. For the control add 0.02 mg. of lead ion (Pb) to a 5-ml. aliquot of the solution and dilute to 25 ml. For the sample use the remaining 25-ml. portion. Adjust the pH of the control and sample solutions to between 3 and 4 (using a pH meter) with $1N$ acetic acid or ammonium hydroxide (10 per cent NH$_3$), dilute to 40 ml., and mix. Add 10 ml. of freshly prepared hydrogen sulfide water to each and mix. Any color in the solution of the sample should not exceed that in the control.

Iron.   Dissolve 5 grams in about 40 ml. of water, add 2 ml. of hydrochloric acid, and dilute to 50 ml. Add 30 to 50 mg. of ammonium persulfate crystals and 3 ml. of ammonium thiocyanate reagent solution. Any red color should not exceed that produced by 0.015 mg. of iron (Fe) in an equal volume of solution containing the quantities of reagents used in the test.

Notes

Sodium Nitrite

NaNO$_2$ Formula Wt. 69.00

REQUIREMENTS

Insoluble matter. Not more than 0.010 per cent.
Assay. Not less than 97 per cent NaNO$_2$.
Chloride (Cl). Not more than 0.005 per cent.
Sulfate (SO$_4$). Not more than 0.010 per cent.
Calcium (Ca). Not more than 0.01 per cent.
Heavy metals (as Pb). Not more than 0.001 per cent.
Iron (Fe). Not more than 0.001 per cent.
Potassium (K). Not more than 0.005 per cent.

TESTS

Insoluble matter. Dissolve 10 grams in 100 ml. of water, heat to boiling, and digest in a covered beaker on the steam bath for 1 hour. Filter through a tared filtering crucible, wash thoroughly, and dry at 105°C. The weight of the residue should not exceed 0.0010 gram.

Sample Solution A. Weigh accurately 10 grams, dissolve in water, and dilute to 100 ml. in a volumetric flask (1 ml. = 0.1 gram).

Assay. Dilute a 10.0-ml. aliquot of Sample Solution A to 100 ml. in a volumetric flask. Add 5 ml. of sulfuric acid to 300 ml. of water and, while the solution is still warm, add 0.1N potassium permanganate until a faint pink color that persists for 2 minutes is produced. Then add 40.0 ml. of 0.1N potassium permanganate and mix gently. Add, slowly and with constant agitation, 10.0 ml. of the diluted sample solution, holding the tip of the pipet well below the surface of the liquid. Add 15.0 ml. of 0.1N ferrous ammonium sulfate, allow the solution to stand for 5 minutes, and titrate the excess ferrous ammonium sulfate with 0.1N potassium permanganate. Each milliliter of 0.1N potassium permanganate consumed by the sodium nitrite corresponds to 0.003450 gram of NaNO$_2$.

Chloride. To 2 ml. of Sample Solution A (0.2-gram sample) add 10 ml. of water, slowly add 1 ml. of glacial acetic acid, and boil gently for 5 minutes. Cool, dilute to 20 ml., and filter if necessary through a chloride-free filter. Add 1 ml. of nitric acid and 1 ml. of silver nitrate reagent solution. Any turbidity should not exceed that produced by 0.01 mg. of chloride ion (Cl) in an equal volume of solution containing the quantities of reagents used in the test.

Sulfate. To 4 ml. of Sample Solution A (0.4-gram sample) add slowly 1 ml. of hydrochloric acid, evaporate to dryness on the steam bath, and dissolve the residue in 4 ml. of water plus 1 ml. of dilute hydrochloric acid (1 + 19). Filter if necessary through a small filter, wash with two 2-ml. portions of water, dilute to 10 ml., and add 1 ml. of barium chloride reagent solution. Any turbidity should not exceed that produced by 0.04 mg. of sulfate ion (SO_4) in an equal volume of solution containing the quantities of reagents used in the test. Compare 10 minutes after adding the barium chloride to the sample and standard solutions.

Calcium. To 10 ml. of Sample Solution A (1-gram sample) add slowly 1 ml. of glacial acetic acid. Heat to expel oxides of nitrogen, cool, dilute to 10 ml., and add 2 ml. of ammonium oxalate reagent solution. Any turbidity should not exceed that produced by 0.1 mg. of calcium ion (Ca) in an equal volume of solution containing the quantities of reagents used in the test.

Heavy metals. To 30 ml. of Sample Solution A (3-gram sample) add 5 ml. of hydrochloric acid. For the control add 0.02 mg. of lead ion (Pb) and 5 ml. of hydrochloric acid to a 10-ml. aliquot of Sample Solution A. Evaporate the solutions to dryness on the steam bath, add 5 ml. of hydrochloric acid to each, and again evaporate to dryness. Dissolve the residues in about 20 ml. of water and dilute to 25 ml. Adjust the pH of the control and sample solutions to between 3 and 4 (using a pH meter) with 1N acetic acid or ammonium hydroxide (10 per cent NH_3), dilute to 40 ml., and mix. Add 10 ml. of freshly prepared hydrogen sulfide water to each and mix. Any color in the solution of the sample should not exceed that in the control.

Iron. To 10 ml. of Sample Solution A (1-gram sample) add 5 ml. of hydrochloric acid and evaporate to dryness on the steam bath. Dissolve in 2 ml. of hydrochloric acid plus 15 to 20 ml. of water and filter if necessary. Dilute to 50 ml., and add 30 to 50 mg. of ammonium persulfate crystals and 3 ml. of ammonium thiocyanate reagent solution. Any red color should not exceed that produced by 0.01 mg. of iron (Fe) in an equal volume of solution containing the quantities of reagents used in the test.

Potassium. Determine the potassium by the flame photometric method described on page 14. Dissolve 10 grams in water and dilute to 100 ml.

> **Sample Solution A.** Dilute a 10-ml. aliquot (1-gram sample) of the solution to 100 ml.

> **Control Solution B.** Add 0.05 mg. of potassium ion (K) to another 10-ml. aliquot of the solution and dilute to 100 ml.

Observe the emission of Control Solution B at the 767-mμ potassium line. Observe the emission of Sample Solution A at the 767-mμ potassium line and at a wavelength of 750 mμ. The difference (D_1) between the intensities observed for Sample Solution A at 767 mμ and 750 mμ should not exceed the difference (D_2) observed at 767 mμ between Sample Solution A and Control Solution B.

Notes

Sodium Nitroferricyanide

$Na_2Fe(CN)_5NO \cdot 2H_2O$ Formula Wt. 297.95

REQUIREMENTS

Insoluble matter.   Not more than 0.010 per cent.
Chloride (Cl).   Not more than 0.020 per cent.
Sulfate (SO$_4$).   To pass test (limit about 0.01 per cent).

TESTS

Insoluble matter.   Dissolve 10 grams in 50 ml. of water at room temperature, filter promptly through a tared filtering crucible, wash thoroughly, and dry at 105°C. The weight of the residue should not exceed 0.0010 gram.

Chloride.   Dissolve 1 gram in 175 ml. of water, add 1.25 grams of cupric sulfate crystals dissolved in 25 ml. of water, mix thoroughly, and allow to stand until the precipitate has settled. Filter through a chloride-free filter, rejecting the first 50 ml. of the filtrate. Dilute 10 ml. of the filtrate to 20 ml., and add 1 ml. of nitric acid and 1 ml. of silver nitrate reagent solution. Any turbidity should not exceed that produced by 0.01 mg. of chloride ion (Cl) in an equal volume of solution containing the quantities of reagents used in the test, with enough cupric sulfate added to match the color of the test.

Sulfate.   Dissolve 5 grams in 100 ml. of water without heating, filter, and to the filtrate add 0.25 ml. of glacial acetic acid and 5 ml. of barium chloride reagent solution. Stir and pour into a Nessler tube for observation. No turbidity should be produced in 10 minutes.

Notes

Sodium Oxalate

(COONa)$_2$

Formula Wt. 134.00

REQUIREMENTS

Insoluble matter.   Not more than 0.005 per cent.
Loss on drying at 105°C.   Not more than 0.010 per cent.
Neutrality.   To pass test.
Chloride (Cl).   Not more than 0.002 per cent.
Sulfate (SO$_4$).   Not more than 0.002 per cent.
Ammonium (NH$_4$).   Not more than 0.002 per cent.
Heavy metals (as Pb).   Not more than 0.002 per cent.
Iron (Fe).   Not more than 0.001 per cent.
Potassium (K).   Not more than 0.005 per cent.
Substances darkened by hot sulfuric acid.   To pass test.

TESTS

Insoluble matter.   Dissolve 20 grams in 500 ml. of water, heat to boiling, and digest in a covered beaker on the steam bath for 1 hour. Filter through a tared filtering crucible, wash thoroughly, and dry at 105°C. The weight of the residue should not exceed 0.0010 gram.

Loss on drying at 105°C.   Accurately weigh 10 grams in a tared dish or crucible and dry to constant weight at 105°C.   The loss in weight should not exceed 0.0010 gram.

Neutrality.   Dissolve 2 grams in 200 ml. of water, and add 10.0 ml. of 0.01N oxalic acid and 0.20 ml. of a 1 per cent solution of phenolphthalein. Boil the solution in a flask for 10 minutes, passing through it a stream of carbon dioxide-free air. Cool the solution rapidly to room temperature while keeping the flow of carbon dioxide-free air passing through it. Titrate with 0.01N sodium hydroxide. Not less than 9.2 nor more than 10.5 ml. of 0.01N sodium hydroxide should be required to match the pink color of a buffer solution containing 0.20 ml. of a 1 per cent solution of phenolphthalein. The buffer solution contains in 1 liter 3.1 grams of boric acid (H$_3$BO$_3$), 3.8 grams of potassium chloride (KCl), and 5.90 ml. of 1N sodium hydroxide.

Chloride.   Ignite 2.5 grams to carbonate in a platinum container, protected from the absorption of chlorides. Dissolve in 50 ml. of water, neutralize with nitric acid, filter if necessary through a chloride-free filter, and dilute to 100 ml. To 20 ml. of the solution add 1 ml. of nitric acid and 1 ml. of silver nitrate reagent solution. Any turbidity should not exceed that produced by 0.01 mg. of chloride ion (Cl) in an equal volume of solution containing the quantities of reagents used in the test.

Sulfate. Mix 20 grams with 50 ml. of water, add 25 ml. of nitric acid and 25 ml. of 30 per cent hydrogen peroxide, and digest in a covered beaker on the steam bath until reaction ceases. Remove the cover and evaporate to dryness. Add 80 ml. of dilute hydrochloric acid (1 + 1) and again evaporate to dryness. Repeat the evaporation with dilute hydrochloric acid. Dissolve the residue in 200 ml. of water, add 2 ml. of hydrochloric acid, and filter if necessary. Heat the filtrate to boiling, add 10 ml. of barium chloride reagent solution, digest in a covered beaker on the steam bath for 2 hours, and allow to stand overnight. If a precipitate is formed, filter, wash thoroughly, and ignite. The weight of the precipitate should not be more than 0.0010 gram greater than the weight obtained in a complete blank test.

Ammonium. Dissolve 1 gram in 50 ml. of ammonia-free water and add 2 ml. of Nessler reagent. Any color should not exceed that produced by 0.02 mg. of ammonium ion (NH_4) in an equal volume of solution containing 2 ml. of Nessler reagent.

Heavy metals. Mix 2 grams with 2 ml. of water, add 2 ml. of nitric acid and 2 ml. of 30 per cent hydrogen peroxide, and digest in a covered beaker on the steam bath until reaction ceases. Remove the cover and evaporate to dryness. Dissolve the residue in 2 ml. of nitric acid plus 2 ml. of water and again evaporate to dryness. Dissolve the residue in about 20 ml. of water and dilute to 32 ml. For the control evaporate on the steam bath one half the quantities of hydrogen peroxide and nitric acid used in preparing the sample solution. Dissolve the residue in about 10 ml. of water, add an 8-ml. aliquot of the sample solution plus 0.02 mg. of lead ion (Pb), and dilute to 25 ml. For the sample dilute the remaining 24-ml. portion to 25 ml. Adjust the pH of the control and sample solutions to between 3 and 4 (using a pH meter) with $1N$ acetic acid or ammonium hydroxide (10 per cent NH_3), dilute to 40 ml., and mix. Add 10 ml. of freshly prepared hydrogen sulfide water to each and mix. Any color in the solution of the sample should not exceed that in the control.

Iron. Mix 2 grams with 2 ml. of water, add 2 ml. of nitric acid and 2 ml. of 30 per cent hydrogen peroxide, and digest in a covered beaker on the steam bath until reaction ceases. Remove the cover and evaporate to dryness. Add 5 ml. of hydrochloric acid and again evaporate to dryness. Dissolve the residue in water, add 4 ml. of hydrochloric acid, and dilute to 100 ml. To 50 ml. of the solution add 30 to 50 mg. of ammonium persulfate crystals and 3 ml. of ammonium thiocyanate reagent solution. Any red color should not exceed that produced by 0.01 mg. of iron (Fe) in an equal volume of solution containing the quantities of reagents used in the test, including the residue from evaporation of 1 ml. of nitric acid, 1 ml. of 30 per cent hydrogen peroxide, and 2 ml. of hydrochloric acid.

Potassium. Determine the potassium by the flame photometric method described on page 14.

Sample Solution A. Dissolve 1 gram in water and dilute to 100 ml.

Control Solution B. Dissolve 1 gram in water, add 0.05 mg. of potassium ion (K), and dilute to 100 ml.

Observe the emission of Control Solution B at the 767-mμ potassium line. Observe the emission of Sample Solution A at the 767-mμ potassium line and at a wavelength of 750 mμ. The difference (D_1) between the intensities observed for Sample Solution A at 767 mμ and 750 mμ should not exceed the difference (D_2) observed at 767 mμ between Sample Solution A and Control Solution B.

Substances darkened by hot sulfuric acid. Heat 1 gram in a recently ignited test tube with 10 ml. of sulfuric acid until the appearance of dense fumes. The acid when cooled should have no more color than a mixture of the following composition: 0.2 ml. of cobaltous chloride solution (5.95 grams of $CoCl_2 \cdot 6H_2O$ and 2.5 ml. of hydrochloric acid in 100 ml.), 0.3 ml. of ferric chloride solution (4.50 grams of $FeCl_3 \cdot 6H_2O$ and 2.5 ml. of hydrochloric acid in 100 ml.), 0.3 ml. of cupric sulfate solution (6.24 grams of $CuSO_4 \cdot 5H_2O$ and 2.5 ml. of hydrochloric acid in 100 ml.), and 9.2 ml. of water.

Notes

Sodium Periodate

Sodium Metaperiodate

(Suitable for determination of manganese)

NaIO$_4$ Formula Wt. 213.89

REQUIREMENTS

Assay. Not less than 99.8 nor more than 100.3 per cent NaIO$_4$.
Other halogens (as Cl). Not more than 0.02 per cent.
Manganese (Mn). Not more than 0.0003 per cent.

TESTS

Assay. Weigh accurately about 1 gram, previously dried over sulfuric acid for 6 hours, dissolve in water, and dilute to 500 ml. in a volumetric flask. To a 50-ml. aliquot in a glass-stoppered flask, add 10 grams of potassium iodide and 10 ml. of a cooled solution of dilute sulfuric acid (1 + 5). Allow to stand for 5 minutes, add 100 ml. of cold water, and titrate the liberated iodine with 0.1N sodium thiosulfate, adding starch indicator solution near the end point. Correct for a blank test. One milliliter of 0.1N sodium thiosulfate corresponds to 0.002674 gram of NaIO$_4$.

Other halogens. Dissolve 0.5 gram in 25 ml. of a dilute solution of sulfurous acid (3 + 2). Boil for 3 minutes, cool, and add 5 ml. of ammonium hydroxide and 20 ml. of 2.5 per cent silver nitrate solution. Allow the precipitate to coagulate, filter through a chloride-free filter, and dilute the filtrate to 200 ml. To 20 ml. of this solution add 1.5 ml. of nitric acid. Any turbidity should not exceed that produced by 0.01 mg. of chloride ion (Cl) in an equal volume of solution containing 0.5 ml. of ammonium hydroxide, 1.5 ml. of nitric acid, and 1 ml. of silver nitrate reagent solution.

Manganese. Dissolve 2.5 grams in 40 ml. of 10 per cent sulfuric acid reagent solution. For the control add 0.5 gram of the sample and 0.006 mg. of manganese ion (Mn) to 40 ml. of 10 per cent sulfuric acid reagent solution. Add 5 ml. of nitric acid and 5 ml. of phosphoric acid to each, boil gently for 10 minutes, and cool. Any pink color in the solution of the sample should not exceed that in the control.

Sodium Peroxide

Na₂O₂

Formula Wt. 77.98

REQUIREMENTS

Assay. Not less than 93.0 per cent Na₂O₂.
Chloride (Cl). Not more than 0.002 per cent.
Nitrogen compounds (as N). Not more than 0.003 per cent.
Phosphate (PO₄). Not more than 0.0005 per cent.
Sulfate (SO₄). Not more than 0.001 per cent.
Heavy metals (as Pb). Not more than 0.002 per cent.
Iron (Fe). Not more than 0.005 per cent.

Caution. This reagent should be stored in airtight containers in a cool place. Avoid contact with organic materials; fire or explosion may result.

Note. When dissolving sodium peroxide, the material should be added slowly and in small portions to well cooled water; when neutralizing, the acid must be added cautiously in small portions, and the solution kept cool.

TESTS

Assay. Weigh accurately about 0.7 gram and add slowly to 400 ml. of dilute sulfuric acid (1 + 99) that has been cooled to 10°C. Dilute to 500 ml., in a volumetric flask, with dilute sulfuric acid (1 + 99), mix well, and titrate 100.0 ml. with 0.1N potassium permanganate. One milliliter of 0.1N potassium permanganate corresponds to 0.003899 gram of Na₂O₂.

Chloride. Add 1 gram in small portions to 35 ml. of water, cool, and slowly add 4 ml. of nitric acid. Filter if necessary through a chloride-free filter and dilute the filtrate to 40 ml. To 20 ml. of the filtrate add 1 ml. of silver nitrate reagent solution. Any turbidity should not exceed that produced by 0.01 mg. of chloride ion (Cl) in an equal volume of solution containing the quantities of reagents used in the test.

Nitrogen compounds. Dissolve 1 gram in 20 ml. of water cooled to 10°C., add acetic acid until neutral plus an excess of 0.15 ml., and boil down to a volume of 10 ml. Cool and add to 50 ml. of water in a flask connected through a spray trap to a condenser, the end of which dips beneath the surface of 10 ml. of 0.1N hydrochloric acid. Add to the flask 10 ml. of freshly boiled 10 per cent sodium hydroxide reagent solution and 0.5 gram of aluminum wire in small pieces. Allow to stand for 1 hour, distill about 35 ml., and dilute the distillate to 60 ml. To 20 ml.

of the diluted distillate add 1 ml. of 10 per cent sodium hydroxide reagent solution, dilute to 50 ml., and add 2 ml. of Nessler reagent. Any color should not exceed that produced when the residue from evaporation of the quantity of acetic acid used in the test and a quantity of an ammonium salt containing 0.03 mg. of nitrogen (N) are together treated exactly like the sample.

Phosphate. Dissolve 4 grams in 50 ml. of water, cautiously add 10 ml. of nitric acid, and evaporate to dryness on the steam bath. Dissolve the residue in 25 ml. of approximately $0.5N$ sulfuric acid, add 1 ml. of ammonium molybdate reagent solution and 1 ml. of p-methylaminophenol sulfate reagent solution, and allow to stand for 2 hours at room temperature. Any blue color should not exceed that produced by 0.02 mg. of phosphate ion (PO_4) in an equal volume of solution containing the quantities of reagents used in the test.

Sulfate. Completely dissolve 20 grams in 300 ml. of cold water (10°C.), neutralize with hydrochloric acid, and note the volume used. Add an excess of 2 ml. of the acid and evaporate to a volume of about 200 ml. Filter if necessary, heat the filtrate to boiling, add 10 ml. of barium chloride reagent solution, digest in a covered beaker on the steam bath for 2 hours, and allow to stand overnight. If a precipitate is formed, filter, wash thoroughly, and ignite. The weight of the precipitate should not be more than 0.0005 gram greater than the weight obtained in a complete blank test.

For the blank add about 10 mg. of sodium carbonate and 1 ml. of bromine water to the volume of hydrochloric acid used to neutralize the sodium peroxide, and evaporate to dryness. Dissolve in 2 ml. of hydrochloric acid, add 200 ml. of water, boil, and filter if necessary. Add 10 ml. of barium chloride reagent solution and carry along with the sample.

Heavy metals. Add 2 grams cautiously to 15 ml. of dilute hydrochloric acid (1 + 2) cooled to 10°C. For the control add 0.02 mg. of lead ion (Pb) to 15 ml. of dilute hydrochloric acid (1 + 2), and then add cautiously 1 gram of the sample. Evaporate both solutions to dryness on the steam bath. Add 15 ml. of dilute hydrochloric acid and repeat the evaporation. Dissolve each residue in about 20 ml. of water and dilute to 25 ml. Adjust the pH of the control and sample solutions to between 3 and 4 (using a pH meter) with $1N$ acetic acid or ammonium hydroxide (10 per cent NH_3), dilute to 40 ml., and mix. Add 10 ml. of freshly prepared hydrogen sulfide water to each and mix. Any color in the solution of the sample should not exceed that in the control.

Iron. Add 10 grams cautiously to 75 ml. of a cooled solution of dilute hydrochloric acid (1 + 2). Evaporate to dryness on the steam bath. Add 10 ml. of hydrochloric acid and again evaporate to dryness. Dissolve in 80 ml. of dilute hydrochloric acid (1 + 40) and dilute to 100 ml. with water. To 2 ml. of this solution add 2 ml. of hydrochloric acid, dilute to 50 ml., and add 30 to 50 mg. of ammonium persulfate crystals and 3 ml. of ammonium thiocyanate reagent solution. Any red color should not exceed that produced by 0.01 mg. of iron (Fe) in an equal volume of solution containing the quantities of reagents used in the test.

Notes

Sodium Phosphate, Dibasic, Anhydrous
(Suitable for buffer solutions)

Na_2HPO_4 Formula Wt. 141.96

REQUIREMENTS

> **Insoluble matter.**   Not more than 0.010 per cent.
> **Loss on drying at 105°C.**   Not more than 0.20 per cent.
> **pH of a 0.1M solution.**   From 9.1 to 9.2 at 25°C.
> **Chloride (Cl).**   Not more than 0.002 per cent.
> **Nitrogen compounds (as N).**   Not more than 0.002 per cent.
> **Sulfate (SO_4).**   Not more than 0.005 per cent.
> **Heavy metals (as Pb).**   Not more than 0.001 per cent.
> **Iron (Fe).**   Not more than 0.002 per cent.

TESTS

Insoluble matter.   Dissolve 10 grams in 100 ml. of water, heat to boiling, and digest in a covered beaker on the steam bath for 1 hour. Filter through a tared filtering crucible (not glass), wash well with hot water, and dry at 105°C. The weight of the residue should not exceed 0.0010 gram.

Loss on drying at 105°C.   Weigh accurately about 2 grams and dry at 105°C. to constant weight. The loss in weight should not exceed 0.20 per cent. Save the material for the determination of pH.

pH of a 0.1M solution.   Dissolve 1.42 grams, previously dried, in carbon dioxide- and ammonia-free water and dilute to 100 ml. Determine the pH by the method described on page 18. The pH should be from 9.1 to 9.2 at 25°C.

Chloride.   Dissolve 1 gram in 30 ml. of water, filter if necessary through a chloride-free filter, add 3 ml. of nitric acid, and dilute to 40 ml. To 20 ml. of this solution add 1 ml. of silver nitrate reagent solution. Any turbidity should not exceed that produced by 0.01 mg. of chloride ion (Cl) in an equal volume of solution containing the quantities of reagents used in the test.

Nitrogen compounds.   Dissolve 0.5 gram in 60 ml. of water in a flask connected through a spray trap to a condenser, the end of which dips beneath the surface of 10 ml. of 0.1N hydrochloric acid. Add to the flask 10 ml. of freshly boiled 10 per cent sodium hydroxide reagent solution and 0.5 gram of aluminum wire in small pieces, allow to stand for 1 hour, and distill 35 ml. To the distillate add 1 ml. of 10 per cent sodium hydroxide reagent solution, dilute to 50 ml., and add 2 ml. of Nessler reagent. Any color should not exceed that produced when a solution of an ammonium salt containing 0.01 mg. of nitrogen (N) is treated exactly like the sample.

Sulfate. Dissolve 10 grams in 200 ml. of water, add 14 ml. of hydrochloric acid, and heat to boiling. Filter and reheat the filtrate to boiling. Add 10 ml. of barium chloride reagent solution, digest in a covered beaker on the steam bath for 2 hours, and allow to stand overnight. If a precipitate is formed, filter, wash thoroughly, and ignite. The weight of the precipitate should not be more than 0.0012 gram greater than the weight obtained in a complete blank test.

Heavy metals. Dissolve 4 grams in about 20 ml. of water, add 14.5 ml. of $2N$ hydrochloric acid, and dilute to 40 ml. For the control add 0.02 mg. of lead ion (Pb) to a 10-ml. aliquot of the solution and dilute to 30 ml. For the sample use the remaining 30-ml. portion. Adjust the pH of the control and sample solutions to between 3 and 4 (using a pH meter) with $1N$ acetic acid or ammonium hydroxide (10 per cent NH_3), dilute to 40 ml., and mix. Add 10 ml. of freshly prepared hydrogen sulfide water to each and mix. Any color in the solution of the sample should not exceed that in the control.

Iron. Dissolve 1 gram in water and dilute to 20 ml. To 10 ml. of the solution add 6 ml. of hydroxylamine hydrochloride reagent solution and 4 ml. of 1,10-phenanthroline reagent solution, and dilute to 25 ml. Any red color should not exceed that produced by 0.01 mg. of iron (Fe) in an equal volume of solution containing the quantities of reagents used in the test. Compare 1 hour after adding the reagents to the sample and standard solutions.

Notes

Sodium Phosphate, Dibasic, Heptahydrate

$Na_2HPO_4 \cdot 7H_2O$ Formula Wt. 268.07

REQUIREMENTS

Insoluble matter.   Not more than 0.005 per cent.
Loss on drying at 105°C.   Not less than 43 nor more than 50 per cent.
pH of a 5 per cent solution.   From 8.7 to 9.3 at 25°C.
Chloride (Cl).   Not more than 0.001 per cent.
Nitrogen compounds (as N).   Not more than 0.001 per cent.
Sulfate (SO_4).   Not more than 0.005 per cent.
Arsenic (As).   Not more than 0.0005 per cent.
Heavy metals (as Pb).   Not more than 0.001 per cent.
Iron (Fe).   Not more than 0.001 per cent.

TESTS

Insoluble matter.   Dissolve 20 grams in 200 ml. of water, heat to boiling, and digest in a covered beaker on the steam bath for 1 hour. Filter through a tared filtering crucible (not glass), wash thoroughly, and dry at 105°C. The weight of the residue should not exceed 0.0010 gram.

Loss on drying at 105°C.   Weigh accurately about 1 gram. Dry to constant weight at 105°C. The loss in weight should be not less than 43 nor more than 50 per cent.

pH of a 5 per cent solution.   Dissolve 10 grams in 200 ml. of carbon dioxide- and ammonia-free water. Determine the pH by the method described on page 18. The pH should be from 8.7 to 9.3 at 25°C. The pH of a 5 per cent solution of pure sodium phosphate, dibasic, heptahydrate would be 9.0 at 25°C.

Chloride.   Dissolve 1 gram in 20 ml. of water, filter if necessary through a chloride-free filter, and add 3 ml. of nitric acid and 1 ml. of silver nitrate reagent solution. Any turbidity should not exceed that produced by 0.01 mg. of chloride ion (Cl) in an equal volume of solution containing the quantities of reagents used in the test.

Nitrogen compounds.   Dissolve 1 gram in 60 ml. of water in a flask connected through a spray trap to a condenser, the end of which dips beneath the surface of 10 ml. of 0.1N hydrochloric acid. Add to the flask 10 ml. of freshly boiled 10 per cent sodium hydroxide reagent solution and 0.5 gram of aluminum wire in small pieces, allow to stand for 1 hour, and distill about 35 ml. To the distillate add 2 ml. of 10 per cent sodium hydroxide reagent solution, dilute to 50 ml., and add 2 ml. of

Nessler reagent. Any color should not exceed that produced when a quantity of an ammonium salt containing 0.01 mg. of nitrogen (N) is treated exactly like the sample.

Sulfate. Dissolve 10 grams in 100 ml. of water, add 7 ml. of hydrochloric acid, and heat to boiling. Add 5 ml. of barium chloride reagent solution, digest in a covered beaker on the steam bath for 2 hours, and allow to stand overnight. If a precipitate is formed, filter, wash thoroughly and ignite. The weight of the precipitate should not be more than 0.0012 gram greater than the weight obtained in a complete blank test.

Arsenic. Determine the arsenic in 0.5 gram by the Gutzeit method (page 11). The amount of stain should not exceed that produced by 0.0025 mg. of arsenic (As).

Heavy metals. Dissolve 4 grams in about 20 ml. of water, add 8 ml. of 2N hydrochloric acid, and dilute to 32 ml. For the control add 0.02 mg. of lead ion (Pb) to an 8-ml. aliquot of the solution and dilute to 25 ml. For the sample dilute the remaining 24-ml. portion to 25 ml. Adjust the pH of the control and sample solutions to between 3 and 4 (using a pH meter) with 1N acetic acid or ammonium hydroxide (10 per cent NH_3), dilute to 40 ml., and mix. Add 10 ml. of freshly prepared hydrogen sulfide water to each and mix. Any color in the solution of the sample should not exceed that in the control.

Iron. Dissolve 1 gram in 10 ml. of water. Add 6 ml. of hydroxylamine hydrochloride reagent solution and 4 ml. of 1,10-phenanthroline reagent solution, and dilute to 25 ml. Any red color should not exceed that produced by 0.01 mg. of iron (Fe) in an equal volume of solution containing the quantities of reagents used in the test. Compare 1 hour after adding the reagents to the sample and standard solutions.

Notes

Sodium Phosphate, Monobasic

$NaH_2PO_4 \cdot H_2O$ Formula Wt. 137.99

REQUIREMENTS

Insoluble matter, calcium and ammonium hydroxide precipitate. Not more than 0.010 per cent.
pH of a 5 per cent solution. From 4.1 to 4.5 at 25°C.
Chloride (Cl). Not more than 0.0005 per cent.
Nitrogen compounds (as N). Not more than 0.001 per cent.
Sulfate (SO_4). Not more than 0.003 per cent.
Arsenic (As). Not more than 0.00005 per cent.
Heavy metals (as Pb). Not more than 0.001 per cent.
Iron (Fe). Not more than 0.001 per cent.

TESTS

Insoluble matter, calcium and ammonium hydroxide precipitate. Dissolve 10 grams in 100 ml. of water. Add 5 ml. of ammonium oxalate reagent solution and ammonium hydroxide until the solution is distinctly alkaline to litmus, add an excess of 15 ml. of ammonium hydroxide, and allow to stand overnight. Filter, wash with water containing 2.5 per cent ammonia and about 0.1 per cent ammonium oxalate, and ignite at 800° ± 25°C. for 15 minutes. The weight of the residue should not exceed 0.0010 gram.

pH of a 5 per cent solution. Dissolve 10 grams in 200 ml. of carbon dioxide- and ammonia-free water. Determine the pH by the method described on page 18. The pH should be from 4.1 to 4.5 at 25°C. The pH of a 5 per cent solution of pure sodium phosphate, monobasic, would be 4.2 at 25°C.

Chloride. Dissolve 2 grams in 20 ml. of water, filter if necessary through a chloride-free filter, and add 2 ml. of nitric acid and 1 ml. of silver nitrate reagent solution. Any turbidity should not exceed that produced by 0.01 mg. of chloride ion (Cl) in an equal volume of solution containing the quantities of reagents used in the test.

Nitrogen compounds. Dissolve 1 gram in 60 ml. of water in a flask connected through a spray trap to a condenser, the end of which dips beneath the surface of 10 ml. of $0.1N$ hydrochloric acid. Add to the flask 20 ml. of freshly boiled 10 per cent sodium hydroxide reagent solution and 0.5 gram of aluminum wire in small pieces, allow to stand for 1 hour, and slowly distill about 35 ml. To the distillate add 1 ml. of 10 per cent sodium hydroxide reagent solution, dilute to 50 ml., and add

2 ml. of Nessler reagent. Any color should not exceed that produced when a quantity of an ammonium salt containing 0.01 mg. of nitrogen (N) is treated exactly like the sample.

Sulfate.   Dissolve 15 grams in 200 ml. of water, add 2 ml. of hydrochloric acid, heat to boiling, and filter. Heat the filtrate to boiling, add 10 ml. of barium chloride reagent solution, digest in a covered beaker on the steam bath for 2 hours, and allow to stand overnight. If a precipitate is formed, filter, wash thoroughly, and ignite. The weight of the precipitate should not be more than 0.0011 gram greater than the weight obtained in a complete blank test.

Arsenic.   Determine the arsenic in 6 grams by the Gutzeit method (page 11). The amount of stain should not exceed that produced by 0.003 mg. of arsenic (As).

Heavy metals.   Dissolve 4 grams in about 20 ml. of water and dilute to 32 ml. For the control add 0.02 mg. of lead ion (Pb) to an 8-ml. aliquot of the solution and dilute to 25 ml. For the sample dilute the remaining 24-ml. portion to 25 ml. Adjust the pH of the control and sample solutions to between 3 and 4 (using a pH meter) with $1N$ acetic acid or ammonium hydroxide (10 per cent NH_3), dilute to 40 ml., and mix. Add 10 ml. of freshly prepared hydrogen sulfide water to each and mix. Any color in the solution of the sample should not exceed that in the control.

Iron.   Dissolve 1 gram in water and dilute to 10 ml. Add 6 ml. of hydroxylamine hydrochloride reagent solution and 4 ml. of 1,10-phenanthroline reagent solution and dilute to 25 ml. Any red color should not exceed that produced by 0.01 mg. of iron (Fe) in an equal volume of solution containing the quantities of reagents used in the test. Compare 1 hour after adding the reagents to the sample and standard solutions.

Notes

Sodium Phosphate, Tribasic

$Na_3PO_4 \cdot 12H_2O$ Formula Wt. 380.12

Note. This salt when stored under ordinary conditions may lose some water of crystallization. Any loss in water will result in an assay of more than 100 per cent $Na_3PO_4 \cdot 12H_2O$ but does not affect the determination of the relative amount of free alkali present.

REQUIREMENTS

Assay. Not less than 98.0 per cent $Na_3PO_4.12H_2O$.
Excess alkali (as NaOH). Not more than 2.5 per cent.
Insoluble matter. Not more than 0.010 per cent.
Chloride (Cl). Not more than 0.001 per cent.
Nitrogen compounds (as N). Not more than 0.001 per cent.
Sulfate (SO$_4$). Not more than 0.010 per cent.
Arsenic (As). Not more than 0.0005 per cent.
Heavy metals (as Pb). Not more than 0.001 per cent.
Iron (Fe). Not more than 0.001 per cent.

TESTS

Assay. Accurately weigh 13 to 14 grams and dissolve in 40 ml. of water in a 400-ml. beaker. Add 100.0 ml. of $1N$ hydrochloric acid and pass a stream of carbon dioxide-free air, in fine bubbles, through the solution for 30 minutes to expel carbon dioxide. The beaker must be covered with a perforated cover to prevent loss of any of the solution by spraying. Wash down cover and sides of beaker. Titrate the solution with $1N$ sodium hydroxide to a pH of 4.00 as measured with a standardized pH meter and glass electrode system. Calculate (A) the milliliters of $1N$ hydrochloric acid consumed in this titration. Protect the solution from absorbing carbon dioxide from the air and continue the titration to pH 8.80 with $1N$ sodium hydroxide. Calculate (B) the milliliters of $1N$ sodium hydroxide consumed in this titration.

If A is equal to or greater than $2B$, then

$$\frac{B \times 0.3801}{\text{Wt. of sample}} \times 100 = \text{per cent } Na_3PO_4.12H_2O$$

If A is less than $2B$, then

$$\frac{(A - B) \times 0.3801}{\text{Wt. of sample}} \times 100 = \text{per cent } Na_3PO_4.12H_2O$$

Excess alkali. Calculate the amount of excess alkali as NaOH from the titration values obtained in the test for *Assay*. If A is equal to or less than $2B$, there is no excess alkali present when the salt is dissolved. If A is greater than $2B$, then

$$\frac{(A - 2B) \times 0.040}{\text{Wt. of sample}} \times 100 = \text{per cent NaOH}$$

Insoluble matter. Dissolve 10 grams in 100 ml. of water, add 0.10 ml. of methyl red indicator solution, and add hydrochloric acid until the solution is slightly acid to the methyl red indicator. Heat the solution to boiling and digest in a covered beaker on the steam bath for 1 hour. Filter through a tared filtering crucible, wash thoroughly, and dry at 105°C. The weight of the residue should not exceed 0.0010 gram.

Chloride. Dissolve 1 gram in 20 ml. of water, filter if necessary through a chloride-free filter, and add 3 ml. of nitric acid and 1 ml. of silver nitrate reagent solution. Any turbidity should not exceed that produced by 0.01 mg. of chloride ion (Cl) in an equal volume of solution containing the quantities of reagents used in the test.

Nitrogen compounds. Dissolve 1 gram in 60 ml. of water in a flask connected through a spray trap to a condenser, the end of which dips beneath the surface of 10 ml. of $0.1N$ hydrochloric acid. Add to the flask 10 ml. of freshly boiled 10 per cent sodium hydroxide reagent solution and 0.5 gram of aluminum wire in small pieces, allow to stand for 1 hour, and distill about 35 ml. To the distillate add 1 ml. of 10 per cent sodium hydroxide reagent solution, dilute to 50 ml., and add 2 ml. of Nessler reagent. Any color should not exceed that produced when a quantity of an ammonium salt containing 0.01 mg. of nitrogen (N) is treated exactly like the sample.

Sulfate. Dissolve 5 grams in 100 ml. of water, filter if necessary, add 4 ml. of hydrochloric acid, and heat to boiling. Add 5 ml. of barium chloride reagent solution, digest in a covered beaker on the steam bath for 2 hours, and allow to stand overnight. If a precipitate is formed, filter, wash thoroughly, and ignite. The weight of the precipitate should not be more than 0.0012 gram greater than the weight obtained from a complete blank test.

Arsenic. Determine the arsenic in 0.5 gram by the Gutzeit method (page 11). The amount of stain should not exceed that produced by 0.0025 mg. of arsenic (As).

Heavy metals. Dissolve 4 grams in about 20 ml. of water, add 8 ml. of 2N hydrochloric acid, and dilute to 32 ml. For the control add 0.02 mg. of lead ion (Pb) to an 8-ml. aliquot of the solution and dilute to 25 ml. For the sample dilute the remaining 24-ml. portion to 25 ml. Adjust the pH of the control and sample solutions to between 3 and 4 (using a pH meter) with 1N acetic acid or ammonium hydroxide (10 per cent NH_3), dilute to 40 ml., and mix. Add 10 ml. of freshly prepared hydrogen sulfide water to each and mix. Any color in the solution of the sample should not exceed that in the control.

Iron. Dissolve 1 gram in 10 ml. of water and add 3 ml. of 1N hydrochloric acid. Add 6 ml. of hydroxylamine hydrochloride reagent solution and 4 ml. of 1,10-phenanthroline reagent solution and dilute to 25 ml. Any red color should not exceed that produced by 0.01 mg. of iron (Fe) in an equal volume of solution containing the quantities of reagents used in the test, except the 3 ml. of 1N hydrochloric acid. Compare 1 hour after adding the reagents to the sample and standard solutions.

Notes

Sodium Sulfate, Anhydrous

Na₂SO₄   Formula Wt. 142.04

REQUIREMENTS

Insoluble matter.   Not more than 0.010 per cent.
Loss on ignition.   Not more than 0.50 per cent.
pH of a 5 per cent solution.   From 5.2 to 8.2 at 25°C.
Chloride (Cl).   Not more than 0.002 per cent.
Nitrogen compounds (as N).   Not more than 0.0005 per cent.
Arsenic (As).   Not more than 0.0001 per cent.
Calcium, magnesium, and R₂O₃ precipitate.   Not more than 0.020 per cent.
Heavy metals (as Pb).   Not more than 0.0005 per cent.
Iron (Fe).   Not more than 0.001 per cent.

TESTS

Insoluble matter.   Dissolve 10 grams in 100 ml. of water, heat to boiling, and digest in a covered beaker on the steam bath for 1 hour. Filter through a tared filtering crucible, wash thoroughly, and dry at 105°C. The weight of the residue should not exceed 0.0010 gram.

Loss on ignition.   Weigh accurately about 2 grams in a tared dish or crucible and ignite at 800° ± 25°C. for 15 minutes. The loss in weight should not exceed 0.50 per cent of the weight of the sample.

pH of a 5 per cent solution.   Dissolve 10 grams in 200 ml. of carbon dioxide- and ammonia-free water. Determine the pH by the method described on page 18. The pH should be from 5.2 to 8.2 at 25°C. The pH of a 5 per cent solution of pure sodium sulfate, anhydrous, would be 7.2 at 25°C.

Chloride.   Dissolve 1 gram in 50 ml. of water and filter if necessary through a chloride-free filter. To 25 ml. of the solution add 1 ml. of nitric acid and 1 ml. of silver nitrate reagent solution. Any turbidity should not exceed that produced by 0.01 mg. of chloride ion (Cl) in an equal volume of solution containing the quantities of reagents used in the test.

Nitrogen compounds.   Dissolve 2 grams in 60 ml. of water in a flask connected through a spray trap to a condenser, the end of which dips beneath the surface of 10 ml. of 0.1N hydrochloric acid. Add to the flask 10 ml. of freshly boiled 10 per cent sodium hydroxide reagent solution and 0.5 gram of aluminum wire in small pieces, allow to stand for 1 hour, and distill about 35 ml. To the distillate add 1 ml. of 10 per cent sodium hydroxide reagent solution, dilute to 50 ml., and add 2 ml. of Nessler reagent. Any color should not exceed that produced when a quantity of an ammonium salt containing 0.01 mg. of nitrogen (N) is treated exactly like the sample.

Arsenic. Determine the arsenic in 3 grams by the Gutzeit method (page 11). The amount of stain should not exceed that produced by 0.003 mg. of arsenic (As).

Calcium, magnesium, and R₂O₃ precipitate. Dissolve 5 grams in 75 ml. of water, filter if necessary, and add 5 ml. of ammonium oxalate reagent solution, 2 ml. of ammonium phosphate reagent solution, and 10 ml. of ammonium hydroxide. Allow to stand overnight. If a precipitate is formed, filter, wash with water containing 2.5 per cent ammonia and about 0.1 per cent ammonium oxalate, and ignite. The weight of the residue should not exceed 0.0010 gram.

Heavy metals. Dissolve 6 grams in water and dilute to 42 ml. For the control add 0.02 mg. of lead ion (Pb) to a 7-ml. aliquot of the solution and dilute to 35 ml. For the sample use the remaining 35-ml. portion. Adjust the pH of the control and sample solutions to between 3 and 4 (using a pH meter) with $1N$ acetic acid or ammonium hydroxide (10 per cent NH_3), dilute to 40 ml., and mix. Add 10 ml. of freshly prepared hydrogen sulfide water to each and mix. Any color in the solution of the sample should not exceed that in the control.

Iron. Dissolve 1 gram in 30 ml. of water plus 2 ml. of hydrochloric acid and dilute to 50 ml. Add 30 to 50 mg. of ammonium persulfate crystals and 3 ml. of ammonium thiocyanate reagent solution. Any red color should not exceed that produced by 0.01 mg. of iron (Fe) in an equal volume of solution containing the quantities of reagents used in the test.

Notes

Sodium Sulfide

Na₂S·9H₂O

Formula Wt. 240.18

REQUIREMENTS

Appearance.   Crystals, colorless or with no more than a slight yellow color.

Ammonium (NH₄).   Not more than 0.002 per cent.

Sulfite and thiosulfate (as SO₂).   To pass test (limit about 0.10 per cent.

Iron.   To pass test.

TESTS

Ammonium.   Dissolve 1 gram in 80 ml. of water, add 20 ml. of lead acetate reagent solution, and allow to stand until the precipitate has settled. Decant 50 ml. and transfer it, with the aid of 10 ml. of water, to a flask. Connect the flask by means of a spray trap to a condenser, the end of which dips beneath the surface of 10 ml. of 0.1N hydrochloric acid. Prepare a standard in a similar distillation apparatus containing 0.01 mg. of ammonium ion (NH₄) and 10 ml. of lead acetate reagent solution and dilute to 60 ml. with water. To each flask add 10 ml. of freshly boiled 10 per cent sodium hydroxide reagent solution and distill 35 ml. from each. To each distillate add 1 ml. of 10 per cent sodium hydroxide reagent solution and 2 ml. of Nessler reagent solution. Any brownish color in the solution of the sample should not exceed that in the standard.

Sulfite and thiosulfate.   (Note.   The water used in this test must be free from dissolved oxygen.) Dissolve 3 grams in 200 ml. of water and add 100 ml. of 5 per cent zinc sulfate solution. Mix thoroughly; allow to stand for 30 minutes. Filter and titrate 100 ml. of the filtrate with 0.1N iodine, using starch indicator. Not more than 0.3 ml. of the iodine solution should be required.

Iron.   Dissolve 5 grams in 100 ml. of water. The solution should be clear and colorless.

Notes

Sodium Sulfite, Anhydrous

Na_2SO_3 Formula Wt. 126.04

REQUIREMENTS

Assay.   Not less than 98.0 per cent Na_2SO_3.
Insoluble matter.   Not more than 0.005 per cent.
Free acid.   To pass test.
Free alkali (as Na_2CO_3).   Not more than 0.15 per cent.
Chloride (Cl).   Not more than 0.02 per cent.
Arsenic (As).   Not more than 0.0001 per cent.
Heavy metals (as Pb).   Not more than 0.001 per cent.
Iron (Fe).   Not more than 0.001 per cent.

TESTS

Assay.   Weigh accurately about 2.5 grams, dissolve in water, and dilute to 500 ml. in a volumetric flask. Add a 50-ml. aliquot to 50-ml. of a $0.1N$ iodine solution (the sulfite must be added to the iodine). Allow to stand for 5 minutes, add 1 ml. of hydrochloric acid, and titrate the excess iodine with $0.1N$ thiosulfate, using starch indicator solution near the end of the titration. One milliliter of $0.1N$ iodine corresponds to 0.006302 gram of Na_2SO_3.

Insoluble matter.   Dissolve 20 grams in 200 ml. of water, heat to boiling, and digest in a covered beaker on the steam bath for 1 hour. Filter through a tared filtering crucible, wash thoroughly, and dry at 105°C. The weight of the residue should not exceed 0.0010 gram.

Free acid.   Dissolve 1 gram in 10 ml. of water and add 0.10 ml. of phenolphthalein indicator solution. A pink color should be produced.

Free alkali.   Dissolve 1 gram in 10 ml. of water and add 3 ml. of 30 per cent hydrogen peroxide which has been previously neutralized to methyl red. Shake well and allow to stand for 5 minutes. Titrate with $0.1N$ hydrochloric acid, using methyl red indicator. Not more than 0.30 ml. of the acid should be required to neutralize the solution.

Chloride.   Dissolve 1 gram in 10 ml. of water, filter if necessary through a small chloride-free filter, add 3 ml. of 30 per cent hydrogen peroxide, and dilute to 100 ml. Dilute 5 ml. of this solution to 20 ml., and add 1 ml. of nitric acid and 1 ml. of silver nitrate reagent solution. Any turbidity should not exceed that produced by 0.01 mg. of chloride ion (Cl) in an equal volume of solution containing the quantities of nitric acid and silver nitrate used in the test.

ACS SPECIFICATIONS   **571**

Arsenic. Dissolve 2 grams in 10 ml. of water, add 1 ml. of sulfuric acid, evaporate to about 1 ml. on the steam bath, and determine the arsenic by the Gutzeit method (page 11). The amount of stain should not exceed that produced by 0.002 mg. of arsenic (As).

Heavy metals. Dissolve 3 grams in 20 ml. of dilute hydrochloric acid (1 + 1). For the control dissolve 1 gram in 20 ml. of dilute hydrochloric acid (1 + 1) and add 0.02 mg. of lead ion (Pb). Evaporate both solutions to dryness on the steam bath. Add 10 ml. more of dilute hydrochloric acid (1 + 1) to each and again evaporate to dryness. Dissolve each in about 20 ml. of water and dilute to 25 ml. Adjust the pH of the control and sample solutions to between 3 and 4 (using a pH meter) with 1N acetic acid or ammonium hydroxide (10 per cent NH₃), dilute to 40 ml., and mix. Add 10 ml. of freshly prepared hydrogen sulfide water to each and mix. Any color in the solution of the sample should not exceed that in the control.

Iron. Dissolve 1 gram in 20 ml. of dilute hydrochloric acid (1 + 9), and evaporate to dryness on the steam bath. Dissolve the residue in 5 ml. of dilute hydrochloric acid (1 + 1), and again evaporate to dryness. Dissolve the residue in 4 ml. of dilute hydrochloric acid (1 + 1), dilute to 50 ml., and add 30 to 50 mg. of ammonium persulfate crystals and 3 ml. of ammonium thiocyanate reagent solution. Any red color should not exceed that produced by 0.01 mg. of iron (Fe) in an equal volume of solution containing the quantities of reagents used in the test.

Notes

Sodium Tartrate

$(CHOHCOONa)_2 \cdot 2H_2O$ Formula Wt. 230.08

Note. This reagent is suitable for standardization of Karl Fischer reagent as used for the determination of water.

REQUIREMENTS

Loss on drying at 150°C. Not less than 15.61 per cent nor more than 15.71 per cent.
Insoluble matter. Not more than 0.005 per cent.
pH of a 5 per cent solution. From 7.0 to 9.0 at 25°C.
Chloride (Cl). Not more than 0.0005 per cent.
Phosphate (PO$_4$). Not more than 0.0005 per cent.
Sulfate (SO$_4$). Not more than 0.005 per cent.
Ammonium (NH$_4$). Not more than 0.003 per cent.
Calcium (Ca). Not more than 0.01 per cent.
Heavy metals (as Pb). Not more than 0.0005 per cent.
Iron (Fe). Not more than 0.001 per cent.

TESTS

Loss on drying at 150°C. Weigh accurately about 3 grams and dry at 150°C. in a low-form weighing bottle to constant weight (minimum 4 hours). The loss in weight should not be less than 15.61 per cent nor more than 15.71 per cent.

Insoluble matter. Dissolve 20 grams in 200 ml. of water, heat to boiling, and digest in a covered beaker on the steam bath for 1 hour. Filter through a tared filtering crucible (retain filtrate without the washings for the test for *Sulfate*), wash thoroughly, and dry at 105°C. The weight of the residue should not exceed 0.0010 gram.

pH of a 5 per cent solution. Dissolve 10 grams in 200 ml. of carbon dioxide- and ammonia-free water. Determine the pH by the method described on page 18. The pH should be from 7.0 to 9.0 at 25°C. The pH of a 5 per cent solution of pure sodium tartrate would be 8.4 at 25°C.

Chloride. Dissolve 2 grams in 20 ml. of water, filter if necessary through a chloride-free filter, and add 1 ml. of nitric acid and 1 ml. of silver nitrate reagent solution. Any turbidity should not exceed that produced by 0.01 mg. of chloride ion (Cl) in an equal volume of solution containing the quantities of reagents used in the test.

Phosphate. Ignite 4 grams in a platinum dish. Dissolve the residue in 5 ml. of water, add 5 ml. of nitric acid, and evaporate to dryness. Dissolve the residue in 25 ml. of approximately 0.5N sulfuric acid, add 1 ml. of ammonium molybdate reagent solution and 1 ml. of p-methylamino-phenol sulfate reagent solution, and allow to stand at room temperature for 2 hours. Any blue color should not exceed that produced by a standard containing the residue from 5 ml. of nitric acid and 0.02 mg. of phosphate ion (PO_4) in an equal volume of solution containing the quantities of reagents used in the test.

Sulfate. To the filtrate (without washings) retained from the test for *Insoluble matter,* add 16 ml. of hydrochloric acid, heat to boiling, add 10 ml. of barium chloride reagent solution, digest in a covered beaker on the steam bath for 2 hours, and allow to stand overnight. If a precipitate is formed, filter, wash thoroughly, and ignite. The weight of the precipitate should not be more than 0.0024 gram greater than the weight obtained in a complete blank test.

Ammonium. Dissolve 1 gram in 60 ml. of water. To 20 ml. add 1 ml. of 10 per cent sodium hydroxide reagent solution, dilute to 50 ml., and add 2 ml. of Nessler reagent. Any color should not exceed that produced by 0.01 mg. of ammonium ion (NH_4) in an equal volume of solution containing the quantities of reagents used in the test.

Calcium. Determine the calcium by the flame photometric method described on page 14. Dissolve 5 grams in 80 ml. of dilute hydrochloric acid ($1 + 7$) and digest in a covered beaker on the steam bath for 20 minutes. Cool and dilute to 100 ml. with water.

Sample Solution A. Dilute a 20-ml. aliquot of this solution to 100 ml. with water.

Control Solution B. Add 0.10 mg. of calcium ion (Ca) to another 20-ml. aliquot of the same solution and dilute to 100 ml. with water.

Observe the emission of Control Solution B at 422.7-mμ calcium line. Observe the emission of Sample Solution A at the 422.7-mμ calcium line and at a wavelength of 416.7 mμ. The difference (D_1) between the intensities observed for Sample Solution A at 422.7 mμ and 416.7 mμ should not exceed the difference (D_2) observed at 422.7 mμ between Sample Solution A and Control Solution B.

Heavy metals. Dissolve 6 grams in about 20 ml. of water and dilute to 30 ml. For the control add 0.02 mg. of lead ion (Pb) to a 5-ml. aliquot of the solution and dilute to 25 ml. For the sample use the remaining 25-ml. portion. Adjust the pH of the control and sample solutions to between 3 and 4 (using a pH meter) with 1N acetic acid or ammonium hydroxide (10 per cent NH_3), dilute to 40 ml., and mix. Add 10 ml. of freshly prepared hydrogen sulfide water to each and mix. Any color in the solution of the sample should not exceed that in the control.

Iron.   Dissolve 1 gram in 10 ml. of water, add 2 ml. of hydrochloric acid, and dilute to 50 ml. Add 30 to 50 mg. of ammonium persulfate crystals and 3 ml. of ammonium thiocyanate reagent solution. Any red color should not exceed that produced by 0.01 mg. of iron (Fe) in an equal volume of solution containing the quantities of reagents used in the test.

Notes

Sodium Tetraphenylborate
Sodium Tetraphenylboron

$NaB(C_6H_5)_4$ Formula Wt. 342.23

REQUIREMENTS

Assay.   Not less than 99.5 per cent $NaB(C_6H_5)_4$.
Loss on drying at 105°C.   Not more than 0.5 per cent.
Clarity of solution.   To pass test.

TESTS

Assay.   Weigh accurately about 0.5 gram, dissolve in 100 ml. of water, and add 1 ml. of acetic acid. Add, with constant stirring, 25 ml. of 5 per cent potassium hydrogen phthalate solution, and allow to stand for 2 hours. Filter through a tared filtering crucible, wash with three 5-ml. portions of saturated potassium tetraphenylborate solution, and dry at 105°C. for 1 hour. The weight of the potassium tetraphenylborate multiplied by 0.9551 corresponds to the weight of the sodium tetraphenylborate.

Loss on drying at 105°C.   Weigh accurately about 1.5 grams and dry to constant weight at 105°C. The loss in weight should not be more than 0.5 per cent.

Clarity of solution.   Weigh 1.5 grams, add 250 ml. of water and 0.75 gram of hydrated aluminum oxide, stir for 5 minutes, and filter through a filter paper. Filter the first 25-ml. portion again. The filtrate should be clear.

Notes

Sodium Thiocyanate

NaSCN   Formula Wt. 81.07

REQUIREMENTS

Insoluble matter. Not more than 0.005 per cent.
Carbonate (as Na$_2$CO$_3$). Not more than 0.2 per cent.
Chloride (Cl). Not more than 0.005 per cent.
Sulfate (SO$_4$). Not more than 0.010 per cent.
Sulfide (S). Not more than 0.001 per cent.
Ammonium (NH$_4$). Not more than 0.002 per cent.
Heavy metals (as Pb). Not more than 0.0005 per cent.
Iron (Fe). Not more than 0.0002 per cent.

TESTS

Insoluble matter. Dissolve 20 grams in 150 ml. of water, heat to boiling, and digest in a covered beaker on the steam bath for 1 hour. Filter through a tared filtering crucible, wash thoroughly, and dry at 105°C. The weight of the residue should not exceed 0.0010 gram.

Carbonate. Dissolve 10 grams in 100 ml. of carbon dioxide-free water, add 0.10 ml. of methyl orange indicator, and titrate with 0.1N sulfuric acid. Not more than 3.8 ml. of the acid should be required.

Chloride. Dissolve 1 gram in 20 ml. of water, filter if necessary through a chloride-free filter, and add 10 ml. of 25 per cent sulfuric acid solution and 7 ml. of 30 per cent hydrogen peroxide. Evaporate to 20 ml. by boiling *in a well ventilated hood*, add 15 to 20 ml. of water, and evaporate again. Repeat until all of the cyanide has been volatilized, cool, and dilute to 100 ml. To 20 ml. of this solution add 1 ml. of nitric acid and 1 ml. of silver nitrate reagent solution. Any turbidity should not exceed that produced by 0.01 mg. of chloride ion (Cl) in an equal volume of solution containing the quantities of reagents used in the test.

Sulfate. Dissolve 1 gram in 30 ml. of water, filter if necessary, and add 1 ml. of 1N hydrochloric acid and 2 ml. of barium chloride reagent solution. Any turbidity should not exceed that produced by 0.1 mg. of sulfate ion (SO$_4$) in an equal volume of solution containing the quantities of reagents used in the test. Compare 10 minutes after adding the barium chloride to the sample and standard solutions.

Sulfide. Add 5 grams to 80 ml. of solution prepared by mixing 10 ml. of ammonium hydroxide and 10 ml. of silver nitrate reagent solution in 60 ml. of water. Heat on the steam bath with occasional shaking for

20 minutes and transfer to a color comparison tube. Any color should not exceed that produced by 0.05 mg. of sulfide ion (S) in an equal volume of solution containing the quantities of reagents used in the test.

Ammonium. Dissolve 1 gram in 50 ml. of water in a flask connected through a spray trap to a condenser, the end of which dips beneath the surface of 10 ml. of 0.1N hydrochloric acid. Add to the flask 10 ml. of freshly boiled 10 per cent sodium hydroxide reagent solution, distill about 45 ml., and dilute the distillate to 100 ml. To 50 ml. of this solution add 1 ml. of 10 per cent sodium hydroxide reagent solution and 2 ml. of Nessler reagent. Any color should not exceed that produced when a quantity of an ammonium salt containing 0.02 mg. of ammonium ion (NH_4) is treated exactly like the sample.

Heavy metals. Dissolve 6 grams in about 20 ml. of water and dilute to 30 ml. For the control add 0.02 mg. of lead ion (Pb) to a 5-ml. aliquot of the solution and dilute to 25 ml. For the sample use the remaining 25-ml. portion. Adjust the pH of the control and sample solutions to between 3 and 4 (using a pH meter) with 1N acetic acid or ammonium hydroxide (10 per cent NH_3), dilute to 40 ml., and mix. Add 10 ml. of freshly prepared hydrogen sulfide water to each and mix. Any color in the solution of the sample should not exceed that in the control.

Iron. Dissolve 10 grams in 60 ml. of water. To 30 ml. of the solution add 0.1 ml. of hydrochloric acid, 6 ml. of hydroxylamine hydrochloride reagent solution, and 4 ml. of 1,10-phenanthroline reagent solution, and add ammonium hydroxide to bring the pH to approximately 5. Any red color should not exceed that produced by 0.01 mg. of iron (Fe) in an equal volume of solution containing the quantities of reagents used in the test. Compare 1 hour after adding the reagents to the sample and standard solutions.

Notes

Sodium Thiosulfate

Na$_2$S$_2$O$_3$·5H$_2$O   Formula Wt. 248.18

REQUIREMENTS

> **Insoluble matter.**   Not more than 0.005 per cent.
> **pH of a 5 per cent solution.**   From 6.0 to 8.4 at 25°C.
> **Nitrogen compounds (as N).**   Not more than 0.002 per cent.
> **Sulfate and sulfite (as SO$_4$).**   Not more than 0.10 per cent.
> **Sulfide (S).**   To pass test (limit about 0.0001 per cent).

TESTS

Insoluble matter.   Dissolve 20 grams in 100 ml. of water, heat to boiling, and digest in a covered beaker on the steam bath for 1 hour. Filter through a tared filtering crucible, wash thoroughly, and dry at 105°C. The weight of the residue should not exceed 0.0010 gram.

pH of a 5 per cent solution.   Dissolve 5 grams in 100 ml. of carbon dioxide- and ammonia-free water. Determine the pH by the method described on page 18. The pH should be from 6.0 to 8.4 at 25°C. The pH of a 5 per cent solution of pure sodium thiosulfate would be 7.9 at 25°C.

Nitrogen compounds.   Dissolve 1.5 grams in 10 ml. of water in a flask, and add 10 ml. of 25 per cent sulfuric acid reagent solution. Connect the flask to a water-cooled reflux condenser, heat to boiling, and reflux for about 5 minutes. Cool and rinse down the condenser with a small amount of water. Filter, using a filter that has been washed free of ammonia, into a flask, and wash the residue with 10 to 15 ml. of water. Connect the flask through a spray trap to a condenser, the tip of which dips beneath the surface of 10 ml. of 0.1N hydrochloric acid. Add to the flask 30 ml. of freshly boiled 10 per cent sodium hydroxide reagent solution and 0.5 gram of aluminum wire in small pieces, allow to stand for 1 hour, and distill about 35 ml. To the distillate add 2 ml. of 10 per cent sodium hydroxide reagent solution, dilute to 100 ml., and to 50 ml. of the diluted distillate add 2 ml. of Nessler reagent solution. Any color should not exceed that produced when a control composed of 0.5 gram of the sample and a quantity of an ammonium salt containing 0.02 mg. of nitrogen (N) is treated exactly like the sample.

Sulfate and sulfite.   Dissolve 1 gram in 50 ml. of water and add approximately 0.1N iodine until the liquid has a faint yellow color. Dilute to a volume of 100 ml. and mix thoroughly. To 5 ml. of the solution add 5 ml. of water, 1 ml. of 1N hydrochloric acid, and 1 ml. of barium chloride reagent solution. Any turbidity should not exceed that produced by 0.05 mg. of sulfate ion (SO_4) in an equal volume of solution containing the quantities of reagents used in the test. Compare 10 minutes after adding the barium chloride to the sample and standard solutions.

Sulfide. Dissolve 1 gram in 10 ml. of water and add 0.5 ml. of alkaline lead solution (made by adding sufficient 10 per cent sodium hydroxide reagent solution to 10 per cent lead acetate reagent solution to redissolve the precipitate that is first formed). No dark color should be produced in 1 minute.

Notes

Sodium Tungstate

Na$_2$WO$_4 \cdot$2H$_2$O   Formula Wt. 329.86

REQUIREMENTS

>**Insoluble matter.**   Not more than 0.010 per cent.
>**Alkalinity (as Na$_2$CO$_3$).**   Not more than 0.20 per cent.
>**Chloride (Cl).**   Not more than 0.005 per cent.
>**Molybdenum (Mo).**   Not more than 0.001 per cent.
>**Nitrogen compounds (as N).**   Not more than 0.001 per cent.
>**Sulfate (SO$_4$).**   Not more than 0.01 per cent.
>**Arsenic (As).**   Not more than 0.0005 per cent.
>**Heavy metals and iron (as Pb).**   Not more than 0.001 per cent.

TESTS

Insoluble matter.   Dissolve 10 grams in 100 ml. of water, heat to boiling, and digest in a covered beaker on the steam bath for 1 hour. Filter through a tared filtering crucible, other than glass, wash thoroughly, and dry at 105°C. The weight of the residue should not exceed 0.0010 gram.

Alkalinity.   Dissolve 2 grams in 50 ml. of cold water and add 0.10 ml. of thymol blue indicator solution. A blue color should be produced which is changed to yellow by the addition of not more than 0.40 ml. of 0.1N acid.

Chloride.   Dissolve 1 gram in 20 ml. of water, filter if necessary through a chloride-free filter, add 3 ml. of phosphoric acid, mix well, and dilute to 50 ml. Dilute 10 ml. of the solution to 25 ml. and add 1 ml. of nitric acid and 1 ml. of silver nitrate reagent solution. Any turbidity should not exceed that produced by 0.01 mg. of chloride ion (Cl) in an equal volume of solution containing the quantities of reagents used in the test.

Molybdenum.   Dissolve 2 grams in 10 ml. of water and make slightly alkaline if necessary with dilute sodium hydroxide solution. Dissolve in this solution 0.5 gram of potassium xanthate without warming. Add 10 ml. of chloroform and then add, drop by drop, dilute sulfuric acid (1 + 9), shaking after each addition, until the color in the chloroform is no longer intensified. Any pink color in the chloroform should not exceed that produced in a control made with 0.03 mg. of molybdic anhydride (MoO$_3$), corresponding to 0.02 mg. of molybdenum ion (Mo).

Nitrogen compounds.   Dissolve 1 gram in 60 ml. of water in a flask connected through a spray trap to a condenser, the end of which dips beneath the surface of 10 ml. of 0.1N hydrochloric acid. Add to the flask

10 ml. of freshly boiled 10 per cent sodium hydroxide reagent solution and 0.5 gram of aluminum wire in small pieces, allow to stand for 1 hour, and distill about 35 ml. To the distillate add 1 ml. of 10 per cent sodium hydroxide reagent solution, dilute to 50 ml., and add 2 ml. of Nessler reagent. Any color should not exceed that produced when a quantity of an ammonium salt containing 0.01 mg. of nitrogen (N) is treated exactly like the sample.

Sulfate. Dissolve 2 grams in 100 ml. of water and add slowly with stirring 5 ml. of hydrochloric acid. Evaporate to dryness and heat for 20 minutes at 110°C. Add 30 ml. of water, 2.5 ml. of hydrochloric acid, and 2 ml. of cinchonine solution [made by dissolving 5 grams of cinchonine in 50 ml. of dilute hydrochloric acid (1 + 3)] and heat just below the boiling point for 30 minutes. Dilute to 30 ml. and allow to stand until cool. Filter, and to 15 ml. of the filtrate add ammonium hydroxide drop by drop until a slight permanent precipitate forms. Add just enough hydrochloric acid to redissolve the precipitate and add 2 ml. of barium chloride reagent solution. Any turbidity should not exceed that produced in a standard made as follows: To 1 ml. of the cinchonine solution add 0.10 mg. of sulfate (SO_4), dilute to 15 ml., and add 2 ml. of barium chloride reagent solution. Compare 10 minutes after adding the barium chloride to the sample and standard solutions.

Arsenic. Transfer 1 gram to a distilling flask fitted with a gas inlet tube, a dropping funnel, a thermometer inserted to within a few millimeters of the bottom, an outlet tube, and an efficient water condenser. Add 5 ml. of phosphoric acid, 5 grams of potassium bromide, 5 grams of calcium chloride, and 0.1 gram of cuprous chloride. Add 50 ml. of hydrochloric acid through the dropping funnel, pass a slow stream of carbon dioxide or nitrogen (2 to 3 bubbles per second) into the flask, and boil the liquid gently. Absorb the distillate in 20 ml. of cold water in a large test tube immersed in an ice bath. The reaction is complete when the temperature reaches 111°C. Neutralize the distillate with 50 per cent sodium hydroxide and apply the Gutzeit test (page 11). Any stain should not exceed that produced by 0.005 mg. of arsenic (As).

Heavy metals and iron. Dissolve 2 grams in 90 ml. of water plus 2 ml. of ammonium hydroxide, and dilute to 100 ml. To 10 ml. of this solution in a separatory funnel add 10 ml. of dithizone extraction solution in chloroform. Shake well for 20 seconds and discard the aqueous layer. Wash the chloroform layer with successive 10-ml. portions of 0.5 per cent ammonium hydroxide until the ammonium hydroxide solution remains nearly colorless. The pink color remaining in the chloroform should not exceed that produced by 0.002 mg. of lead ion (Pb) in 10 ml. of dilute ammonium hydroxide (1 + 99) treated exactly like the 10-ml. portion of the solution of the sample.

Notes

Stannous Chloride

SnCl$_2$·2H$_2$O   Formula Wt. 225.63

REQUIREMENTS

Solubility in hydrochloric acid.   To pass test.
Sulfate (SO$_4$).   To pass test (limit about 0.003 per cent).
Arsenic (As).   Not more than 0.0002 per cent.
Substances not precipitated by hydrogen sulfide (as sulfates).   Not
 more than 0.05 per cent.
Iron (Fe).   Not more than 0.003 per cent.
Other metals (as Pb).   Not more than 0.010 per cent.

TESTS

Solubility in hydrochloric acid.   Dissolve 5 grams in 5 ml. of hydrochloric
acid, heat to 40°C. if necessary, and dilute with 5 ml. of water. The salt
should dissolve completely.

Sulfate.   Dissolve 5 grams in 5 ml. of hydrochloric acid, dilute the solution to 50 ml. with water, filter if necessary, and heat to boiling. Add 5
ml. of barium chloride reagent solution, digest in a covered beaker on
the steam bath for 2 hours, and allow to stand overnight. No precipitate
should be formed.

Arsenic.   Dissolve 1 gram in 5 ml. of hydrochloric acid and dilute to 40
ml. Determine the arsenic by the Gutzeit method (page 11) omitting
the addition of the potassium iodide solution. The amount of stain should
not exceed that produced by 0.002 mg. of arsenic (As).

Substances not precipitated by hydrogen sulfide.   Dissolve 4 grams in
5 ml. of hydrochloric acid, dilute to 200 ml. with water, and precipitate
the tin with hydrogen sulfide. Filter without washing, and evaporate 100
ml. of the filtrate in a tared dish to a few milliliters. Add 0.10 to 0.20 ml.
of sulfuric acid, evaporate to dryness, and ignite at 800° ± 25°C. for 15
minutes. The weight of the residue should not exceed 0.0010 gram. Retain the residue for the test for *Iron*.

Iron.   To the residue from the preceding test add 3 ml. of dilute hydrochloric acid (1 + 1), cover with a watch glass, and digest on the steam
bath for 15 minutes. Remove the cover, evaporate to dryness, dissolve
the residue in water plus 8 ml. of hydrochloric acid, and dilute to 100 ml.
Dilute 25 ml. of the solution to 50 ml. with water and add 30 to 50 mg.
of ammonium persulfate crystals and 3 ml. of ammonium thiocyanate
reagent solution. Any red color should not exceed that produced by

0.015 mg. of iron (Fe) in an equal volume of solution containing the quantities of reagents used in the test.

Other metals. Dissolve 1 gram in 5 ml. of aqua regia (2 ml. of hydrochloric acid plus 3 ml. of nitric acid). Boil until dissolution is complete and brown fumes are no longer given off in abundance. Cool and dilute to 50 ml. with water. To 10 ml. of the solution add 8 ml. of 10 per cent sodium hydroxide reagent solution, dilute to 40 ml., and add 10 ml. of freshly prepared hydrogen sulfide water. Any brown color should not exceed that produced upon the addition of 10 ml. of hydrogen sulfide water to a solution that contains in a volume of 40 ml., 8 ml. of 10 per cent sodium hydroxide reagent solution and 0.02 mg. of lead ion (Pb).

Notes

Starch, Soluble

(For iodometry)

REQUIREMENTS

Solubility. To pass test.
pH of a 2 per cent solution. From 4.5 to 6.0 at 25°C.
Residue after ignition. Not more than 0.30 per cent.
Sensitivity. To pass test.

TESTS

Solubility. Prepare a paste of 2 grams of the sample with a little cold water and add to it with stirring 100 ml. of boiling water. The solution should be no more than opalescent, and on cooling it should remain liquid and not increase in opalescence.

pH of a 2 per cent solution. Determine the pH of the solution obtained in the test for *Solubility* by the method described on page 18. The pH should be from 4.5 to 6.0 at 25°C.

Residue after ignition. Gently ignite 1 gram in a tared crucible or dish until charred. Cool, moisten the char with 1 ml. of sulfuric acid, and ignite again slowly until all carbon and excess sulfuric acid are removed. Finally, ignite at 800° ± 25°C. for 15 minutes. The weight of the residue should not exceed 0.0030 gram.

Sensitivity. Prepare a paste of 1.0 gram of the sample with a little cold water and add it with stirring to 200 ml. of boiling water. Cool and add 5 ml. of this solution to 100 ml. of water containing 50 mg. of potassium iodide, and add 0.05 ml. of 0.1N iodine solution. A deep blue color should be produced which will be discharged by 0.05 ml. of 0.1N sodium thiosulfate solution.

Notes

Strontium Nitrate

Sr(NO₃)₂   Formula Wt. 211.63

Sr(NO$_3$)$_2$

Formula Wt. 211.63

REQUIREMENTS

Insoluble matter. Not more than 0.010 per cent.
Loss on drying at 105°C. Not more than 0.10 per cent.
pH of a 5 per cent solution. From 5.0 to 7.0 at 25°C.
Chloride (Cl). Not more than 0.002 per cent.
Sulfate (SO$_4$). Not more than 0.005 per cent.
Barium (Ba). To pass test (limit about 0.050 per cent).
Calcium (Ca). Not more than 0.050 per cent.
Magnesium and alkali salts (as sulfates). Not more than 0.15 per cent.
Heavy metals (as Pb). Not more than 0.0005 per cent.
Iron (Fe). Not more than 0.0005 per cent.

TESTS

Insoluble matter. Dissolve 10 grams in 100 ml. of water, heat to boiling, and digest in a covered beaker on the steam bath for 1 hour. Filter through a tared filtering crucible, wash thoroughly, and dry at 105°C. The weight of the residue should not exceed 0.0010 gram.

Loss on drying at 105°C. Weigh accurately about 2 grams and dry at 105°C. for 4 hours. The loss in weight should not exceed 0.10 per cent.

pH of a 5 per cent solution. Dissolve 10 grams in 200 ml. of carbon dioxide- and ammonia-free water. Determine the pH by the method described on page 18. The pH should be from 5.0 to 7.0 at 25°C. The pH of a 5 per cent solution of pure strontium nitrate would be 7.0 at 25°C.

Chloride. Dissolve 1 gram in 50 ml. of water, and filter if necessary through a chloride-free filter. To 25 ml. of the solution add 1 ml. of nitric acid and 1 ml. of silver nitrate reagent solution. Any turbidity should not exceed that produced by 0.01 mg. of chloride ion (Cl) in an equal volume of solution containing the quantities of reagents used in the test.

Sulfate. Dissolve 10 grams in 35 ml. of water, add 30 ml. of hydrochloric acid, and evaporate to dryness. Treat the residue with 20 ml. of water and 20 ml. of hydrochloric acid, and again evaporate to dryness. Dissolve the residue in 100 ml. of water. Reserve 20 ml. of this solution for the test for *Iron*. To 80 ml. add 1 ml. of hydrochloric acid, filter if not perfectly clear, heat to boiling, add 5 ml. of barium chloride reagent solution, digest in a covered beaker on the steam bath for 2 hours, and allow to stand overnight. If a precipitate is formed, filter, wash thoroughly, and ignite. The weight of the precipitate should not be more than 0.0010 gram greater than the weight obtained in a complete blank test in which the residue from 40 ml. of hydrochloric acid is included.

Barium. Dissolve 2 grams in 20 ml. of water and add 1 gram of sodium acetate, 0.05 ml. of acetic acid, and 1 ml. of 10 per cent potassium dichromate solution. Allow to stand for 30 minutes. Any turbidity should not be greater than that produced by 1.0 mg. of barium ion (Ba) in an equal volume of solution containing the quantities of reagents used in the test.

Calcium. Determine the calcium by the flame photometric method described on page 14. To 5 grams in a small beaker add 10 ml. of water and 1 ml. of nitric acid, evaporate just to dryness on the steam bath, and add 10 ml. of concentrated nitric acid. Crush the large crystals with a stirring rod, warm the mixture short of boiling, and immediately cool in an ice bath.

> **Sample Solution A.** Dilute a 2-ml. aliquot of the supernatant liquid to 100 ml. with water.

> **Control Solution B.** Add 0.50 mg. of calcium ion (Ca) to another 2-ml. aliquot of the supernatant liquid and dilute to 100 ml. with water.

Observe the emission of Control Solution B at the 422.7-mμ calcium line. Observe the emission of Sample Solution A at the 422.7-mμ calcium line and at a wavelength of 416.7 mμ. The difference (D_1) between the intensities observed for Sample Solution A at 422.7 mμ and 416.7 mμ should not exceed the difference (D_2) observed at 422.7 mμ between Sample Solution A and Control Solution B.

Magnesium and alkali salts. Dissolve 2 grams in 80 ml. of water plus 0.15 ml. of hydrochloric acid, heat to boiling, and add 20 ml. of dilute sulfuric acid $(1 + 9)$. Cool, dilute to 100 ml., add 100 ml. of ethyl alcohol, mix, and allow to stand overnight. Decant through a dry filtering crucible or paper. Evaporate 100 ml. of the filtrate to dryness in a tared dish and ignite at 800° ± 25°C. for 15 minutes. The weight of the residue should not exceed 0.0015 gram.

Heavy metals. Dissolve 6 grams in about 20 ml. of water and dilute to 30 ml. For the control add 0.02 mg. of lead ion (Pb) to a 5-ml. aliquot of the solution and dilute to 25 ml. For the sample use the remaining 25-ml. portion. Adjust the pH of the control and sample solutions to between 3 and 4 (using a pH meter) with 1N acetic acid or ammonium hydroxide (10 per cent NH$_3$), dilute to 40 ml., and mix. Add 10 ml. of freshly prepared hydrogen sulfide water to each and mix. Any color in the solution of the sample should not exceed that in the control.

Iron. To the 20 ml. of solution reserved from the test for *Sulfate* add 2 ml. of hydrochloric acid. For the standard add 0.01 mg. of iron (Fe) to 10 ml. of hydrochloric acid and evaporate to dryness. Dissolve the residue in 20 ml. of water and add 2 ml. of hydrochloric acid. To each solution add 0.10 ml. of potassium permanganate, dilute to 50 ml., and allow to stand for 5 minutes. Add 3 ml. of ammonium thiocyanate reagent solution to each. Any red color in the solution of the sample should not exceed that in the standard.

Notes

Sucrose

$C_{12}H_{22}O_{11}$ Formula Wt. 342.30

REQUIREMENTS

Specific rotation $[\alpha]_D^{25\,°C\cdot}$ Not less than $+66.3°$ nor more than $+66.8°$.
Insoluble matter.   Not more than 0.005 per cent.
Loss on drying at 105°C.   Not more than 0.03 per cent.
Residue after ignition.   Not more than 0.010 per cent.
Acidity (as CH_3COOH).   Not more than 0.005 per cent.
Chloride (Cl).   Not more than 0.005 per cent.
Sulfate and sulfite (as SO_4).   Not more than 0.005 per cent.
Heavy metals (as Pb).   Not more than 0.0005 per cent.
Iron (Fe).   Not more than 0.0005 per cent.
Invert sugar.   Not more than 0.05 per cent.

TESTS

Specific rotation. Weigh accurately about 26 grams and dissolve in 90 ml. of water in a 100-ml. volumetric flask. Dilute to volume at 25°C. Observe the optical rotation in a polarimeter at 25°C. using sodium light, and calculate the specific rotation. It should not be less than $+66.3°$ nor more than $+66.8°$.

Insoluble matter. Dissolve 40 grams in 150 ml. of water, heat to boiling, and digest on the steam bath in a covered beaker for 1 hour. Filter through a tared filtering crucible, wash thoroughly, and dry at 105°C. The weight of the residue should not exceed 0.0020 gram. Reserve the filtrate, without the washings, for preparation of Sample Solution A.

Loss on drying at 105°C. Weigh accurately 4.9 to 5.1 grams in a tared dish or crucible and dry at 105°C. for 2 hours. The loss in weight should not exceed 0.0015 gram.

Residue after ignition. Gently ignite 10 grams in a tared crucible or dish until charred. Cool, moisten the char with 1 ml. of sulfuric acid, and ignite again slowly until the remaining carbon and excess sulfuric acid have been volatilized. Finally, ignite at $800° \pm 25°C.$ for 15 minutes. The weight of the residue should not exceed 0.0010 gram.

Acidity. To 100 ml of carbon dioxide-free water add 0.10 ml. of phenolphthalein indicator solution and 0.01N sodium hydroxide until a pink color is produced. Dissolve 10 grams of the sample in this solution and titrate with 0.01N sodium hydroxide to the same end point. Not more than 0.83 ml. should be required.

Sample Solution A. Transfer the filtrate from the test for *Insoluble matter* to a volumetric flask and dilute to 200 ml.

Chloride. Dilute 10 ml. of Sample Solution A to 50 ml. Dilute 5 ml. of this solution to 25 ml. and add 1 ml. of nitric acid and 1 ml. of silver nitrate reagent solution. Any turbidity should not exceed that produced by 0.01 mg. of chloride ion (Cl) in an equal volume of solution containing the quantities of reagents used in the test.

Sulfate and sulfite. Dilute 5 ml. of Sample Solution A to 10 ml., add 1 ml. of bromine water, and boil. Cool and add 1 ml. of dilute hydrochloric acid $(1 + 19)$ and 1 ml. of barium chloride reagent solution. Any turbidity should not exceed that produced by 0.05 mg. of sulfate ion (SO_4) in an equal volume of solution containing the quantities of reagents used in the test. Compare 10 minutes after adding the barium chloride to the sample and standard solutions.

Heavy metals. For the sample use a 25-ml. aliquot of Sample Solution A. For the control add 0.02 mg. of lead ion (Pb) to a 5-ml. aliquot of Sample Solution A and dilute to 25 ml. Adjust the pH of the control and sample solutions to between 3 and 4 (using a pH meter) with $1N$ acetic acid or ammonium hydroxide (10 per cent NH_3), dilute to 40 ml., and mix. Add 10 ml. of freshly prepared hydrogen sulfide water to each and mix. Any color in the solution of the sample should not exceed that in the control.

Iron. Dilute 10 ml. of Sample Solution A to 40 ml. and add 2 ml. of hydrochloric acid. Dilute to 50 ml. and add 30 to 50 mg. of ammonium persulfate crystals and 3 ml. of ammonium thiocyanate reagent solution. Any red color should not exceed that produced by 0.01 mg. of iron (Fe) in an equal volume of solution containing the quantities of reagents used in the test.

Invert sugar. Prepare a reagent solution containing in 1 liter 150 grams of potassium bicarbonate, 100 grams of potassium carbonate, anhydrous, and 6.928 grams of cupric sulfate $(CuSO_4 \cdot 5H_2O)$. Transfer 50 ml. of this reagent to a 400-ml. beaker, cover, heat to boiling, and allow to boil for 1 minute. Dissolve 10 grams of the sample in water, dilute to 50 ml., and add this solution to the solution in the 400-ml. beaker. Heat to boiling and boil for 5 minutes. At the end of this period stop the reaction by adding 100 ml. of cold, recently boiled water. Filter through a tared filtering crucible, wash thoroughly, and dry at 105°C. The weight of the precipitate should not exceed 0.0277 gram.

Sulfanilic Acid

4-NH$_2$C$_6$H$_4$SO$_3$H·H$_2$O   Formula Wt. 191.21

REQUIREMENTS

Residue after ignition.   Not more than 0.010 per cent.
Insoluble in sodium carbonate solution.   Not more than 0.02 per cent.
Chloride (Cl).   Not more than 0.002 per cent.
Nitrite (NO$_2$).   Not more than 0.00005 per cent.
Sulfate (SO$_4$).   Not more than 0.01 per cent.

TESTS

Residue after ignition.   Gently ignite 10 grams in a tared crucible or dish until charred. Slowly raise the temperature until all carbon is removed, and finally heat at 800° ± 25°C. for 15 minutes. The weight of the residue should not exceed 0.0010 gram.

Insoluble in sodium carbonate solution.   Dissolve 5 grams in 50 ml. of a clear 5 per cent solution of sodium carbonate and allow to stand in a covered beaker for 1 hour. If an insoluble residue remains, filter through a tared porous porcelain or a platinum filtering crucible, wash with cold water, and dry at 105°C. The weight of the residue should not exceed 0.0010 gram.

Chloride.   Boil 5 grams with 100 ml. of water until dissolved. Cool, dilute to 100 ml., mix well, and filter through a chloride-free filter. Dilute 10 ml. of the filtrate to 20 ml., and add 1 ml. of nitric acid and 1 ml. of silver nitrate reagent solution. Any turbidity should not exceed that produced by 0.01 mg. of chloride ion (Cl) in an equal volume of solution containing the quantities of reagents used in the test. Reserve the remaining filtrate for the test for *Sulfate*.

Nitrite.   Dissolve 0.7 gram in 100 ml. of water, warming if necessary but keeping the temperature below 30°C. For the control dissolve 0.2 gram in about 75 ml. of water, add 0.00025 mg. of nitrite ion (NO$_2$), and dilute to 100 ml. To each solution add 5 ml. of sulfanilic-1-naphthylamine reagent solution and allow to stand for 10 minutes. Any pink color produced in the solution of the sample should not exceed that in the control.

The sulfanilic-1-naphthylamine solution is made as follows: dissolve 0.5 gram of sulfanilic acid in 150 ml. of 36 per cent acetic acid. Dissolve 0.1 gram of 1-naphthylamine hydrochloride in 150 ml. of 36 per cent acetic acid. Mix the two solutions. If a pink color develops on standing, it may be discharged with a little zinc dust.

Sulfate. Cool about 30 ml. of the solution reserved from the test for *Chloride* to about 0°C. and filter. To 10 ml. of the filtrate add 1 ml. of dilute hydrochloric acid (1 + 19) and 1 ml. of barium chloride reagent solution. Any turbidity should not exceed that produced by 0.05 mg. of sulfate ion (SO_4) in an equal volume of solution containing the quantities of reagents used in the test. Compare 10 minutes after adding the barium chloride to the sample and standard solutions.

Notes

5-Sulfosalicylic Acid

$HOC_6H_3(COOH)SO_3H \cdot 2H_2O$ Formula Wt. 254.22

REQUIREMENTS

Assay. Not less than 99.0 nor more than 101.0 per cent HOC_6H_3 $(COOH)SO_3H \cdot 2H_2O$.

Insoluble matter. Not more than 0.02 per cent.

Residue after ignition. Not more than 0.10 per cent.

Chloride (Cl). Not more than 0.001 per cent.

Salicylic acid (HOC_6H_4COOH). Not more than 0.04 per cent.

Sulfate (SO_4). To pass test (limit about 0.02 per cent).

Heavy metals (as Pb). Not more than 0.002 per cent.

Iron (Fe). Not more than 0.001 per cent.

TESTS

Assay. Weigh accurately about 5 grams, dissolve in 50 ml. of water, add phenolphthalein indicator solution, and titrate with $1N$ sodium hydroxide. One milliliter of $1N$ sodium hydroxide corresponds to 0.1271 gram of $HOC_6H_3(COOH)SO_3H \cdot 2H_2O$.

Insoluble matter. Dissolve 5 grams in 50 ml. of water, heat to boiling, and digest in a covered beaker on the steam bath for 1 hour. Filter through a tared filtering crucible, wash thoroughly, and dry at 105°C. The weight of the residue should not exceed 0.0010 gram.

Residue after ignition. Gently ignite 1 gram in a tared crucible or dish, other than platinum, until charred. Cool, moisten the char with 1 ml. of sulfuric acid, and ignite again slowly until all carbon and excess sulfuric acid have been volatilized. Finally, ignite at $800° \pm 25°C$. for 15 minutes. The weight of the residue should not exceed 0.0010 gram.

Chloride. Dissolve 1 gram in 20 ml. of water, filter if necessary through a chloride-free filter, and add 1 ml. of nitric acid and 1 ml. of silver nitrate reagent solution. Any turbidity should not exceed that produced by 0.01 mg. of chloride ion (Cl) in an equal volume of solution containing the quantities of reagents used in the test.

Salicylic acid. Dissolve 5.0 grams in 15 ml. of cold water, add 10 ml. of dilute hydrochloric acid $(1 + 1)$, and extract with 50.0 ml. of benzene in a 250-ml. separatory funnel. Shake for 1.5 minutes, allow the layers to separate, and discard the aqueous layer. Add about 2 grams of anhydrous sodium sulfate to the benzene layer, shake for 1 minute, and allow the sodium sulfate to settle. Pour some of the clear benzene extract into a beaker, transfer a 10.0-ml. aliquot to a test tube, and add 10 ml. of ferric ammonium sulfate solution.* Shake the tube vigorously for 15 seconds and centrifuge at about 2500 r.p.m. (about 1700 r.c.f.) for 3 minutes. The color in the clear lower aqueous layer should not exceed that produced by 2.0 mg. of salicylic acid treated in exactly the same manner as the sample. In cases of borderline results or apparent nonconformity, aspirate off the benzene layer and determine the absorbance of the aqueous layer from the sample and the standard in 1-cm. cells at 540 mμ, using the ferric ammonium sulfate solution as the reference liquid in the spectrophotometer. Calculate the per cent of salicylic acid as follows:

$$\text{Per cent salicylic acid} = \frac{C \times \dfrac{A_u}{A_s} \times 100}{W \times 1000}$$

where:

C = weight, in mg., of salicylic acid in standard
A_u = absorbance of sample solution
A_s = absorbance of standard solution
W = weight, in grams, of sample

*Ferric Ammonium Sulfate Solution.   To 200 ml. of water in a beaker add 10 per cent sulfuric acid until the pH is about 3, dissolve 200 mg. of ferric ammonium sulfate, $FeNH_4(SO_4)_2 \cdot 12H_2O$, in the solution, and adjust the pH to 2.45 (using a pH meter) with 10 per cent sulfuric acid.

Sulfate.   Dissolve 1 gram in 20 ml. of water, neutralize with dilute ammonium hydroxide (1 + 9) to a phenolphthalein end point, and dilute to 40 ml. To 10 ml. of this solution add 1 ml. of dilute hydrochloric acid (1 + 19) and 1 ml. of barium chloride reagent solution. Any turbidity should not exceed that produced by 0.05 mg. of sulfate ion (SO_4) in an equal volume of solution containing the quantities of reagents used in the test. Compare 10 minutes after adding the barium chloride to the sample and standard solutions.

Sample Solution A.   Gently ignite 4 grams in a crucible or dish, other than platinum, until charred. Cool, moisten the char with 1 ml. of sulfuric acid, and ignite again slowly until all the carbon and excess sulfuric acid have been volatilized. Add 3 ml. of hydrochloric acid and 0.5 ml. of nitric acid, cover, and digest on the steam bath until dissolved. Remove the cover, evaporate to dryness on the steam bath, dissolve the residue in 4 ml. of $1N$ acetic acid, and dilute to 100 ml. with water (1 ml. = 0.04 grams).

Heavy metals. For the sample use a 25-ml. aliquot of Sample Solution A (1-gram sample). For the standard dilute a solution containing 0.02 mg. of lead ion (Pb) to 25 ml. Adjust the pH of the standard and sample solutions to between 3 and 4 (using a pH meter) with $1N$ acetic acid or ammonium hydroxide (10 per cent NH_3), dilute to 40 ml., and mix. Add 10 ml. of freshly prepared hydrogen sulfide water to each and mix. Any color in the solution of the sample should not exceed that in the standard.

Iron. To 25 ml. of Sample Solution A (1-gram sample) add 2 ml. of hydrochloric acid and dilute to 50 ml. Add 30 to 50 mg. of ammonium persulfate crystals and 3 ml. of ammonium thiocyanate reagent solution. Any red color should not exceed that produced by 0.01 mg. of iron (Fe) in an equal volume of solution containing the quantities of reagents used in the test.

Notes

Sulfuric Acid

H_2SO_4 Formula Wt. 98.08

REQUIREMENTS

Appearance. Free from suspended or insoluble matter as received and after dilution to $2N$.

Assay. Not less than 95.0 nor more than 98.0 per cent H_2SO_4.

Color (APHA). Not more than 10 as received and after dilution to $2N$.

Residue after ignition. Not more than 0.0005 per cent.

Chloride (Cl). Not more than 0.00002 per cent.

Nitrate (NO_3). Not more than 0.00005 per cent.

Ammonium (NH_4). Not more than 0.0002 per cent.

Substances reducing permanganate. To pass test (limit about 0.0002 per cent as SO_2).

Arsenic (As). Not more than 0.000001 per cent.

Heavy metals (as Pb). Not more than 0.0001 per cent.

Iron (Fe). Not more than 0.00002 per cent.

TESTS

Assay. Tare a small glass-stoppered flask, add about 1 ml. of the sample, and weigh accurately. Cautiously add 30 ml. of water, cool, add methyl orange indicator solution, and titrate with $1N$ sodium hydroxide. One milliliter of $1N$ sodium hydroxide corresponds to 0.04904 gram of H_2SO_4.

Color (APHA). For the color standard dilute a 2-ml. aliquot of platinum-cobalt stock solution (APHA No. 500) to 100 ml. with water. Compare this solution (APHA No. 10) with 100 ml. of the sulfuric acid in 100-ml. Nessler tubes, viewed vertically over a white background. Dilute a portion of the acid with water until $2N$ (approximately 60 ml. of acid added to 940 ml. of water), and compare as before.

Residue after ignition. Evaporate 110 ml. (200 grams) to dryness in a tared platinum dish and ignite at $800° \pm 25°C$. for 15 minutes. The weight of the residue should not exceed 0.0010 gram.

Chloride. Carefully pour 13.6 ml. (25 grams) into 40 ml. of water. Cool and add 1 ml. of nitric acid and 1 ml. of silver nitrate reagent solution. Any turbidity should not exceed that produced by 0.005 mg. of chloride ion (Cl) in an equal volume of solution containing the quantities of reagents used in the test.

Nitrate.

Sample Solution A. Cautiously add 22 ml. (40 grams) to 2.0 ml. of water, dilute to 50 ml. with brucine sulfate reagent solution, and mix.

Control Solution B. Cautiously add 22 ml. (40 grams) to 2.0 ml. of the standard nitrate solution containing 0.01 mg. of nitrate ion (NO_3) per ml., dilute to 50 ml. with brucine sulfate reagent solution, and mix.

Blank Solution C. Use 50 ml. of brucine sulfate reagent solution.

Heat the three solutions in a preheated (boiling) water bath for 10 minutes. Cool rapidly in an ice bath to room temperature. Set a spectrophotometer at 410 mμ and, using 1-cm. cells, adjust the instrument to read 0 absorbance with Blank Solution C in the light path, then determine the absorbance of Sample Solution A. Adjust the instrument to read 0 absorbance with Sample Solution A in the light path and determine the absorbance of Control Solution B. The absorbance of Sample Solution A should not exceed that of Control Solution B.

Ammonium. Carefully add 2.7 ml. (5 grams) to 30 ml. of cold water in a flask suitable for an ammonia distillation. Cool in ice, cautiously add 30 ml. of freshly boiled 10 per cent sodium hydroxide reagent solution, keeping the temperature low, cool, add 30 ml. more of the sodium hydroxide solution, and connect the flask through a spray trap to a condenser, the end of which dips beneath the surface of 10 ml. of 0.1N hydrochloric acid. Distill about 35 ml., add to the distillate 1 ml. of 10 per cent sodium hydroxide reagent solution, dilute to 50 ml., and add 2 ml. of Nessler reagent. Any color should not exceed that produced when a solution of an ammonium salt containing 0.01 mg. of ammonium ion (NH_4) is treated exactly like the sample.

Substances reducing permanganate. Carefully dilute 43.5 ml. (80 grams) with 60 ml. of ice-cold water, keeping the solution cool during the addition. Add 0.05 ml. of 0.1N potassium permanganate solution. The solution should remain pink for not less than 5 minutes.

Arsenic. Add 3 ml. of nitric acid to 165 ml. (300 grams) of the acid and evaporate to about 10 ml. Cool, carefully dilute with about 20 ml. of water, and evaporate again to about 5 ml. Cool, dilute with about 20 ml. of water, and determine arsenic by the Gutzeit method (page 11). The stain should not exceed that produced by 0.003 mg. of arsenic (As).

Heavy metals. Add 11 ml. (20 grams) to about 10 mg. of sodium carbonate dissolved in a small quantity of water. Heat over a low flame till nearly dry, then add 1 ml. of nitric acid. Evaporate to dryness, add about 20 ml. of water, and dilute to 25 ml. For the standard dilute a solution containing 0.02 mg. of lead ion (Pb) to 25 ml. Adjust the pH of the standard and sample solutions to between 3 and 4 (using a pH meter) with $1N$ acetic acid or ammonium hydroxide (10 per cent NH_3), dilute to 40 ml., and mix. Add 10 ml. of freshly prepared hydrogen sulfide water to each and mix. Any color in the solution of the sample should not exceed that in the standard.

Iron. Add 27 ml. (50 grams) to about 10 mg. of sodium carbonate dissolved in a small quantity of water. Evaporate to dryness by heating with a small flame or on an electric hot plate. Cool, add 5 ml. of dilute hydrochloric acid $(1 + 1)$, cover with a watch glass, and digest on the steam bath for 15 minutes. Dilute to 50 ml., and add 30 to 50 mg. of ammonium persulfate crystals and 3 ml. of ammonium thiocyanate reagent solution. Any red color should not exceed that produced by 0.01 mg. of iron (Fe) in an equal volume of solution containing the quantities of reagents used in the test.

Notes

Sulfuric Acid, Fuming

Note. This specification applies to fuming sulfuric acid with nominal content of 15, 20, or 30 per cent free SO_3.

REQUIREMENTS

Appearance. Colorless to very light brown color.
Assay (free SO_3). 15.0 to 18.0 per cent, 20.0 to 23.0 per cent, or 30.0 to 33.0 per cent.
Residue after ignition. Not more than 0.002 per cent.
Nitrate (NO_3). Not more than 0.0001 per cent.
Ammonium (NH_4). Not more than 0.0003 per cent.
Arsenic (As). Not more than 0.000003 per cent.
Iron (Fe). Not more than 0.0002 per cent.

TESTS

Assay. Accurately weigh about 4 grams in a tared Dely tube. Carefully transfer to a casserole containing 100 ml. of carbon dioxide–free water by placing the tip of the tube beneath the surface and flushing the tube with carbon dioxide–free water. Cool, add phenolphthalein indicator solution, and titrate with $1N$ sodium hydroxide.

$$\text{Per cent } H_2SO_4 = \frac{4.904\ V}{W}$$

Per cent free $SO_3 = 4.445\ (\% H_2SO_4 - 100)$
V = volume of $1N$ sodium hydroxide
W = weight of sample

Notes. 1. For accurate results a weight buret should be used.
2. The Dely tube and its use are described in standard reference books, such as Scott's "Standard Methods of Analysis."

Residue after ignition. Evaporate 27 ml. (50 grams) to dryness in a tared platinum dish and ignite at $800° \pm 25°C$. for 15 minutes. The weight of the residue should not exceed 0.0010 gram.

Nitrate.

Sample Solution A. Cautiously add 5.0 ml (10 grams) to 1.0 ml. of water, dilute to 50 ml. with brucine sulfate reagent solution, and mix.

Control Solution B. Cautiously add 5.0 ml. (10 grams) to 1.0 ml. of the standard nitrate solution containing 0.01 mg. of nitrate ion

(NO_3) per ml., dilute to 50 ml. with brucine sulfate reagent solution, and mix.

Blank Solution C. Use 50 ml. of brucine sulfate reagent solution.

Heat the three solutions in a preheated (boiling) water bath for 10 minutes. Cool rapidly in an ice bath to room temperature. Set a spectrophotometer at 410 mμ and, using 1-cm. cells, adjust the instrument to read 0 absorbance with Blank Solution C in the light path, then determine the absorbance of Sample Solution A. Adjust the instrument to read 0 absorbance with Sample Solution A in the light path and determine the absorbance of Control Solution B. The absorbance of Sample Solution A should not exceed that of Control Solution B.

Ammonium. Carefully add 1.7 ml. (3 grams) to 30 ml. of cold water in a flask suitable for an ammonia distillation. Cool in ice, cautiously add 20 ml. of freshly boiled 10 per cent sodium hydroxide reagent solution, keeping the temperature low, cool, add 25 ml. more of the sodium hydroxide solution, and connect the flask through a spray trap to a condenser, the end of which dips beneath the surface of 10 ml. of 0.1N hydrochloric acid. Distill about 35 ml., add to the distillate 1 ml. of 10 per cent sodium hydroxide reagent solution, dilute to 50 ml., and add 2 ml. of Nessler reagent. Any color should not exceed that produced when a solution of an ammonium salt containing 0.01 mg. of ammonium ion (NH_4) is treated exactly like the sample.

Arsenic. Add 3 ml. of nitric acid to 52 ml. (100 grams) of the acid and evaporate to about 10 ml. Cool, carefully dilute with about 20 ml. of water, and evaporate again to about 5 ml. Cool, dilute with about 20 ml. of water, and determine arsenic by the Gutzeit method (page 11). The amount of stain should not exceed that produced by 0.003 mg. of arsenic (As).

Iron. Cautiously add 2.6 ml. (5 grams) to about 10 mg. of sodium carbonate and evaporate to dryness with a small flame or on an electric hot plate. Cool, add 5 ml. of dilute hydrochloric acid (1 + 1), cover with a watch glass, and digest on the steam bath for 15 minutes. Dilute to 50 ml., and add 30 to 50 mg. of ammonium persulfate crystals and 3 ml. of ammonium thiocyanate reagent solution. Any red color should not exceed that produced by 0.01 mg. of iron (Fe) in an equal volume of solution containing the quantities of reagents used in the test.

Sulfurous Acid

(A solution of SO_2 in water)

REQUIREMENTS

> **Assay.** Not less than 6.0 per cent SO_2.
> **Residue after ignition.** Not more than 0.005 per cent.
> **Chloride (Cl).** Not more than 0.0005 per cent.
> **Arsenic (As).** Not more than 0.00005 per cent.
> **Heavy metals (as Pb).** Not more than 0.0002 per cent.
> **Iron (Fe).** Not more than 0.0005 per cent.

TESTS

Assay. Tare a glass-stoppered Erlenmeyer flask containing 50.0 ml. of $0.1N$ iodine. Quickly introduce about 2 ml. of the sample, stopper, and weigh accurately. Titrate the excess iodine with $0.1N$ sodium thiosulfate, adding starch indicator solution near the end of the titration. One milliliter of $0.1N$ iodine corresponds to 0.003203 gram of SO_2.

Residue after ignition. Evaporate 20 ml. (20 grams) to dryness on the steam bath in a tared crucible or dish and ignite at $800° \pm 25°C$. for 15 minutes. The weight of the residue should not exceed 0.0010 gram.

Chloride. Digest 10 ml. (10 grams) with 2 ml. of nitric acid on the steam bath for 1 hour. Cool and dilute to 100 ml. To 20 ml. of the solution add 1 ml. of nitric acid and 1 ml. of silver nitrate reagent solution. Any turbidity should not exceed that produced by 0.01 mg. of chloride ion (Cl) in an equal volume of solution containing the quantities of reagents used in the test.

Arsenic. To 4 ml. (4 grams) add 0.5 ml. of sulfuric acid and evaporate on the steam bath until free from sulfur dioxide and the volume is reduced to about 2 ml. Dilute to about 5 ml. and determine the arsenic by the Gutzeit method (page 11). The amount of stain should not exceed that produced by 0.002 mg. of arsenic (As).

Heavy metals. To 10 ml. (10 grams) add 10 ml. of water, boil to expel the sulfur dioxide, and dilute to 25 ml. For the standard dilute a solution containing 0.02 mg. of lead ion (Pb) to 25 ml. Adjust the pH of the standard and sample solutions to between 3 and 4 (using a pH meter) with $1N$ acetic acid or ammonium hydroxide (10 per cent NH_3), dilute to 40 ml., and mix. Add 10 ml. of freshly prepared hydrogen sulfide water to each and mix. Any color in the solution of the sample should not exceed that in the standard.

Iron. To 2 ml. (2 grams) add about 10 mg. of sodium carbonate and evaporate to dryness. Treat the residue with 0.5 ml. of hydrochloric acid and 0.15 ml. of nitric acid and repeat the evaporation. Dissolve with 2 ml. of hydrochloric acid, dilute to 50 ml., and add 30 to 50 mg. of ammonium persulfate crystals and 3 ml. of ammonium thiocyanate reagent solution. Any red color should not exceed that produced by 0.01 mg. of iron (Fe) in an equal volume of solution containing the quantities of reagents used in the test.

Notes

Tartaric Acid

HOOC(CHOH)₂COOH

Formula Wt. 150.09

HOOC(CHOH)$_2$COOH

Formula Wt. 150.09

REQUIREMENTS

Insoluble matter. Not more than 0.005 per cent.
Residue after ignition. Not more than 0.020 per cent.
Chloride (Cl). Not more than 0.001 per cent.
Oxalate (C₂O₄). To pass test (limit about 0.10 per cent).
Phosphate (PO₄). Not more than 0.001 per cent.
Sulfur compounds (as S). Not more than 0.002 per cent.
Heavy metals (as Pb). Not more than 0.0005 per cent.
Iron (Fe). Not more than 0.0005 per cent.

TESTS

Insoluble matter. Dissolve 20 grams in 200 ml. of water, heat to boiling, and digest in a covered beaker on the steam bath for 1 hour. Filter through a tared filtering crucible, wash thoroughly, and dry at 105°C. The weight of the residue should not exceed 0.0010 gram.

Residue after ignition. Gently ignite 5 grams in a tared crucible or dish until charred. Cool, moisten the char with 2 ml. of sulfuric acid, and ignite again until all carbon and excess sulfuric acid have been volatilized. Finally, ignite at 800° ± 25°C. for 15 minutes. The weight of the residue should not exceed 0.0010 gram.

Chloride. Dissolve 1 gram in 20 ml. of water, filter if necessary through a chloride-free filter, and add 1 ml. of nitric acid and 1 ml. of silver nitrate reagent solution. Any turbidity should not exceed that produced by 0.01 mg. of chloride ion (Cl) in an equal volume of solution containing the quantities of reagents used in the test.

Oxalate. Dissolve 5 grams in 30 ml. of water and divide into two equal portions. Neutralize one portion with ammonium hydroxide, using litmus paper as indicator. Add the other portion and dilute with water to 40 ml. Shake well, cool, and allow to stand at 15°C. for 15 minutes. Filter, and to 20 ml. of the filtrate add an equal volume of a saturated solution of calcium sulfate. No turbidity or precipitate should appear in 2 hours.

Sample Solution A. To 10 grams add about 10 mg. of sodium carbonate, 5 ml. of nitric acid, and 5 ml. of 30 per cent hydrogen peroxide. Digest in a covered beaker on the steam bath until the reaction ceases. Wash down the cover glass and the sides of the beaker and evaporate to dryness. Repeat the treatment with nitric acid and peroxide and again evaporate to dryness. Dissolve the residue in about 30 ml. of water, filter if necessary, and dilute to 50 ml. (1 ml. = 0.2 gram).

Phosphate. Dilute 10 ml. of Sample Solution A (2-gram sample) to 20 ml. and add 5 ml. of 2.5N sulfuric acid. Add 1 ml. of ammonium molybdate reagent solution and 1 ml. of p-methylaminophenol sulfate reagent solution. Allow to stand for 2 hours at room temperature. Any blue color should not exceed that produced by 0.02 mg. of phosphate ion (PO_4) in an equal volume of solution containing the quantities of reagents used in the test.

Sulfur compounds. Dilute 5 ml. of Sample Solution A (1-gram sample) to 10 ml. Add 1 ml. of dilute hydrochloric acid (1 + 19) and 1 ml. of barium chloride reagent solution. Any turbidity should not exceed that produced by 0.06 mg. of sulfate ion (SO_4) in an equal volume of solution containing the quantities of reagents used in the test. Compare 10 minutes after adding the barium chloride to the sample and standard solutions.

Heavy metals. Dilute 20 ml. of Sample Solution A (4-gram sample) to 25 ml. For the standard dilute a solution containing 0.02 mg. of lead ion (Pb) to 25 ml. Adjust the pH of the standard and sample solutions to between 3 and 4 (using a pH meter) with 1N acetic acid or ammonium hydroxide (10 per cent NH_3), dilute to 40 ml., and mix. Add 10 ml. of freshly prepared hydrogen sulfide water to each and mix. Any color in the solution of the sample should not exceed that in the standard.

Iron. Dissolve 2 grams in 40 ml. of water plus 2 ml. of hydrochloric acid, dilute to 50 ml., and add 30 to 50 mg. of ammonium persulfate crystals and 3 ml. of ammonium thiocyanate reagent solution. Any red color should not exceed that produced by 0.01 mg. of iron (Fe) in an equal volume of solution containing the quantities of reagents used in the test.

Notes

Thioacetamide

CH$_3$CSNH$_2$ Formula Wt. 75.13

Note. This reagent when stored under ordinary conditions may decompose slightly and fail the test for *Clarity of a 2 per cent solution.*

REQUIREMENTS

Assay. Not less than 99 per cent CH$_3$CSNH$_2$.
Melting point. Not below 111°C. nor above 114°C.
Residue after ignition. Not more than 0.050 per cent.
Clarity of a 2 per cent solution. To pass test.

TESTS

Assay. Weigh accurately about 1.5 grams, dissolve in water, and dilute to 500 ml. in a volumetric flask. To a 50.0-ml. aliquot add 1 ml. of ammonium hydroxide and 50.0 ml. of 0.1N silver nitrate. Allow to stand for 20 minutes, carefully filter through a filtering crucible or a sintered glass funnel which has been cleaned with dilute nitric acid, and wash the funnel and flask well with water. To the clear solution add 5 ml. of nitric acid and 2 ml. of ferric ammonium sulfate indicator solution, and titrate with 0.1N thiocyanate. One milliliter of 0.1N silver nitrate corresponds to 0.003757 gram of CH$_3$CSNH$_2$.

Residue after ignition. Gently ignite 2 grams in a tared crucible or dish until charred. Cool, moisten the char with 1 ml. of sulfuric acid, and ignite again slowly until the remaining carbon and excess sulfuric acid have been volatilized. Finally, ignite at 800° ± 25°C. for 15 minutes. The weight of the residue should not exceed 0.0010 gram.

Clarity of a 2 per cent solution. Dissolve 2 grams in 100 ml. of water. The solution should be clear and colorless.

Notes

Thorium Nitrate

Th(NO₃)₄·4H₂O

REQUIREMENTS

Insoluble matter. Not more than 0.010 per cent.
Chloride (Cl). Not more than 0.002 per cent.
Sulfate (SO₄). Not more than 0.010 per cent.
Substances not precipitated by ammonium hydroxide. Not more than 0.20 per cent.
Heavy metals (as Pb). Not more than 0.002 per cent.
Iron (Fe). Not more than 0.002 per cent.
Rare earths (as La). To pass test (limit about 0.2 per cent).
Titanium (Ti). Not more than 0.01 per cent.

TESTS

Insoluble matter. Dissolve 10 grams in 100 ml. of water, heat to boiling, and digest in a covered beaker on the steam bath for 1 hour. Filter through a tared filtering crucible, wash thoroughly, and dry at 105°C. The weight of the residue should not exceed 0.0010 gram. Reserve the filtrate and washings for the preparation of Sample Solution A.

> **Sample Solution A for the determination of Chloride, Sulfate, Substances not precipitated by ammonium hydroxide, Heavy metals, Iron, Rare earths, and Titanium.** Transfer the filtrate and washings reserved from the test for *Insoluble matter* to a 200-ml. volumetric flask and dilute to 200 ml. with water (1 ml. = 0.05 gram).

Chloride. Dilute 10 ml. (0.5-gram sample) of Sample Solution A to 20 ml., filter if necessary through a chloride-free filter, and add 1 ml. of nitric acid and 1 ml. of silver nitrate reagent solution. Any turbidity should not exceed that produced by 0.01 mg. of chloride ion (Cl) in an equal volume of solution containing the quantities of reagents used in the test.

Sulfate. Dilute 10 ml. (0.5-gram sample) of Sample Solution A to 20 ml. with water. Add 5 ml. of 2N ammonium acetate and transfer the solution to a separatory funnel. Extract with successive 10-ml. portions of 0.2M N-phenylbenzohydroxamic acid in chloroform until the color of the chloroform layer remains unchanged. Wash the aqueous layer twice with 5-ml. portions of chloroform. Transfer the aqueous solution to a beaker and evaporate on the steam bath to 2 to 3 ml. Add 2 ml. of nitric acid and 2 ml. of hydrochloric acid, cover, and digest on the steam bath until any reaction ceases. Uncover, wash down the sides of the beaker, and evaporate to dryness. Dissolve the residue in 4 ml. of water plus 1 ml. of dilute hydrochloric acid (1 + 19). Filter if necessary through a small filter, wash with two 2-ml. portions of water, and dilute to 10 ml. Add 1 ml. of barium chloride reagent solution. Any turbidity should not exceed that produced by 0.05 mg. of sulfate ion (SO_4) in an equal volume of solution which has been treated exactly like the sample. Compare 10 minutes after adding the barium chloride to the sample and standard solutions.

Substances not precipitated by ammonium hydroxide. Dilute 40 ml. (2-gram sample) of Sample Solution A to 100 ml. Add 0.10 ml. of methyl red indicator solution and add ammonium hydroxide until the solution is alkaline to methyl red. Heat the solution to boiling and digest on the steam bath for 15 minutes. Dilute the solution to 150 ml., mix thoroughly, and filter. Evaporate 75 ml. (1-gram sample) to dryness in a tared dish on the steam bath. Moisten the residue with 0.10 ml. of sulfuric acid. Heat gently to volatilize the excess salts and acid, and finally ignite at 800° ± 25°C. for 15 minutes. The weight of the residue should not exceed 0.0020 gram.

Heavy metals. For the sample use a 30-ml. aliquot (1.5-gram sample) of Sample Solution A. For the control add 0.02 mg. of lead ion (Pb) to a 10-ml. aliquot (0.5-gram sample) of Sample Solution A and dilute to 30 ml. Adjust the pH of the control and sample solutions to between 3 and 4 (using a pH meter) with 1N acetic acid or ammonium hydroxide (10 per cent NH_3), dilute to 40 ml., and mix. Add 10 ml. of freshly prepared hydrogen sulfide water to each and mix. Any color in the solution of the sample should not exceed that in the control.

Iron. Add 2 ml. of hydrochloric acid to 10 ml. (0.5-gram sample) of Sample Solution A and dilute to 50 ml. Add 20 to 30 mg. of ammonium persulfate crystals and 3 ml. of ammonium thiocyanate reagent solution. Any red color should not exceed that produced by 0.01 mg. of iron (Fe) in an equal volume of solution containing the quantities of reagents used in the test.

Rare earths. Dilute 5 ml. (0.25-gram sample) of Sample Solution A to 90 ml. with water. Adjust to pH 4.5 with sodium acetate–acetic acid buffer solution and dilute to 100 ml. To a 10-ml. aliquot in a separatory funnel add 10 ml. of N-phenylbenzohydroxamic acid reagent solution, shake vigorously, allow the layers to separate, and draw off and discard the chloroform layer. Repeat the extraction with 5-ml. portions of N-phenylbenzohydroxamic acid reagent solution two more times, drawing off and discarding the chloroform layer each time. Wash the aqueous layer with 5 ml. of chloroform and draw off and discard the chloroform.

Add 2 ml. of Alizarin Red S solution and dilute to 50 ml. Adjust the pH of the solution to 4.68 with 0.5N sodium acetate. Any red color should not exceed that produced by 0.05 mg. of lanthanum ion (La) which has been treated exactly like the 10-ml. aliquot of the sample.

Sodium Acetate–Acetic Acid Buffer. Dissolve 54.4 grams of sodium acetate in water, add 23 ml. of acetic acid, and dilute to 200 ml. with water.

N-Phenylbenzohydroxamic Acid Reagent Solution. Dissolve 4.26 grams of N-phenylbenzohydroxamic acid in chloroform and dilute to 100 ml. with chloroform.

Alizarin Red S Solution. Dissolve 0.10 gram of alizarin sodium monosulfonate in water and dilute to 100 ml.

Titanium. Dilute 10 ml. (0.5-gram sample) of Sample Solution A to 20 ml. and add 0.5 ml. of 30 per cent hydrogen peroxide. Any yellow color should not exceed that produced by 0.05 mg. of titanium ion (Ti) in an equal volume of solution containing the quantities of reagents used in the test.

Notes

Thymol Blue

Thymolsulfonphthalein
α-Hydroxy-α,α-bis(5-hydroxycarvacryl)-p-toluenesulfonic Acid

Note. This specification applies both to the free acid form and to the salt form of this indicator.

REQUIREMENTS

Insoluble matter. To pass test.
Visual transition interval (acid range). From pH 1.2 (red) to pH 2.8 (yellow).
Visual transition interval (alkaline range). From pH 8.0 (yellow) to pH 9.2 (blue).

TESTS

Insoluble matter. If the indicator is the acid form, dissolve 0.1 gram in 100 ml. of alcohol. If the indicator is a salt form, dissolve 0.1 gram in 100 ml. of water. Not more than a faint trace of turbidity or insoluble matter should remain. Reserve the solution for the tests for *Visual transition interval.*

Visual transition interval (acid range). Dissolve 1 gram of potassium chloride in 100 ml. of water. Adjust the pH of the solution to 1.20 (using a pH meter as described on page 18) with 1.0N acid. Add 0.1 to 0.3 ml. of the 0.1 per cent solution reserved from the test for *Insoluble matter.* The color of the solution should be pink. Titrate the solution with 1.0N sodium hydroxide until the pH is 2.2 (using the pH meter). The color of the solution should be orange. Continue the titration until the pH is 2.8. The color of the solution should be yellow. Not more than 8.6 ml. of the 1.0N sodium hydroxide should be consumed in the titration.

Visual transition interval (alkaline range). Dissolve 1 gram of potassium chloride in 100 ml. of water. Adjust the pH of the solution to 8.00 (using a pH meter as described on page 18) by adding 0.01N acid or alkali. Add 0.1 to 0.3 ml. of the 0.1 per cent solution reserved from the test for *Insoluble matter.* The color of the solution should be yellow. Titrate the solution with 0.01N sodium hydroxide until the pH is 8.4 (using the pH meter). The color of the solution should be green. Continue the titration until the pH is 9.2. The color of the solution should be blue. Not more than 0.50 ml. of the 0.01N sodium hydroxide should be consumed in the titration.

Thymolphthalein

5',5"-Diisopropyl-α',α"-dimethylphenolphthalein

REQUIREMENTS

Insoluble matter.   To pass test.
Visual transition interval.   From pH 8.6 (colorless) to pH 10 (blue).

TESTS

Insoluble matter.   Dissolve 0.1 gram in 100 ml. of alcohol. Not more than a faint trace of turbidity or insoluble matter should remain. Reserve the solution for the test for *Visual transition interval.*

Visual transition interval.   Dissolve 1 gram of potassium chloride in 100 ml. of water. Adjust the pH of the solution to 8.60 (using a pH meter as described on page 18) with 0.01N acid or alkali. Add 0.5 to 1.0 ml. of the 0.1 per cent solution reserved from the test for *Insoluble matter.* The solution should be colorless. Titrate the solution with 0.01N sodium hydroxide to pH 9.0 (using the pH meter). The solution should have a pale grayish blue color. Continue the titration to pH 9.2. The solution should have a light blue color. Not more than 0.30 ml. of 0.01N sodium hydroxide should be consumed in the titration. Each additional 0.20 ml. of 0.01N sodium hydroxide should increase the amount of blue color until at pH 10 the color should be an intense blue.

Notes

Tin

Sn

Atomic Wt. 118.69

REQUIREMENTS

Nonvolatile with hydrobromic acid and bromine. Not more than 0.02 per cent.

Antimony (Sb). Not more than 0.02 per cent.

Arsenic (As). Not more than 0.0001 per cent.

TESTS

Nonvolatile with hydrobromic acid and bromine. Dissolve 10 grams in 65 ml. of HBr-Br mixture (4HBr + 1Br) in a 300-ml. tall-form beaker. (It is safe to pour bromine into hydrobromic acid, but tin must be added with care.) After dissolution is complete, add 6 ml. of perchloric acid and evaporate to light fumes of perchloric acid. Then grip the beaker with a pair of tongs and swirl over a free flame for about 15 seconds. If the perchloric acid is cloudy, indicating incomplete removal of tin or antimony, wash down the sides of the beaker with 5 ml. of hydrobromic acid–bromine solution and evaporate and fume as above. Continue the addition of 5 ml. of hydrobromic acid–bromine solution and the subsequent heating until a clear perchloric acid solution is obtained. Run a complete blank, using the same quantities of reagents as used in the test. Transfer each to a tared evaporating dish, add 0.1 ml. of sulfuric acid, and carefully evaporate to dryness. Finally, ignite at 800° ± 25°C. for 15 minutes. The weight of the residue from the sample should not be more than 0.0020 gram greater than that from a complete blank.

Antimony. Dissolve 0.5 gram by heating with 10 ml. of sulfuric acid in a beaker. Cool and add 30 ml. of water. Filter, add 50 ml. of hydrochloric acid, and dilute to 100 ml. Dilute 5 ml. to 10 ml., and add 0.5 ml. of a 1 per cent solution of sodium bisulfite. Cool below 25°C. and add 3 ml. of ceric solution (prepared by adding 3 ml. of sulfuric acid to 3 grams of ceric ammonium nitrate and diluting to 100 ml.) and 0.5 ml. of a 1 per cent solution of hydroxylamine hydrochloride. Allow to stand until the solution becomes colorless, then dilute to 60 ml. and transfer to a separatory funnel. Add 10 ml. of isopropyl ether and shake for 30 seconds. Allow to separate and draw off the aqueous layer. Wash twice with 2-ml. portions of 1N hydrochloric acid, drawing off and discarding the aqueous layer each time. Add 2 ml. of Rhodamine B solution (0.02 gram in 100 ml. of 1N hydrochloric acid) and shake for 10 seconds. Draw off the aqueous layer. The ether layer should contain no more pink color than an equal volume of a solution containing 0.005 mg. of antimony ion (Sb), 1 ml. of sulfuric acid, and 5 ml. of hydrochloric acid which has been treated exactly like the 5-ml. aliquot of the sample.

Arsenic. Dissolve 3 grams in 15 ml. of sulfuric acid plus 1 ml. of water in a 250-ml. Erlenmeyer flask. Dissolve the sample by carefully heating with a Bunsen burner and rotating the flask in the open flame. When the sample is dissolved, cool, add 0.2 gram of hydrazine sulfate, and again boil gently for a few minutes. Cool, cautiously dilute the solution with an equal volume of water, and cool. Add 100 ml. of hydrochloric acid, filter if necessary, and transfer to an apparatus suitable for distilling arsenic trichloride. Replace the air in the distilling apparatus with carbon dioxide and keep a stream of carbon dioxide passing through the apparatus throughout the distillation. Distill 60 ml., keeping the temperature in the distilling flask below 111°C. The end of the condenser should dip below the surface of 50 ml. of dilute nitric acid (1 + 9). Add 5 ml. of sulfuric acid to the distillate and evaporate to dense fumes of sulfur trioxide. Cool, cautiously add 10 ml. of water, and again evaporate to dense fumes of sulfur trioxide. Determine the arsenic by the Gutzeit method (page 11). The stain should not exceed that produced by 0.003 mg. of arsenic (As) treated exactly like the sample.

Notes

Toluene

C₆H₅CH₃

REQUIREMENTS

Color (APHA). Not more than 10.
Boiling range. 1 ml. to 95 ml., not more than 1.0°C.; 95 ml. to dryness, not more than 1.0°C.
Residue after evaporation. Not more than 0.001 per cent.
Substances darkened by sulfuric acid. To pass test.
Sulfur compounds (as S). Not more than 0.003 per cent.
Water (H₂O). Not more than 0.03 per cent.

TESTS

Color (APHA). For the color standard dilute a 2-ml. aliquot of platinum-cobalt stock solution (APHA No. 500) to 100 ml. with water. Compare this solution (APHA No. 10) with 100 ml. of the toluene in 100-ml. Nessler tubes, viewed vertically over a white background.

Boiling range. Distill 100 ml. by the method described on page 12. The difference between the temperatures when 1 ml. and 95 ml. have distilled should not exceed 1.0°C., and the difference in the temperatures when 95 ml. have distilled and when the dry point is reached should not exceed 1.0°C. The boiling point of pure toluene at 760-mm. mercury pressure is 110.6°C.

Residue after evaporation. Evaporate 115 ml. (100 grams) to dryness in a tared dish on the steam bath and dry the residue at 105°C. for 30 minutes. The weight of the residue should not exceed 0.0010 gram.

Substances darkened by sulfuric acid. Shake 15 ml. with 5 ml. of sulfuric acid for 15 to 20 seconds and allow to stand for 15 minutes. The toluene layer should be colorless and the color of the acid should not exceed that of a color standard composed of 2 volumes of water plus 1 volume of a color standard containing 5 grams of CoCl₂.6H₂O, 40 grams of FeCl₃.6H₂O, and 20 ml. of hydrochloric acid in a liter.

Sulfur compounds. Place 30 ml. of approximately 0.5N potassium hydroxide in methanol in an Erlenmeyer flask, add 6 ml. (5 grams) of the sample, and boil the mixture gently for 30 minutes under a reflux condenser, avoiding the use of a rubber stopper or connection. Detach the condenser, dilute with 50 ml. of water, and heat on the steam bath until the toluene and methanol are evaporated. Add 50 ml. of saturated bromine water and heat for 15 minutes longer. Transfer the solution to a beaker, neutralize with dilute hydrochloric acid $(1 + 3)$, add an excess of 1 ml. of the acid, and evaporate to about 50 ml. Filter if necessary, heat the filtrate to boiling, add 5 ml. of barium chloride reagent solution, digest in a covered beaker on the steam bath for 2 hours, and allow to stand overnight. If a precipitate is formed, filter, wash thoroughly, and ignite. The weight of the precipitate should not be more than 0.0012 gram greater than the weight obtained in a complete blank test.

Water. Place 25 ml. of methanol in a dry titration flask and add Karl Fischer reagent to a visually or electrometrically determined end point. Add 20 ml. (17.4 grams) of the sample, taking care to protect the sample and contents of the flask from moisture. Stir vigorously and titrate with Karl Fischer reagent to the same end point. Calculate the water content of the sample from the titer and volume of Karl Fischer reagent consumed by the sample.

Notes

Toluene

(Suitable for use in ultraviolet spectrophotometry)

$C_6H_5CH_3$

Formula Wt. 92.14

REQUIREMENTS

Absorbance.　To pass test.

Boiling range.　1 ml. to 95 ml., not more than 1.0°C.; 95 ml. to dryness, not more than 1.0°C.

Residue after evaporation.　Not more than 0.001 per cent.

Substances darkened by sulfuric acid.　To pass test.

Sulfur compounds (as S).　Not more than 0.003 per cent.

Water (H_2O).　Not more than 0.03 per cent.

TESTS

Absorbance.　Determine the absorbance of the sample in a 1.00-cm. cell throughout the range of 286 mμ to 400 mμ, against water in a similar matched cell set at zero absorbance as the reference liquid. The absorbance should not exceed 1.00 at 286 mμ, 0.50 at 288 mμ, 0.20 at 293 mμ, 0.10 at 300 mμ, 0.05 at 310 mμ, 0.02 at 335 mμ, and 0.01 at 350 mμ to 400 mμ. The spectral absorbance curve recorded through the wavelengths indicated should be smooth throughout the prescribed range and should not show any extraneous impurity peaks within this range.

Other tests are the same as for **Toluene**, page 614, except *Color* (*APHA*), which is superseded by the *Absorbance* test.

Notes

Trichloroacetic Acid

CCl₃COOH

REQUIREMENTS

Assay. Not less than 99.0 per cent CCl_3COOH.
Residue after ignition. Not more than 0.03 per cent.
Chloride (Cl). Not more than 0.001 per cent.
Nitrate (NO_3). Not more than 0.002 per cent.
Phosphate (PO_4). Not more than 0.0005 per cent.
Sulfate (SO_4). Not more than 0.02 per cent.
Heavy metals (as Pb). Not more than 0.002 per cent.
Iron (Fe). Not more than 0.001 per cent.
Substances darkened by sulfuric acid. To pass test.

TESTS

Assay. Weigh accurately about 5 grams, previously dried for 24 hours over an efficient desiccant, and dissolve in 20 ml. of water in a 500-ml. reflux flask. Add 0.05 ml. of methyl red indicator solution and titrate with 1N sodium hydroxide to a distinct yellow color, then add 50.0 ml. of 1N sulfuric acid. Add sufficient dioxane to make the final solution at least 55 per cent dioxane. Add silicon carbide boiling chips and boil gently under complete reflux for 1 hour. Cool, add more methyl red indicator solution, and titrate the excess sulfuric acid with 1N sodium hydroxide, the end point being the distinct transition from a light orange color to a definite yellow color. Correct for the acid present in the dioxane by running a complete blank.

$$\text{Per cent } CCl_3COOH = \frac{V \times 0.1634 \times 100}{\text{wt. of sample}}$$

where V = volume of 1N sulfuric acid consumed by the sample. This quantity is the volume of 1N sodium hydroxide consumed by the blank minus the volume of 1N sodium hydroxide consumed by the sample.

Residue after ignition. Ignite 5 grams in a tared crucible or dish. The rate of heating should be such that from 1 to 2 hours is required to volatilize the sample. When nearly all of the sample has been volatilized, cool and moisten the residue with 0.10 ml. of sulfuric acid. Continue the heating until the remainder of the sample and excess sulfuric acid have been volatilized. Finally, ignite at 800° ± 25°C. for 15 minutes. The weight of the residue should not exceed 0.0015 gram.

Chloride. Dissolve 1 gram in 23 ml. of water, filter if necessary through a chloride-free filter, and add 1 ml. of nitric acid and 1 ml. of silver nitrate reagent solution. Any turbidity should not exceed that produced by 0.01 mg. of chloride ion (Cl) in an equal volume of solution containing the quantities of reagents used in the test.

Nitrate.

Sample Solution A. Dissolve 0.25 gram in 3 ml. of water by heating in a boiling water bath. Dilute to 50 ml. with brucine sulfate reagent solution.

Control Solution B. Dissolve 0.25 gram in 2.5 ml. of water and 0.5 ml. of the standard nitrate solution containing 0.01 mg. of nitrate ion (NO_3) per ml. by heating in a boiling water bath. Dilute to 50 ml. with brucine sulfate reagent solution.

Blank Solution C. Use 50 ml. of brucine sulfate reagent solution.

Heat the three solutions in a preheated (boiling) water bath for 10 minutes. Cool rapidly in an ice bath to room temperature. Set a spectrophotometer at 410 mμ and, using 1-cm. cells, adjust the instrument to read 0 absorbance with Blank Solution C in the light path, then determine the absorbance of Sample Solution A. Adjust the instrument to read 0 absorbance with Sample Solution A in the light path and determine the absorbance of Control Solution B. The absorbance of Sample Solution A should not exceed that of Control Solution B.

Sample Solution A. Evaporate 5 grams to dryness in a beaker on the steam bath. Dissolve in about 10 ml. of water, filter if necessary, and dilute to 100 ml. (1 ml. = 0.05 gram).

Phosphate. Dilute 40 ml. of Sample Solution A (2-gram sample) to about 80 ml. Add 0.5 gram of ammonium molybdate and adjust the pH to 1.8 (using a pH meter) with dilute hydrochloric acid (1 + 9). Heat to boiling, cool to room temperature, dilute to 90 ml., and add 10 ml. of hydrochloric acid. For the standard treat 0.01 mg. of phosphate ion (PO_4) exactly like the 40 ml. of Sample Solution A. Transfer the solutions to separatory funnels, add 35 ml. of ether, shake vigorously, and allow to separate. Draw off and discard the aqueous phase. Wash the ether phases once with 10-ml. portions of dilute hydrochloric acid (1 + 9), drawing off and discarding the aqueous phases. Add 0.5 ml. of a freshly prepared 2 per cent solution of stannous chloride in hydrochloric acid to each ether phase. Any blue color in the solution of the sample should not exceed that in the standard. If the ether extracts are turbid, wash with 10 ml. of dilute hydrochloric acid $(1 + 9)$.

Sulfate. Dilute 5 ml. of Sample Solution A (0.25-gram sample) to 10 ml. Add 1 ml. of dilute hydrochloric acid $(1 + 19)$, and 1 ml. of barium chloride reagent solution. Any turbidity should not exceed that produced by 0.05 mg. of sulfate ion (SO_4) in an equal volume of solution containing the quantities of reagents used in the test. Compare 10 minutes after adding the barium chloride to the sample and standard solutions.

Heavy metals. Dilute 20 ml. of Sample Solution A (1-gram sample) to 25 ml. For the standard dilute a solution containing 0.02 mg. of lead ion (Pb) to 25 ml. Adjust the pH of the standard and sample solutions to between 3 and 4 (using a pH meter) with $1N$ acetic acid or ammonium hydroxide (10 per cent NH_3), dilute to 40 ml., and mix. Add 10 ml. of freshly prepared hydrogen sulfide water to each and mix. Any color in the solution of the sample should not exceed that in the standard.

Iron. Add 2 ml. of hydrochloric acid to 20 ml. of Sample Solution A (1-gram sample) and dilute to 50 ml. Add 30 to 50 mg. of ammonium persulfate crystals and 3 ml. of ammonium thiocyanate reagent solution. Any red color should not exceed that produced by 0.01 mg. of iron (Fe) in an equal volume of solution containing the quantities of reagents used in the test.

Substances darkened by sulfuric acid. Dissolve 1 gram in 10 ml. of sulfuric acid and digest in a covered beaker on the steam bath for 15 minutes. Any color should not exceed that produced when 10 ml. of sulfuric acid is added to 1 ml. of water containing 0.1 mg. of sucrose and heated in the same way as the sample.

Notes

Trichloroethylene

Trichloroethene

CHCl:CCl$_2$

Formula Wt. 131.39

Note. This material usually contains a stabilizer. If a stabilizer is present, the amount and kind will be stated on the label.

REQUIREMENTS

Color (APHA). Not more than 10.

Density (grams per ml.) at 25°C. Not less than 1.455 nor more than 1.460.

Boiling range. 1 ml. to 95 ml., not more than 0.5°C.; 95 ml. to dryness, not more than 0.5°C.

Residue after evaporation. Not more than 0.001 per cent.

Acidity (as HCl). Not more than 0.0005 per cent.

Alkalinity (as NaOH). Not more than 0.001 per cent.

Water (H$_2$O). Not more than 0.05 per cent.

Heavy metals (as Pb). Not more than 0.0001 per cent.

Free halogens. To pass test.

TESTS

Color (APHA). For the color standard dilute a 2-ml. aliquot of platinum-cobalt stock solution (APHA No. 500) to 100 ml. with water. Compare this solution (APHA No. 10) with 100 ml. of the trichloroethylene in 100-ml. Nessler tubes, viewed vertically over a white background.

Boiling range. Distill 100 ml. by the method described on page 12. The difference between the temperatures when 1 ml. and 95 ml. have distilled should not exceed 0.5°C., and the difference in the temperatures when 95 ml. have distilled and when the dry point is reached should not exceed 0.5°C. The boiling point of pure trichloroethylene at 760-mm. mercury pressure is 87.1°C.

Residue after evaporation. Evaporate 69 ml. (100 grams) to dryness in a tared dish on the steam bath in a well ventilated hood and dry the residue at 105°C. for 30 minutes. The weight of the residue should not exceed 0.0010 gram.

Acidity and alkalinity. To 25 ml. of water and 0.10 ml. of phenolphthalein indicator solution in a 250-ml. glass-stoppered flask, add 0.01N sodium hydroxide until a slight pink color appears. Add 25 ml. (36 grams) of sample and shake for 30 seconds. If the pink color persists, titrate with

0.01N hydrochloric acid, shaking repeatedly, until the pink color just disappears. Not more than 0.90 ml. of 0.01N hydrochloric acid should be required (alkalinity). If the pink color is discharged when the sample is added, titrate with 0.01N sodium hydroxide until the pink color is restored. Not more than 0.50 ml. of 0.01N sodium hydroxide should be required (acidity).

Water. Place 25 ml. of methanol in a dry titration flask and add Karl Fischer reagent to a visually or electrometrically determined end point. Add 25 ml. (36 grams) of the sample, taking care to protect the sample and contents of the flask from moisture. Stir vigorously and titrate with Karl Fischer reagent to the same end point. Calculate the water content of the sample from the titer and volume of Karl Fischer reagent consumed by the sample.

Heavy metals. Evaporate 7 ml. (10 grams) to dryness in a glass evaporating dish on the steam bath inside a well ventilated hood. For the standard evaporate a solution containing 0.01 mg. of lead ion (Pb) to dryness. Cool, add 2 ml. of hydrochloric acid to each, and slowly evaporate to dryness on the steam bath. Moisten the residues with 0.05 ml. of hydrochloric acid, add 10 ml. of hot water, and digest for 2 minutes. Filter if necessary through a small filter, wash the evaporating dish and the filter with about 10 ml. of water, and dilute each to 25 ml. Adjust the pH of the standard and sample solutions to between 3 and 4 (using a pH meter) with 1N acetic acid or ammonium hydroxide (10 per cent NH_3), dilute to 40 ml., and mix. Add 10 ml. of freshly prepared hydrogen sulfide water to each and mix. Any color in the solution of the sample should not exceed that in the standard.

Free halogens. Shake 10 ml. vigorously for 2 minutes with 10 ml. of 10 per cent potassium iodide reagent solution and 1 ml. of starch indicator solution. A blue color should not appear in the water layer.

Notes

2,2,4-Trimethylpentane

Isooctane

$(CH_3)_3CCH_2CH(CH_3)_2$ Formula Wt. 114.23

REQUIREMENTS

Color (APHA).   Not more than 10.
Density (gram per ml.) at 25°C.   Not above 0.690.
Boiling range.   1 ml. to 95 ml., not more than 2.0°C.
Residue after evaporation.   Not more than 0.001 per cent.
Acidity (as CH_3COOH).   To pass test (limit about 0.002 per cent).
Sulfur compounds (as S).   Not more than 0.005 per cent.

TESTS

Color (APHA).   For the color standard dilute a 2-ml. aliquot of platinum-cobalt stock solution (APHA No. 500) to 100 ml. with water. Compare this solution (APHA No. 10) with 100 ml. of the 2,2,4-trimethylpentane in 100-ml. Nessler tubes, viewed vertically over a white background.

Boiling range.   Distill 100 ml. by the method described on page 12. The difference between the temperatures when 1 ml. and 95 ml. have distilled should not exceed 2.0°C. The boiling point of pure 2,2,4-trimethylpentane at 760-mm. mercury pressure is 99.2°C.

Residue after evaporation.   Evaporate 145 ml. (100 grams) to dryness in a tared dish on the steam bath and dry the residue at 105°C. for 30 minutes. The weight of the residue should not exceed 0.0010 gram.

Acidity.   To 44 ml. (30 grams) in a separatory funnel, add 50 ml. of water, and shake vigorously for 2 minutes. Allow the layers to separate, draw off the aqueous layer, and add 0.05 ml. of phenolphthalein indicator solution to the aqueous layer. Not more than 0.10 ml. of 0.1N sodium hydroxide should be required to produce a pink color.

Sulfur compounds.   To 30 ml. of 0.5N potassium hydroxide in methanol in an Erlenmeyer flask, add 8 ml. (5.5 grams) of the sample, and boil the mixture gently for 30 minutes under a reflux condenser, avoiding the use of a rubber stopper or connection. Detach the condenser, dilute with 50 ml. of water, and heat on the steam bath until the 2,2,4-trimethylpentane and methanol are evaporated. Add 50 ml. of saturated bromine water, heat for 15 minutes longer, and transfer to a beaker. Neutralize with dilute hydrochloric acid (1 + 3), add an excess of 1 ml. of the acid, evaporate to about 50 ml., and filter if necessary. Heat the filtrate to boiling, add 5 ml. of barium chloride reagent solution, digest in a covered beaker on the steam bath for 2 hours, and allow to stand overnight. If a precipitate is formed, filter, wash thoroughly, and ignite. The weight of the precipitate should not be more than 0.0020 gram greater than the weight obtained in a complete blank test.

Notes

2,2,4-Trimethylpentane

Isooctane

(Suitable for use in ultraviolet spectrophotometry)

$(CH_3)_3CCH_2CH(CH_3)_2$ Formula Wt. 114.23

REQUIREMENTS

>**Absorbance.** To pass test.
>**Density** (gram per ml.) at 25°C. Not above 0.690.
>**Boiling range.** 1 ml. to 95 ml., not more than 2.0°C.
>**Residue after evaporation.** Not more than 0.001 per cent.
>**Acidity** (as CH_3COOH). To pass test (limit about 0.002 per cent).
>**Sulfur compounds** (as S). Not more than 0.005 per cent.

TESTS

Absorbance. Determine the absorbance of the sample in a 1.00-cm. cell throughout the range of 210 mμ to 400 mμ, against water in a similar matched cell set at zero absorbance as the reference liquid. The absorbance should not exceed 1.00 at 210 mμ, 0.20 at 220 mμ, 0.10 at 230 mμ, 0.04 at 240 mμ, and 0.01 at 250 mμ to 400 mμ. The spectral absorbance curve recorded through the wavelengths cited should be smooth throughout the prescribed range and should not show any extraneous impurity peaks within this range.

Other tests are the same as for **2,2,4-Trimethylpentane,** page 622, except *Color (APHA),* which is superseded by the *Absorbance* test.

Notes

Uranyl Acetate

$UO_2(CH_3COO)_2 \cdot 2H_2O$ Formula Wt. 424.15

Note. The formula weight of this reagent is likely to deviate from the value cited above, since the natural distribution of uranium isotopes is often altered in current sources of uranium compounds.

REQUIREMENTS

Insoluble matter. Not more than 0.010 per cent.
Chloride (Cl). Not more than 0.003 per cent.
Sulfate (SO_4). Not more than 0.01 per cent.
Alkalies and alkaline earths (as sulfates). Not more than 0.05 per cent.
Heavy metals (as Pb). Not more than 0.002 per cent.
Iron (Fe). Not more than 0.001 per cent.
Substances reducing permanganate (as U^{IV}). To pass test (limit about 0.06 per cent).

TESTS

Insoluble matter. Dissolve 10 grams in 185 ml. of water plus 5 ml. of glacial acetic acid at room temperature. Filter through a tared filtering crucible, wash thoroughly with water, and dry at 105°C. The weight of the residue should not exceed 0.0010 gram.

Sample Solution A. Dissolve 15 grams in 275 ml. of water plus 5 ml. of glacial acetic acid, add 10 ml. of 30 per cent hydrogen peroxide, and heat to coagulate the precipitate. Decant through a fritted-glass filter, without washing, and dilute to 300 ml. (1 ml. = 0.05 gram).

Chloride. Dilute 10 ml. of Sample Solution A (0.5-gram sample) to 20 ml. Add 1 ml. of nitric acid and 1 ml. of silver nitrate reagent solution. Any turbidity should not exceed that produced by 0.015 mg. of chloride ion (Cl) in an equal volume of solution containing the quantities of reagents used in the test.

Sulfate. To 8 ml. of Sample Solution A (0.4-gram sample) add 2 ml. of water, 1 ml. of dilute hydrochloric acid (1 + 19), and 1 ml. of barium chloride reagent solution. Any turbidity should not exceed that produced by 0.04 mg. of sulfate ion (SO_4) in an equal volume of solution containing the quantities of reagents used in the test. Compare 10 minutes after adding the barium chloride to the sample and standard solutions.

Alkalies and alkaline earths. To 40 ml. of Sample Solution A (2-gram sample) add 0.10 ml. of sulfuric acid, evaporate to dryness, and gently ignite at about 450°C. Digest the residue with 25 ml. of hot water, filter, evaporate the filtrate to dryness in a tared dish, and ignite at 800° ± 25°C. for 15 minutes. The weight of the residue should not exceed 0.0010 gram.

Heavy metals. Evaporate 20 ml. of Sample Solution A (1-gram sample) to dryness, dissolve in about 20 ml. of water, and dilute to 25 ml. For the standard dilute a solution containing 0.02 mg. of lead ion (Pb) to 25 ml. Adjust the pH of the standard and sample solutions to between 3 and 4 (using a pH meter) with 1N acetic acid or ammonium hydroxide (10 per cent NH_3), dilute to 40 ml., and mix. Add 10 ml. of freshly prepared hydrogen sulfide water to each and mix. Any color in the solution of the sample should not exceed that in the standard.

Iron. Evaporate 20 ml. of Sample Solution A (1-gram sample) to dryness. Dissolve the residue in 2 ml. of hydrochloric acid and dilute to 50 ml. Add 30 to 50 mg. of ammonium persulfate crystals and 3 ml. of ammonium thiocyanate reagent solution. Any red color should not exceed that produced by 0.01 mg. of iron (Fe) in an equal volume of solution containing the quantities of reagents used in the test.

Substances reducing permanganate. Prepare two solutions, each containing 3 grams in 200 ml. of dilute sulfuric acid (1 + 99). Titrate one solution with 0.1N potassium permanganate. Not more than 0.20 ml. of permanganate should be required to cause a color change that can be observed by comparison with the solution not titrated. The 0.20 ml. includes the 0.05 ml. allowed to produce the color change in the absence of uranous compounds.

Notes

Uranyl Nitrate

$UO_2(NO_3)_2 \cdot 6H_2O$ Formula Wt. 502.13

Note. The formula weight of this reagent is likely to deviate from the value cited above, since the natural distribution of uranium isotopes is often altered in current sources of uranium compounds.

REQUIREMENTS

Insoluble matter. Not more than 0.005 per cent.
Chloride (Cl). Not more than 0.002 per cent.
Sulfate (SO_4). Not more than 0.005 per cent.
Alkalies and alkaline earths (as sulfates). Not more than 0.10 per cent.
Heavy metals (as Pb). Not more than 0.002 per cent.
Iron (Fe). Not more than 0.002 per cent.
Substances reducing permanganate (as U^{IV}). To pass test (limit about 0.06 per cent).

TESTS

Insoluble matter. Dissolve 20 grams in 200 ml. of water, heat to boiling, and digest in a covered beaker on the steam bath for 1 hour. Filter through a tared filtering crucible, wash thoroughly, and dry at 105°C. The weight of the residue should not exceed 0.0010 gram.

Sample Solution A. Dissolve 15 grams in 275 ml. of water, add 7 grams of ammonium acetate and 10 ml. of 30 per cent hydrogen peroxide, and heat to coagulate the precipitate. Decant through a fritted-glass filter, without washing, and dilute to 300 ml. (1 ml. = 0.05 gram).

Chloride. Dilute 10 ml. of Sample Solution A (0.5-gram sample) to 20 ml. Add 1 ml. of nitric acid and 1 ml. of silver nitrate reagent solution. Any turbidity should not exceed that produced by 0.01 mg. of chloride ion (Cl) in an equal volume of solution containing the quantities of reagents used in the test.

Sulfate. To 20 ml. of Sample Solution A (1-gram sample) add 2 ml. of dilute hydrochloric acid (1 + 19) and 2 ml. of barium chloride reagent solution. Any turbidity should not exceed that produced by 0.05 mg. of sulfate ion (SO_4) in an equal volume of solution containing the quantities of reagents used in the test. Compare 10 minutes after adding the barium chloride to the sample and standard solutions.

Alkalies and alkaline earths. To 20 ml. of Sample Solution A (1-gram sample) add 0.10 ml. of sulfuric acid, evaporate to dryness in a tared evaporating dish, and ignite at $800° \pm 25°C$. for 15 minutes. The weight of the residue should not exceed 0.0010 gram.

Heavy metals. Evaporate 20 ml. of Sample Solution A (1-gram sample) to dryness, dissolve in about 20 ml. of water, and dilute to 25 ml. For the standard dilute a solution containing 0.02 mg. of lead ion (Pb) to 25 ml. Adjust the pH of the standard and sample solutions to between 3 and 4 (using a pH meter) with $1N$ acetic acid or ammonium hydroxide (10 per cent NH_3), dilute to 40 ml., and mix. Add 10 ml. of freshly prepared hydrogen sulfide water to each and mix. Any color in the solution of the sample should not exceed that in the standard.

Iron. To 10 ml. of Sample Solution A (0.5-gram sample) add 2 ml. of hydrochloric acid and dilute to 50 ml. Add 30 to 50 mg. of ammonium persulfate crystals and 3 ml. of ammonium thiocyanate reagent solution. Any red color should not exceed that produced by 0.01 mg. of iron (Fe) in an equal volume of solution containing the quantities of reagents used in the test.

Substances reducing permanganate. Prepare two solutions each containing 3 grams in 200 ml. of dilute sulfuric acid (1 + 99). Titrate one solution with $0.1N$ potassium permanganate. Not more than 0.20 ml. of permanganate should be required to cause a color change that can be observed by comparison with the solution not titrated. The 0.20 ml. includes 0.05 ml. allowed to produce the color change in the absence of uranous compounds.

Notes

Urea

NH$_2$CONH$_2$ Formula Wt. 60.06

REQUIREMENTS

Melting point.   Not below 132°C. nor above 135°C.
Insoluble matter.   Not more than 0.010 per cent.
Residue after ignition.   Not more than 0.01 per cent.
Chloride (Cl).   Not more than 0.0005 per cent.
Sulfate (SO$_4$).   Not more than 0.001 per cent.
Heavy metals (as Pb).   Not more than 0.001 per cent.
Iron (Fe).   Not more than 0.001 per cent.

TESTS

Insoluble matter.   Dissolve 10 grams in 100 ml. of water, heat to boiling, and digest in a covered beaker on the steam bath for 1 hour. Filter through a tared filtering crucible, other than glass, wash thoroughly, and dry at 105°C. The weight of the residue should not exceed 0.0010 gram.

Residue after ignition.   Ignite 10 grams in a tared crucible or dish. The rate of heating should be such that from 1 to 2 hours is required to volatilize the sample. When nearly all of the sample has been volatilized, cool, and moisten the residue with 0.10 ml. of sulfuric acid. Continue the heating until the remainder of the sample and excess sulfuric acid have been volatilized. Finally, ignite at 800° ± 25°C. for 15 minutes. The weight of the residue should not exceed 0.0010 gram.

Chloride.   Dissolve 2 grams in 20 ml. of water, filter if necessary through a chloride-free filter, and add 1 ml. of nitric acid and 1 ml. of silver nitrate reagent solution. Any turbidity should not exceed that produced by 0.01 mg. of chloride ion (Cl) in an equal volume of solution containing the quantities of reagents used in the test.

Sulfate.   Dissolve 4 grams and about 10 mg. of sodium carbonate in 10 ml. of hydrochloric acid. Add 10 ml. of nitric acid and digest in a covered beaker on the steam bath until reaction ceases. Add 5 ml. of hydrochloric acid and 10 ml. of nitric acid and again digest in a covered beaker on the steam bath until reaction ceases. Remove the cover and evaporate to dryness. Dissolve the residue in 4 ml. of water plus 1 ml. of dilute hydrochloric acid (1 + 19) and filter through a small filter. Wash with two 2-ml. portions of water, dilute to 10 ml., and add 1 ml. of barium chloride reagent solution. Any turbidity should not exceed that produced when a solution containing 0.04 mg. of sulfate ion (SO$_4$) is treated exactly like the 4-gram sample. Compare 10 minutes after adding the barium chloride to the sample and standard solutions.

Heavy metals. Dissolve 2 grams in about 20 ml. of water and dilute to 25 ml. For the standard dilute a solution containing 0.02 mg. of lead ion (Pb) to 25 ml. Adjust the pH of the standard and sample solutions to between 3 and 4 (using a pH meter) with $1N$ acetic acid or ammonium hydroxide (10 per cent NH_3), dilute to 40 ml., and mix. Add 10 ml. of freshly prepared hydrogen sulfide water to each and mix. Any color in the solution of the sample should not exceed that in the standard.

Iron. Dissolve 1 gram in 50 ml. of water and add 2 ml. of hydrochloric acid, 30 to 50 mg. of ammonium persulfate crystals, and 3 ml. of ammonium thiocyanate reagent solution. Any red color should not exceed that produced by 0.01 mg. of iron (Fe) in an equal volume of solution containing the quantities of reagents used in the test.

Notes

Water, Reagent

Distilled Water, Deionized Water

H_2O

Formula Wt. 18.02

REQUIREMENTS

Specific conductance at 25°C.   Not more than $2.0 \times 10^{-6} ohm^{-1} cm.^{-1}$
Silicate (as SiO_2).   Not more than 0.01 p.p.m.
Heavy metals (as Pb).   Not more than 0.01 p.p.m.
Substances reducing permanganate.   To pass test.

TESTS

Specific conductance.   Fill a conductance cell that has been properly standardized. Take precautions to prevent the water from absorbing carbon dioxide, ammonia, hydrogen chloride, or any other gases normally present in a laboratory. Immerse in a constant temperature bath at 25°C., equilibrate, and measure the resistance with a suitable conductance bridge. The calculated specific conductance should not exceed $2.0 \times 10^{-6} ohm^{-1} cm.^{-1}$

Silicate.   Evaporate 1500 ml. to 80 ml. in a platinum dish on the steam bath (in aliquots, if necessary). Add 10 ml. of silica-free ammonium hydroxide,* cool, and add 5 ml. of a 10 per cent solution of ammonium molybdate. Adjust the pH to between 1.7 and 1.9 (using a pH meter) with hydrochloric acid or silica-free ammonium hydroxide. Heat the solution just to boiling, cool to room temperature, and dilute to 90 ml. Transfer the solution to a separatory funnel, add 10 ml. of hydrochloric acid and 35 ml. of ethyl ether, and shake vigorously for a few minutes. Allow the two layers to separate, draw off the aqueous layer into another separatory funnel, and add 10 ml. of hydrochloric acid and 50 ml. of butyl alcohol. Shake vigorously, allow to separate, draw off the aqueous phase, and discard. Wash the butyl alcohol phase 3 times with 20 ml. of dilute hydrochloric acid (1 + 99), discarding the aqueous solution each time. Add 0.5 ml. of freshly prepared 2 per cent stannous chloride solution in hydrochloric acid to the butyl alcohol. Any blue color should not exceed that produced by 0.015 mg. of silica (SiO_2)** when treated exactly like the sample. Since the blue color fades on standing, compare immediately after the reduction with stannous chloride. Treatment again with stannous chloride will restore a fading blue color to its original intensity.

Heavy metals.   Add 10 mg. of sodium chloride and 1 ml. of 1N hydrochloric acid to 2 liters, evaporate to dryness on the steam bath, and dissolve the residue in 25 ml. of the water. For the standard evaporate 1 ml. of the 1N hydrochloric acid to dryness on the steam bath, dissolve in about 20 ml. of the water, add 0.02 mg. of lead ion (Pb), and dilute to 25 ml. with the water. Adjust the pH of the standard and sample solutions to between 3 and 4 (using a pH meter) with 1N acetic acid or ammonium hydroxide (10 per cent NH_3), dilute to 40 ml., and mix. Add 10 ml. of freshly prepared hydrogen sulfide water to each and mix. Any color in the solution of the sample should not exceed that in the standard.

Substances reducing permanganate.   To 500 ml. add 1 ml. of sulfuric acid and 0.03 ml. of 0.1N permanganate and allow to stand for 1 hour at room temperature. The pink color should not be entirely discharged.

*Ammonium Hydroxide (Silica-free).** Aqueous ammonia in contact with glass, even momentarily, will dissolve sufficient silica to make the reagent useless for this test. Since ammonium hydroxide is ordinarily supplied in glass containers by commercial sources, silica-free ammonium hydroxide must be prepared in the laboratory. The most convenient method is the saturation of water with ammonia gas from a cylinder of compressed anhydrous ammonia. Plastic tubing and bottles—for example, polyethylene—must be used throughout.

Silicate Solution in Ammonium Hydroxide (0.01 mg. SiO₂ in 1 ml.). To prepare a stock solution of silica dissolve 9.46 grams of assayed sodium silicate, $Na_2SiO_3.9H_2O$, in 9 ml. of silica-free ammonium hydroxide and dilute to 200 ml. (199.4 grams at 25°C.) with water. Dilute a 1-ml. aliquot of this solution plus 5 ml. of silica-free ammonium hydroxide to 1 liter (997.1 grams at 25°C.) with water. If volumetric polyethylene ware is unavailable, dilute the silica solution by weight.

Notes

Xylene

$C_6H_4(CH_3)_2$ Formula Wt. 106.17

REQUIREMENTS

Color (APHA).   Not more than 10.
Boiling range.   From 137° to 140°C.
Residue after evaporation.   Not more than 0.002 per cent.
Substances darkened by sulfuric acid.   To pass test.
Sulfur compounds (as S).   Not more than 0.003 per cent.
Water (H$_2$O).   Not more than 0.05 per cent.

TESTS

Color (APHA).   For the color standard dilute a 2-ml. aliquot of platinum-cobalt stock solution (APHA No. 500) to 100 ml. with water. Compare this solution (APHA No. 10) with 100 ml. of the xylene in 100-ml. Nessler tubes, viewed vertically over a white background.

Boiling range.   Distill 100 ml. by the method described on page 12. The temperatures when 1 ml. and 95 ml. have distilled should be from 137° to 140°C. at 760-mm. mercury pressure.

Residue after evaporation.   Evaporate 115 ml. (100 grams) to dryness in a tared dish on the steam bath and dry the residue at 105°C. for 30 minutes. The weight of the residue should not exceed 0.0020 gram.

Substances darkened by sulfuric acid.   Shake 15 ml. with 5 ml. of sulfuric acid for 15 to 20 seconds and allow to stand for 15 minutes. The xylene layer should be colorless, and the color of the acid should not exceed that of a color standard composed of 1 volume of water and 3 volumes of a color standard containing 5 grams of $CoCl_2 \cdot 6H_2O$, 40 grams of $FeCl_3 \cdot 6H_2O$, and 20 ml. of hydrochloric acid in a liter.

Sulfur compounds.   Place 30 ml. of approximately 0.5N potassium hydroxide in methanol in an Erlenmeyer flask, add 6 ml. of the sample, and boil the mixture gently for 30 minutes under a reflux condenser, avoiding the use of a rubber stopper or connection. Detach the condenser, dilute with 50 ml. of water, and heat on the steam bath until the xylene and methanol have evaporated. Add 50 ml. of saturated bromine water and heat for 15 minutes longer. Transfer the solution to a beaker, neutralize with dilute hydrochloric acid (1 + 3), add an excess of 1 ml. of the acid, and concentrate to about 50 ml. Filter if necessary, heat the filtrate to boiling, add 5 ml. of barium chloride reagent solution, digest in a covered beaker on the steam bath for 2 hours, and allow to stand overnight.

If a precipitate is formed, filter, wash thoroughly, and ignite. The weight of the precipitate should not be more than 0.0012 gram greater than the weight obtained in a complete blank test.

Water. Place 25 ml. of methanol in a dry titration flask and add Karl Fischer reagent to a visually or electrometrically determined end point. Add 20 ml. (17.4 grams) of the sample, taking care to protect the sample and contents of the flask from moisture. Stir vigorously and titrate with Karl Fischer reagent to the same end point. Calculate the water content of the sample from the titer and volume of Karl Fischer reagent consumed by the sample.

Notes

Zinc

Zn

Atomic Wt. 65.37

REQUIREMENTS

> **Arsenic (As).** Not more than 0.00001 per cent.
> **Iron (Fe).** Not more than 0.01 per cent.
> **Lead (Pb).** Not more than 0.01 per cent.

TESTS

Arsenic. Test 20 grams of sample by the Gutzeit method (page 11), using 24 ml. of sulfuric acid or 40 ml. of hydrochloric acid diluted with about 70 ml. of water. Any stain should not be greater than is produced by 0.002 mg. of arsenic (As). If the zinc does not dissolve completely, the spent acid should be decanted and the apparatus filled with fresh acid; the evolved gas is passed over the same test paper.

> **Sample Solution A.** Dissolve 2 grams in 15 ml. of dilute hydrochloric acid (1 + 1). When the solution is nearly complete, add 1 ml. of nitric acid and heat to boiling, or until any residue from the zinc is dissolved. Cool and dilute to 100 ml. (1 ml. = 0.02 gram).

Iron. To 5 ml. of Sample Solution A (0.1-gram sample) add 2 ml. of hydrochloric acid, dilute to 50 ml., and add 30 to 50 mg. of ammonium persulfate crystals and 3 ml. of ammonium thiocyanate reagent solution. Any red color should not exceed that produced by 0.01 mg. of iron (Fe) in an equal volume of solution containing the quantities of reagents used in the test.

Lead. Dilute 10 ml. of Sample Solution A (0.2-gram sample) to 20 ml. and add ammonium hydroxide until a small amount of permanent precipitate is formed. Carefully add nitric acid in sufficient amount just to dissolve the precipitate. Pour the solution into 20 ml. of 10 per cent sodium cyanide reagent solution, dilute to 50 ml., mix thoroughly, and add 0.20 ml. of a 10 per cent solution of sodium sulfide. Any brown color should not exceed that produced by 0.02 mg. of lead ion (Pb) in an equal volume of solution containing the quantities of reagents used in the test.

Notes

Zinc Chloride

$ZnCl_2$ Formula Wt. 136.28

REQUIREMENTS

Assay.   Not less than 95 per cent $ZnCl_2$.
Oxychloride.   To pass test.
Insoluble matter.   Not more than 0.005 per cent.
Nitrate (NO_3).   Not more than 0.003 per cent.
Sulfate (SO_4).   Not more than 0.010 per cent.
Ammonium (NH_4).   Not more than 0.005 per cent.
Iron (Fe).   To pass test (limit about 0.001 per cent).
Lead (Pb).   Not more than 0.005 per cent.
Substances not precipitated by ammonium sulfide (as sulfates).   Not more than 0.20 per cent.

TESTS

Assay.   Using precautions to avoid absorption of moisture, weigh accurately about 0.3 gram, dissolve in about 100 ml. of water in a 200-ml. volumetric flask, and add 5 ml. of nitric acid and 50.0 ml. of 0.1N silver nitrate. Shake vigorously, dilute to volume, mix well, and filter through a dry paper into a dry flask or beaker, rejecting the first 20 ml. of the filtrate. To 100 ml. of the filtrate subsequently collected, add 2 ml. of ferric ammonium sulfate indicator solution, and titrate the excess silver nitrate with 0.1N ammonium thiocyanate. One milliliter of 0.1N silver nitrate corresponds to 0.006814 gram of $ZnCl_2$.

Oxychloride.   Dissolve 20 grams in 200 ml. of water. On the addition of 6 ml. of 1N hydrochloric acid any flocculent precipitate should entirely dissolve. Retain the solution for the test for *Insoluble matter*.

Insoluble matter.   To the solution obtained in the test for *Oxychloride* add 6 ml. of 1N hydrochloric acid. If insoluble matter is present, filter through a tared filtering crucible, wash thoroughly with water containing about 0.2 per cent hydrochloric acid, and dry at 105°C. The weight of the residue should not exceed 0.0010 gram.

Nitrate.

Sample Solution A.   Dissolve 0.5 gram in 3 ml. of water by heating in a boiling water bath. Dilute to 50 ml. with brucine sulfate reagent solution.

Control Solution B.   Dissolve 0.5 gram in 1.5 ml. of water and 1.5 ml. of the standard nitrate solution containing 0.01 mg. of nitrate ion

(NO_3) by heating in a boiling water bath. Dilute to 50 ml. with brucine sulfate reagent solution.

Blank Solution C. Use 50 ml. of brucine sulfate reagent solution.

Heat the three solutions in a preheated (boiling) water bath for 10 minutes. Cool rapidly in an ice bath to room temperature. Set a spectrophotometer at 410 mμ and, using 1-cm. cells, adjust the instrument to read 0 absorbance with Blank Solution C in the light path, then determine the absorbance of Sample Solution A. Adjust the instrument to read 0 absorbance with Sample Solution A in the light path and determine the absorbance of Control Solution B. The absorbance of Sample Solution A should not exceed that of Control Solution B.

Sulfate. Dissolve 10 grams in 120 ml. of water, filter if necessary, and add 2 ml. of hydrochloric acid. Heat to boiling, add 5 ml. of barium chloride reagent solution, digest in a covered beaker on the steam bath for 2 hours, and allow to stand overnight. If a precipitate is formed, filter, wash with water containing about 0.2 per cent of hydrochloric acid, wash finally with plain water, and ignite. The weight of the precipitate should not be more than 0.0025 gram greater than the weight obtained in a complete blank test.

Ammonium. Dissolve 1 gram in water and dilute to 50 ml. Pour 10 ml. of the solution into 10 ml. of freshly boiled 10 per cent sodium hydroxide reagent solution. Dilute to 50 ml. and add 2 ml. of Nessler reagent. Any color should not exceed that produced by 0.01 mg. of ammonium ion (NH_4) in an equal volume of solution containing the quantities of reagents used in the test.

Iron. Dissolve 1 gram in 40 ml. of water, add 2 ml. of hydrochloric acid, and dilute to 50 ml. Add 30 to 50 mg. of ammonium persulfate crystals and 3 ml. of ammonium thiocyanate reagent solution. Any red color should not exceed that produced by 0.01 mg. of iron (Fe) in an equal volume of solution containing the quantities of reagents used in the test.

Lead. Dissolve 2 grams in 10 ml. of water and add a few drops of nitric acid. Add ammonium hydroxide dropwise with constant stirring until a faint but permanent precipitate is produced, clear this turbidity with a few drops of 10 per cent nitric acid reagent solution, and dilute to 50 ml. Add 10 ml. of this solution to 20 ml. of 10 per cent sodium cyanide reagent solution, stirring constantly during the addition, dilute to 50 ml., and add 0.2 ml. of 10 per cent sodium sulfide solution. Any color should not exceed that produced by 0.02 mg. of lead ion (Pb) in an equal volume of solution containing the quantities of reagents used in the test.

Substances not precipitated by ammonium sulfide. To 2 grams in 140 ml. of water add 10 ml. of ammonium hydroxide, pass hydrogen sulfide through the solution to precipitate the zinc completely, and decant through a filter paper. To 75 ml. of the filtrate add 0.25 ml. of sulfuric acid, evaporate to dryness in a tared dish, ignite carefully until the ammonium salts are volatilized, and finally ignite at 800° ± 25°C. for 15 minutes. The weight of the residue should not exceed 0.0020 gram.

Notes

Zinc Oxide

ZnO   Formula Wt. 81.37

REQUIREMENTS

Insoluble in dilute sulfuric acid.   Not more than 0.010 per cent.
Alkalinity.   To pass test.
Chloride (Cl).   Not more than 0.001 per cent.
Nitrate (NO$_3$).   Not more than 0.003 per cent.
Sulfur compounds (as SO$_4$).   Not more than 0.010 per cent.
Arsenic (As).   Not more than 0.0002 per cent.
Iron (Fe).   To pass test (limit about 0.001 per cent).
Lead (Pb).   Not more than 0.005 per cent.
Manganese (Mn).   Not more than 0.0005 per cent.
Substances not precipitated by ammonium sulfide.   Not more than 0.10 per cent.

TESTS

Insoluble in dilute sulfuric acid.   Dissolve 10 grams by heating in a covered beaker on a steam bath with 160 ml. of dilute sulfuric acid (1 + 15) for 1 hour. Filter through a tared filtering crucible, wash thoroughly, and dry at 105°C. The weight of the residue should not exceed 0.0010 gram.

Alkalinity.   Suspend 2 grams in 20 ml. of water, boil for 1 minute, and filter. Add 0.10 ml. of phenolphthalein indicator solution to 10 ml. of the filtrate. No red color should be produced.

Chloride.   Suspend 1 gram in 20 ml. of water, dissolve by adding 3 ml. of nitric acid, filter if necessary through a chloride-free filter, and add 1 ml. of silver nitrate reagent solution. Any turbidity should not exceed that produced by 0.01 mg. of chloride ion (Cl) in an equal volume of solution containing the quantities of reagents used in the test.

Nitrate.

Sample Solution A.   Suspend 0.5 gram in 3 ml. of water. Dilute to 50 ml. with brucine sulfate reagent solution.

Control Solution B.   Suspend 0.5 gram in 1.5 ml. of water and 1.5 ml. of the standard nitrate solution containing 0.01 mg. of nitrate ion (NO$_3$) per ml. Dilute to 50 ml. with brucine sulfate reagent solution.

Blank Solution C.   Use 50 ml. of brucine sulfate reagent solution.

ACS SPECIFICATIONS   **639**

Heat Sample Solution A, Control Solution B, and Blank Solution C in a preheated (boiling) water bath until the zinc oxide is dissolved in A and B, then heat for 10 more minutes. Cool rapidly in an ice bath to room temperature. Set a spectrophotometer at 410 mμ and, using 1-cm. cells, adjust the instrument to read 0 absorbance with Blank Solution C in the light path, then determine the absorbance of Sample Solution A. Adjust the instrument to read 0 absorbance with Sample Solution A in the light path and determine the absorbance of Control Solution B. The absorbance of Sample Solution A should not exceed that of Control Solution B.

Sulfur compounds.   Suspend 5 grams in 50 ml. of water and add about 50 mg. of sodium carbonate and 1 ml. of saturated bromine water. Boil for 5 minutes, cautiously add hydrochloric acid in small portions until the zinc oxide is dissolved, then add 1 ml. more of the acid. Filter, wash, and dilute the filtrate to about 150 ml. Heat the filtrate to boiling, add 5 ml. of barium chloride reagent solution, digest in a covered beaker on the steam bath for 2 hours, and allow to stand overnight. If a precipitate is formed, filter, wash 2 or 3 times with dilute hydrochloric acid (1 + 99), complete the washing with water alone, and ignite. The weight of the precipitate should not be more than 0.0012 gram greater than the weight obtained in a complete blank test.

Arsenic.   Determine the arsenic in 1 gram by the Gutzeit method (page 11). The amount of stain should not exceed that produced by 0.002 mg. of arsenic (As).

Iron.   Dissolve 1 gram in 10 ml. of dilute hydrochloric acid (1 + 1) and dilute to 50 ml. Add 30 to 50 mg. of ammonium persulfate crystals and 3 ml. of ammonium thiocyanate reagent solution. Any red color should not exceed that produced by 0.01 mg. of iron (Fe) in an equal volume of solution containing the quantities of reagents used in the test.

Lead.   Suspend 2 grams in 10 ml. of water, add just enough hydrochloric acid (about 2.5 ml.) to dissolve the oxide, and add a few drops of nitric acid. Add ammonium hydroxide dropwise with constant stirring until a faint but permanent precipitate is produced, clear this turbidity with a few drops of 10 per cent nitric acid reagent solution, and dilute to 50 ml. Add 10 ml. of this solution to 20 ml. of 10 per cent sodium cyanide solution, stirring constantly during the addition, dilute to 50 ml., add 0.2 ml. of 10 per cent sodium sulfide solution, and transfer to a Nessler tube. Any color should not exceed that produced by 0.02 mg. of lead ion (Pb) in an equal volume of solution containing the quantities of reagents used in the test.

Manganese. Dissolve 2 grams in 35 ml. of water. For the standard dilute a solution containing 0.01 mg. of manganese ion (Mn) to 35 ml. To each add 10 ml. of nitric acid, 5 ml. of sulfuric acid, and 5 ml. of phosphoric acid. Boil the solutions for 5 minutes, cool, and add 0.25 gram of potassium periodate. Boil again for 5 minutes, cool, and compare in Nessler tubes. Any pink color in the solution of the sample should not exceed that in the standard.

Substances not precipitated by ammonium sulfide. Dissolve 2 grams by warming with 20 ml. of dilute acetic acid (1 + 3). Dilute to 140 ml. and pass hydrogen sulfide through the solution until the zinc is mostly precipitated. Neutralize with ammonium hydroxide, add an excess of 1 ml., dilute to 150 ml., pass hydrogen sulfide through the solution for 2 minutes more, and filter. If the filtrate comes through turbid at first, pass it through the filter a second time. Evaporate 75 ml. of the clear filtrate nearly to dryness in a tared dish, add 0.5 ml. of sulfuric acid, evaporate, ignite gently until the ammonium salts are volatilized, and finally ignite at $800° \pm 25°C$. for 15 minutes. The weight of the residue should not exceed 0.0010 gram.

Notes

Zinc Sulfate

ZnSO$_4 \cdot 7$H$_2$O   Formula Wt. 287.54

REQUIREMENTS

Insoluble matter.   Not more than 0.010 per cent.
pH of a 5 per cent solution.   From 4.4 to 6.0 at 25°C.
Chloride (Cl).   Not more than 0.0005 per cent.
Nitrate (NO$_3$).   Not more than 0.002 per cent.
Ammonium (NH$_4$).   Not more than 0.001 per cent.
Arsenic (As).   Not more than 0.0001 per cent.
Iron (Fe).   To pass test (limit about 0.001 per cent).
Lead (Pb).   Not more than 0.003 per cent.
Manganese (Mn).   Not more than 0.0003 per cent.
Substances not precipitated by ammonium sulfide (as sulfates).   Not more than 0.20 per cent.

TESTS

Insoluble matter.   Dissolve 10 grams in 100 ml. of water, heat to boiling, and digest in a covered beaker on the steam bath for 1 hour. Filter through a tared filtering crucible, wash thoroughly, and dry at 105°C. The weight of the residue should not exceed 0.0010 gram.

pH of a 5 per cent solution.   Dissolve 10 grams in 200 ml. of carbon dioxide- and ammonia-free water. Determine the pH by the method described on page 18. The pH should be from 4.4 to 6.0 at 25°C. The pH of a 5 per cent solution of pure zinc sulfate would be 5.4 at 25°C.

Chloride.   Dissolve 2 grams in water, filter if necessary through a small chloride-free filter, dilute to 20 ml., and add 1 ml. of nitric acid and 1 ml. of silver nitrate reagent solution. Any turbidity should not exceed that produced by 0.01 mg. of chloride ion (Cl) in an equal volume of solution containing the quantities of reagents used in the test.

Nitrate.

Sample Solution A.   Dissolve 1 gram in 3 ml. of water by heating in a boiling water bath. Dilute to 50 ml. with brucine sulfate reagent solution.

Control Solution B.   Dissolve 1 gram in 1 ml. of water and 2 ml. of the standard nitrate solution containing 0.01 mg. of nitrate ion (NO$_3$) per ml. by heating in a boiling water bath. Dilute to 50 ml. with brucine sulfate reagent solution.

Blank Solution C.   Use 50 ml. of brucine sulfate reagent solution.

Heat the three solutions in a preheated (boiling) water bath for 10 minutes. Cool rapidly in an ice bath to room temperature. Set a spectrophotometer at 410 mμ and, using 1-cm. cells, adjust the instrument to read 0 absorbance with Blank Solution C in the light path, then determine the absorbance of Sample Solution A. Adjust the instrument to read 0 absorbance with Sample Solution A in the light path and determine the absorbance of Control Solution B. The absorbance of Sample Solution A should not exceed that of Control Solution B.

Ammonium. Dissolve 1 gram in 25 ml. of water, pour into 25 ml. of freshly boiled and cooled 10 per cent sodium hydroxide reagent solution, and add 2 ml. of Nessler reagent. Any color should not exceed that produced by 0.01 mg. of ammonium ion (NH_4) in an equal volume of solution containing the quantities of reagents used in the test.

Arsenic. Determine the arsenic in 2 grams by the Gutzeit method (page 11). The amount of stain should not exceed that produced by 0.002 mg. of arsenic (As).

Iron. Dissolve 1 gram in 40 ml. of water and add 2 ml. of hydrochloric acid. Dilute to 50 ml. and add 30 to 50 mg. of ammonium persulfate crystals and 3 ml. of ammonium thiocyanate reagent solution. Any red color should not exceed that produced by 0.01 mg. of iron (Fe) in an equal volume of solution containing the quantities of reagents used in the test.

Lead. Dissolve 2 grams in 10 ml. of water and add a few drops of nitric acid. Add ammonium hydroxide dropwise with constant stirring until a faint but permanent precipitate is produced. Clear this turbidity by adding a few drops of 10 per cent nitric acid. Pour this solution slowly into 20 ml. of 10 per cent sodium cyanide reagent solution, stirring constantly during the addition, and dilute to 60 ml. Dilute 20 ml. of this solution to 50 ml. and add 0.2 ml. of 10 per cent sodium sulfide solution. Any color should not exceed that produced by 0.02 mg. of lead ion (Pb) in an equal volume of solution containing the quantities of reagents used in the test.

Manganese. Dissolve 3.3 grams in 35 ml. of water. For the standard dilute a solution containing 0.01 mg. of manganese ion (Mn) to 35 ml. To each add 10 ml. of nitric acid, 5 ml. of sulfuric acid, and 5 ml. of phosphoric acid, and boil for 5 minutes. Cool, add 0.25 gram of potassium periodate, and boil again for 5 minutes. Cool, and compare in Nessler tubes. Any pink color in the solution of the sample should not exceed that in the standard.

INDEX

A